INTRODUCTION TO
INFRARED AND RAMAN SPECTROSCOPY

INTRODUCTION TO INFRARED AND RAMAN SPECTROSCOPY

Norman B. Colthup

AMERICAN CYANAMID COMPANY
STAMFORD, CONNECTICUT

Lawrence H. Daly

STATE UNIVERSITY OF
NEW YORK AT ALBANY
ALBANY, NEW YORK

Stephen E. Wiberley

DEPARTMENT OF CHEMISTRY
WALKER LABORATORY
RENSSELAER POLYTECHNIC INSTITUTE
TROY, NEW YORK

1964

ACADEMIC PRESS • New York and London

PREFACE

The idea for this book originated about five years ago because the authors felt there was a definite need for a book dealing with an elementary treatment of infrared and Raman spectroscopy. For a complete theoretical analysis of a molecule both the infrared and Raman spectra are needed; so it seemed logical to include the two subjects in a single text. In the past two years a considerable number of books dealing primarily with infrared spectroscopy have been published, but as yet no book has had the general plan of this one.

The intent was to cover rather broadly the theory and instrumentation aspects of infrared and Raman spectroscopy, and with greater emphasis, group frequency correlations mainly based on infrared data, and finally to analyze one typical molecule in detail.

The theory presented in this text is on an elementary level and no attempt has been made to cover any involved or sophisticated aspects. The excellent texts of Herzberg and Wilson, Decius, and Cross leave little room for improvement in this area. In regard to instrumentation one chapter has been devoted to such major subjects as sources, monochromators, receptors, sample handling technique and quantitative analysis—to mention a few.

Symmetry elements are presented and point groups explained in Chapter 3. The basis for the character table is developed and the selection rules are calculated in detail for a C_{3v} molecule. Extensive chemical examples of each point group are also given with references.

A large portion of the book is devoted to group correlations. The vibrational origin of group frequencies is emphasized with a discussion of the effects of vibrational interaction and coupling. Group frequencies are presented in text form with selected references, and in chart form with spectral examples. A large number of infrared spectra of carefully chosen compounds are presented with group frequencies indicated on the spectra. The authors feel that these spectral examples are an important aspect of the book because experience has shown that band shape and the general appearance of the complete spectrum supplement correlation tables. Many representative spectra are given for illustration.

A method for calculating fundamental frequencies is discussed and a detailed example (chloroform) is worked out. This approach is not necessarily new but the emphasis lies with developing all the steps required in a detailed manner not readily available elsewhere. While some use of group theory and matrix algebra is made, no previous knowledge of these fields is necessary. A chapter on calculation of thermodynamic functions follows the same format. It is realized that many texts discuss statistical thermodynamics, and the emphasis here is again on a detailed example showing the method in convenient form for easy calculation. Enough material is included, however, to show the origin of the equations.

In the study of the typical molecule (chloroform), considerable effort has been devoted to presenting the analysis in such a fashion that the average student should have little difficulty in following each step. Care has been exercised in eliminating the time-honored "it readily follows that" mathematical approach which leaves the student in a puzzled quandary.

In short, this book has been written for the student or the organic or analytical chemist who does not feel qualified to call himself a spectroscopist.

The help of Mr. Solomon Levine in the literature survey and preparation of the cesium bromide correlation charts is gratefully acknowledged. The assistance of Miss Esther Wight in typing the final manuscript and checking references proved invaluable to the authors. One of the authors (N. B. C.) wishes to acknowledge the help he has received from the spectroscopists and chemists of the Stamford Research Laboratories of the American Cyanamid Company. Their suggestions and contributions for this book were greatly appreciated.

March, 1964   NORMAN B. COLTHUP
                                                                LAWRENCE H. DALY
                                                                STEPHEN E. WIBERLEY

CONTENTS

PREFACE v

Chapter 1

VIBRATIONAL AND ROTATIONAL SPECTRA 1

1.1 Introduction, 1; 1.2 Normal Modes of Vibration, 3; 1.3 Mechanical Molecular Models, 4; 1.4 Doubly Degenerate Modes of Vibration, 6; 1.5 Dipole Moment, 7; 1.6 Theoretical Linear Harmonic Oscillator, 8; 1.7 Actual Diatomic Oscillator, 10; 1.8 Molecular Rotation, 12; 1.9 Types of Rotators, 16; 1.10 Rotation of Symmetrical Top Molecules, 16; 1.11 Vibrational-Rotational Spectra, 19; 1.12 Spherical Top Molecules, 23; 1.13 Symmetrical Top Molecules, 25; 1.14 Asymmetrical Top Molecules, 27; 1.15 The Raman Effect, 27; 1.16 Polarizability, 31; 1.17 Change in Polarizability, 33; 1.18 Pure Rotational Raman Spectra, 34; 1.19 Depolarization Ratio, 35

Chapter 2

EXPERIMENTAL CONSIDERATIONS 37

2.1 Source of Infrared Radiation, 37; 2.2 Infrared Monochromators and Filters, 43; 2.3 Infrared Detectors, 52; 2.4 Typical Commercial Instruments, 55; 2.5 Instrument Calibration, 59; 2.6 Sample Handling Techniques, 60; 2.7 Quantitative Analysis, 71; 2.8 Polarized Infrared Radiation, 79; 2.9 Raman Sources, 85; 2.10 Raman Spectrographs, 88; 2.11 Raman Measurements, 90

Chapter 3

CLASSIFICATION OF MOLECULES 98

3.1 Symmetry Properties, 98; 3.2 Point Groups, 104; 3.3 Group Theory, 108; 3.4 Group Theory Applied to Point Groups, 109; 3.5 Characters and Representations of Groups, 112; 3.6 The Number of Fundamentals of Each Type, 122; 3.7 Infrared Activity, 123; 3.8 Raman Activity, 124; 3.9 Overtone and Combination Bands, 124; 3.10 Selection Rules, Character Tables, and Chemical Examples, 128; 3.11 Techniques of Band Assignments, 162

Chapter 4

THE ORIGIN OF GROUP FREQUENCIES 168

4.1 Introduction, 168; 4.2 Introduction to Mass and Force Constant Effects, 168; 4.3 Interaction and Coupling Effects, 169; 4.4 Individual Oscillator Groups, 172; 4.5 Multiple Oscillator Groups, 174; 4.6 Single Bond Interactions, 176; 4.7 Bending Interaction, 178; 4.8 Bending-Stretching Interaction, 181; 4.9 Overtone-Fundamental Interaction, 181; 4.10 The Effect of Bond Angle, 182; 4.11 Introduction to Inductive and Mesomeric Effects, 186; 4.12 Hydrogen Bonding, 189

Chapter 5

ALIPHATIC GROUPS 191

5.1 Methyl Groups, 191; 5.2 Methylene Groups, 195; 5.3 Carbon-Hydrogen Group, 199

Chapter 6

TRIPLE BONDS AND CUMULATED DOUBLE BONDS 200

6.1 Introduction, 200; 6.2 Monosubstituted Acetylenes, 200; 6.3 Disubstituted Acetylenes, 202; 6.4 Allenes, 202; 6.5 Nitriles, 202; 6.6 Nitrile N-oxides, 203; 6.7 Isocyanates, 203; 6.8 Thiocyanates, 204; 6.9 Isothiocyanates, 204; 6.10 Nitriles on a Nitrogen Atom, 204; 6.11 Carbodiimides, 205; 6.12 Ketene Imines, 205; 6.13 Diazo Compounds, 205; 6.14 Azides, 206; 6.15 Aryl Diazonium Salts, 207; 6.16 Isocyanides, 207; 6.17 Ketenes, 208; 6.18 Cyanide Ions, 208; 6.19 Cyanate Ions, 208; 6.20 Thiocyanate Ions, 208; 6.21 Metal Carbonyls, 209

Chapter 7

OLEFIN GROUPS 210

7.1 Noncyclic Olefins, 210; 7.2 Olefinic Hydrogen Wagging Vibrations, 213; 7.3 Cyclic C=C, 216

Chapter 8

AROMATIC AND HETEROAROMATIC RINGS 220

8.1 Benzene Rings, 220;   8.2 The Carbon-Carbon Vibrations, 220;
8.3 Symmetry Considerations, 223;   8.4 The 1600 cm^{-1} Region, 224;
8.5 The 1500 cm^{-1} Region, 224;   8.6 The 700 cm^{-1} Region, 225;   8.7 The
450 cm^{-1} Region, 226;   8.8 Carbon-Hydrogen Vibrations, 226;   8.9 The
900-675 cm^{-1} Region, 226;   8.10 The 1300-1000 cm^{-1} Region, 228;
8.11 The 2000-1750 cm^{-1} Region, 228;   8.12 The 3100-3000 cm^{-1}
Region, 230;   8.13 Raman Correlations for Substituted Benzenes, 230;
8.14 Condensed Ring Aromatic Compounds, 231;   8.15 Pyridines, 233;
8.16 Pyridine N-oxides, 233; 8.17 Pyrimidines, 234; 8.18 Triazines, 234;
8.19 Alkyl or Aryl Substituted Triazines, 234;   8.20 Melamines and
Guanamines, 235; 8.21 Chloro, Oxy, and Thiosubstituted Triazines, 235;
8.22 Tetrazines, 236;   8.23 Heteroaromatic Five Membered Ring
Compounds, 236;   8.24 Cyclopentadienyl Ring-Metal Complexes, 238

Chapter 9

CARBONYL COMPOUNDS 239

9.1 Introduction, 239; 9.2 Mass Effects, 239; 9.3 Bond Angle Effects,
239; 9.4 Inductive Effects, 241; 9.5 Mesomeric Effects, 242; 9.6 Ketones, 243;   9.7 α-Chloro Ketones, 243;   9.8 Conjugated Ketones, 243;
9.9 Conjugated Hydrogen Bonded Ketones, 244;   9.10 Bond Angle
Effects in Ketones, 246; 9.11 Aldehyde CH Vibrations, 247; 9.12 Aldehyde Carbonyl Vibrations, 248;   9.13 Aldehyde C−C, 248;   9.14 Ester
C=O, 248;   9.15 Ester C−O, 249;   9.16 Out-of-Plane Hydrogen
Vibrations in Unsaturated Esters, 251;   9.17 Groups Next to the
Carbonyl in Esters, 252; 9.18 Groups on the Oxygen Atom in Esters, 253;
9.19 Lactones, 253; 9.20 Thiol Esters and Related Compounds, 254;
9.21 Organic Carbonate Derivatives and Related Compounds, 254;
9.22 Anhydrides, 255; 9.23 Peroxides, 256; 9.24 Acid Chlorides, 256;
9.25 Chloroformates, 257;   9.26 Carboxylic Acid OH Stretch, 257;
9.27 Carboxyl-Carbonyl Stretch, 258; 9.28 Carboxyl OH Bending and
C−O Stretching, 259; 9.29 Monomeric Acids, 260;   9.30 Aliphatic
Peroxy Acids, 260; 9.31 Aromatic Acids, 261; 9.32 Aliphatic Bands in
Long Chain n-Aliphatic Carboxylic Acids, Esters, and Soaps, 261;
9.33 Carboxyl Salts, 262; 9.34 Amino Acids, 262; 9.35 Amido Acids,
263;   9.36 Unsubstituted Amides, 263;   9.37 N-Substituted Amides
(trans), 264; 9.38 N-Substituted Amides (cis) (Lactams), 264; 9.39 Disubstituted Amides, 265; 9.40 Ureas, 265; 9.41 Carbamates, 266;
9.42 Hydroxamic Acids, 266; 9.43 Imides, 266; 9.44 Isocyanurates, 267;
9.45 Acid Hydrazides, 267

Chapter 10

ETHERS, ALCOHOLS, AND PHENOLS 269

10.1 Aliphatic Ethers, 269; 10.2 Aromatic Ethers, 270; 10.3 Vinyl Ethers, 271; 10.4 Cyclic Ether Linkages, 272; 10.5 Oxirane Ring Compounds, 273; 10.6 OH Stretch in Alcohols and Phenols, 273; 10.7 C—O Stretch, 274; 10.8 OH Deformation, 275; 10.9 Phenols, 275; 10.10 Noncyclic Acetals and Related Compounds, 276; 10.11 Cyclic Acetals, 276; 10.12 Carbohydrates, 276; 10.13 Peroxides, 276

Chapter 11

AMINES, C=N, AND N=O COMPOUNDS 278

11.1 NH_2 Stretch in Amines, 278; 11.2 NH_2 Deformation in Amines, 278; 11.3 NH, 279; 11.4 C—N in Aliphatic Amines, 279; 11.5 C—N in Aromatic Amines, 280; 11.6 Aliphatic Bands in Amines, 280; 11.7 The Ammonium Ion, 281; 11.8 Amine Salts, 281; 11.9 C=N Groups, 282; 11.10 Nitro Group, 285; 11.11 Organic Nitrates, 286; 11.12 Nitramines, 287; 11.13 Organic Nitrites, 287; 11.14 Inorganic Nitrates and Nitrites, 287; 11.15 N=N Azo, 287; 11.16 Azoxy and Azothio Groups, 288; 11.17 C-Nitroso Compounds, 289; 11.18 Nitrosamines, 290

Chapter 12

COMPOUNDS CONTAINING BORON, SILICON, PHOSPHORUS, SULFUR, OR HALOGEN 291

12.1 Boron Compounds, 291; 12.2 B—O, 291; 12.3 B—OH, 292; 12.4 B—N, 292; 12.5 B—H, 293; 12.6 B—Cl, 293; 12.7 B—CH$_3$, 294; 12.8 B-Phenyl, 294; 12.9 Silicon Compounds, 294; 12.10 Si—H, 295; 12.11 Si—CH$_3$, 295; 12.12 Si—CH$_2$—R, 296; 12.13 Si—C$_6$H$_5$, 296; 12.14 Si—CH=CH$_2$, 296; 12.15 Si—O—R, 296; 12.16 Si—O—C$_6$H$_5$, 297; 12.17 Si—O—Si, 297; 12.18 Si—OH, 297; 12.19 Si—Halogen, 297; 12.20 Si—N, 298; 12.21 Phosphorus Compounds, 298; 12.22 P—H, 299; 12.23 P=O, 299; 12.24 P—OH, 300; 12.25 P—O—P, 300; 12.26 PO$_2^-$, POS$^-$, PO$_3^{2-}$, PO$_4^{3-}$, 300; 12.27 P—O—C (Aliphatic), 301; 12.28 P—O—C (Phenyl), 301; 12.29 P—CH$_2$, 302; 12.30 P—CH$_3$, 302; 12.31 P—Phenyl, 302; 12.32 P=S, 302; 12.33 P—SH, 304; 12.34 P—N, 304; 12.35 P=N, 305; 12.36 P—F, P—Cl, P—C, 305; 12.37 S—H, 305; 12.38 Sulfides and Disulfides, 306; 12.39 CH$_2$—S, 306; 12.40 CH$_3$—S, 306; 12.41 S—CH=CH$_2$, 307; 12.42 S—Aryl, 307; 12.43 S—F, 307; 12.44 SO, 307; 12.45 SO$_2$, 308; 12.46 Sulfones, 308; 12.47 Sulfonamides, 308; 12.48 Sulfonic Acids,

310; 12.49 Sulfonic Acid Salts, 310; 12.50 Sulfinic Acids, 310; 12.51 HSO_4^-, 310; 12.52 SO_4^{2-}, 311; 12.53 SO_3^{2-}, 311; 12.54 $S-O-CH_2$, 311; 12.55 Thionylamine, 311; 12.56 $C=S$, 311; 12.57 (FHF)−, 313; 12.58 FCH, 313; 12.59 $FC=C$, 314; 12.60 $FC=O$, 314; 12.61 F-Aryl, 314; 12.62 CF Stretch, 314; 12.63 $C-Cl$, 315; 12.64 $C-Br$, 316; 12.65 $C-I$, 317; 12.66 Aryl Halides, 317; 12.67 Organometallic Compounds, 317

Chapter 13

MAJOR SPECTRA-STRUCTURE
CORRELATIONS BY SPECTRAL REGIONS 319

13.1 Introduction, 319; 13.2 3700-3100 cm^{-1} (OH, NH, and $\equiv$CH), 319; 13.3 3100-3000 cm^{-1} (Aryl, Olefinic, and Three Membered Ring CH), 319; 13.4 3000-2700 cm^{-1} (Aliphatic CH), 320; 13.5 3100-2400 cm^{-1} (Acidic and Strongly Bonded Hydrogens), 320; 13.6 2600-2100 cm^{-1} (SH, BH, PH, and SiH), 320; 13.7 2300-1900 cm^{-1} ($X\equiv Y$ and $X=Y=Z$), 320; 13.8 2000-1700 cm^{-1} (Aryl and Olefinic Overtones), 321; 13.9 1900-1550 cm^{-1} ($C=O$), 321; 13.10 1700-1550 cm^{-1} ($C=C$ and $C=N$), 321; 13.11 1660-1450 cm^{-1} ($N=O$), 322; 13.12 1660-1500 cm^{-1} (NH_2, NH_3^+, and CNH), 322; 13.13 1620-1420 cm^{-1} (Aromatic and Heteroaromatic Rings), 322; 13.14 1500-1250 cm^{-1} (CH_3 and CH_2), 322; 13.15 1470-1310 cm^{-1} ($B-O$, $B-N$, NO_3^-, CO_3^{2-}, and NH_4^+), 323; 13.16 1400-1000 cm^{-1} (SO_2, SO_3^{2-}, SO, and SO_4^{2-}), 323; 13.17 1300-1140 cm^{-1} ($P=O$), 323; 13.18 1350-1120 cm^{-1} (CF_3 and CF_2), 323; 13.19 1350-1150 cm^{-1} (CH_2 and CH wag), 323; 13.20 1300-1000 cm^{-1} ($C-O$), 324; 13.21 1100-830 cm^{-1} ($Si-O$ and $P-O$), 324; 13.22 1000-600 cm^{-1} (Olefinic CH Wag), 324; 13.23 900-700 cm^{-1} (Aromatic CH Wag), 325; 13.24 830-500 cm^{-1} (CCl, CBr, and Cl), 325; 13.25 Near Infrared Region Correlation Chart, 325; 13.26 Carbon-Hydrogen Stretching Region Correlation Chart, 329; 13.27 Sodium Chloride Region Correlation Charts, 336; 13.28 Cesium Bromide Region Correlation Charts, 336; 13.29 Selected Infrared Spectra Illustrating Functional Group Frequencies, 349; 13.30 Documentation of Spectra, 420

Chapter 14

THE THEORETICAL ANALYSIS OF
MOLECULES 422

14.1 Normal Modes of Vibration, 423; 14.2 Internal Coordinates, 425; 14.3 Symmetry Coordinates, 426; 14.4 The Calculation of Frequencies, 427; 14.5 The $CHCl_3$ Molecule, 432; 14.6 The Internal Coordinates for $CHCl_3$, 432; 14.7 The Symmetry Coordinates for $CHCl_3$, 433;

14.8 The F Matrix for $CHCl_3$, 440; 14.9 The G Matrix for $CHCl_3$, 445; 14.10 The Secular Determinants for $CHCl_3$, 452; 14.11 The Infrared and Raman Spectra of $CHCl_3$ and $CDCl_3$, 457; 14.12 Band Assignments for $CHCl_3$, and $CDCl_3$, 458; 14.13 Comparison of Experimental and Calculated Values, 460; 14.14 The General Application of Theoretical Analysis, 461

Chapter 15

THE CALCULATION OF THERMODYNAMIC
FUNCTIONS 463

15.1 The Partition Function, 463; 15.2 The Partition Function and the Total Energy, 464; 15.3 The Partition Function and the Thermodynamic Functions, 464; 15.4 Evaluation of the Partition Function, 469; 15.5 Evaluation of the Thermodynamic Functions for $CHCl_3$, 476

AUTHOR INDEX 485

SUBJECT INDEX 498

INTRODUCTION TO
INFRARED AND RAMAN SPECTROSCOPY

CHAPTER 1

VIBRATIONAL
AND ROTATIONAL SPECTRA

1.1 Introduction

The energy of a molecule consists partly of translational energy, partly of rotational energy, partly of vibrational energy, and partly of electronic energy. For a first approximation these energy contributions can be treated separately. Electronic energy transitions normally give rise to absorption or emission in the ultraviolet and visible regions of the electromagnetic spectrum. Pure rotation gives rise to absorption in the microwave region. Molecular vibrations give rise to absorption bands throughout most of the infrared region of the spectrum. In this book we shall mainly be concerned with the interaction of electromagnetic radiation with molecular vibrations and rotations.

According to the quantum theory the frequency ν' in cycles per second of a photon is proportional to its energy E in ergs so that

$$E = h\nu' \tag{1.1}$$

where h is Planck's constant, 6.62391×10^{-27} erg-sec. The frequency ν' is related to the wavelength λ in cm and to the wavenumber, ν in cm^{-1} as follows,

$$\nu' = \frac{c}{\lambda} = \nu c \tag{1.2}$$

where c is the velocity of light, 2.997930×10^{10} cm/sec (see Fig. 1.1).

If fundamental units, centimeters and seconds, are used in Eq. (1.2), then the ultraviolet, visible, infrared, and microwave regions of the electromagnetic spectrum assume the values shown in Table 1.1.

As can be seen from Table 1.2 the micron is a more convenient unit than the millimicron for the infrared region. In actual practice the usual absorption spectrum in the infrared region is shown as a plot of absorption versus the

1

TABLE 1.1

VALUES FOR λ, ν, AND ν' (FUNDAMENTAL UNITS)[a]

Region	λ (cm)	ν (cm^{-1})	ν' (sec^{-1})
Ultraviolet			
(far)	1×10^{-6} to 2×10^{-5}	1×10^6 to 50,000	3×10^{16} to 1.5×10^{15}
(near)	2×10^{-5} to 3.8×10^{-5}	50,000 to 26,320	1.5×10^{15} to 7.9×10^{14}
Visible	3.8×10^{-5} to 7.8×10^{-5}	26,320 to 12,820	7.9×10^{14} to 3.8×10^{14}
Infrared			
(near)	7.8×10^{-5} to 3×10^{-4}	12,820 to 3333	3.8×10^{14} to 1×10^{14}
(middle)	3×10^{-4} to 3×10^{-3}	3333 to 333	1×10^{14} to 1×10^{13}
(far)	3×10^{-3} to 3×10^{-2}	333 to 33.3	1×10^{13} to 1×10^{12}
Microwave	3×10^{-2} to 1×10^{2}	33.3 to 0.01	1×10^{12} to 3×10^{8}

[a] Since fundamental units yield awkward numbers particularly in the case of wavelength and frequency values, the following units are more practical. For wavelength: 1 micron designated $\mu = 1 \times 10^{-4}$ cm; or 1 millimicron* designated $m\mu = 1 \times 10^{-7}$ cm. For frequency: 1 fresnel $= \nu'/10^{12}$. With these units, the values shown in Table 1.2 result.

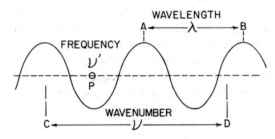

FIG. 1.1. Relationship between wavelength, wavenumber, and frequency. The wavelength, λ, is the distance between adjacent waves (A and B). The wavenumber, ν, is the number of waves in a unit length (C to D). The frequency, ν', is the number of waves passing a fixed point P in a unit time.

* In emission spectroscopy line spectra are measured in angstroms (i.e., $1\text{Å} = 1 \times 10^{-8}$ cm) rather than millimicrons because the sharpness of emission lines can be measured to 1 Å even with instruments of moderate resolution. In absorption spectroscopy the bands are broad and there is little need for the additional significant figure. Hence, in the ultraviolet and visible regions absorption band maxima are reported in millimicrons. In Raman spectroscopy, the lines in most cases are sharp and measured in angstroms or cm^{-1}. At one time the angstrom was defined as a unit of length equal to $1/6438.4696$ of the wavelength of the red line of cadmium. This value was almost but not exactly 10^{-8} cm or 10^{-10} meter. Recently, the standard unit of length, the meter, has been redefined to be $1,650,763.73$ wavelengths (in vacuum) of the orange-red line of Kr^{86}. With this definition, the angstrom is again exactly 1×10^{-8} cm.

TABLE 1.2

VALUES FOR λ, ν, AND ν' (PRACTICAL UNITS)

Region	λ (millimicrons)		ν (cm^{-1})	ν' (fresnels)
Ultraviolet				
(far)	10	–200	1×10^6–50,000	30,000–1500
(near)	200	–380	50,000–26,320	1500– 790
Visible	380	–780	26,320–12,820	790– 385
		microns		
Infrared				
(near)	0.78–	3.0	12,820– 3333	385– 100
(middle)	3.0 –	30	3333 – 333	100– 10
(far)	30	–300	333 – 33.3	10– 1
Microwave	300	–1,000,000	33.3– 0.01	1– 3×10^{-4}

wavelength in microns or absorption versus wavenumber in cm^{-1}.* The term "frequency in cm^{-1}" is often used for wavenumbers. For many instruments both units are shown on the printed graph. Recently the word, Kaysers, to replace wavenumbers has been recommended but has not been adopted as yet in most publications. Some confusion has also arisen because ν and ν' are both called frequency.

1.2 Normal Modes of Vibration

If a nonlinear molecule is placed in a three-dimensional (x, y, and z) coordinate system, it will require three coordinates to specify the position of each atom. If the molecule contains N atoms, then $3N$ coordinates are required and the molecule is said to have $3N$ degrees of freedom. Considering the molecule as a distinct unit, translation of the center of gravity to any point on the x, y, z coordinate system can be described with three coordinates. Rotation of the molecule as a whole about its center of gravity can be described by three angular coordinates specifying rotation about three mutually perpendicular axes intersecting at the center of gravity. The remaining $3N$-6 degrees of freedom describe vibrational motions of the atoms of the molecule. Thus, for a nonlinear molecule there are $3N$-6 fundamental vibrations or normal modes. However, in the case of a linear molecule only two rotational coordinates are needed about two axes at right angles to the molecular axis since it is not necessary to specify

* Since the velocity of light varies according to the medium, there is a small difference for ν measured in air (ν_a) versus that in vacuum (ν_v). For example, at 1000 cm^{-1} $\nu_a - \nu_v$ = 0.26 and at 3000 cm^{-1}, $\nu_a - \nu_v$ = 0.78. In practical spectroscopy no attention is given to this difference, but in high resolution work the correction is often made.

rotation about the molecular axis. Linear molecules therefore have $3N-5$ funda-mental vibrational modes.

The modes of vibration of a molecule may be demonstrated by a classical analogy where nuclei are represented by weights and intramolecular forces by springs. If such a molecular model is freely supported and is struck with a hammer, it will usually perform complicated types of motion where the indi-vidual weights move in complex nonrepetitive fashions. It can be shown that these complex motions are combinations of $3N-6$ (or $3N-5$) modes of vibration in each of which all the atoms perform simple harmonic motions with the same frequency, all atoms passing through their equilibrium positions simultaneously. These are the so called normal or fundamental modes of vibration.

1.3 Mechanical Molecular Models

Figure 1.2 illustrates an apparatus for a mechanical analogy of molecular vibrations.[1] A source of oscillation is provided by an eccentric on the shaft of a motor whose rotational speed is adjustable. This oscillating eccentric is attached

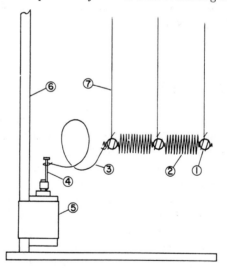

FIG. 1.2. Apparatus for a mechanical analogy of molecular vibrations. A freely suspend-ed ball and spring model representing the CO_2 molecule is attached through a loose coupling to an oscillating eccentric on a motor. (1) $\frac{7}{16}$-in. diameter steel ball bearings held within shaped coils. (2) 16 mil helical spring, 12 coils $\frac{7}{8}$-in. diameter, $2\frac{1}{2}$-in. between "atoms." (3) 10 mil coupling wire. (4) Nail taped to side of motor shaft to form an eccen-tric. (5) Variable speed motor (1–7 revolutions/sec). (6) Tall ringstand. (7) Long threads.

[1] C. F. Kettering, L. W. Shutts and D. H. Andrews, *Phys. Rev.* **36**, 531 (1930).

through a fine spring coupling wire to the suitably suspended weight and spring molecular model. As the motor speed is altered the oscillating eccentric "disturbs" the molecular model with a varying frequency through the loose coupling. When the "disturbing" frequency coincides with the frequency of one of the normal modes of vibration of the model, resonance occurs. The model responds by performing this normal mode of vibration (see Fig. 1.3). It can be seen that all weights either remain motionless or perform simple harmonic motions with identical frequencies. At a different "disturbing" frequency another normal mode may be "excited." When the "disturbing" frequency does not coincide with the frequency of a normal mode, the model remains quiet.

The helical spring is only an approximate representation of the molecular force field, and this rough approximation is one of the limitations of models. For demonstration purposes, however, the relative frequencies obtained agree sufficiently well with the relative frequencies of the actual molecules. The

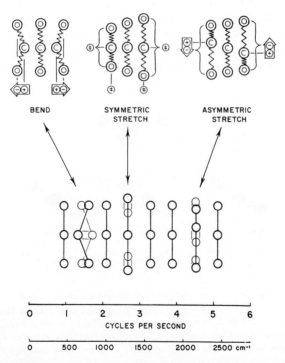

FIG. 1.3. Frequency response and representation of the vibrations of a spring model of carbon dioxide. The ball and spring model responds to different "disturbing" mechanical frequencies which are proportional to frequencies (cm^{-1}) in the actual case. The bending and asymmetric stretching vibrations cause a change in the dipole moment of the molecule and thus are infrared active. The symmetric stretching vibration causes no change in dipole moment and so is infrared inactive.

stretching and bending force constants of the spring can be adjusted so that their ratio is about eight or ten to one which is approximately the ratio found in real molecules. This ratio can be increased if too small by permanently stretching out the spring a little. Planar vibrations of planar molecules can be studied by suspending the molecular plane horizontally and supporting every weight by a long thread as in Fig. 1.2.

1.4 Doubly Degenerate Modes of Vibration

The linear CO_2 molecule has $3N$-5 or 4 fundamental modes of vibration three of which are illustrated in Fig. 1.3. The fourth fundamental is another bending vibration identical in character and frequency to the one illustrated but where each atom moves in a direction perpendicular to that of the first case. Such pairs of vibrations which have the same frequency are called doubly degenerate vibrations. The two bending fundamental modes of vibration for the CO_2 molecule are illustrated in the upper part of Fig. 1.4. Cartesian coor-

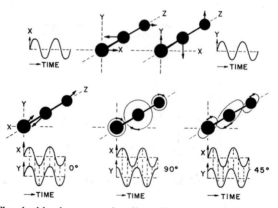

FIG. 1.4. The doubly degenerate bending vibrations of carbon dioxide. The two top figures illustrate the two fundamental bending modes of vibration. Graphs of end atom displacements in the X and Y directions as a function of time are illustrated. The bottom three figures illustrate motions which result from combinations of the two fundamental components with various phase differences (0°, 90°, and 45°) and equal amplitudes.

dinates are drawn with an end atom at the origin and the molecular axis coincident with the Z axis. In one vibration every atom performs a simple harmonic motion with the same frequency where the graph of the displacement in the X direction versus time is a sine wave. The graphs in the illustration describe the motion of an end atom. In the second vibration, a graph of Y versus time is a sine wave. These two vibrations have the same frequency and can both be activated at the same time. The molecule actually performs a motion which is a resultant of the two component simple harmonic motions.

Three possible resultant motions are illustrated in the lower part of Fig. 1.4. The graphs illustrate separately the X and Y components of end atom displacement as a function of time both of which are sine waves with the same frequency. If the phase difference between the two fundamental components is zero (or 180°) then $X = 0$ when $Y = 0$. Each atom goes through the equilibrium position as it performs a simple harmonic motion in a direction intermediate between the X and Y directions. If the phase difference is not zero (or 180°) the atoms move in circles or ellipses around the molecular axis and do not go through the equilibrium position since when $X = 0$, $Y \neq 0$. All these relatively simple resultant motions are periodic in nature, all atoms moving with the same frequency. These motions differ from the complex and usually nonperiodic motions which result from the mixing of two vibrations with different frequencies.

Although the fundamental components of doubly degenerate vibrations have a definite relationship to each other they are not uniquely defined. In this case, for example, the same resultant motions could result from mixing two other mutually perpendicular fundamental components perpendicular to the molecular axis in any direction intermediate between X and Y.

1.5 Dipole Moment

In order for a normal mode of vibration to be infrared active, that is, to give rise to an observable infrared band there must be a change in the dipole moment of the molecule during the course of the vibration. When a positive charge $+ z$ and a negative charge $- z$ are separated by a distance d, the dipole moment μ is equal to the magnitude of either charge multiplied by the distance

$$\mu = zd \tag{1.3}$$

When the units of z equal 10^{-10} electrostatic units and d is expressed in angstroms (10^{-8} cm) the dipole moment is expressed in debye units where 1 debye $= 1 \times 10^{-18}$ e.s.u. cm.

The hydrogen chloride molecule consists of two atoms of different electronegativities and has a permanent dipole moment. During the vibration of the hydrogen chloride molecule the internuclear distance varies thus changing the dipole moment. This vibration is infrared active. Due to its symmetry, the hydrogen molecule has no charge displacement and no permanent dipole moment. No charge displacement is caused by the vibration of the H_2 molecule as symmetry is retained at all times. This vibration is infrared inactive.

In the CO_2 molecule in Fig. 1.3 the center of positive charge is considered to be in the carbon atom and the center of negative charge halfway between the two oxygen atoms. The molecule has no permanent dipole moment. But during the bending and asymmetric stretching vibrations there are changes in the dipole moment so these vibrations are infrared active. The symmetric stretching vibration which causes no net charge displacement is infrared inactive.

Pure rotational infrared spectra can be observed if the rotating molecule has a permanent dipole moment since in this case a change in dipole moment can occur, as seen by the incident radiation.

1.6 Theoretical Linear Harmonic Oscillator

A weight and spring model of the hydrogen chloride molecule is shown in Fig. 1.5. During the vibration of the model the internuclear distance changes. The difference between the internuclear distance r at any time from the equilibrium distance r_0 is represented by Δr. If it is assumed that the model behaves as a simple harmonic oscillator the restoring force f is proportional to Δr.

$$f = -k\Delta r \tag{1.4}$$

The proportionality constant k is called the force constant. It is also true that the force at a given point is equal to the negative derivative of the potential energy, U_r, with respect to Δr at that point.

$$f = -\frac{dU_r}{d(\Delta r)} \tag{1.5}$$

and

$$-\frac{dU_r}{d(\Delta r)} = -k\Delta r \tag{1.6}$$

The variation of the potential energy with Δr is given by integrating Eq. (1.6)

$$U_r = 1/2\, k(\Delta r)^2. \tag{1.7}$$

A plot of U_r vs. r yields a parabola as shown in Fig. 1.5. At the minimum of this parabola where the potential energy is zero, the internuclear distance is labeled r_0.

For a harmonic oscillator the frequency of oscillation or vibration is independent of both the amplitude and the energy of the oscillation and is given by an equation derived from Hooke's law,

$$\nu' = \frac{1}{2\pi}\sqrt{\frac{k}{u}} \quad \text{or} \quad \nu = \frac{1}{2\pi c}\sqrt{\frac{k}{u}} \tag{1.8}$$

where ν' is the frequency of the vibration in cycles per second, ν is the frequency in cm^{-1},* k is the force constant in dynes per centimeter, c is the velocity of

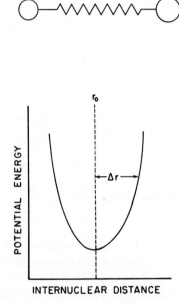

FIG. 1.5. Schematic spring model of hydrogen chloride and potential energy diagram of a harmonic oscillator.

light, and u is the reduced mass of the vibrating atoms defined by the equation $(1/u) = (1/m_1) + (1/m_2)$ where m_1 and m_2 are the masses in grams of the vibrating atoms.

A quantum mechanical treatment[2] of the linear harmonic oscillator yields the following equation

$$E_{\text{vib.}} = (v + \tfrac{1}{2})hc\nu_0 \tag{1.9}$$

[2] B. Bak, "Elementary Introduction to Molecular Structure," pp. 47-50. Interscience, New York, 1954.

* A photon which has the same frequency as the oscillator will have a "frequency in cm^{-1}" or wavenumber equal to ν.

where $E_{\text{vib.}}$ is the vibrational energy, v is the vibrational quantum number which can assume the integer values 0, 1, 2, 3 ..., ν_0 is the fundamental vibrational frequency in cm^{-1}, h is Planck's constant, and c is the velocity of light.

In the classical oscillator the amplitude and energy can vary continuously. In the quantum mechanical oscillator the vibrational energy has discrete values or energy levels described by quantum numbers. In the lowest possible energy state each particle in the classical oscillator is stationary and is found at a fixed position, the equilibrium position. In the quantum mechanical oscillator [Eq. (1.9)] it can be seen that when $v = 0$ the energy is not zero but $\frac{1}{2} hc \nu_0$. This is the zero point energy of the vibrator which exists at the temperature of absolute zero when all translational motion has stopped. Even at absolute zero with all the quanta of vibrational energy removed, the molecule still vibrates. The zero point energy is a result of the Heisenberg uncertainty principle. According to this principle the uncertainty in the position of a particle multiplied by the uncertainty in the momentum of the particle is approximately equal to h, Planck's constant. In order to completely define the position of a particle the momentum must approach infinity. In order to completely specify the momentum the position must be infinitely variable.

1.7 Actual Diatomic Oscillator

In an actual molecule such as hydrogen chloride there is considerable deviation from the simple harmonic oscillator approximation. The potential energy curve resembles that shown in Fig. 1.6. Around the minimum of the curve the quantized energy levels are represented by the horizontal lines labeled $v = 0, 1, 2, 3, 4, \ldots$. These initial levels are almost equally spaced since the vibrational amplitudes are small and the vibrations are essentially harmonic. However as the vibrational quantum number increases, the vibrational levels come closer together and ultimately dissociation occurs. The spectroscopic energy of dissociation D_e is the energy of dissociation measured from the minimum while D_0, the chemical energy required for dissociation, is the height of the asymptote measured from $v = 0$, the ground vibrational state. Thus, $D_e = D_0 + \frac{1}{2} hc \nu_0$ [see Eq. (1.9)]. On the potential energy curve r_e is the equilibrium internuclear distance while r_0 is the internuclear distance at the lowest energy state. These two internuclear distances do not coincide because the curve is not quite symmetrical near the minimum.

It can be shown that if the vibrations of a molecule were strictly harmonic, the vibrational energy could only change one step at a time, that is $\Delta v = \pm 1$.

If the harmonic oscillator energy Eq. (1.9) is solved for $v = 0$ and $v = 1$, the result is

$$E_{\text{vib.}} = (v + \tfrac{1}{2}) h \, cv_0 = \tfrac{1}{2} hc \, v_0 \quad \text{for } v = 0 \qquad (1.10)$$

$$= \tfrac{3}{2} hc \, v_0 \quad \text{for } v = 1 \qquad (1.11)$$

The difference between these two equations is

$$\Delta E_{\text{vib.}} = hcv_0 \quad \text{or} \quad \frac{\Delta E_{\text{vib.}}}{hc} = v_0 \quad (\text{cm}^{-1}) \qquad (1.12)$$

The energy difference between these two energy levels is equivalent to the energy of an infrared photon whose frequency in cm^{-1} is v_0. This photon is totally absorbed when it changes the molecule in the ground state $v = 0$ to

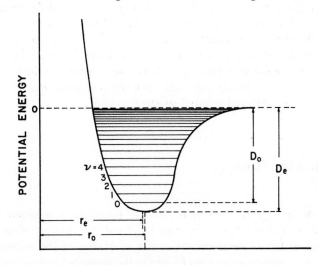

INTERNUCLEAR DISTANCE

FIG. 1.6. Potential energy diagram of an actual diatomic oscillator.

the first excited vibrational state $v = 1$. (We assume there is no rotational interaction here). Other $\Delta v = 1$ transitions such as $v = 1 \rightarrow v = 2$ yield the same result as Eq. (1.12). These transitions which originate from elevated vibrational states are more probable at higher temperatures. Most molecules at room temperature are in the ground state but at higher temperatures the population in the excited states increases. Transitions from a higher vibrational level to a lower level involving $\Delta v = -1$ result in emission rather than absorption of radiation.

Because the vibrations of a real molecule are anharmonic, Eq. (1.9) must be modified with the vibrational energy levels being given by

$$E_{\text{vib.}} = hc \left[\nu_0 \left(v + \tfrac{1}{2}\right) - x\nu_0 \left(v + \tfrac{1}{2}\right)^2 + \ldots \right] \qquad (1.13)$$

where x is the anharmonicity constant. The values of x vary from 0.01 to 0.05 for single bonds. Because of the anharmonicity, the spacings between the vibrational levels become smaller as the vibrational quantum number increases. Now $v = 1 \rightarrow v = 2$ transitions give rise to slightly lower frequencies of absorption than $v = 0 \rightarrow v = 1$ transitions. No longer is the variation in vibrational quantum number simply ± 1 but now variations of ± 1, ± 2, ... are allowed. The vibrational spectrum may therefore contain so-called harmonics or overtones ($v = 0 \rightarrow v = 2, 3, 4, \ldots$) as well as the fundamental ($v = 0 \rightarrow v = 1$) vibrational band. These overtones may occur at values approximately equal to two, three, or four times the fundamental expressed in wavenumbers. For example, if the fundamental vibration occurs at 2886 cm^{-1}, one might expect the first overtone at a value somewhat less than 5772 cm^{-1}. In polyatomic molecules both combination bands (i.e., linear combinations of the fundamentals in cm^{-1}) or difference bands also occur in many instances, thus adding to the complexity of the observed infrared spectrum.

1.8 Molecular Rotation

As shown in Fig. 1.7 hydrogen chloride resembles a lopsided dumbbell since the masses of the hydrogen atom (m_{H}) and the chlorine atom (m_{Cl}) are quite different. Let G represent the center of gravity of the molecule, d the distance of the chlorine atom from G, and r_0 the apparent internuclear distance. According to the lever principle,

$$m_{\text{H}}(r_0 - d) = m_{\text{Cl}}d \qquad (1.14)$$

$$d = \frac{m_{\text{H}}r_0}{m_{\text{H}} + m_{\text{Cl}}} \qquad (1.15)$$

If it is assumed that the molecule rotates as a rigid rotator about the axis b which passes through the center of gravity, G, and is perpendicular to the internuclear axis, then the moment of inertia I_b about the axis is given by

$$I_b = m_{\text{H}}(r_0 - d)^2 + m_{\text{Cl}}d^2 \qquad (1.16)$$

Substituting from Eq. (1.15)

$$I_b = \frac{m_H m_{Cl}}{m_H + m_{Cl}} r_0^2 \qquad (1.17)$$

and recalling the definition of the reduced mass, u,

$$u = \frac{m_H m_{Cl}}{m_H + m_{Cl}}$$

$$I_b = u r_0^2 \qquad (1.18)$$

where in this case u is the reduced mass of the hydrogen and chlorine atoms. In other words, the molecule rotating about the axis b has the same moment of inertia I_b as a particle of effective mass, u, moving in a circle of radius r_0.

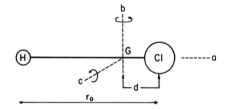

FIG. 1.7. Hydrogen chloride as a rigid rotator.

A quantum mechanical treatment of the rigid rotator yields the following equation.

$$E_{rot.} = \frac{J(J+1) h^2}{8\pi^2 u r_0^2} = \frac{J(J+1) h^2}{8\pi^2 I_b} \qquad (1.19)$$

where $E_{rot.}$ is the rotational energy, and J is the rotational quantum number which can assume the values $0, 1, 2, 3, \ldots$. This equation can be rewritten as

$$E_{rot.} = Bhc\, J(J+1) \qquad (1.20)$$

where B which is called the rotational constant is defined by*

$$B = \frac{h}{8\pi^2 I_b c} \qquad (1.21)$$

* In place of B some authors use b (in ergs) where $b = h^2/8\pi^2 I_b$.

In the classical rigid rotator the angular momentum can vary continuously. In the quantum mechanical rigid rotator the angular momentum P has discrete values described by quantum numbers where

$$P = \frac{h}{2\pi} \sqrt{J(J+1)} \qquad (1.22)$$

The selection rule for allowed rotational energy transitions is $\Delta J = \pm 1$. Let J be the quantum number for a rotational state and $J + 1$ be the quantum number for the next higher rotational state. The transition $J \rightarrow J + 1$ results in the absorption of infrared radiation whose energy is the same as the increase in rotational energy of the molecule. If we substitute $J + 1$ for J in Eq. (1.20) we obtain

$$E_{\text{rot.}} = Bhc(J + 1)(J + 2) \qquad (1.23)$$

By substracting Eq. (1.20) which is the rotational energy of the J state from Eq. (1.23) which is the rotational energy of the $J + 1$ state we obtain for the energy difference

$$\Delta E_{\text{rot.}} = 2Bhc(J + 1) \qquad (1.24)$$

or

$$\frac{\Delta E_{\text{rot.}}}{hc} \text{ (cm}^{-1}) = 2B(J + 1) \qquad (1.25)$$

This equation shows that the moment of inertia of the molecule (included in B) can be evaluated from the spectrum (see Fig. 1.8).

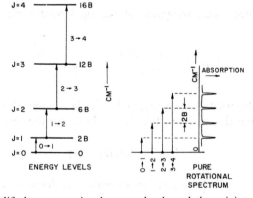

FIG. 1.8. Simplified pure rotational energy levels and the origin of pure rotational lines in an X-Y diatomic molecule. The pure rotational energy levels in cm^{-1} are equal to $BJ(J + 1)$; for $J = 1, 2, 3, \ldots$, the energy levels in cm^{-1} = $2B, 6B, 12B$. Allowed transitions for absorption ($\Delta J = +1$) are indicated by arrows on the left. The differences between adjacent levels in cm$^{-1} \uparrow$ are indicated graphically on the right as being equal to the wavenumbers of the absorption lines of the pure rotational spectrum.

The pure rotational spectrum of HCl has been measured by Hansler and Oetjen.[3] Their data and treatment of these data are shown in Table 1.3.

TABLE 1.3

FAR INFRARED ABSORPTION BANDS OF HCl AND RELATED CALCULATIONS

Frequency, ν (cm^{-1})	Quantum numbers associated with energy levels		$\dfrac{\nu}{(J+1)} = 2B$
	Lower $J \rightarrow J + 1$	Upper	
83.32	3	4	20.83
104.13	4	5	20.83
124.73	5	6	20.79
145.37	6	7	20.79
165.89	7	8	20.74
186.23	8	9	20.69
206.60	9	10	20.66
226.86	10	11	20.62

Evidently the values for the lower transitions could not be observed with the instrumentation available. The decreases in the values shown in the last column are caused by centrifugal stretching. In the upper rotational levels the molecule rotates faster and the bond is elongated slightly resulting in a decrease in the spacing between levels and a slight increase in the moment of inertia. To accurately fit the energy levels a correction term must be added to Eq. (1.20) as follows:

$$E_{\text{rot.}} = BhcJ(J + 1) - Dhc[J(J + 1)]^2 \qquad (1.26)$$

where D is the centrifugal distortion constant.

If the small deviation caused by centrifugal stretching is ignored, then $2B$ equals approximately 20.8 cm^{-1} and $B = 10.4$ cm^{-1}. Now from Eq. (1.21)

$$I_b = \frac{h}{8\pi^2 Bc} = \frac{6.624 \times 10^{-27}}{8 \times (3.14)^2 \times 10.4 \times 3 \times 10^{10}} \qquad (1.27)$$

and

$$I_b = 2.69 \times 10^{-40} \text{ gm-cm}^2$$

and since the reduced mass of HCl* is

$$u = \frac{35.5 \times 1}{35.5 + 1} \times \frac{1}{6.02 \times 10^{23}} = 1.616 \times 10^{-24} \text{ gm/molecule}$$

[3] R. L. Hansler and R. A. Oetjen, *J. Chem. Phys.* **21**, 1340 (1953).
* The data for HCl was obtained on the gas containing both the Cl^{35} and Cl^{37} isotopes; so the mass based on the normal isotopic abundances has been used in this calculation.

then

$$r_0^2 = \frac{2.69 \times 10^{-40}}{1.616 \times 10^{-24}} = 1.665 \times 10^{-16} \text{ cm}^2$$

and

$$r_0 = 1.29 \times 10^{-8} \text{ cm} = 1.29 \text{ Å}$$

1.9   Types of Rotators

In considering the rotation of hydrogen chloride only rotation about the b axis has been discussed. If the rotation were performed about the c axis (see Fig. 1.7) which passes through G and is perpendicular to the b axis, the same result would be obtained. Hence, $I_b = I_c$. The moment of inertia about the a axis which joins the hydrogen and chlorine atoms is equal to zero. Therefore, for a linear molecule $I_a = 0$ and $I_b = I_c$. The moments of inertia are conventionally designated in this manner with I_a having the smallest moment, I_b the next largest and I_c the largest moment. With moments of inertia as a basis molecules can be classified as rotators then into the four distinct types shown in Table 1.4.

Polyatomic linear molecules and diatomic molecules have identical rotational energy equations. However, pure rotational spectra can only be observed for those molecules which possess a permanent dipole moment. Linear molecules such as carbon dioxide and acetylene do not have a permanent dipole moment because of their symmetry.

Spherical top molecules, which have three equal moments of inertia, have a rotational energy equation identical to the equation for linear molecules. However, these molecules do not have a permanent dipole moment so pure rotation for such molecules does not give rise to a changing dipole moment.

An asymmetrical top molecule has three different moments of inertia. Although the rotational spectrum and the rotational energy expression is complex, some individual molecules such as water have been successfully treated.

1.10   Rotation of Symmetrical Top Molecules

Molecules with a 3-fold or higher axis of symmetry (see Section 3.1) are symmetrical tops (or symmetrical rotators) and have two equal moments of inertia. A few molecules of lower symmetry may by chance have two moments

TABLE 1.4

TYPES OF ROTATORS

Type	Moments of inertia	$E_{rot.}$	Structure	Examples[a]
(1) Linear	$I_a = 0, I_b = I_c$	$J(J+1)Bhc$	Linear	HCl, HBr, all diatomic molecules, CO_2, C_2H_2, etc.
(2) Spherical top	$I_a = I_b = I_c$	$J(J+1)Bhc$	Tetrahedron Octahedron	CH_4, CCl_4, SiH_4, etc. SF_6, UF_6, etc.
(3) Symmetric top (oblate)	$I_a = I_b \neq I_c$	$J(J+1)Bhc + K^2(C-B)hc$	Structure with one 3-fold or higher-fold axis	BF_3, C_6H_6, $CHCl_3$
(prolate)	$I_a \neq I_b = I_c$	$J(J+1)Bhc + K^2(A-B)hc$	Structure with one 3-fold or higher-fold axis	C_2H_6, CH_3Cl, etc.
(4) Asymmetric top	$I_a \neq I_b \neq I_c$	No simple equation	Structure lacking a 3-fold or higher-fold axis	H_2O, CH_2O, CH_3OH, etc.

[a] For a more complete list of compounds belonging to each type see Table 3.8.

of inertia almost equal and are almost symmetrical tops. The 3-fold or higher symmetry axis is called the unique axis of the molecule. If the two smaller moments are equal, i.e., $I_a = I_b \neq I_c$, then the molecule is an oblate or coinlike rotator. If the two larger moments are equal, i.e., $I_a \neq I_b = I_c$, then the molecule is a prolate or rodlike rotator.

For an oblate rotator the rotational energy is given by

$$E_{\text{rot.}} = J(J + 1)Bhc + K^2(C - B)hc \qquad (1.28)$$

where J is the quantum number characterizing the total angular momentum of the molecule and may have the values 0, 1, 2, 3 ... . K is the quantum number characterizing the angular momentum about the unique axis of the molecule. K may have integer values 0, 1, 2, 3, ... which may equal but not exceed J numerically. B and C are rotational constants defined by

$$B = \frac{h}{8\pi^2 I_b c} \qquad (1.29)$$

$$C = \frac{h}{8\pi^2 I_c c} \qquad (1.30)$$

The rotational energy of the prolate rotator is given by

$$E_{\text{rot.}} = J(J + 1)Bhc + K^2(A - B)hc \qquad (1.31)$$

where the symbols have been previously defined except for A which is given by

$$A = \frac{h}{8\pi^2 I_a c} \qquad (1.32)$$

No infrared absorption can result from the pure rotation of a symmetrical top molecule about the unique or symmetry axis since this rotation yields no change in dipole moment. The selection rules are $\Delta K = 0$ and $\Delta J = \pm 1$ for a symmetrical top with a permanent dipole moment. When the energy difference between two successive energy levels $(J \rightarrow J + 1)$ is evaluated by subtracting Eq. (1.28) from the same equation where $J + 1$ has been substituted for J we obtain,

$$\Delta E_{\text{rot.}} = 2Bhc(J + 1) \qquad (1.33)$$

A similar treatment for Eq. (1.31) yields the same result which is identical with that obtained for the linear molecule Eq. (1.24). Thus, analysis of the pure rotational spectrum of a symmetrical top molecule can yield only one moment of inertia, the one not about the symmetry axis.

1.11 Vibrational-Rotational Spectra

A vibrational-rotational band in the infrared spectrum of a gas has a complex structure because a change in the vibrational energy, E_v, of a molecule may be accompanied by a change in the rotational energy, E_r. We are assuming initially that these energies are additive. By combining Eqs. (1.9) and (1.20) for the linear molecule, the total energy is given by,

$$E_{v+r} = (v + \tfrac{1}{2})hcv_0 + Bhc J(J + 1) \qquad (1.34)$$

Let J represent the rotational quantum number in the ground vibrational state $v = 0$ and J' represent the rotational quantum number in the first excited vibrational state $v = 1$. Subtracting Eq. (1.34) where $v = 0$, $J = J$ from the same equation with the substitution $v = 1$, $J = J'$ yields,

$$\frac{\Delta E_{v+r}}{hc}\ (\text{cm}^{-1}) = v_0 + B[J'(J' + 1) - J(J + 1)] \qquad (1.35)$$

A polyatomic linear molecule can have two types of vibrational-rotational bands. A *parallel* band results when the change in dipole moment is parallel to the molecular axis. A *perpendicular* band results when the dipole moment change is perpendicular to the molecular axis.

For the parallel band the selection rule is $\Delta J = \pm 1$. For the perpendicular band the selection rule is $\Delta J = 0, \pm 1$.

When $\Delta J = 0$ and $J' = J$, Eq. (1.35) becomes

$$\frac{\Delta E_{v+r}}{hc} = Q(\text{cm}^{-1}) = v_0 \qquad (1.36)$$

This equation which is independent of the value of J gives the frequency in cm^{-1} of the so called Q branch of the band.

When $\Delta J = 1$ and $J' = J + 1$ Eq. (1.35) becomes

$$\frac{\Delta E_{v+r}}{hc} = R(\text{cm}^{-1}) = v_0 + 2B(J + 1) \qquad J = 0, 1, 2, ... \qquad (1.37)$$

This equation gives the frequencies in cm^{-1} of the rotational lines which make up the R branch whose values depend on J (the rotational quantum number of the lower vibrational state.)

When $\Delta J = -1$ and $J' = J - 1$ Eq. (1.35) becomes

$$\frac{\Delta E_{v+r}}{hc} = P(\text{cm}^{-1}) = \nu_0 - 2B(J) \qquad J = 1, 2, 3 \dots \qquad (1.38)$$

This is the equation for the frequencies of the rotational lines which make up the P branch whose values depend on J. In this equation J cannot be zero since J' is one integer lower than J (see Fig. 1.9).

Parallel and perpendicular bands in linear molecules have identical P and R branches with a spacing of $2B$ between the rotational lines according to these equations. The perpendicular band has a central Q branch which distinguishes

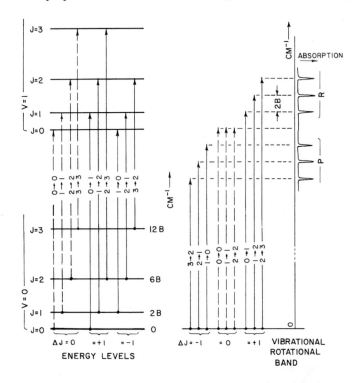

FIG. 1.9. Simplified vibrational-rotational energy levels and the origin of a parallel vibrational-rotational band for a linear molecule. The rotational levels in cm^{-1} for the vibrational ground state $v = 0$ are equal to $BJ(J + 1)$; for $J = 1, 2, 3, \dots$, the energy levels in cm^{-1} = $2B, 6B, 12B, \dots$ Allowed transitions ($\Delta J = \pm 1$) are indicated on the left between $v = 0$ and $v = 1$, the first excited vibrational state which has similar rotational levels. The differences between specified levels in cm^{-1} ↑ are indicated graphically on the right as being equal to the frequency (cm^{-1}) of the absorption lines which make up the band. Only the first three rotational lines of each series are shown. Transitions involving $\Delta J = 0$ are forbidden for parallel bands.

it from parallel bands.* Under conditions of low resolution the P and R branches of the parallel band appear as a broad doublet where the fine structure is not resolved. The doublet spacing, $\Delta\nu$, of the intensity maxima of the P and R branches is given by

$$\Delta\nu = \frac{1}{\pi c}\sqrt{\frac{kT}{I}} \qquad (1.39)$$

where c is the velocity of light, k is the Boltzmann constant, T is the absolute temperature, and I is the moment of inertia. The contour of the P or R branch reflects the relative molecular population of the rotational states. The most intense lines result from transitions from the most highly populated states. The population distribution will change as the temperature changes.

In the vibrational-rotational band of hydrogen chloride in Fig. 1.10 the

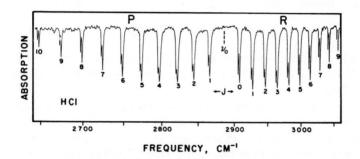

FIG. 1.10.   The hydrogen chloride vibrational-rotational band. The P and R branches are labeled. The Q branch (ν_0) is missing since ΔJ cannot equal zero for a parallel band of a linear molecule. Each rotational line is labeled with its rotational quantum number in the ground vibrational state. In this high resolution spectrum each rotational line is a doublet since chlorine has two naturally occurring isotopes. The peaks for HCl^{37} occur at slightly lower frequencies in cm^{-1} than the peaks for HCl^{35} [see Eq. (1.8)].

individual lines which make up the band are not uniformly spaced as they should be according to the equations presented but become more closely spaced at higher wavenumbers. In the stretching vibration the average internuclear distance and hence the moment of inertia increases as the vibrational quantum number increases. Since the rotational constant is proportional to the reciprocal of the moment of inertia, the rotational constant has a smaller value in the excited state than in the ground state. The rotational constant B is, therefore not constant as has been assumed.

* An exception to this is the NO molecule. In this odd electron molecule there is a resultant electronic angular momentum about the molecular axis which gives rise to a Q branch in a parallel band.

Let B_0 represent the rotational constant in the ground vibrational state and B_1 in the first-excited vibrational state. Equation (1.35) must be modified to yield,

$$\frac{\Delta E_{v+r}}{hc} \text{ (cm}^{-1}\text{)} = \nu_0 + B_1[J'(J'+1)] - B_0[J(J+1)] \qquad (1.40)$$

For the Q branch where $\Delta J = 0$ and $J' = J$ we obtain,

$$Q(\text{cm}^{-1}) = \nu_0 + (B_1 - B_0)\, J^2 + (B_1 - B_0)\, J \qquad J = 0, 1, 2, 3, \ldots$$

For the R branch where $\Delta J = +1$ and $J' = J + 1$ we obtain,

$$R(\text{cm}^{-1}) = \nu_0 + 2B_1 + (3B_1 - B_0)\, J + (B_1 - B_0)\, J^2 \quad J = 0, 1, 2, 3, \ldots \quad (1.41)$$

For the P branch where $\Delta J = -1$ and $J' = J - 1$ we obtain,

$$P(\text{cm}^{-1}) = \nu_0 - (B_1 + B_0)\, J + (B_1 - B_0)\, J^2 \qquad J = 1, 2, 3, \ldots$$

According to these equations there is no requirement for uniform spacing in the P and R branches. The Q branch (when present) no longer consists of a single line.

In the determination of the rotational constants a pair of rotational lines is selected whose separation is dependent on the rotational constant of the ground state (B_0) and a second pair of rotational lines whose separation is dependent on the rotational constant of the excited state (B_1). Two particularly valuable combinations are

$$R_{(J-1)} - P_{(J+1)} = 2B_0(2J + 1) \qquad (1.42)$$

and

$$R_J - P_J = 2B_1(2J + 1) \qquad (1.43)$$

Here R_J or P_J stand for the frequency in cm^{-1} of a rotational line in the R or P branch with a quantum number J. These equations come from Eq. (1.41), R and P branches, respectively. The rotational lines of the vibrational-rotational bands of both HCl^{35} and HCl^{37} have been accurately measured by several investigators.[4,5] For simplicity only HCl^{35} lines will be considered and Table 1.5 is constructed listing values for Eq. (1.42) and (1.43).

It can be seen in Table 1.5 that the rotational constants B_0 and B_1 vary somewhat as the quantum number changes and again this variation can be explained by centrifugal stretching (see Section 1.8). The average values for

[4] E. K. Plyler and E. D. Tidwell, *Z. Elektrochem.* **64**, 717 (1960).
[5] H. M. Mould, W. C. Price and G. R. Wilkinson, Kings College, London, unpublished data.

TABLE 1.5

TREATMENT OF DATA ON VIBRATIONAL-ROTATIONAL BAND OF HCl[35]

J	R_J	P_J	$R_J - P_J$	$R_{(J-1)} - P_{(J+1)}$	$2J+1$	$^a B_1$	$^b B_0$
0	2906.24						
1	2925.90	2865.10	60.80	62.62[c]	3	10.13	10.37
2	2944.90	2843.62	101.28	104.34	5	10.13	10.43
3	2963.29	2821.56	141.73	145.96	7	10.12	10.43
4	2981.00	2798.94	182.06	187.53	9	10.11	10.42
5	2998.04	2775.76	222.28	228.96	11	10.10	10.41
6	3014.41	2752.04	262.37	270.26	13	10.09	10.39
7	3030.09	2727.78	302.31	311.40	15	10.08	10.38
8	3045.06	2703.01	342.05	352.36	17	10.06	10.36
9	3059.32	2677.73	381.59	393.10	19	10.04	10.34
					Average	10.10	10.39

$^a B_1$ = column four $\div$ 2 $\times$ column six.
$^b B_0$ = column five $\div$ 2 $\times$ column six.
^{c} If $J = 1$, then $R_{(J-1)} = R_0$ and $P_{(J+1)} = P_2$; thus, 2906.24 − 2843.62 = 62.62.

the rotational constants in the upper and lower states are 10.10 and 10.39 respectively. A better average value could be obtained by plotting $R_J - P_J$ and $R_{(J-1)} - P_{(J+1)}$ versus $2J + 1$ on a large scale graph. As illustrated in Fig. 1.11 the slopes of these two plots give $2B_1$ and $2B_0$, respectively. The values of B_1 and B_0 obtained by this method for HCl are 10.06 and 10.36, respectively. The moment of inertia in the upper state is then 2.78×10^{-40} gm-cm² and in the lower state 2.70×10^{-40} gm-cm². The latter value agrees well with that calculated from the pure rotational spectrum [see Eq. (1.27)].

1.12 Spherical Top Molecules

Spherical top molecules such as methane and carbon tetrachloride have three equal moments of inertia. All infrared active bands have the same selection rule $\Delta J = 0, \pm 1$. Since the rotational energy equation is the same as that for linear molecules (see Table 1.4) the vibrational-rotational bands resemble the perpendicular bands of a linear molecule with simple P, Q, and R branches (see Fig. 1.12).

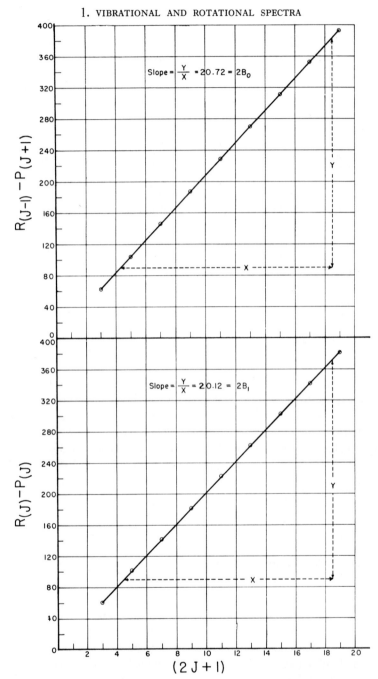

FIG. 1.11.   Plots of $R_{(J)} - P_{(J)}$ and $R_{(J-1)} - P_{(J+1)}$ versus $2J + 1$ for determination of rotational constants B_1 and B_0 respectively.

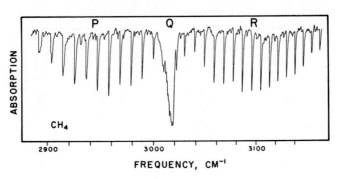

FIG. 1.12. Vibrational-rotational band of methane.

1.13 Symmetrical Top Molecules

Molecules in this class have two equal moments of inertia which differ from the third moment. The normal modes of a symmetrical top molecule can be divided into parallel and perpendicular vibrations. In the parallel vibrations the dipole moment change occurs parallel to the molecule's major symmetry axis which must be a 3-fold or higher symmetry axis (see Section 3.1). In the perpendicular vibrations the dipole moment change occurs perpendicular to the major symmetry axis.

The rotational energy equations for symmetrical top molecules (see Table 1.4) involve two different moments of inertia and two rotational quantum numbers, namely, J, characterizing the total angular momentum of the molecule and K, the angular momentum about the major symmetry axis. For *parallel* bands the selection rule is $\Delta J = 0, \pm 1$ with $\Delta K = 0$, except when $K = 0$, in which case $\Delta J = \pm 1$, $\Delta K = 0$. When a difference in energy levels is taken, only the quantum number J is involved and as a result only one moment of inertia is involved, the one not about the symmetry axis. The parallel bands of a symmetric top molecule resemble the perpendicular bands of the linear molecule having P, Q, and R branches corresponding to $\Delta J = -1$ (Poorer), $\Delta J = 0$ (Equal) and $\Delta J = +1$ (Richer). The unresolved band has a broad doublet and a sharp central peak (see Fig. 1.13).

For the *perpendicular* bands the selection rule is $\Delta J = 0, \pm 1$ with $\Delta K = \pm 1$. Since two quantum numbers and two moments of inertia are involved, the band structure is more complex than the parallel bands. The unresolved band shape will vary depending on the relative magnitudes of the moments of inertia. When the moment of inertia about the symmetry axis is relatively small, as in acetonitrile, the perpendicular band contour may be broad and round,

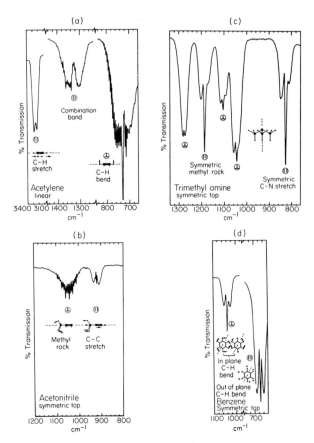

FIG. 1.13.   Gas phase contours of absorption bands of acetylene, acetonitrile, tri-methylamine, and benzene measured in a 10-cm cell with a rock salt prism. (a) Acetylene[6] at 81 mm pressure. The parallel and perpendicular bands are marked. The perpendicular band has a central peak which is absent in the parallel bands. There is partial resolution of some rotational fine structure.   (b) Acetonitrile[6] at 67 mm pressure. The moment of inertia about the symmetry axis is relatively small. The perpendicular band has a round contour with some fine structure resolved. The parallel band is a triplet. (c) Trimethyl-amine[7] at 27 mm pressure. The parallel bands are a little wider than the perpendicular bands and show a more distinct central peak. The triplet bands are asymmetrical because of centrifugal distortion. (d) Benzene[8] at 26 mm pressure. The parallel and perpendicular bands are not very different. *

[6] G. Herzberg, "Infrared and Raman Spectra of Polyatomic Molecules." Van Nostrand, New York, 1945.

[7] J. R. Barceló Matutano and J. Bellanato, *Spectrochim. Acta* 8, 27 (1956).

[8] C. R. Bailey, J. B. Hale, C. K. Ingold and J. W. Thompson, *J. Chem. Soc.* **1936**, 931.

* The references cited refer to the band assignments; the spectra shown were obtained by the authors of this text.

differing distinctly in this case from the parallel band. When the moments of inertia are more nearly equal, the perpendicular and parallel bands are more similar in shape and may be difficult to distinguish (see Fig. 1.13).

1.14 Asymmetrical Top Molecules

Molecules in this class have three unequal moments of inertia $I_a \neq I_b \neq I_c$ and therefore have the most complex band contours. If, during a vibration, the dipole moment changes parallel to the a, b, or c axis a band contour results which is designated as an A, B, or C type band, respectively.

The contours of the pure A, B, and C type bands are dependent upon the relative values of the moments of inertia.[9] The A and C bands both have a sharp central peak and symmetrical broad wing bands. The B type band is unique in that it has no central peak. In molecules where the moment of inertia about the c axis is relatively large the central peak of the C type band is comparatively stronger than the central peak of the A type band (see Fig. 1.14). The wing bands of the A, B, and C bands are made up of two components, $\Delta J = 0$ which causes a doublet of narrow spacing and $\Delta J = \pm 1$ which causes a doublet of somewhat wider spacing. This doubling of each wing band contour is not always apparent but it is clearly illustrated by the B type band in ethylene oxide in Fig. 1.14.

If the dipole moment does not change exactly parallel to the a, b, or c axis a mixed contour will result. Band asymmetry can also result from centrifugal distortion.

1.15 The Raman Effect

When electromagnetic radiation of energy content hvc irradiates a molecule, the energy may be transmitted, absorbed, or scattered. In the Tyndall effect the radiation is scattered by particles (smoke or fog for example). In Rayleigh scattering the molecules scatter the light. Lord Rayleigh showed that the blue sky results because air molecules scatter sunlight. No change in wavelength of individual photons occurs in either Tyndall or Rayleigh scattering.

[9] R. M. Badger and L. R. Zumwalt, *J. Chem. Phys.* **6**, 711 (1938).

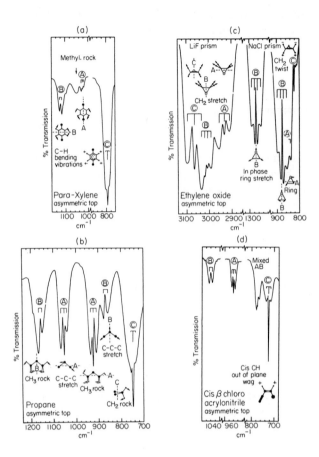

FIG. 1.14.   Gas phase contours of absorption bands of *para*-xylene, propane, ethylene oxide and *cis-β*-chloroacrylonitrile measured in a 10-cm cell (unless noted otherwise) with a rock salt prism. (a) *Para*-xylene[10] at 7 mm pressure in a 100-cm cell. The *B* type bands have a doublet structure and the *A* and *C* bands have a triplet structure. The *C* type band has a relatively strong central peak. (b) Propane[11] at 679 mm pressure. The *A*, *B*, and *C* type bands have the same structure as discussed for *para*-xylene. (c) Ethylene oxide[12] at 72 mm pressure except for the 800-900 cm⁻¹ band which is at 41 mm pressure. The *A* and *C* bands have a triplet structure. The *B* type bands show four components. (d) *Cis-β*-chloroacrylonitrile at its vapor pressure at 25° C. In this planar molecule the out-of-plane CH wag band has a *C* type contour with the prominent central peak. This band is easily distinguished from nearby-in-plane vibrations.

[10] K. S. Pitzer and D. W. Scott, *J. Am. Chem. Soc.* **65**, 803 (1943).
[11] H. L. McMurry and V. Thornton, *J. Chem. Phys.* **19**, 1014 (1951).
[12] F. Halverson, private communication.

In 1928 C. V. Raman described another type of scattering known as the Raman effect. This effect had been theoretically predicted by Smekal before the successful experimental demonstration of this effect by Raman and is therefore often referred to as the Smekal-Raman effect in the German literature. In the Raman effect photons of the exciting radiation interact with molecules of the sample being irradiated. The energies of the scattered photons are either increased or decreased relative to the exciting photons by quantized increments which correspond to the energy differences in the vibrational and rotational energy levels of the molecule (see Fig. 1.15). It has been shown previously that the infrared absorption also depends on these same vibrational and rotational energy levels.

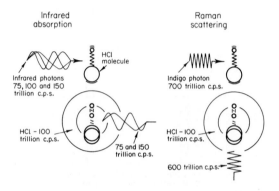

FIG. 1.15. Schematic representation of infrared absorption and Raman scattering.

While infrared and Raman spectra have this similarity, they are not exact duplicates since the selection rules and relative band intensities differ in many cases. For example, when a molecule has a center of symmetry, all vibrations which are symmetrical with respect to the center are infrared inactive and all vibrations which are antisymmetrical with respect to the center are Raman inactive. An example of such a molecule is carbon dioxide. Only the symmetrical stretching vibration gives rise to a band in the Raman effect (see Fig. 1.3).

In Fig. 1.16 the lines designated $v = 0$ and $\nu = 1$ represent the vibrational energy levels of the molecule. When a photon interacts with a molecule in the ground state ($v = 0$), the molecule is raised momentarily to a higher energy level (indicated by a dashed line) which is not a stable energy level at room temperature for the molecule. Since the molecule cannot remain in this unstable level, it may scatter a photon and return to the ground state as illustrated in Fig. 1.16. The scattered photon has therefore the same energy content and frequency as the individual exciting photon, and gives rise to Rayleigh scattering.

However, the molecule may not return to the ground state but may only drop in energy to an excited vibrational state such as $v = 1$ (see Fig. 1.16).

The energy of the scattered photon is equal to the energy of the exciting photon *minus* the energy difference between the $v = 1$ and $v = 0$ levels. Therefore, the wavelength of the scattered photon is longer than that of the incident light. The Raman lines at longer wavelengths (or lower frequencies) than the incident exciting radiation are called Stokes lines. This terminology arose from Stokes' rule of fluorescence which stated that fluorescent radiation always occurs at longer wavelengths than that of the exciting radiation.

The final possibility is that the molecule in an excited level (such as $v = 1$) is raised to a higher unstable level by interaction with the exciting photon. The molecule may then scatter a photon and return to the ground state ($v = 0$).

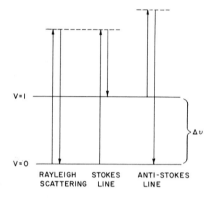

FIG. 1.16.   Energy level diagram for the Raman effect.

The energy of the scattered photon is equal to the energy of the exciting photon *plus* the energy difference between the $v = 1$ and $v = 0$ levels. The spectral line observed has a shorter wavelength (and a higher frequency) than the incident radiation and is called an anti-Stokes line. At room temperature most of the molecules are in the ground state rather than in an excited state. Consequently, the anti-Stokes lines are of lower intensity than the Stokes lines, particularly those anti-Stokes lines originating from the highest energy levels since these have lower molecular population than levels of lower energy.

A diagram of the Raman spectrum of carbon tetrachloride is shown in Fig. 1.17. The mercury line at 4358.4 Å (22.945 cm^{-1}) is the incident monochromatic exciting radiation. Mercury has other lines each of which produce similar Raman shifts. Since Raman lines excited by one wavelength could overlap with those excited by another wavelength, suitable filter solutions are used to produce effectively monochromatic radiation of 4358.4 Å. In certain cases other exciting wavelengths are more advantageous. In Fig. 1.17 there are five Stokes lines shown but only three anti-Stokes lines. The anti-Stokes lines are less intense than the corresponding Stokes lines for reasons previously discussed.

For both the Stokes and anti-Stokes lines the 459 cm^{-1} line is the most intense. The unaltered exciting line appears in the Raman spectrum because of Rayleigh scattering. It is much more intense than the Raman lines.

Since Raman lines represent frequency differences, they are also called Raman shifts and are designated as $\Delta\nu$ in cm^{-1} and are calculated by means of the formula

$$\Delta\nu \,(\text{cm}^{-1}) = \frac{10^8}{\lambda_E} - \frac{10^8}{\lambda_R} \qquad (1.44)$$

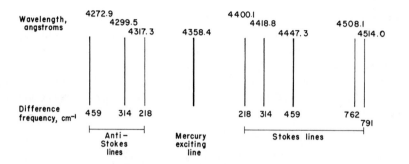

FIG. 1.17.   The Raman spectrum of carbon tetrachloride.

where λ_E is the wavelength in angstroms of the exciting line and λ_R is the wavelength in angstroms of the Raman line. This equation gives the Stokes lines; for anti-Stokes lines both signs on the right hand side of the equation should be reversed.

1.16   Polarizability

It has been stated that a molecular vibration which causes a change in the dipole moment is infrared active. In order for a molecular vibration to be Raman active there must be a change in the "induced" dipole moment resulting from a *change in the polarizability* of the molecule. The complex nature of the polarizability will be discussed below.

A hypothetical atom with a spherically symmetrical electron cloud has no permanent dipole moment. When such an atom is placed between the plates of a charged condenser, the electrons will be attracted to the positive plate and the protons to the negative plate. The polarized atom now has an induced dipole moment caused by the external field. If **E** represents the vector of the electric force of the field and **μ** represents the induced dipole moment oriented parallel to the direction of **E** then

$$\boldsymbol{\mu} = \alpha\mathbf{E} \tag{1.45}$$

where α is the polarizability of the atom. When the electric field is resolved into cartesian coordinates this equation may be rewritten as

$$\mu_x = \alpha E_x, \qquad \mu_y = \alpha E_y, \qquad \mu_z = \alpha E_z \tag{1.46}$$

where μ_x, μ_y, and μ_z are the components of the induced dipole moment and E_x, E_y, and E_z are the x, y, and z components of the electric field. Equation (1.46) is only applicable to completely symmetrical systems.

Since most molecules generally have a structure which is not spherically symmetrical, the polarizability α may be different in the x, y, and z directions. Such a molecule is said to be anisotropic. For this general case the following equations apply:

$$\mu_x = \alpha_{xx}E_x + \alpha_{xy}E_y + \alpha_{xz}E_z$$
$$\mu_y = \alpha_{yx}E_x + \alpha_{yy}E_y + \alpha_{yz}E_z$$
$$\mu_z = \alpha_{zx}E_x + \alpha_{zy}E_y + \alpha_{zz}E_z \tag{1.47}$$

where α_{xx}, α_{xy}, α_{xz}, ... are the proportionality constants respectively between μ_x and E_x, μ_x and E_y and μ_x and E_z, ..., etc. The over-all polarizability is then the whole system of these constants or coefficients. Such a system of coefficients which establishes a linear relationship between vectors is termed a tensor[13] and thus the polarizability is a tensor.

The polarizability tensor is a symmetric tensor, that is, $\alpha_{xy} = \alpha_{yx}$, $\alpha_{yz} = \alpha_{zy}$, and $\alpha_{xz} = \alpha_{zx}$. Symmetric tensors have the property that a particular set of coordinates, x', y', and z', can be chosen such that only $\alpha_{x'x'}$, $\alpha_{y'y'}$, and $\alpha_{z'z'}$ are different from zero (all terms involving $\alpha_{x',y'}$, $\alpha_{x',z'}$, and $\alpha_{y',z'}$, are equal to zero).[14] These special axes are three mutually perpendicular directions in the molecule for which the induced moments are parallel to the electric field. Equation (1.47) then reduces to

$$\mu_{x'} = \alpha_{x'x'}E_{x'}$$
$$\mu_{y'} = \alpha_{y'y'}E_{y'}$$
$$\mu_{z'} = \alpha_{z'z'}E_{z'} \tag{1.48}$$

[13] H. Margenau and G. M. Murphy, "The Mathematics of Physics and Chemistry." Van Nostrand, New York, 1943.

[14] J. C. D. Brand and J. C. Speakman, "Molecular Structure," p. 175. Edward Arnold, London, 1960.

The three axes in these three directions are called the principal axes of polarizability. The locus of points formed by plotting $1/\sqrt{\alpha}$ in any direction from the origin yields a surface called the polarizability ellipsoid whose axes are x', y', and z'. For a molecule which is completely anisotropic, $\alpha_{x'x'} \neq \alpha_{y'y'} \neq \alpha_{z'z'}$, and the ellipsoid has three axes of unequal length. If two of the three axes have the same magnitude (i.e., $\alpha_{x'x'} = \alpha_{y'y'} \neq \alpha_{z'z'}$) the ellipsoid becomes a rotational ellipsoid and the polarizability will be the same in the x' and y' direction. If all three axes are equal then a polarizability sphere results. The molecule is said to be isotropic and has the same polarizability in all three directions.

While the ellipsoid may have higher symmetry than the molecule all the symmetry elements possessed by the molecule will also be possessed by the ellipsoid. If the polarizability ellipsoid is changed in size, shape, or orientation as a result of molecular vibration or rotation a Raman spectrum will result.

1.17 Change in Polarizability

The varying electric field E of a light wave whose frequency (sec^{-1}) is ν' is given by

$$E = E_0 \sin 2\pi \nu' t \qquad (1.49)$$

where E_0 is a constant, the maximum value of the field, and t is time. For the case of the spherically symmetrical atom discussed previously $\mu = \alpha E$. An incident light wave will induce an oscillating dipole moment μ in the atom whose frequency will be the same as that of the light wave

$$\mu = \alpha E_0 \sin 2\pi \nu' t \qquad (1.50)$$

Classically the atom can now emit radiation of frequency ν' which is the same as the exciting frequency, yielding Rayleigh scattering.

In molecules α is not constant since certain vibrations and rotations can cause α to vary. During the vibration of a diatomic molecule, the molecular shape is alternately compressed and extended. Since the electron cloud is not identical at the extremes of the vibration, a change in polarizability results. For small displacements, the polarizability of the diatomic molecule is given by

$$\alpha = \alpha_0 + \frac{\partial \alpha}{\partial (\Delta r)} \Delta r \qquad (1.51)$$

Where α_0 is the equilibrium polarizability, Δr is the difference between the internuclear distance at any time and the equilibrium internuclear distance and

$\partial\alpha/\partial(\Delta r)$ is the rate of change of the polarizability with respect to Δr. Since the vibration is considered to be a simple harmonic motion, Δr is given by

$$\Delta r = a \sin 2\pi v'_v t \qquad (1.52)$$

where v'_v is the vibrational frequency ($\sec^{-1}$), a is a constant, the maximum value of Δr, and t is time. Equation (1.51) becomes

$$\alpha = \alpha_0 + \frac{\partial\alpha}{\partial(\Delta r)} a \sin 2\pi v'_v t \qquad (1.53)$$

Substituting this value of α into Eq. (1.50) yields,

$$\mu = \alpha_0 \sin 2\pi v' t + \alpha E_0 \frac{\partial\alpha}{\partial(\Delta r)} (\sin 2\pi v'_v t)(\sin 2\pi v' t) \qquad (1.54)$$

and

$$\mu = \alpha_0 \sin 2\pi v' t + \frac{\alpha E_0}{2} \frac{\partial\alpha}{\partial(\Delta r)} [\cos 2\pi(v' - v'_v) t - \cos 2\pi(v' + v'_v) t] \qquad (1.55)$$

It can be seen from this equation that the induced dipole moment varies with three component frequencies v', $v' - v'_v$, and $v' + v'_v$ and can therefore give rise to Rayleigh scattering, Stokes, and anti-Stokes frequencies respectively. The Raman line intensities depend on $\partial\alpha/\partial(\Delta r)$ and the Rayleigh scattering intensity depends on α_0. For polyatomic molecules $\partial\alpha/\partial\Delta r$ is replaced by the general expression $\partial\alpha/\partial Q$, which is the rate at which α changes during a given normal mode of vibration (Q) as the atoms pass through their equilibrium positions.

1.18 Pure Rotational Raman Spectra

The pure rotation of a molecule will give rise to a pure rotational Raman spectrum if the polarizability of the molecule varies in different directions at right angles to the axis of rotation. Therefore, symmetrical molecules such as H_2 and CO_2 have pure rotational Raman spectra. The selection rule for pure rotational energy changes is $\Delta J = 0$ and ± 2 for linear molecules. Applying this selection rule to the rotational energy equation (1.20) for the linear molecule we obtain for the frequencies in cm^{-1} of the Stokes lines $(J \to J + 2)$

$$\frac{\Delta E_{\text{rot.}}}{hc} = B(4J + 6) \qquad J = 0, 1, 2, ... \qquad (1.56)$$

and for the anti-Stokes lines $(J \to J - 2)$

$$\frac{\Delta E_{\text{rot.}}}{hc} = B(4J - 2) \qquad J = 2, 3, 4, ... \qquad (1.57)$$

where J is the quantum number of the initial rotational state. Both sets of lines have a spacing equal to $4B$ with the space between the first line and the exciting line equal to $6B$. When $\Delta J = 0$ the lines coincide with the exciting line.

All symmetrical top molecules should possess pure rotational Raman spectra. However, the polarizability is unaffected by rotation about the major symmetry axis. The selection rule is $\Delta J = 0, \pm 1, \pm 2$ with $\Delta K = 0$ and can be applied to Eqs. (1.28) and (1.31). The spacing between the lines is equal to $2B$. Therefore the moment of inertia about the symmetry axis cannot be obtained from the spacing.

Spherical top molecules which are isotropic can not have a pure rotational Raman spectrum. Asymmetrical top molecules have no simple rotational energy equation.

1.19 Depolarization Ratio

Let the direction of propagation of the incident radiation be the z axis and the direction of observation be perpendicular to the z axis in the xy plane. If natural unpolarized incident light is the exciting agent, then the depolarization ratio ρ_n is defined as the ratio of the intensity of scattered light polarized perpendicular to the xy plane, $I_\perp$, to that polarized parallel to the xy plane, $I_{//}$.

$$\rho_n = \frac{I_\perp}{I_{//}} \tag{1.58}$$

By averaging over all orientations of the polarizability ellipsoid Born[15] has shown that for natural unpolarized incident light the depolarization ratio, ρ_n, is given by

$$\rho_n = \frac{I_\perp}{I_{//}} = \frac{6\beta^2}{45(\alpha')^2 + 7\beta^2} \tag{1.59}$$

where α' is the isotropic or spherical part of the polarizability defined as the average of the three principal polarizabilities

$$\alpha' = \tfrac{1}{3}(\alpha_{x'x'} + \alpha_{y'y'} + \alpha_{z'z'}) \tag{1.60}$$

and β is the completely anisotropic part of the polarizability defined by

$$\beta^2 = \tfrac{1}{2}[(\alpha_{x'x'} - \alpha_{y'y'})^2 + (\alpha_{y'y'} - \alpha_{z'z'})^2$$
$$+ (\alpha_{z'z'} - \alpha_{x'x'})^2 + 6(\alpha_{x'y'}^2 + \alpha_{y'z'}^2 + \alpha_{z'x'}^2)]. \tag{1.61}$$

[15] M. Born, "Optik." Edwards Brothers, Ann Arbor, Michigan, 1943.

Equations (1.60) and (1.61) apply for Rayleigh scattering. For Raman scattering the polarizability components $\alpha_{x'x'}$, $\alpha_{y'y'}$, etc. in Eqs. (1.60) and (1.61) should be replaced by the *change* in polarizability during the vibration $(\partial \alpha_{x'x'}/\partial Q)$, etc. Equation (1.59) is used with these new values for α' and β for a particular vibration.

The maximum value of Eq. (1.59) is $\frac{6}{7}$ which occurs when $\alpha' = 0$. A Raman line with a depolarization ratio of $\frac{6}{7}$ is said to be depolarized. If the depolarization ratio is less than $\frac{6}{7}$, the Raman line is said to be polarized. It has been found that only totally symmetric vibrations can yield polarized Raman lines. A measurement of the depolarization ratio can thus distinguish totally symmetrical vibrations ($\rho_n = 0$ to $\frac{6}{7}$) from non-totally symmetrical vibrations ($\rho_n = \frac{6}{7}$).

In measuring the depolarization ratio, the polarizer may be placed in two orientations between the sample and the spectrometer. An equivalent ratio may be measured with the polarizer placed in two orientations between the source of incident radiation and the sample as long as the source irradiates the sample at right angles to the scattering direction. These measurements will be discussed in more detail in the next chapter.

CHAPTER 2

EXPERIMENTAL CONSIDERATIONS

In this chapter the experimental techniques and equipment needed to measure infrared absorption spectra will be discussed first and then the methods and instrumentation required to determine Raman spectra.

The techniques and equipment in the infrared region are dependent upon the characteristics of each of the following: the source, the monochromator and the receptor. Each of these items shall now be considered in the order mentioned.

2.1 Source of Infrared Radiation

Molecules in a gas, a liquid or a solid are in constant thermal agitation except at the temperature of absolute zero ($-273°C$). As the temperature of a body is increased, the thermal motion and amplitude increase. All of the molecules are not excited to the same degree of thermal agitation but follow a Boltzmann distribution curve. Although most of the molecules have approximately the same degree of thermal agitation, smaller numbers of molecules have lower or higher degrees of thermal agitation. Since molecules consist of atoms containing electrical charges, these oscillating centers of electrical charge give off electromagnetic radiation. The distribution of this energy corresponds to the distribution of the number of molecules in the various states of thermal excitation and hence a hot body emits electromagnetic radiation covering a wide range of wavelengths.

Infrared radiation is normally considered as heat radiation because in approaching an infrared source, a person is certainly aware of its heat aspect. Heat or thermal energy can be transferred by infrared radiation or by conduction and convection. These latter two methods require a physical medium so that the heat can be carried directly from point to point. By contrast infrared transfers heat indirectly as radiation and does not require a direct physical medium. When infrared radiation is absorbed by an object, the radiation is converted to heat.

An object which is white-hot emits considerable energy in the infrared region of the electromagnetic spectrum but a great deal of the radiation is also in the visible region. The fact that the object appears white proves that a continuous spectrum of all visible wavelengths is present. As the object cools, it becomes red in color indicating that the visible radiation is now confined to the red end or the long wavelength end of the visible spectrum. On cooling further, the radiation decreases and is confined to the infrared region where it is no longer visible to the human eye. The total amount of radiation decreases with temperature and the energy peak shifts toward longer wavelengths.

In this discussion it is well to introduce the concept of a blackbody which may be defined as a body which absorbs all radiation striking it. A blackbody has the maximum possible absorption and emission and is a theoretical entity since no perfect blackbody exists. The first attempt to predict the spectral distribution of the energy E of a blackbody radiator in a quantitative fashion was made by Wien using the laws of classical physics. Although the equation derived by Wien holds for frequencies in the ultraviolet and visible regions, it fails for infrared frequencies. Lord Rayleigh and Jeans derived a distribution law also based on classical theory which holds for long wavelengths but fails when applied to the spectral region in which Wien's equation is valid. Using the quantum hypothesis, Planck derived a distribution law for blackbody radiation which holds over all wavelengths. Planck's distribution law giving the radiant energy between the wavelengths λ to $\lambda + d\lambda$ may be expressed in the form

$$E_\lambda \, d\lambda = \frac{c_1 \lambda^{-5}}{e^{(c_2/\lambda T)} - 1} \, d\lambda \tag{2.1}$$

where $e =$ the Naperian base, 2.718, and the constants c_1 and c_2 are given by

$$c_1 = 2\pi c^2 h = 3.740 \times 10^{-12} \text{ watts cm}^2 \tag{2.2}$$

and

$$c_2 = ch/k = 1.438 \text{ cm } °K \tag{2.3}$$

where c is the speed of light, 2.998×10^{10} cm/sec, h is Planck's constant, 6.624×10^{-34} watt-sec^2, and k is the Boltzmann constant, 1.380×10^{-23} watt-sec/°K. $E_\lambda d\lambda$ is the radiant energy emitted per unit area per unit increment of wavelength. With the units shown and $d\lambda$ in microns, the units of $E_\lambda d\lambda$ are watts/cm^2/micron.

For $c_2 > \lambda T$, the exponential factor in the denominator of Eq. (2.1) is very large compared to unity and consequently this equation becomes

$$E_\lambda d\lambda = c_1 \lambda^{-5} e^{-(c_2/\lambda T)} d\lambda \tag{2.4}$$

which is Wien's radiation law.

For $\lambda T \gg c_2$, the exponential factor which can be expressed as an infinite series of the type

$$e^x = 1 + x + \frac{x^2}{2!} + \frac{x^3}{3!} \cdots$$

becomes approximately

$$e^{c_2/\lambda T} = 1 + c_2/\lambda T \tag{2.5}$$

and

$$E_\lambda d\lambda = (c_1/c_2)\lambda^{-5} \cdot \lambda T d\lambda \tag{2.6}$$

$$= 2\pi c k T \lambda^{-4} d\lambda \tag{2.7}$$

which is the Rayleigh-Jeans radiation law.

The wavelength λ_m at which the energy is at a maximum at any temperature is found by differentiating E_λ with respect to λ and setting the derivative $dE_\lambda/d\lambda$ equal to zero. The solution[1] of the resulting equation yields Wien's displacement law.

$$\lambda_m = \frac{b}{T} \tag{2.8}$$

where $b =$ Wien's displacement constant, 2897μ °K, and $T =$ absolute temperature, °K.

The actual energy distribution of a blackbody radiator at three different temperatures is shown in Fig. 2.1. The energy at any wavelength is given by the

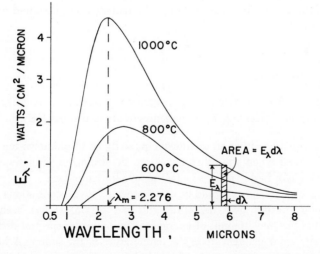

FIG. 2.1. Energy distribution of a blackbody radiator at 600°, 800°, and 1000° C.

[1] F. W. Sears, "Optics," p. 314. Addison-Wesley, Reading, Massachusetts, 1949.

area of the vertical strip under the curve at that wavelength. If the height of the strip is E_λ and the width is $d\lambda$, then the area is $E_\lambda \, d\lambda$ as indicated on the 1000° C curve in Fig. 2.1.

Figure 2.1 also shows how the peak of the energy curve is temperature dependent. For example, at a temperature of 1000° C the wavelength at which the energy is at a maximum, E_{λ_m}, is given by Eq. (2.8) and would be $(2.897 \times 10^3)/(1000 + 273) = 2.276\ \mu$ (see Fig. 2.1). At a lower temperature of 600° C the energy peak shifts to a longer wavelength, namely 3.318 microns. It is also important to note that the energy output falls off very rapidly at long wavelengths. In the usual infrared spectrometer a slit located between the source and the receptor is programmed to open as the wavelength increases, resulting in a constant energy level as the spectrum is traversed. Nevertheless the low energy output of the source at long wavelengths presents problems in the design of instruments for the far infrared.

Integrating of $E_\lambda \, d\lambda$ [Eq. (2.1)] between the limits 0 and ∞ yields[2]

$$\int_0^\infty E_\lambda \, d\lambda = \sigma T^4 \tag{2.9}$$

which is the Stefan-Boltzmann law and σ is the Stefan-Boltzmann constant. The Stefan-Boltzmann law states that the total radiation from a blackbody is proportional to the fourth power of its absolute temperature. When a source has less radiation than a theoretical blackbody, the ratio of its emission to that of a blackbody at the same temperature is called the emissivity, ρ. For a theoretical blackbody, the emissivity ρ equals 1.00. The radiant energy emitted by a body then becomes

$$E = \rho \sigma T^4 \tag{2.10}$$

where in practical units

E = radiant energy, watt-cm^{-2}, ρ = emissivity factor, $\sigma = 5.672 \times 10^{-12}$ watt-cm^{-2} degree^{-4} (Kelvin), T = the temperature in degrees Kelvin.

With this equation either an unknown emissivity or an unknown temperature can be calculated when the other terms are determinable. Emissivity factors range from 0.02 for highly polished silver to 0.95 for lampblack.

The ideal infrared source would be one that would give a continuous and high radiant energy output over the entire infrared region. It has been shown, however, that the total amount of energy radiated and the spectral distribution of this energy are dependent upon the temperature of the source. A blackbody slit cavity at high temperature would be ideal from the continuous high radiant

[2] I. Kaplan, "Nuclear Physics," p. 81. Addison-Wesley, Reading, Massachusetts, 1955.

energy standpoint, but is impractical for spectrometers. However, several infrared sources have been developed which follow the characteristics of the blackbody radiator rather closely in the infrared region. The two in most common use are the Nernst Glower and the Globar.

The Nernst Glower is a source which is composed mainly of oxides of the rare earths such as zirconium, yttrium, and thorium. These oxides are molded in the shape of a rod about 20 mm long and 1 mm wide. The ends of the rod are attached to ceramic tubes for mounting and have platinum leads for the electrical connection. The source is nonconducting at room temperature and must be preheated to bring it to a conducting state. Like most semiconductors, it has a negative coefficient of resistivity and must be operated with a ballast resistance in a constant voltage circuit. Nernst Glowers are operated generally at 1900° C using 1.2 amperes and 75 volts alternating current.

Conn[3] has described a method of repairing Nernst Glowers and Ebers and Nielsen[4] have published a method of increasing the life of Nernst Glowers.

The Globar is a silicon carbide rod, usually about two inches long and $\frac{3}{16}$ in. in diameter. The rod is silvered at the ends to ensure better electrical contact. It is easily mounted and has about the same radiator properties as the Nernst Glower and has the advantage of being more rugged. It is operated at about 50 volts and 4–5 amperes at 1200° C. The resistance of the Globar increases with the length of time it is operated and provision must be made for increasing the voltage by means of a variable transformer. The main disadvantage is that it must have a water-cooled jacket to protect the electrical contacts. The life of the Globar decreases as the temperature is increased because the bonding material boils out, causing high resistance hot spots and eventual failure.

Comparison of the spectral energy distribution of the Globar and the Nernst Glower[5] indicates that the Glower has an advantage in the short wavelength region but at 15 microns the two sources are comparable.

The Sauereisen source[6] developed in 1949 is a porcelain rod fitted with aluminum terminals and wrapped with platinum wire. The rod is then covered with Sauereisen cement.

This source has the desirable rugged and self-starting characteristics of the Globar and some distinct advantages. It has low emissivity in the 2–4 micron region with high emissivity throughout the remainder of the rock salt range. It does not change resistance with age and has a positive temperature coefficient of resistivity so that the power input tends to be self-regulating. The construction minimizes the variation in contact resistance and allows it to be operated directly or in a series with a ballast lamp at 115 volts.

[3] G. K. T. Conn, *J. Sci. Instr.* **15**, 414 (1938).
[4] E. S. Ebers and H. H. Nielsen, *Rev. Sci. Instr.* **11**, 429 (1940).
[5] R. A. Friedel and A. G. Sharkey, Jr., *Rev. Sci. Instr.* **18**, 928 (1947).
[6] L. W. Herscher, *Rev. Sci. Instr.* **20**, 833 (1949).

The Welsbach mantle is an illuminating gas mantle consisting largely of thorium oxide.[7] This is a good source for the long wavelength infrared region and closely approaches that of a blackbody above 6 microns.

Pfund[8] has developed an electric Welsbach mantle which gives emission comparable to the Nernst Glower in the 0.7–15 micron region. The heating unit consists of an ashed Welsbach mantle heated by glow or arc discharge formed between terminals connected to the secondary of a high voltage transformer. When operating in air, a small, pointed gas flame is applied to the mantle to steady the electrical discharge and increase the temperature. From 0.7 to 15 microns, gas plus electricity is used; beyond that to 150 microns gas alone is employed.

A carbon rod source has been described by Smith.[9] It consists of a carbon rod heated electrically in a vacuum. The rod is 6 mm in diameter and has a V-shaped 1-in. cavity in the center. It is operated at 1800° C with a power consumption of 600 watts and has a life of about 100 hr. Emission is comparable to that of the Globar from 1 to 10 microns and considerably greater beyond 10 microns.

Probably the most recent infrared source is the one designed for a low-cost double-beam spectrometer, the Perkin-Elmer Model 137. The Model 137 source, for which a patent application has been made, is the invention of Kurt H. Opperman of the Perkin-Elmer Corporation and dates to 1956. Its principle is the utilization of the infrared-radiative properties of incandescent aluminum oxide. A rhodium high-temperature heating coil is inserted in a sintered aluminum oxide tube which is then filled with a slurry of zirconium silicate and aluminum oxide powders and water, to prevent deterioration of the rhodium coil in atmosphere. Under vacuum, all air entrapments are removed. The slurry becomes a tightly-packed dry powder mass. Electrical contacts are soldered into the rhodium wire. The solder also caps the aluminum oxide tube at both ends. In use, the source is partially enclosed in a metal shield and ceramic (porcelain) caps to prevent temperature transience due to air currents. A diagram of this source is shown in Fig. 2.2.

The source is powered by 2.8 volts, 30 watts, and develops an external temperature of 1200° C. It provides radiant infrared energy from 2.5 to 25 microns.

For all the infrared sources discussed the radiant energy is low in the far infrared and to obtain sufficient energy the slit width has to be opened considerably with a corresponding decrease in resolution. One might compensate for this low emissivity in the far infrared by raising the temperature of the radiator, say from 2000° K to 3000° K.

[7] V. Z. Williams, *Rev. Sci. Instr.* **19**, 135 (1948).

[8] A. H. Pfund, *J. Opt. Soc. Am.* **26**, 439 (1936).

[9] L. G. Smith, *Rev. Sci. Instr.* **13**, 63 (1942).

It can be seen from the Stefan-Boltzmann law [Eq. (2.9)] that the total emissivity would increase about fivefold:

$$\frac{E_2}{E_1} = \frac{\sigma T_2^4}{\sigma T_1^4} = \frac{81 \times 10^{12}}{16 \times 10^{12}} = \sim 5 : 1. \qquad (2.11)$$

If the radiation is calculated using Planck's law [Eq. (2.1)] there is only a slight increase in the long wavelength radiation compared with a much greater increase in the short wavelength radiation. Since stray high frequency radiation can cause a considerable error in the absorption measurements, raising the temperature has just as bad an effect as increasing the slit width and it reduces the life of the source.

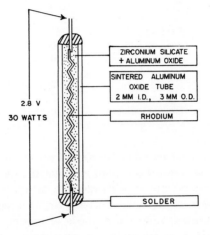

FIG. 2.2   Schematic diagram of the infrared source for the Perkin-Elmer Model 137 Spectrometer.

2.2   Infrared Monochromators and Filters

Prior to discussing infrared monochromators, some mention should be made of the transmittance of optical materials in the infrared region. Table 2.1 lists approximate transmission limits in wavenumbers for some optical materials.

The substances in Table 2.1 are not soluble in water except for sodium chloride, potassium bromide, cesium bromide and cesium iodide which are very soluble in water. Irtran-2 is a trademark of the Eastman Kodak Company and is a new optical material which can stand elevated temperature and can be polished to good optical tolerances. KRS-5 is a synthetic optical crystal consisting of about 42% thallium bromide and 58% thallium iodide. All the substances listed in Table 2.1 with the exception of mica and Irtran-2 have been employed for prism materials.

TABLE 2.1

APPROXIMATE TRANSMISSION LIMITS FOR OPTICAL MATERIALS

Glass	3000 cm^{-1}
Quartz	2500
Mica	2000
Lithium fluoride	1500
Calcium fluoride	1200
Barium fluoride	850
Irtran-2	750
Sodium chloride	600
Potassium bromide	350
Silver chloride	350
KRS-5	250
Cesium bromide	250
Cesium iodide	200

Although some of the most recent infrared spectrometers being made today are of the grating type, most infrared spectrometers contain prisms of alkali halides. Prisms of adequate size covering a wide range of materials are now available through the development of methods of making large synthetic crystals.

Valuable information regarding the methods of making these crystals and their optical properties is contained in a manual entitled "Synthetic Optical Crystals" available from the Harshaw Chemical Company, Cleveland, Ohio.

For spectroscopic work a prism must be transparent to the particular wavelength region of interest and the dispersion of the prism must be as large as possible. These two requirements are not entirely unrelated as the following discussion will show.

The angular dispersion of a prism can be represented mathematically as $d\theta/d\lambda$ which is the rate of change of the angle of emergence from the prism with respect to wavelength. The angular dispersion may be considered as the product of two terms.

$$\frac{d\theta}{d\lambda} = \frac{d\theta}{dn} \cdot \frac{dn}{d\lambda} \tag{2.12}$$

The first term, $d\theta/dn$, the rate of change of angular dispersion with index of refraction n, is a function of the angle between the two refracting faces. For the case of minimum deviation, where the incident and emergent rays make equal angles with the normals to the prism faces at which the rays enter and emerge, the evaluation of $d\theta/dn$ yields,[10]

$$\frac{d\theta}{dn} = \frac{2 \sin(\alpha/2)}{\cos i} \tag{2.13}$$

where as illustrated in Fig. 2.3, α equals the apex angle of the prism, and i equals the incident or emergent angle.

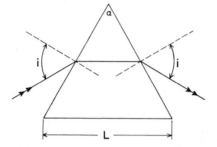

FIG. 2.3. Passage of a ray at minimum deviation through a prism.

From this expression it can be seen that a prism must have a large apex angle to make the first term of the angular dispersion large. Prisms usually have a 60° angle as a compromise between smaller angles which give less dispersion and larger angles which cause greater reflection loss and require more material.

In the expression for angular dispersion, the second term, $dn/d\lambda$, is a function of the prism material and is commonly called the dispersion. This term can be evaluated for a substance by plotting n, the index of refraction against wavelength, λ. Such a plot is shown in Fig. 2.4 for lithium fluoride, calcium fluoride, and sodium chloride from approximately 2 to 18 microns and in Fig. 2.5 for potassium bromide, KRS-5 and cesium bromide from approximately 2 to 40 microns. Values of $dn/d\lambda$ can be taken at suitable wavelength intervals and plotted to yield the dispersion curves shown. For reference, transmission curves are also plotted for these materials at an approximate thickness of 1 mm.

It can be seen that the index of refraction of a given material decreases as the wavelength increases. Secondly the dispersion, $dn/d\lambda$, approaches a maximum as the substance reaches its wavelength boundary of effective transmission. In other words a prism made of a given alkali halide will show maximum dispersion in the infrared wavelength region just below that wavelength where the prism

[10] F. A. Jenkins and H. E. White, "Fundamentals of Optics," p. 465. McGraw-Hill, New York, 1957.

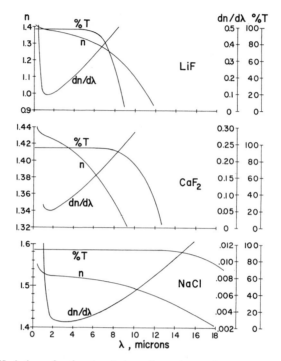

FIG. 2.4. Variation of refractive index, dispersion and per cent transmission with wavelength of lithium fluoride, calcium fluoride, and sodium chloride.

becomes opaque. In order to obtain maximum dispersion over the entire infrared region it is therefore necessary to have several prisms of different materials. Since most data are obtained in the infrared region from 2.5 to 15 microns, a compromise is made by using a sodium chloride prism because it has adequate

TABLE 2.2

REGIONS OF OPTIMUM DISPERSION FOR VARIOUS PRISMS

Prism	Wavelength, microns	Wavenumbers,[a] cm⁻¹
Lithium fluoride	2.0–5.3	5000–1885
Calcium fluoride	5.3–8.5	1885–1175
Sodium chloride	8.5–15.4	1175–650
Potassium bromide	15.4–25	650–400
KRS-5	20–35	500–285
Cesium bromide	25–40	400–250

[a] Values rounded to the nearest 5 cm⁻¹.

dispersion in this region. However, most commercial infrared spectrometers are designed with prism interchange assemblies so the sodium chloride prism can readily be replaced by other prisms. Table 2.2 lists the region of optimum dispersion for various prisms.

With prisms of lithium fluoride, sodium chloride and cesium bromide the wavelength region from 2 to 40 microns is well covered.

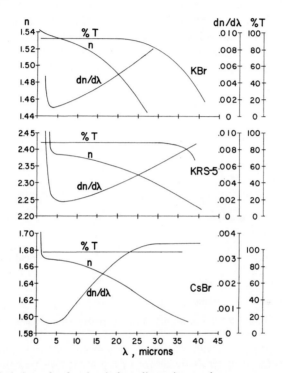

FIG. 2.5. Variation of refractive index, dispersion, and per cent transmission with wavelength of potassium bromide, KRS-5, and cesium bromide.

The resolving power of a prism can be defined mathematically as $\lambda/d\lambda$ and is a convenient measure of the ability of the prism to separate two spectral bands with a wavelength difference of $d\lambda$. The ultimate resolving power is equal to the product of the length of the prism base, L, and $dn/d\lambda$, the dispersion.[11] Thus, the resolution can be increased by increasing the size of the prism, by using N prisms in series in which case L becomes LN and, as previously discussed, by choosing a prism with high dispersion in the desired wavelength region. Most infrared spectrometers have a Littrow arrangement similar to the one shown in

[11] F. W. Sears, "Optics," p. 278. Addison-Wesley, Reading, Massachusetts, 1949.

Fig. 2.6. In a Littrow arrangement radiation passes through the prism two or more times. Some instruments have a double monochromator in a Littrow arrangement to yield four equivalent prisms, i.e., N equals four. Extension of such multimonochromator techniques is limited because of energy losses at reflecting surfaces.

At the start of this section mention was made of diffraction gratings for infrared work, and it is pertinent to consider their value as monochromators at this point. The function of a grating, like that of a prism, is to provide monochromatic radiation from radiation composed of many wavelengths. A diffraction grating consists of a number of equally-spaced slits, which diffract light by interference. There is presently a marked emphasis on diffraction gratings which

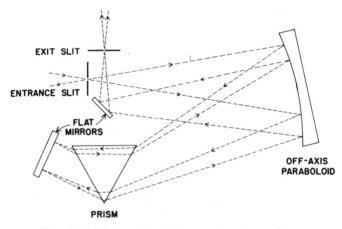

FIG. 2.6.   Diagram of a Littrow prism arrangement.

are slowly but surely replacing prisms because of their inherent higher resolving power. The theoretical resolving power of a grating may be expressed as mN where m is the order of the spectrum and N is the number of grooves or rulings on the grating. It is apparent that the highest resolution is obtained by having gratings with a large number of grooves or using large gratings to increase N and by working with higher order spectra. However, the number of grooves is restricted by several factors including the longest wavelength which is to be measured. The size of the grating is limited by cost and space available while for higher order spectra the grating efficiency falls off rapidly. In spite of these limitations gratings will eventually replace prisms in infrared spectrometers.

For monochromatic light of wavelength, λ, the grating law is

$$m\lambda = d(\sin i \pm \sin r)$$

$$m = 1, 2, 3, ...,$$

(2.14)

i.e., the order of the spectra, and as illustrated in Fig. 2.7, i = angle of incidence, r = angle of reflectance or diffraction, d = distance between grooves—that is, the grating constant. The plus-sign applies when i and r are on the same side of the grating normal and the minus-sign when they are on opposite sides. The two basic types of diffraction gratings are the transmission and the reflectance types. For the transmission grating, the grooves, which are ruled by an elaborate ruling engine on a plane glass or quartz surface with a diamond needle, are opaque and scatter any incident radiation. The clear undisturbed portions between the grooves transmit the incident radiation and act as slits. Reflecting

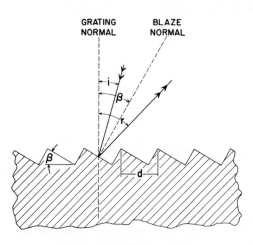

$$m\lambda = d(\sin i \pm \sin r)$$

FIG. 2.7. Cross sectional diagram of a plane diffraction grating.

diffraction gratings are usually made by ruling from 50 to 50 thousand equally spaced grooves per millimeter on borosilicate glass coated with aluminum by vacuum evaporation. The diamond does not mark the glass at all but burnishes grooves into the aluminum. This method has the advantage that the diamond does not wear as fast and the groove shape can be controlled better.

From the master grating replica gratings are made, having their grooves formed in a thin layer of clear plastic that adheres to the surface of a glass backing plate. The optical surface of the reflectance grating is coated with aluminum. These gratings have an advantage over the master grating in that they can be re-aluminized in the event the aluminum is attacked or stained.

As previously discussed, the number of grooves per millimeter or its reciprocal, called the grating constant, is important in determining the resolving power of the grating. There is a finite limit to the number of grooves per millimeter for transmission gratings because adjacent grooves are so close that the maximum angle that the radiation can leave the grating is limited. In addition, since transmission gratings are formed on glass or quartz plates, they are only valuable in the near infrared region. For infrared instruments plane reflectance type gratings are most valuable.

Another factor to be considered is that the longest wavelength in the spectral region under consideration should be less than the width of the groove face on which the incident radiation falls. If the wavelength of the incident light is materially longer than the width of groove face, the grating acts as a mirror and most of the radiation goes into the zero order rather than being diffracted into the desired orders. By this means visible light can be separated from infrared radiation with the diffraction grating acting as a mirror for the infrared region.

A potential disadvantage of a grating for infrared instrumentation is that the grating, unlike the prism, distributes energy into a number of orders. However this disadvantage can be overcome by controlling the groove shape to a specific blaze angle (see Fig. 2.7) thereby concentrating the spectral energy in the desired region of the spectrum for a given order. Undesired overlapping orders can also be eliminated with a fore prism or by appropriate filters.

For reflectance gratings the blaze angle is calculated on the basis that the angle of incidence, i, equals the angle of reflectance, r. Details of this calculation and other valuable information on gratings are given in a bulletin entitled "Diffraction Gratings" available from the Bausch and Lomb Optical Co., Rochester, New York.

Most infrared instruments have filters which pass infrared radiation within a particular wavelength range. Appropriate filters can reduce stray radiation in a prism spectrometer and remove the undesired higher orders obtained with a grating spectrometer.

Four types of filters involved in infrared measurements are the transmission, reflectance, interference and scattering filters.

Transmission filters consist of a thin single filter coating evaporated on a substrate. They have high transmission above and below the wavelength where high absorption produces a sharp cutoff or cuton. (A cutoff is the wavelength where the filter has almost complete absorption of incident radiation; a cuton, where absorption ceases to be high.) Many crystalline materials show a preferential reflection at certain wavelengths corresponding in frequency with the predominant vibration rate of ions in the particular crystal lattice. For example, quartz is valuable at 9 microns, calcium fluoride at 23 microns and cesium bromide at 125 microns. The spectral purity of such a selective reflection increases with the number of reflections. Reflectance filters are of main value in the far infrared region.

An interference filter consists of a series of thin, multilayer films of various castings on a substrate. These layers are either deposited on the substrate or evaporated on in a vacuum. By use of various coatings and substrates and a variation in film thickness, the cutoff or cuton wavelength can be accurately controlled over a fairly wide range. The wavelengths which are to be left out of the spectrum are reflected; the rest are transmitted through the filter.

A great deal of stray radiation in prism spectrometers falls between 1.5 and 3.5 microns. If a mirror or KBr plate is roughened, this stray radiation can be reduced and these filters are called scattering filters.

Infrared filters can be further conveniently classified in the following manner. The short wavelength pass filter absorbs or reflects wavelengths longer than the cutoff wavelengths. There is a sharp drop in transmission at the cutoff which is less than 5% of the maximum transmission. The long wavelength pass filter will transmit all wavelengths longer than a particular cuton, absorbing or reflecting those below this wavelength. The third classification is the band-pass filter which has high transmittance between two wavelengths. Transmission is low at both ends of this range, which may be wide or narrow depending on the filter characteristics. In choosing a suitable filter, transmission curves, cutoff sharpness, optical efficiency, cost, availability, stability (how the filter will hold up under prolonged radiation), and surface hardness are important considerations.

Many substances have been used as filter coatings in the infrared region. Antimony, magnesium oxide and tellurium are coated on substrates having not too high refractive indices such as lithium chloride for the near and middle infrared regions. Cellophane is also a common substrate and is readily coated with various materials. Lead sulphide, lead selenide, and lead telluride were developed as filter coatings because of their value in transmitting middle and slightly long infrared wavelengths, but rejecting the visible through the near infrared regions.[12]

Filters of polycrystalline germanium, selenium, indium arsenide, and indium antimonide have also been described.[13]

Pure alkali halides are normally transparent to infrared radiation. However, if certain impurities are introduced (such as another alkali metal), the impurity becomes trapped between the alkali halide molecules and absorption bands are developed. The concentration of the impurity determines how far these F-center filters, as they are called, can be extended into the infrared region. However, if the impurity concentration becomes too great the filter is not only opaque to the ultraviolet and visible regions, but also to the infrared.

The popularity of filters and gratings in infrared instruments is rapidly developing. For example, Mattraw and Landis[14] replaced the prism on their Baird Infrared Spectrophotometer with a 60 line/mm Bausch and Lomb replica grating and the standard silver chloride scattering light filter with a germanium

[12] J. G. N. Braithwaite, *J. Sci. Instr.* **32**, 10 (1955).
[13] R. C. Lord and T. K. McCubbin, Jr., *J. Opt. Soc. Am.* **45**, 441 (1955).
[14] H. C. Mattraw and F. P. Landis, *Appl. Spectr.* **11**, 31 (1957).

filter. The modified spectrophotometer had increased resolution over the fairly wide range of 2–26 microns. Lord and McCubbin[13] modified a Perkin-Elmer Model 99 spectrometer with a selenium-coated germanium filter and a 150 line/mm grating to get better resolution in the 3–5 micron region. The commercially available instruments which contain gratings will be described in a subsequent section.

2.3 Infrared Detectors

Perhaps the first infrared detector for spectroscopy was that of Herschel in 1840. Herschel passed the infrared beam through a prism to disperse the radiation, which was then allowed to evaporate alcohol from a soot-covered surface. The resulting pattern was photographed to record the infrared spectrum.[7]

The first real advance came in 1880 when Langley introduced the bolometer. By 1930 one of the best detectors was a thermocouple constructed by Cartwright.[15] His thermocouple was made from strips of Bi-Sn and Bi-Sb alloys and had a sensitivity of about 20 $\mu v/\mu w$, which is comparable to modern detectors.[16] To eliminate the zero-drift of these early detectors, detectors were made with response times fast enough to respond to a chopped radiation beam, which was coupled with an ac amplification system which responded only to the chopped signal. The ac signal enables a transformer to be placed in the detector circuit thereby increasing the impedance so that the galvanometer can be replaced by an amplifier. With this technique the effect of stray background radiation can be eliminated. Lehrer[17] prepared a bolometer from a platinum ribbon which had a time constant fast enough to respond to a chopped beam. Other bolometers were prepared in this period from rolled strip and thin wire nickel, and evaporated gold, and from various organic polymers.[7]

Infrared detectors can be conveniently divided into two general groups, selective and nonselective. Selective detectors include those whose response is markedly dependent upon the wavelength of incident radiation. Photographic plates, photocells, photoconductive cells, and infrared phosphors are in this group. The second group (nonselective) includes detectors whose response is directly proportional to incident energy and relatively independent of wavelength. These detectors are better suited for spectroscopy work, and among the more

[15] C. H. Cartwright, Z. Physik 92, 153 (1934).
[16] R. De Waard and E. M. Wormser, Proc. IRE 47, 1508 (1959).
[17] E. Lehrer, Z. tech. Phys. 18, 393 (1937).

common types are thermocouples, bolometers (metal strip, thermistor, and superconducting), and the pneumatic cell.

Most photographic plates are insensitive to radiation in the infrared region. The use of infrared phosphors in combination with photographic plates has extended their range. These phosphors are usually excited with ultraviolet light and, when the afterglow has diminished, are placed with a photographic plate in the instrument. Absorption of infrared light by the phosphor causes it to emit light in the visible region. This technique was used by Paul[18] to record mercury arc spectra.

The most important type of selective detector is the photoconductive cell, which has a rapid response and high sensitivity. These cells, usually made of materials such as thallous sulfide, lead sulfide, lead telluride,[19] lead selenide,[20] or selenium, show an increase in conductivity when illuminated by infrared light. Jenness[21] has prepared photoconductive cells by coating a dielectric supporting base, transparent to infrared radiation, such as sapphire or calcium fluoride, with the photoconducting material which is in turn coated with a reflection-reducing coating such as magnesium fluoride, antimony sulfide, or arsenic trioxide. The other side of the base is coated with a reflective material such as silver or aluminum. Photoconductive cells are most useful in the range of 0.5–3.5 microns, but this range has been extended by Moss,[19] using lead telluride cells cooled with liquid hydrogen.

A thermocouple is an excellent detector for measuring infrared radiation. By blackening the junction of dissimilar metals, incident radiation is absorbed, causing a temperature rise at the junction and a resultant increase in the electromotive potential developed across the junction leads. Thermocouples are often made by evaporating metals, such as bismuth, antimony, or semiconductor alloys, on a thin film of cellulose nitrate or other supporting base.[7] The thermocouple is placed in an evacuated chamber with a window of NaCl and KBr, or CsI and crystal quartz[22] for long wavelengths, i.e., 50 microns. Common commercial units have sensitivities of about 6–8 $\mu v/\mu w$.[23]

A bolometer is a detecting device which depends on a change of resistance of the material with temperature. The receiving element is made one arm of a Wheatstone bridge circuit, thus providing an easy method of measuring the resistance of the element. Bolometers have an advantage in infrared detection in that they generally have a faster response time than thermocouples.[24] Jones[25]

[18] F. W. Paul, *J. Opt. Soc. Am.* **36**, 175 (1946).
[19] T. S. Moss, *Nature* **161**, 766 (1948).
[20] T. S. Moss, Proc. *IRE* **43**, 1869 (1955).
[21] J. R. Jenness, Jr., U. S. Patent 2,768,265, Oct. 23, 1956.
[22] E. K. Plyler and N. Acquista, *J. Chem. Phys.* **23**, 752 (1955).
[23] Charles M. Reeder and Company, Detroit, Michigan, Catalog 1954-55.
[24] E. B. Baker and C. D. Robb, *Rev. Sci. Instr.* **14**, 356 (1943).
[25] R. C. Jones, *J. Opt. Soc. Am.* **36**, 448 (1946).

has given a good discussion of the theoretical aspects of their behavior.

Metal bolometers have the inherent advantage of a small thermal capacity, and therefore a quick response. Brockman[26] prepared a thin strip nickel bolometer by rolling nickel between layers of silver and then removing the silver by electrolysis. He found that the temperature coefficient of resistivity of nickel bolometers was independent of the strip thickness. Billings[27] prepared a nickel bolometer by evaporating a layer of nickel approximately 200 angstroms thick onto a nitro-cellulose pellicle. Langton[28] made a platinum strip bolometer which was soldered on a taut suspension and operated in an atmosphere of hydrogen at reduced pressure. This detector gave an exceptionally low noise level, with a fair time constant and sensitivity. Gillham[29] prepared a bolometer by sputtering a coating of antimony about 400 angstroms thick on a polystyrene pellicle, but the sensitivity and time constant were not too promising. Markov[30] has obtained a lower threshold of sensitivity with a bismuth-lead alloy.

In recent years, thermistor bolometers have come into prominence largely because of their increased sensitivities. Thermistors are made of semiconducting material in which the resistance decreases exponentially with increasing temperature. The thermal coefficient of resistivity is about 4% per °C, or about ten times that for metal bolometers. Thermistors are prepared in the form of flakes, 1–5 mm long, 0.1–1 mm wide and 0.01–0.02 mm thick, composed of sintered oxides of nickel, cobalt, and manganese. Metal contacts are placed on each end, the assembly is cemented to a backing of glass or quartz, and the whole assembly placed in an evacuated metal case, with an infrared-transparent window.[31] Thermistors have also been prepared of other materials, such as the oxides of uranium.[32]

Commercial thermistor bolometers consist of a matched pair of thermistor flakes, having similar thermal and electrical properties. The second flake serves as a compensating element to eliminate the effect of background radiation. Time constants for thermistors are about the same as for metal bolometers (3 μsec), but the sensitivity is much greater (up to 400 volts/watt).[33]

Superconducting bolometers use metals at cryogenic temperatures. They offer the advantages of extremely high sensitivity and very fast response. Andrews[34] developed a superconducting bolometer employing a columbium nitride ribbon at temperatures of about 15° K.

[26] F. G. Brockman, *J. Opt. Soc. Am.* **36**, 32 (1946).

[27] B. H. Billings, E. E. Barr, and W. L. Hyde, *Rev. Sci. Instr.* **18**, 429 (1947).

[28] W. G. Langton, *J. Opt. Soc. Am.* **36**, 355 (1946).

[29] E. J. Gillham, *J. Sci. Instr.* **33**, 338 (1956).

[30] M. N. Markov, *Dokl. Akad. Nauk S.S.S.R.* **108**, 428 (1956).

[31] W. H. Brattain and J. A. Becker, *J. Opt. Soc. Am.* **36**, 354 (1946).

[32] J. Prigent, *J. Phys. Radium* **10**, 58 (1949).

[33] Servo Corporation of America, New Hyde Park, N. Y., Bulletin SCA-TB-1.

[34] D. H. Andrews, R. M. Milton, and W. De Sorbo, *J. Opt. Soc. Am.* **36**, 518 (1946).

One of the more ingenious detectors was the pneumatic cell, developed primarily by Golay.[35] The Golay cell consisted of a gasfilled 3 mm cell, which was connected by means of a tube to a second small cell, one side of which was closed by a curved diaphragm which acts as a mirror. A change in the radiant energy incident on the first cell caused a change in gas pressure, which in turn moved the mirror on the second cell. A steady beam of light was reflected off the mirror and passed through a grid network to a photocell, which was in turn connected to an amplifier and recorder. A slight movement of the mirror would result in a large change in intensity of the light passing through the grid thereby yielding great sensitivity.

It is beyond the scope of this text to consider the amplifiers used with the various detectors discussed. There are several excellent references[7,36,37] which cover this subject adequately.

Infrared detectors have been greatly improved since the days of Herschel, but they are still the subject of many research investigations in the field of infrared instrumentation.

2.4 Typical Commercial Instruments

Major manufacturers of infrared spectrometers are Baird-Atomic, Inc., Beckman Instruments, Inc., and the Perkin-Elmer Corporation in the United States and Unicam Instruments Limited in England. Because of the constant changes being made in commercial infrared instruments, it is not advisable to describe in detail all of the models available and only a few instruments will be considered.

The first commercial infrared spectrometers were single beam instruments; however, the interference of water vapor and carbon dioxide bands severely limited their application. In 1947 a double beam instrument was described in the literature[38] and made available commercially by Baird Associates, Inc. Since that time single beam instruments have gradually lost their importance except for far infrared measurements.

As an example of a recent economical double beam instrument the Perkin-

[35] M. J. E. Golay, Rev. Sci. Instr. 18, 357 (1947).

[36] R. A. Smith, F. E. Jones and R. P. Chasmar, "The Detection and Measurement of Infra-Red Radiation," Chapter XII. Oxford Univ. Press, London and New York, 1957.

[37] G. K. T. Conn and D. G. Avery, "Infrared Methods," Chapter IV. Academic Press, New York, 1960.

[38] W. S. Baird, H. M. O'Bryan, G. Ogden, and D. Lee, J. Opt. Soc. Am. 37, 754 (1947).

Elmer Model 137 Infracord Spectrophotometer will be briefly described. The optical diagram of this instrument is shown in Fig. 2.8. Radiant energy from the source (previously described in Section 2.1) is split into the sample and reference beams by the plane mirror and the two toroid mirrors. Toroid mirror (1) focuses the sample beam through the sampling area onto the 100% comb; toroid mirror (2) focuses the reference beam onto the optical wedge. The sample

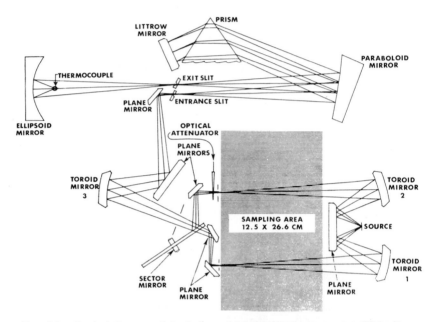

FIG. 2.8. Optical diagram of the Infracord Model 137 Spectrometer. (This diagram and its description are taken from a bulletin entitled "Infracord Spectrophotometer," published by the Perkin-Elmer Corporation, Norwalk, Connecticut.)

is placed just in front of the 100% comb. Sample and reference beams after passing through the sampling area are recombined by the semicircular sector mirror which rotates at 13 revolutions/sec. Oriented in relation to the three plane mirrors shown, the sector mirror alternately reflects the reference beam and passes the sample beam through the aperture stop which assures that both beams are the same size and will follow identical paths through the remainder of the system. The signal beam which now consists of alternate pulses of sample and reference radiation is focused by the toroid mirror (3) and reflected by the plane mirrors through the entrance window of the monochromator and onto the entrance slit (focal point of the toroid mirror). Leaving the slit, the beam diverges until the off-axis paraboloid reflects it as collimated light (parallel rays) onto the prism. At the prism, the component wavelengths are dispersed into infrared wavelengths and reflected by the Littrow mirror back into the prism where it is further dispersed. The dispersed radiation is then focused on the plane of the exit slit by the paraboloid as a band of individual wavelengths falling across the slit. The particular spectral wavelength which emerges from the slit strikes the ellipsoid mirror which focuses it on the thermocouple target.

If the energy in both sample and reference beams is equal, a dc voltage is produced by the thermocouple which is not amplified by the ac amplifier of the instrument. When the sample absorbs radiation at characteristic wavelengths, the intensity of the sample beam is naturally reduced. This produces an unequal signal at the detector which is converted to an alternating voltage and amplified by the 13-cycle amplifier. The amplified signal is used to drive a servo motor which moves an optical wedge into or out of the reference beam to equalize or null the beam intensities. Since the recorder pen is coupled directly to the wedge or optical attenuator, its movements are a record of the wedge position or transmittance.

Instruments of similar design are the KBr Model 137 which contains a potassium bromide prism and is designed for the 12.5–25 micron range and the Model 137-G. This latter instrument has two replica gratings and transmission filters to isolate the desired grating orders and is intended for the 0.83–7.65 micron region.

Other comparatively low-priced double beam instruments for the NaCl region are the Model NK-1 manufactured by Baird-Atomic, Inc. and the Beckman IR-5 manufactured by Beckman Instruments, Inc.

The Beckman IR-7 spectrophotometer is a suitable example of a prism-grating instrument. The optical system[39] is shown in Fig. 2.9. The radiation source is a Nernst Glower composed of bonded zirconium oxide. An auxiliary platinum wire heater raises the refractory oxide to a temperature where it will conduct. The output of the glower is continuously monitored by a cesium oxide phototube. The radiation is split into a sample and reference beam at 11 cycles/sec by two rotating half-mirrors driven in correct phase relation by a synchronous motor. Three precision cams drive the prism, grating and triple-slit system. The entrance, intermediate and exit slits are bilateral, curved slits adjustable from 0 to 6 mm. For optimum balance between energy and stray light, the intermediate slit is maintained 0.5 mm wider than the entrance and exit slits. The fore-prism serves as an order sorter for the replica grating and contributes to the initial dispersion in all four orders of the grating. The detector is a thermocouple with a low mass gold-foil element and a precision lens of potassium bromide. Available as an accessory is a long wavelength interchange containing a cesium iodide prism and a 30-micron blaze, 30 line/mm long wavelength grating. For optimum performance at long wavelengths the manu-

---

[39] Beckman Bulletin 739-B, Beckman Instruments, Inc., Fullerton, California.

facturers[40] recommend a cesium iodide thermocouple detector for operation to 40 microns or a Golay detector for operation to 50 microns.

Another prism-grating instrument commercially available is the Unicam SP.100 Infrared Spectrometer containing the SP.130 grating accessory. This instrument contains two replica gratings ruled at 1500 lines/in. and 3000 lines/in.,

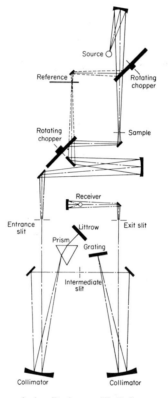

FIG. 2.9. Optical system of the Beckman IR-7 Spectrometer (courtesy Beckman Instruments, Inc., Fullerton, California).

respectively, for the ranges 2150–650 cm^{-1} and 3650–2150 cm^{-1}. These two gratings have ruled areas of 9 × 6 cm and are mounted back to back, slightly out of parallel. The grating assembly is mounted on a turntable which is rotated by means of a lever and cam mechanism to obtain a frequency scan. The radiation enters the grating monochromator through a curved entrance slit, is dispersed, and enters the prism monochromator through a wide intermediate

[40] Beckman Bulletin 782, Beckman Instruments, Inc., Fullerton, California.

slit. The curvature of the entrance slit compensates for image curvature introduced by the prism monochromator. From the prism the radiation passes
through a straight exit slit and is condensed on a Golay detector.

The Perkin-Elmer Model 421 is an all-grating instrument which uses two
gratings in their first orders only to cover the range of 4000–550 cm^{-1}. The
spectrum is recorded continuously without break or overlap. Four filters
automatically inserted in the beam at appropriate regions isolate first-order
energy from that of the higher grating orders. This company also manufactures a
double-beam grating spectrophotometer for the far infrared region. This
instrument has a Globar as a source with several crystal choppers and the various
reststrahlen filters, scatter plates and other filters necessary for elimination of
unwanted grating orders in the wavelength range 400–67 cm^{-1}. The instrument
has a 13-cycle electronic system permitting either single-beam or double-beam
ratio recording operation. The detector assembly includes a Golay detector with
a $\frac{1}{16}$ inch diameter target and a diamond window.

2.5 Instrument Calibration

It is occasionally necessary to check the calibration of an infrared spectrometer
by measuring the spectra of gases whose absorption bands are accurately known.
For example, a lithium fluoride prism can be calibrated in the 3100–2700 cm^{-1}
region by measuring the absorption spectrum of hydrogen chloride (see Fig. 1.10).

The spectra of gases measured on a prism spectrometer often have a different
appearance as compared to those obtained with a grating spectrometer of much
higher resolution. Two problems can result from this difficulty. Identification
of the absorption bands in the calibration traces may be an arduous task and when
a group of bands coalesce, if the bands are not symmetrically placed, the frequency of the absorption maximum may be different from that of the strongest
band. Care should be taken, therefore, in making such comparisons. Articles
showing the spectra of many gases with their band positions tabulated have been
published[41,42] and a recent text[43] deals exclusively with calibration data; so there
is little need to include such information in this text. For a routine check in the
rock salt region a film of polystyrene is convenient since calibration data on
polystyrene are available in most manufacturers' manuals.

[41] A. R. Downie, M. C. Magoon, T. Purcell and B. Crawford, Jr., *J. Opt. Soc. Am.*
43, 941 (1953).

[42] E. K. Plyler, L. R. Blaine and M. Nowak, *J. Res. Natl. Bur. Std.* **58**, 195 (1957).

[43] International Union of Pure and Applied Chemistry Commission on Molecular Structure and Spectroscopy, "Tables of Wavenumbers for the Calibration of Infra-red
Spectrometers." Butterworth, Washington, D. C., 1961.

2.6 Sample Handling Techniques

Since most sample holders have some type of alkali halide window a brief discussion of polishing rock salt crystals as an example is in order. Block rock salt is prepared for polishing by first cleaving the pieces roughly to shape with a single-edged razor blade and a small hammer. The salt crystal is placed on a metal block or firm surface covered with a few layers of paper. The razor blade is held on the crystal edge parallel to the cleavage planes and the sides and then tapped with the hammer. When a cleavage is started, it is followed until complete. Pieces may be split in halves or thirds safely but if much smaller sections are cleaved off, these smaller pieces may break. If small pieces are desired, the big pieces should be cleaved in half and the halves in half etc. The crystals may be finally cut into desired sizes by appropriate cuts perpendicular to the edges.

The cleaved faces can be sanded flat with No. 220 silicon carbide paper such as WETORDRY TRI-M-ITE paper* and fine-sanded with No. 600 paper. Used crystals can be sanded if they are badly scatched or etched. If they have had very light use, they should be repolished without sanding.

One technique for polishing is as follows: two laps are prepared and mounted side by side. One lap is made from a 6-in. diameter metal disc with an indentation in the rim to take a rubber O-ring. Two thicknesses of fine nylon cloth are stretched over the disc and held in place with the O-ring. The other lap is like the first but covered with ordinary diaper cloth.

The nylon lap is moistened completely with water from a medicine dropper and a little Aloxite buffing powder A No. 1 fine[†] or Cerium Oxide Polishing Powder[††] is sprinkled on and spread evenly with the fingers. The lap should be moist—not wet or unevenly damp. The rock salt crystal is held by the ends and polished about thirty strokes on the wet lap and immediately buffed about ten strokes on the dry lap. The operation is repeated until a clear crystal is obtained. If the lap is too dry, a frosted effect results. If the lap is too wet, excessively rounded edges and a ripple "orange peel" effect results.

Using fingers for holding the crystal usually results in marks on the plate ends but, if this area is not in the region of the infrared beam, it can be ignored. If a completely clear crystal is desired, a holder or rubber fingers must be used.

Rock salt can also be well polished with alcohol and rouge as a fine abrasive. A kit which contains ground glass pads, grinding compound and accessories for

* Available from the 3M Company, St. Paul, Minnesota.
† Available from the Carborundum Company.
†† Available from Davison Chemical Co., Pompton Plains, New Jersey.

polishing rock salt is commercially available and includes a brochure[44] with more detailed information on polishing rock salt than has been presented here.

(a) GASES

Absorption spectra of gases can be measured in a wide variety of gas cells ranging from a few centimeters to several meters in path lengths. For compactness the longer path length cells have mirrors which reflect the beam through the cell several times. In cells of one or more meters such a procedure results in a considerable energy loss in the infrared beam. Both glass and metal cells are used although for either very small or very large volumes metal cells are more convenient. To hold a vacuum of 10^{-5} mm or better the glass cells must have carefully polished ends on which the halide windows are cemented with materials such as epoxy resins (see Fig. 2.10). Metal cells of many types have been described

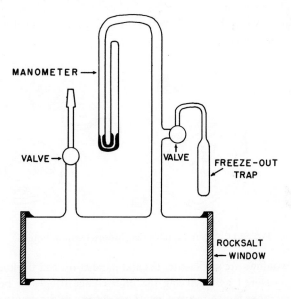

FIG. 2.10. Typical infrared cell for gas samples.

in the literature. The windows in metal cells with O-ring gaskets can be removed more readily for polishing than from glass cells with cemented windows. In addition, metal cells are more suitable for studies at high temperatures. Freezeout traps or manometers can be connected to such cells with glass to metal seals. If a suitable valve is placed between the cell and the freezeout trap, the gas pressure

[44] Instruction Manual for Infrared Sampling Accessories, Connecticut Instrument Corporation, Wilton, Connecticut.

can be readily controlled with suitable freezing mixtures on the trap, particularly if several different gases are in the cell. The manometer serves to monitor the pressure of the gas. For measurements at room temperature neoprene O-rings are suitable but for temperatures above 100° C silicone rubber O-rings are more durable.

Narrow contoured gas cells are particularly valuable if only small samples of gas are available. Such cells having a path length of 10 cm and a volume of only 26 cc are commercially available.[44] Most gases yield suitable spectra at approximately 50-mm pressure. For qualitative analysis an excellent catalog of the infrared spectra of 66 gases has been published by Pierson *et al.*[45]

(b) LIQUIDS

In most instances the spectra of liquids are measured in either a demountable type cell similar to the one shown in Fig. 2.11 or in fixed thickness or sealed cells similar to that shown in Fig. 2.12. Both types of cell are commercially available from a number of sources.

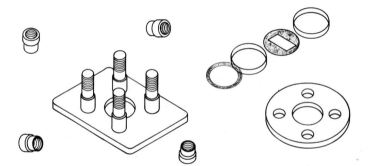

FIG. 2.11.   Demountable type infrared cell for liquids.

If the cell windows are sufficiently flat and parallel the cell thickness of a fixed cell may be measured by observing the interference fringes or percent transmittance undulations which result when the spectrum of the empty cell is taken. The infrared beam which is twice reflected inside the cell is retarded by twice the cell thickness relative to the unreflected beam. The thickness t in cm may be calculated by

$$2\,t = \frac{N}{\nu_1 - \nu_2} \tag{2.15}$$

where N is the number of fringes found between ν_1 and ν_2 (the frequencies in cm^{-1}).

[45] R. H. Pierson, A. N. Fletcher, and E. St. Clair Gantz, *Anal. Chem.* **28**, 1218 (1956).

Liquids which are not too viscous or corrosive to metal or rock salt are normally measured in sealed cells to prevent undue evaporation. These cells may be filled and emptied with a hypodermic syringe. Either corks or plugs made of an inert plastic such as Teflon are used to cap the cells. Viscous or corrosive liquids (including water) are placed in demountable cells. An aluminum spacer foil is

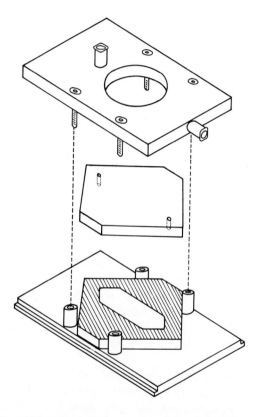

FIG. 2.12.   Fixed thickness or sealed cell for liquids.

placed on the bottom crystal in the metal holder and a drop of sample is placed in the center of the spacer. The second rock salt crystal is placed on top and fastened gently in place. Usually rubber gaskets are placed between the metal holder and the crystal to prevent cracking the crystal. In many instances with very viscous liquids or heavily absorbing liquids the spacer is omitted. Aqueous solutions may be measured in a limited wavelength region with calcium fluoride plates or in most of the rock salt region with barium fluoride or Irtran-2 and in the complete rock salt region using silver chloride plates. Silver chloride, however, is reactive and deformable and darkens on exposure to light which causes a gradual reduction in its transmission in the infrared region also. For qualitative aqueous solution analysis, it is often simpler to use a demountable cell with rock salt plates and resand and polish the plates after the spectrum has been obtained.

Cavity cells first developed by R. N. Jones of the National Research Council of Canada are now commercially available. These cells are made by ultrasonic machining rock salt crystals with a blade of the desired shape which is driven into the block at a frequency of about 20,000 cycles/sec.[44] These cells are economical in cost and suitable for measuring the spectra of most solutions but are less useful for pure liquids since the smallest thickness available at present is 0.05 mm.

For qualitative and quantitative analysis when it is desirable to determine a solute in a solution, the absorption bands of the solvent can be canceled out by filling a second cell of the same thickness as the sample cell with the solvent and placing the second cell in the reference beam. To perform the same function variable space cells which may be quickly set to give any path length within such ranges as 0.015 mm or 0.08 to 1.0 mm are also commercially available.[44]

(c) SOLIDS

Techniques for obtaining the infrared spectra of solids are more diversified than for either gases or liquids. If a suitable solvent is available, the solid may be dissolved and measured in the manner described for liquids. However, suitable solvents are limited in number and none are totally transparent. Those solvents which are less transparent require relatively high concentrations of the solid before adequate spectra can be obtained. Probably carbon tetrachloride, chloroform and carbon disulfide are the most valuable solvents from the standpoint of transparency.

An alternate technique most useful for soluble polymers is to prepare a film of the solid by evaporating a solution of the material directly on a rock salt plate or on a material from which the dried film can be peeled. Water solutions can be readily evaporated on silver chloride plates.

Another method involves melting the sample on the salt plate and allowing it to resolidify. This method is not recommended for crystalline materials because of possible orientation effects or for samples which might be decomposed by heat. It is most applicable for amorphous materials of a tarry or waxy nature.

Orientation effects result from the fact that radiation is a transverse vibration and only interacts with the components of dipole moment changing in a direction normal to the beam direction. For example, if a benzene ring compound is oriented with the ring coplanar with the salt plate, out-of-plane vibrational bands will be weakened and in-plane bands will be strengthened relative to an unoriented preparation. Oriented films are prepared deliberately to observe just such effects for vibrational analysis studies but for qualitative and quantitative analysis orientation is not desirable.

An extremely valuable technique for solid samples is the mineral oil (Nujol) mull method. A small amount of solid sample is mulled in a mortar with a small amount of Nujol to yield a paste which is then transferred to a rock salt plate or the sample may be mulled directly between the salt plates. The small scratches that result from this latter method (which saves time and sample) do no damage and are completely removed when the plate is resurfaced.

The mineral oil technique has the advantage of nonreactivity with samples, reproducibility of results, minor obscuration because of the medium, and rapidity of preparation. The obscured aliphatic carbon-hydrogen region does not always yield definitive information and its loss can usually be tolerated. When information is needed about the carbon-hydrogen region, a second mull can be prepared using either totally fluorinated or chlorinated hydrocarbons such as perfluorokerosene, Halocarbon Oil* or hexachlorobutadiene as the mulling agent. These liquids have strong bands elsewhere but are free of carbon-hydrogen absorption bands. With this complementary preparation, the whole spectral region is available unobscured.

Where there is insufficient sample to fill the sample beam at the desired thickness, the mulled sample should not be thinned further. Instead the regions without sample should be masked off with tape even if this leaves only about three square millimeters clear. Modern double beam instruments will yield a suitable spectrum if the slits are widened a little and a compensating wire screen or attenuator is placed in the reference beam.

Another valuable method involves the potassium bromide disc technique. In this method a very small amount of solid sample is intimately mixed with potassium bromide and then pressed in an evacuated die under high pressure. The resulting discs are transparent and yield excellent spectra. The only infrared absorption by the potassium bromide matrix is from small amounts of adsorbed water in the powder.

There are a wide variety of dies commercially available for the preparation of potassium bromide discs. In general, a die which can be evacuated prior to pressing the disc is preferable; otherwise the entrapped air slowly reappears after the pressure is released. Pressures of approximately eight tons for a pressing time of five minutes or ten tons for one minute are suitable for dies which produce 13-mm discs. For larger diameter dies higher pressures are required. A Carver Laboratory Press of 10-ton capacity is suitable or an economical press can be made from an ordinary hydraulic truck jack and a suitable pressure gauge.

Potassium bromide of infrared quality ground to at least 400 mesh is com-

---

* Halocarbon Products Corp., 82 Burlews Court, Hackensack, New Jersey.

mercially available from the Harshaw Chemical Company, Cleveland, Ohio. Only two weak water bands should be evident in the spectrum of a disc containing pure potassium bromide, the O-H stretching vibration at 3300 cm^{-1} and the O-H bending vibration at approximately 1640 cm^{-1}.

The optimum sample concentration usually varies from 0.1% to as much as 3% in some aromatic compounds. The proper concentration is best determined by trial and 0.5% is a good starting point. Other important variables in obtaining good spectra are the particle size and homogeneity of the sample in the potassium bromide matrix. Both these variables are related to the grinding time. With the same concentration of sample in the potassium bromide the absorption bands increase in intensity as the grinding time is increased and usually reach a maximum constant value in from three to five minutes. Proper particle size and distribution can be achieved by mechanically grinding the sample in a plastic capsule in a commercially available* dental accessory known as the "Wig-L-Bug."

A technique for handling polymers that are difficult to mull, dissolve, or melt consists of placing the polymer and a suitable amount of KBr in a metal Wig-L-Bug capsule with a metal ball inside. The closed capsule is sealed with masking tape and immersed in liquid air. When bubbling stops, the capsule is placed in the Wig-L-Bug and shaken. After the capsule has reached room temperature a normal KBr pellet is made of the contents. The normally tough polymer becomes brittle at low temperatures.

Another technique involves dissolving the sample in a volatile solvent (even water is suitable), adding the solution to the potassium bromide and then evaporating the solvent before grinding. Samples taken from the outlet of a gas chromatograph can be conveniently trapped in a porous plug of potassium bromide and the spectra then obtained by pressing a disc in the usual manner.[46]

An alternate procedure involves the so-called freeze drying technique. In this method solutions of weighed amounts of sample and potassium bromide are cooled rapidly in an acetone-Dry Ice mixture. Such rapid cooling yields sub-microscopic crystals of the organic compound. The resulting mixture is then dried over phosphorus pentoxide at reduced pressures (approximately 10 mm) and slightly elevated temperatures (50° C).

It has been found on occasion that the spectra obtained on powders prepared by the freeze drying method differ from those obtained by grinding. In addition, there have been differences found between the spectrum of a solid when measured in a Nujol mull as compared to its spectrum in potassium bromide. Several authors have reported changes in the spectra of solids in alkali discs caused either

[46] H. W. Leggon, *Anal. Chem.* **33**, 1295 (1961).

* Available from the Crescent Dental Manufacturing Co., Chicago, Illinois.

by metathesis[47,48] or the formation of mixed crystals.[49,50] Padgett[51] has discussed the different spectra obtained for cyanuric acid in potassium bromide, potassium chloride and for a sublimed sample, and concluded that the effect is probably caused by ion interchange. Baker[52] has summarized solid state anomalies in infrared spectroscopy with emphasis on organic compounds. He lists the factors which influence the changes in pellet spectra as follows: (a) crystal energy of the organic phase, (b) total amount of energy used in grinding sample and matrix, (c) lattice energy of matrix, (d) particle size of matrix, (e) stress relaxation involving either the temperature of pellet or powder mixture or the time lapse between grinding the sample mixture and obtaining the spectrum, and (f) occurrence of polymorphic transitions.

Although the potassium bromide method has the disadvantages mentioned, it is still well suited for obtaining spectra of microsamples and of amorphous polymers or resins. It should not displace the mineral oil mull technique but rather act as a complementary method. In combination, these two methods of obtaining spectra can yield more information about a sample than either one alone.

An important new method called attenuated total reflectance for obtaining the infrared spectra of solids or films has recently been described by Fahrenfort.[53] If a beam of radiation traverses a prism so that it is reflected from the back face of the prism as shown in Fig. 2.13(a), some portion of the energy of the beam escapes from the face and is returned into the prism. If an absorbing substance is placed on the reflecting surface, under suitable conditions, the energy that escapes temporarily from the prism is selectively absorbed. The transfer of energy is roughly proportional to the ratio of the indices of refraction of the prism material and the substance. Since the refractive index of a substance changes rapidly at wavelengths of absorption (see for example Figs. 2.4 and 2.5) the plot of the energy transfer versus wavelength is very similar to the conventional infrared absorption spectrum of the substance. The infrared band intensities are the equivalent of a penetration of a few microns into the substance and are independent of the sample thickness. To obtain suitable spectra the angle of incidence of the infrared beam on the internally reflecting face of the prism must be adjustable. In addition, the prism should have a higher index of refraction than the substance to be examined. In this respect KRS-5 with an index of refraction of 2.380 is most suitable. Specially designed liquid and solid sample

[47] W. A. Pliskin and R. P. Eischens, *J. Phys. Chem.* **59**, 1156 (1955).

[48] J. A. A. Ketelaar, C. Haas, and J. van der Elsken, *J. Chem. Phys.* **24**, 624 (1956).

[49] V. C. Farmer, *Chem. Ind. (London)* **1955**, 586.

[50] L. H. Jones and M. M. Chamberlain, *J. Chem. Phys.* **25**, 365 (1956).

[51] W. M. Padgett, II, J. M. Talbert, and W. F. Hamner, *J. Chem. Phys.* **26**, 959 (1957).

[52] A. W. Baker, *J. Phys. Chem.* **61**, 450 (1957).

[53] J. Fahrenfort, *Spectrochim. Acta* **17**, 698 (1961).

holders hold the samples against the reflecting surface of the prism. A novel approach to sampling has been developed by the Connecticut Instrument Company. As a sample holder a specially shaped thin plate of silver chloride provides a semi-expendable reflecting mechanism. The sample is placed on the smooth side of the silver chloride plate. The other side contains a pattern of

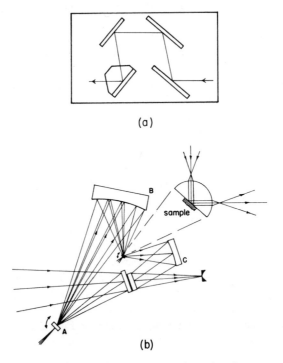

(a)

(b)

FIG. 2.13.   Optical diagrams of the attenuated total reflectance attachments. (a) Attachment for macro samples. (b) Attachment for micro samples (courtesy Connecticut Instrument Co., Wilton, Connecticut.)

parallel prisms (formed by pressing) which place a series of surfaces roughly perpendicular to the incoming radiation beam. Thus, the infrared radiation striking these faces penetrates the plate rather than being reflected from the top surface. Reflection with attenuation takes place at the rear surface.

   The optical schematic of a micro attachment for attenuated total reflectance commercially available from the same company is shown in Fig. 2.13(b). In this attachment the beam is first brought to focus on a source image mirror (A). An adjustable off-axis spherical mirror (B) condenses it at its sampling point. A second spherical mirror (C) refocuses it on the entrance slit of the spectro-photometer. The angle of incidence is adjusted by rotating the source image mirror (A) and the sample mount which are linked to a calibrated dial by a precision gear train assembly. The angle of incidence may be varied from 30 to 60°, with settings reproducible to better than 1°. About 70% of the available energy in a typical spectrophotometer is transmitted by the unit.

The attenuated total reflectance technique is mainly valuable for all types of solid, plastic and highly viscous materials as well as aqueous solutions because the effective beam penetration of the sample is only a few microns.

(d) HIGH AND LOW TEMPERATURE METHODS

It is often desirable to obtain infrared spectra of samples at elevated or low temperatures in addition to room temperature. If a sample has a melting point near room temperature, the spectrum is often measured in the liquid phase for comparison with simpler related compounds which are normally liquids. Other examples include the study of the temperature dependence of bands as well as the study of infrared spectra obtained at different temperatures of a chemical reaction which can be carried out directly in the cell. In order to obtain the vapor spectrum of a material with a relatively low vapor pressure either a multiple reflection cell of several meters or a heated gas cell of conventional length can be used. However, in the case of a compound with very low vapor pressure a heated multiple reflection cell is needed.

One type of heated cell for liquids or solids is a small metal box with windows to transmit the infrared beam and a back flange which fits in the cell holder plate on the instrument. Inside the box a conventional cell is mounted into another cell holder plate identical to the one on the instrument. The box is wound with resistance wire and covered with asbestos. A Variac controls the current while the temperature is measured either with a thermometer or a thermocouple which for best results should be mounted into the body of the salt plates of the cell.

Klemperer[54,55] has studied the thermodynamic properties of aluminum chloride and alkali halides with heated cells. The cells were Pyrex or Vycor tubes about 1.2 meters long and 45 mm in diameter with a side arm to permit evacuation or the addition of an inert atmosphere. The cell was heated in the center by a Nichrome wound external furnace 20 cm long and the temperature was measured in the space between the furnace wall and the cell wall with a thermocouple. The cell and furnace were located so that light from the center of the cell illuminated the entrance slit of the spectrometer. A temperature of 900° C could be obtained. The presence of argon and the long length of the cell outside the furnace prevented the aluminum chloride from condensing

[54] W. Klemperer *J. Chem. Phys.* **24**, 353 (1956).
[55] W. Klemperer and S. A. Rice, *J. Chem. Phys.* **26**, 618 (1957).

on the potassium bromide windows which were at approximately room temperature.

Cole and Minkoff[56] developed a quantitative technique to study the combustion products of a flame by passing the infrared beam through a flat flame burning a homogeneous gas mixture at a constant rate.

Mattraw[57] has described a simple, inexpensive, electrically heated cell purposely built for corrosive materials of low vapor pressure at room temperature. For temperatures to 125° C successful spectra were obtained for such materials as titanium tetrachloride, uranium and iridium hexafluorides as well as chromium, molybdenum, and tungsten carbonyls.

The body of the cell was 10 cm in length and constructed of copper or nickel and contained AgCl or KRS-5 windows placed on Teflon gaskets.

The cell was heated by heating tape wound around the cell body, Hoke valve and trap while the temperature of the tape was controlled by a Variac. The massive cell body wrapped with heating tape held the temperature fairly constant so that once the windows were brought to temperature with infrared lamps the entire spectrum could be measured before condensation took place on the windows.

Hallgren and Greenberg[58] have recently developed two methods for measuring the infrared spectra of fused salts. One technique consists of a reflectance type cell while the other involves supporting the melt on a fine-mesh platinum screen.

In the reflectance cell a mirror was placed in the light path at a 45° angle deflecting the beam downward into a quartz container. The beam passed through the melt to a gold mirror at the bottom of the container. The gold mirror reflected it back upward to a second mirror where it was deflected into the spectrophotometer. As the light beam is a cone focused at the slit, the mirrors must compensate for the change in path length. These mirrors were taken from a standard Perkin-Elmer reflectance attachment and were ground to perform this function.

In the second method a platinum screen supported the melt in the holes of the screen. The screen was placed in the light path in the same manner as the standard cell. The screen was heated either by placing the screen in an electrically heated furnace or by passing a suitable current directly through the screen. The directly heated screen has been operated at temperatures as high as 800° C. A thermocouple was welded on the center of the screen to both measure and control the temperature. Both of the methods have yielded spectra of fused salts in vacuum above and below the melting point.

Infrared spectra are often measured at low temperature to verify the existence of rotational isomers. The more complex spectra at room temperature can usually

[56] D. J. Cole and G. J. Minkoff, *Combust. Flame* 1, 241-9 (1957).
[57] H. C. Mattraw, *Appl. Spectr.* 9, No. 4, 177 (1955).
[58] L. J. Hallgren and J. Greenberg, *Chem. Eng. News* 38, No 39, p. 43 (1960).

be simplified at reduced temperatures yielding the spectrum of the more stable rotational configuration. Absorption bands which are broad and indistinct and overlap in liquids often become sharper as the liquid becomes a solid. Difference bands can sometimes be distinguished from overtone and combination bands by the disappearance of the difference bands at reduced temperatures.

Most designs for low temperature cells[59] include a liquid reservoir for coolants such as Dry Ice and acetone or liquid nitrogen near the sample mounting. A typical design[60] is shown in Fig. 2.14. A circular insert can also be placed in the copper block so that potassium bromide discs can be studied at low temperatures.

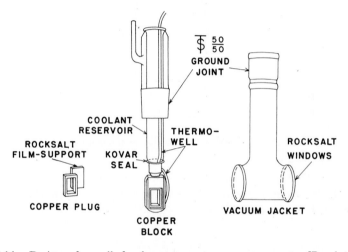

FIG. 2.14. Design of a cell for low temperature measurements. [Reprinted by courtesy of the *J. Chem. Phys.* **18**, 296 (1950).]

2.7 *Quantitative Analysis*

(a) THE ABSORPTION LAW

If P_0 is the incident radiant power impinging on a sample and P is the radiant power after passing through the sample, then the ratio P/P_0 is called the transmittance of the sample and given the symbol T (see Fig. 2.15). Multiplying by 100 gives the percent transmittance ($\% \ T$) of the sample. If the sample is in a

[59] A. Walsh and J. B. Willis, *J. Chem. Phys.* **18**, 552 (1950).
[60] E. L. Wagner and D. F. Hornig, *J. Chem. Phys.* **18**, 296 (1950).

cell of thickness b in cm at a concentration of c in g/liter then the fundamental equation governing the absorption of radiation is

$$\frac{P}{P_0} = 10^{-abc} \tag{2.16}$$

All the terms in this equation have been defined except a which is a constant characteristic of the sample at a given frequency or wavelength and is called the absorptivity.

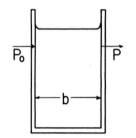

FIG. 2.15.   Graphical illustration of transmission terms.

Equation (2.16) is cumbersome for calculations and can be transformed by taking the logarithm to the base 10 of both sides of the equation and replacing P/P_0 by P_0/P to eliminate the negative sign. The result is

$$\log \frac{P_0}{P} = abc \tag{2.17}$$

The term $\log P_0/P$ is given the symbol A and called the absorbance.* Thus,

$$A = abc \tag{2.18}$$

Historically, the study of the variables in the previous Eq. (2.16) yielded Beer's law denoting conformation with respect to changes in concentration, c, and Bouger's or Lambert's law denoting conformation with respect to changes in thickness, b. Equation (2.16) is obtained by combining[61] the laws just mentioned yielding the Beer-Lambert or Bouger-Beer law. However, for the sake of

---

[61] F. H. Lohman, *J. Chem. Educ.* **32**, 155 (1955).

* There has not been general agreement on the symbols or terminology for Beer's law. Equivalent terms for the absorbance, A, include D, d = density; $O.D.$ = optical density; E = extinction; A_s = absorbancy. For the absorptivity, a, k = specific extinction; E = absorption coefficient; K = specific absorption. I_0 and I representing the intensity of the incident and transmitted radiant energy rather than P_0 and P are frequently employed; d, e, or X in place of b occasionally symbolizes the cell thickness in cm.

simplicity the law is now called Beer's law[62] and written as shown in Eq. (2.18). It is seen that the absorbance, A, is a function of three factors, a constant specific for the substance at a particular frequency, the concentration and the thickness. The product of the concentration and the thickness is a measure of the relative number of molecules in the infrared beam.

A condition implied in this equation is that the radiant energy must be monochromatic, that is, of a single discrete wavelength. This condition is difficult to obtain in practice but is sufficiently approached so that quantitative analyses based on this law may be carried out.

In absorption measurements in the ultraviolet and visible wavelength regions the slit width of the instrument is relatively narrow compared to the widths of the bands in the absorption spectrum. It is worthwhile, therefore, to measure molar absorptivities or ϵ values which are a product of the absorptivity, a, and the molecular weight, M, of the material, i.e., $\epsilon = aM$. ϵ values are measured at band maxima and furnish valuable adjunct information as to the nature of the material. There is little problem in obtaining reproducible ϵ values from one instrument to another. In the infrared region, however, ϵ values or absorptivities are seldom measured and reported for a given compound because of lack of reproducibility from one instrument to another. This problem arises because the slit width of the instrument is relatively wide compared to the band widths observed. Hence, the slit width of the instrument at a given frequency is an important variable that must be considered in quantitative analysis or high resolution work. Robinson[63] in a systematic outline of some errors in infrared analysis has pointed out that deviations from Beer's law are to be expected whenever the slits are wider than the width of the absorption band. When the ratio of slit width to band width was 0.4 there was no appreciable deviation from Beer's law. However, at a ratio of 0.8 the deviations became noticeable, being the largest for measurements made at a wavelength taken on the band where the steepest slope occurred.

Ramsay[64] has shown that measurements made with spectral slit widths one-half the true width of an absorption band yield true and apparent molar absorptivities differing by approximately 20% whereas the difference in the integrated intensity measurement is approximately 2-3%. In the integrated intensity measurements the decrease in peak intensity produced by the finite slit width is roughly compensated by the increase in band width. Ramsay further proved that it was not feasible to characterize band shapes by any one equation. He characterized them by an apparent peak intensity $\ln (T_0/T)_{\nu_{max}}$* and an apparent half

[62] H. K. Hughes et al., *Anal. Chem.* **24**, 1349 (1952).

[63] D. Z. Robinson, *Anal. Chem.* **23**, 273 (1951).

[64] D. A. Ramsay, *J. Am. Chem. Soc.* **74**, 72 (1952).

* Ramsay used ln rather than $\log_{10}$ as has been adopted in this text.

intensity width $(\Delta v_{1/2}^{a})$ and related these quantities to the true peak intensity $\ln (I_0/I)_{v_{\max}}$, the true half intensity width $(\Delta v_{1/2}^{t})$ and the slit width s. For convenience, the ratios

$$\frac{\ln (I_0/I)_{v_{\max}}}{\ln (T_0/T)_{v_{\max}}}$$

and

$$\frac{\Delta v_{1/2}^{a}}{\Delta v_{1/2}^{t}}$$

were calculated as functions of apparent peak intensity and of the ratio of slit width s to the apparent half band width $\Delta v_{1/2}^{a}$. The ratio was found to be at an optimum when $s/\Delta v_{1/2}^{a} = 0.65$, which is approximately the condition for the slit to be equal to $\Delta v_{1/2}^{t}$. The quantity

$$\frac{\ln (I_0/I)_{v_{\max}}}{\ln (T_0/T)_{v_{\max}}}$$

depends mainly on the ratio of slit width to the half band width and to a much lesser extent on the peak intensity of the band, the variation being greater for larger values of $s/\Delta v_{1/2}^{a}$.

Using Ramsay's method, Jones *et al.*[65] caculated integrated band intensities for a large number of steroids and successfully determined the number of carbonyl groups and their positions in these complex compounds.

(b) SINGLE COMPONENT ANALYSIS

In the determination of either a liquid or solid component in a given solvent the spectrum of the pure component is measured and a frequency (cm^{-1}) or wavelength is selected at which the solvent has little or no absorption. A series of known concentrations of the component in the solvent is prepared and the absorbance or per cent transmittance values are measured at the chosen frequency.

Several methods for measuring P_0/P are available. One of these methods[66] is that of "base line density." In this method the spectrum of the mixture is scanned through the analytical band having maximum absorption at frequency v as shown in Fig. 2.16. A base line is drawn between v_1 and v_2 which are the points selected after the most favorable analytical peaks have been determined for all the

[65] R. N. Jones, D. A. Ramsay, D. S. Keir, and K. Dobriner, *J. Am. Chem. Soc.* **74**, 80 (1952).

[66] J. J. Heigl, M. F. Bell, and J. U. White, *Anal. Chem.* **19**, 293 (1947).

compounds in question by a detailed consideration of their spectra. In general, the base line is drawn as nearly parallel as possible to the radiant energy background. The base line density is calculated from the equation:

$$A_b = \log_{10} \frac{P_b}{P} \qquad (2.19)$$

where A_b = the base line absorbance (or optical density); P_b = the distance from zero line to the base line; P = the distance on the spectrum from zero line to the selected absorption peak. P_b and P are measured at the same frequency, ν.

Another technique for making quantitative measurements involves the so-called "cell in, cell out" method. With the spectrophotometer set at the

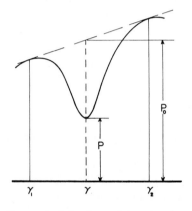

FIG. 2.16. Base line method for determining absorbance or transmittance.

desired wavelength, P_0 and P are measured closely and consecutively in time by recorder deflection. In one modification P_0 is measured by placing in the infrared beam an empty cell containing a single window of thickness equal to that of the combined windows in the cell containing the sample to be analyzed. P is measured with the sample in the cell and $\log_{10} P_0/P$ is plotted versus the concentrations to obtain an analytical working curve. In the other modification of the "cell in, cell out" method a P_0^a is measured for air with no cell in the spectrophotometer and then a P^a for the analytical cell containing the least absorbing component at the frequency involved. Subsequently, a P_0^b for air and P^b for the mixture are measured. The ratio P_0^b/P^b divided by the ratio P_0^a/P^a is then substituted for P_0/P in Eq. (2.17).

If matched cells are available, both cells can be filled with pure solvent and placed in the reference and sample beams respectively and the recorder carefully adjusted to an absorbance reading of 0.0 or a $100\% \, T$ value. The cell in the sample beam can then be removed and used to measure the solutions of known concentration measured in the sample beam versus the solvent in the reference beam. If per cent transmittance values are measured on the recorder paper or scale, these values are plotted on the log axis of semilog paper versus the concentration on the normal coordinate scale. If absorbance values are measured rather than per cent transmittance, the absorbance readings are plotted on normal coordinate paper versus the concentration. In both instances straight line plots should result if Beer's law holds. As has been previously mentioned, deviations from Beer's law can result if the slit width of the instrument at the given frequency exceeds the band width. Or deviations can occur if the actual concentration of the desired molecules differs from the prepared concentration because of association, dissociation, complex formation or a similar process.

Another quantitative technique involves an internal standard. Barnes and associates[67] developed a quantitative infrared method using an internal standard in Nujol mulls and Wiberley et al.[68] applied the method to potassium bromide pellets. The internal standard method eliminates the need to determine the sample thickness. This assumption is readily justified by consideration of Beer's law.[68] The absorbance of the known material to be assayed at ν_k will be given by

$$A_k = a_k b c_k \qquad (2.20)$$

and the absorbance of the internal standard at frequency ν_s by

$$A_s = a_s b c_s \qquad (2.21)$$

Now, dividing the first equation by the second,

$$\frac{A_k = a_k b c_k}{A_s = a_s b c_s} \qquad (2.22)$$

the b's cancel and because a_k and a_s are both constants at the wavenumbers at which the measurements are made, and c_s, the concentration of the internal standard, is constant, these constants can be accumulated in an over-all constant, K, and

$$\frac{A_k}{A_s} = Kc_k. \qquad (2.23)$$

Hence, a plot of A_k/A_s vs. c_k will give a straight line. In this method it is not necessary to determine a_k and a_s, or even to know c_s exactly to obtain an empirical working curve.

[67] R. B. Barnes, R. C. Gore, E. F. Williams, S. G. Linsley, and E. M. Peterson, Ind. Eng. Chem. Anal., Ed. **19**, 620 (1947).
[68] S. E. Wiberley, J. W. Sprague, and J. E. Campbell, *Anal. Chem.* **29**, 210 (1957).

For universal application in quantitative infrared work an internal standard should have a simple spectrum with a few sharp bands, be stable to heat and not absorb excessive moisture, be easily ground to a small particle size, be readily available, and nontoxic. Substances recommended for internal standards in Nujol mulls have been d-alanine, calcium carbonate, lead thiocyanate and naphthalene and in potassium bromide pellets, potassium thiocyanate and sodium azide.[69] Sodium azide has a very strong peak at 2140 cm^{-1} and a weak peak at 1309 cm^{-1}. In the determination of sodium fluoroacetate in dried residues from soil dispersion, sodium azide along with potassium bromide yielded Nujol mulls of medium absorbance values. The addition of the potassium bromide not only decreases the amount of Nujol required, thereby increasing the transmittance of the mull, but also facilitates the grinding of the solids before mulling.

In the quantitative analysis of gases, the absorption law is

$$A = abp \tag{2.24}$$

where p is the pressure of the gas (or partial pressure in a mixture of gases) and replaces c, the concentration, in Eq. (2.18). Thus, a plot of absorbance versus pressure should yield a straight line. However, severe deviation from linearity can result from pressure broadening.[70] Pressure broadening is characterized by unusual changes in band intensity with increasing pressure resulting in different absorbance values than predicted by Beer's law. Pressure broadening may be caused by self-broadening as well as by foreign gas broadening. Self-broadening occurs for single component analysis, i.e., when the vapor pressure of the gas equals the total pressure in the gas cell. Foreign gas broadening occurs when some foreign gas is mixed with the infrared active gas being determined. Self-broadening is not of too great concern in quantitative analysis because empirical curves can be constructed to eliminate the error. However, foreign gas broadening presents serious problems in the analysis of complex gas mixtures.

(c) MULTICOMPONENT ANALYSIS

The analysis of complex mixtures is based on the fact that absorbances are additive, i.e., if the absorbance of component A at 2860 cm^{-1} is 0.400 and that of component B at the same frequency is 0.250, then the total absorbance of the mixture at 2860 cm^{-1} is 0.650. This assumption is usually justified unless the components react with one another, or dissociate, associate or form complexes etc. The effect of spectral slit width previously discussed must also be considered.

[69] R. T. M. Frazer, *Anal. Chem.* **31**, 1602 (1959).
[70] M. G. Mellon, "Analytical Absorption Spectroscopy," p. 498. Wiley, New York, 1950.

For example, consider the analysis of a mixture containing three components all of which absorb in the infrared region. None of these compounds will absorb the same amount at all frequencies. Now the absorbance A of component 1 at frequency ν_1 is given by

$$A = a_1 b c_1$$

and the absorbance of the three components at ν_1 is then

$$A_1 = a_1 b c_1 + a_2 b c_2 + a_3 b c_3$$

and at ν_2

$$A_2 = a_1' b c_1 + a_2' b c_2 + a_3' b c_3 \tag{2.25}$$

and at ν_3

$$A_3 = a_1'' b c_1 + a_2'' b c_2 + a_3'' b c_3 .$$

As a rule b is not measured but the same cell is used for the complete analysis and the b term included in the determination of a. It is of course necessary to experimentally determine the combined absorptivity constant and cell length constant by measurement of pure samples of the individual components separately at ν_1, ν_2, and ν_3. Substitution of these values then yields

$$A_1 = k_1 c_1 + k_2 c_2 + k_3 c_3$$
$$A_2 = k_1' c_1 + k_2' c_2 + k_3' c_3 \tag{2.26}$$
$$A_3 = k_1'' c_1 + k_2'' c_2 + k_3'' c_3$$

where k_1, k_2, k_3, k_1' etc. are now known. Measurement of A_1, A_2, and A_3 on the mixture then yields three equations containing three unknown concentrations, c_1, c_2, and c_3, which can be readily calculated.

If more components are involved, it is simpler to transpose the above equation by electrical computers or reciprocal matrix methods[71] to the form

$$\begin{vmatrix} A_1 \\ A_2 \\ A_3 \end{vmatrix} = \begin{vmatrix} k_1 & k_1' & k_1'' \\ k_2 & k_2' & k_2'' \\ k_3 & k_3' & k_3'' \end{vmatrix} \begin{vmatrix} c_1 \\ c_2 \\ c_3 \end{vmatrix} \tag{2.27}$$

where the terms are as previously defined.

[71] R. P. Bauman, "Absorption Spectroscopy," p. 404. Wiley, New York, 1962.

2.8 *Polarized Infrared Radiation*

The intensity of an infrared absorption band is proportional to the square of the transition moment (or changing dipole moment) of the molecular vibration causing the band. The band intensity also depends on the relative directions of the transition moment and the electric field vector of the incident radiation. The component of the transition moment in the direction of the electric field vector is equal to the transition moment multiplied by the cosine of the included angle. The square of this quantity is proportional to the absorbance.

Polarized infrared radiation can be used to reveal information about the direction of transition moments of normal modes of vibration in solid oriented compounds. When the molecular orientation in a solid is known, polarization studies can be of help in making band assignments. The measured direction of the transition moment of the vibration causing a band must agree with the direction predicted from the known structure if the assignment is correct. Conversely, if the band assignment is known and the molecular orientation in the solid is not known, some information may be deduced about the molecular orientation.

In liquids and gases, the normal modes of the *molecule* interact with radiation. One complication of the solid phase over the liquid phase is that in the crystalline solid state, the normal modes of the *unit cell* are the ones which interact with the radiation. A normal mode has been defined as a vibration where all the atoms are motionless or perform simple harmonic motion with the same frequency, all atoms going through their equilibrium positions simultaneously. Therefore the normal modes of a unit cell consist of the normal modes of the individual molecules taken in as many different phases as there are molecules per unit cell. In a unit cell containing two molecules, each with a carbonyl group, the two carbonyl stretching modes would consist of in-phase and out-of-phase stretching of the two carbonyl groups.

(a) POLARIZERS

Polarized infrared radiation is obtained with transmission polarizers using silver chloride[72] or selenium.[73] A thin plate of silver chloride or thin film of selenium is placed in the beam of unpolarized infrared radiation and is tilted at the polarizing angle relative to the beam.

[72] R. Newman and R. S. Halford, *Rev. Sci. Instr.* **19**, 270 (1948).
[73] A. Elliott, E. J. Ambrose, and R. B. Temple, *J. Opt. Soc. Am.* **38**, 212 (1948).

The polarizing angle of incidence, i, is related to the index of refraction, n, of the material by the equation

$$n = \tan i. \qquad\qquad (2.28)$$

The tilted plate will reflect some radiation to the side which consists of radiation completely polarized in the plane perpendicular to the plane containing the angle of incidence. Some of this polarization component is also transmitted, however, so that the transmitted beam is only partially polarized. Additional plates remove more and more of the unwanted component by reflection, thus improving the degree of polarization of the transmitted beam. Common commercial polarizers consist of about six silver chloride plates (see Fig. 2.17).

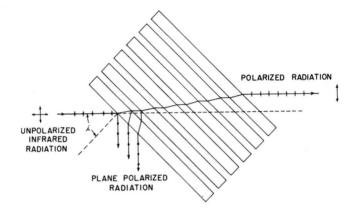

FIG. 2.17. Plane polarization of infrared radiation by several plates. If I is the incident parallel beam of radiation striking at the angle of the incidence, i, the reflected beam (R) is polarized. The incident plane is the plane of the paper, therefore beam R is vibrating normal to the paper. This reflection-polarization process occurs at each face of the stack of plates. After a sufficient number of reflections the transmitted beam (T) has been depleted of vibrations normal to the plane of incidence and consists almost completely of vibrations in this plane. Thus, there are two beams of polarized light produced.

(b) SAMPLE PREPARATION

The molecules in the sample must be oriented in some way. In crystalline compounds, a single crystal of suitable thinness and area or a group of crystals similarly oriented may be prepared. These may be obtained by allowing molten material to crystallize between salt plates separated with a spacer under conditions where a temperature gradient exists on the plate.[74] They may be obtained under

[74] F. Halverson and R. J. Francel, *J. Chem. Phys.* **17**, 694 (1949).

certain conditions from the vapor phase[75] or from solution.[76] Single crystals may be cut and polished to the required size, if possible, the cuts being made parallel to one of the principal axes to avoid double refraction effects.

Thin polymer films may be oriented by stretching, sometimes at elevated temperatures. Such treatment results in uniaxial orientation where some crystallographic axis, usually the long chain axis, will tend to line up parallel to the direction of stretch but there is no preferred orientation of crystallites about this axis. Another technique for polymer orientation consists of rolling the film between rollers which can be heated. The film may also be rolled after sandwiching between silver chloride plates,[77] the silver chloride being removed, if desired, by sodium thiosulfate solution. Rolling results in orientation along the rolling direction (like stretching) but may also result in the orientation of particular crystallographic planes parallel to the film plane (double orientation). X-ray examination can determine the enhancement of orientation.

(c) SAMPLE MEASUREMENT

The oriented sample and the polarizer are placed in the spectrometer beam and spectra are taken with the electric vector of the radiation parallel and perpendicular to the orientation direction of the sample. If the sample is not uniform in thickness or shape, it may be left stationary while the polarizer is rotated so that the same part of the sample is used. Errors are caused by this method because of the inherent polarization in the spectrometer, chiefly caused by the prism.[78] To avoid the above difficulty when rotating the polarizer, measurements may be made with the polarizer oriented 45° with respect to the slit, and then rotated 90° to a position 45° on the other side. If the sample is uniform enough, the polarizer is left stationary in the direction of maximum transmission while the sample is rotated 90°. This is the most satisfactory way to make polarization measurements. Beam condensers may be used for small samples but the additional convergence of the beam has some effect on the results.[79,80]

Dichroism is observed when an absorption band intensity changes when the relative orientation of the polarizer and the sample is altered. The experimentally determined dichroic ratio of a particular mode of vibration is equal to $A_{||}/A_{\perp}$ where A is equal to the absorbance of the band with the electric vector parallel

[75] S. Zwerdling and R. S. Halford, *J. Chem. Phys.* **23**, 2221 (1955).

[76] H. Hallman and M. Pope, "Technical Report on Preparation of Thin Anthracene Single Crystals," ONR Contract No. 285 (25), June 9, 1958.

[77] A. Elliott, E. J. Ambrose, and R. B. Temple, *J. Chem. Phys.* **16**, 877 (1948).

[78] E. Charney, *J. Opt. Soc. Am.* **45**, 980 (1955).

[79] D. L. Wood, *Ann. N.Y. Acad. Sci.* **69**, Article 1, 194 (1957).

[80] R. D. B. Fraser, *J. Chem. Phys.* **21**, 1511 (1953).

and perpendicular to the orientation direction. The experimentally determined dichroic ratio may differ from the true ratio for various reasons[78] such as imperfect polarization by the polarizer, polarization by the spectrometer, imperfectly oriented samples, the presence in partially oriented polymers of some randomly oriented crystallites, birefringence, or the effects of beam convergence in condensing systems.

(d) APPLICATIONS

An application of the use of polarized infrared spectroscopy is found in the study of *ortho*-substituted nitrobenzenes.[81] If the ortho-substituted group is large enough, it may sterically rotate the nitro groups (which are normally coplanar with the ring) out of the ring plane. The oriented crystals were prepared from the molten salt by crystallization between salt plates where a temperature gradient was set up. It was established that in the oriented crystals, the planes of the rings are seen edge on and are perpendicular to the direction of crystal growth. The transition moment of the symmetrical NO_2 stretching frequency near 1350 cm^{-1} is parallel to the C-N bond and is in the plane of the ring regardless of the rotation of the NO_2 group. This planar vibration band shows perpendicular dichroism, the band being more intense when the electric vector is perpendicular to the direction of crystal growth. The transition moment of the asymmetric NO_2 stretching frequency near 1530 cm^{-1} is parallel to the O-O direction. If the NO_2 group is coplanar with the ring, the group will have perpendicular dichroism. If the NO_2 group is rotated 180° out of the ring plane, this band will have parallel dichroism. Thus it was established that *o*-nitrophenol and *o*-nitroaniline had the NO_2 group coplanar with the ring, while *o*-nitro-chlorobenzene and *o*-nitrobromobenzene had a nonplanar NO_2 group due to the presence of the adjacent halogen atoms.[81]

Polarization measurements were made on crystalline acrylamide to verify assignments and to verify a proposed crystal structure[82] which was not as yet known in detail from X-ray work. The model was derived from hydrogen bonding considerations and was in accord with the symmetry elements and unit cell dimensions known from X-ray measurements.[83]

An acetone solution of acrylamide was put on a rock salt plate. After evaporation of the solvent, acrylamide crystallized in patterns on the plate. Under the polarizing microscope extinction was noted, parallel and perpendicular to the direction of crystal growth. An area of uniform extinction and therefore uniform orientation was selected and masked off. It was decided from the above and from

[81] R. J. Francel, *J. Am. Chem. Soc.* **74**, 1265 (1952).

[82] N. B. Colthup, Paper 98, presented at the Pittsburgh Conference on Analytical Chemistry and Applied Spectroscopy (1959).

[83] B. Post and L. A. Siegle, private communication.

the examination of the spectrum that the BC plane (the preferred cleavage plane) was parallel to the rock salt plate face and the direction of crystal growth was parallel to the C axis.

Acrylamide has four molecules per unit cell so that for every normal mode of vibration of the acrylamide molecule there were four modes for the unit cell (see Fig. 2.18). Two modes are infrared inactive because acrylamide crystallizes into two pairs of dimers, each with a center of symmetry.[82] The two infrared active modes will have transition moments parallel and perpendicular to the direction of crystal growth as seen from a direction normal to the BC plane. The parallel and perpendicularly polarized spectra thus isolate the two active modes which have nearly the same but not identical frequencies. The relative band

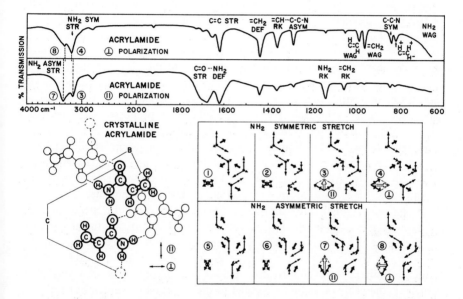

FIG. 2.18. The polarized infrared spectrum of acrylamide. The illustration shows the four repeating molecules of crystalline acrylamide, arranged in two pairs of planar dimers, tilted out of the BC plane (heavy outline molecules above the plane, others below).

The B and C units of the unit cell are shown as well as the direction of the electric vector of the radiation with which the polarized spectra were obtained. The unit cell has four modes of vibration for every molecular mode. These are illustrated schematically for the asymmetric and symmetric NH_2 stretching frequencies. The arrows on the NH_2 groups represent atomic motion. The heavy black arrows represent molecular transition moments. The white arrows represent unit cell transition moments which are the vector resultants of the molecular transition moments. Only modes 3, 4, 7, and 8 are infrared active and these are labeled on the spectra.

The relative magnitudes of the two infrared active unit cell transition moments in each case depend on the orientation of the molecular transition moments.

intensities of the two modes yield information about the direction of the vibrational transition moment of the molecule, projected onto the BC plane (normal to the incident beam). The ratio of the parallel to perpendicular transition moments of the unit cell for a given molecular vibration in this case is equal to the ratio of $\cos \alpha$ to $\sin \alpha$ where α is the acute angle which the BC plane projection of the molecular transition moment makes with the C axis or parallel direction (the direction of crystal growth). The band absorbance ratio $A_{\parallel}/A_{\perp}$ equals the ratio of the squares of the transition moments or $\cos^2 \alpha/\sin^2 \alpha$ or $A_{\parallel}/A_{\perp} = \cot^2 \alpha$.

The angle α obtained indicates the orientation of the BC plane projection of the molecular transition moment. The transition moment does not necessarily lie exactly along the involved molecular bond; for example, the $C{=}O$ stretching, due to interaction with the $C{-}H$ stretching and NH_2 deformation vibrations, has a transition moment direction which may differ appreciably from the $C{=}O$ direction. The NH_2 stretching bands probably give the best idea of the molecular orientation. As the $C{=}C$ stretching band is partially obscured by amide bands, the CH_2 deformation band is the best indicator of the $C{=}C$ orientation. The out-of-plane CH wagging vibrational bands are strong in the perpendicular spectrum, indicating that the planar dimers are rotated out of the BC plane, about the C axis. In this fashion it was decided that the proposed assignments and the proposed structure were mutually compatible, though not necessarily uniquely defined. The Raman spectrum and deuteration studies provide additional information on assignments.[84] A few of the assignments made below 1000 cm^{-1} differ from the data in the literature, because correlations of vinyl frequencies were involved in the present author's assignments.

In polymers which are completely uniaxially oriented by stretching, the dichroic ratio is given by $A_{\parallel}/A_{\perp} = 2 \cot^2 \alpha$ where $A_{\parallel}$ and $A_{\perp}$ are the absorbances of the spectral band in radiation polarized parallel and perpendicular to the direction of stretch, and α is the angle the transition moment makes with the stretching direction.[80] This treatment takes into account that in a long chain polymer, the chains usually lie parallel to the direction of stretch but the crystallites about this axis take all possible orientations. If the parallel polarized absorbance is greater than the perpendicular (parallel dichroism), the angle between the transition moment and the direction of stretch is less than 54°44'. If this angle is greater than 54°44', the perpendicularly polarized absorbance will be the stronger (perpendicular dichroism). This relationship will remain true in the case of incomplete orientation. If quantitative use is to be made of the dichroic ratio, account must be taken of the fact that polymer preparations are usually incompletely oriented.[77,80]

Polarized infrared radiation can distinguish the folded and extended forms of

[84] N. Jonathan, *J. Mol. Spectry.* **6**, 205 (1961).

proteins and polypeptides.[85,86] In the extended form, the backbone chains are lined up side by side and are connected with cross chain hydrogen bonds, the $N-H \cdots O=C$ unit lying approximately perpendicular to the chain direction. The NH stretching band exhibits perpendicular dichroism. In the folded form, the NH of one amide group hydrogen bonds to the $C=O$ of another amide group of the same chain, the $N-H \cdots O=C$ unit lying approximately parallel to the chain progression axis. The NH stretching band exhibits parallel dichroism.

2.9 Raman Sources

In the earliest work on Raman spectra the radiation sources were either sunlight, carbon arcs or mercury arcs. The two general requirements for Raman sources are a high intensity line spectra and a few sharp lines in the visible and ultraviolet region relatively free from continuous light. For work in the near infrared region helium and argon in helical discharge lamps have been used and some recent work involving cesium and rubidium lamps has been initiated. Although lamps of cadmium and other elements such as those mentioned have been tried, the mercury arc is the most suitable source that emits a simple, high intensity line spectrum.

Mercury has strong emission lines at approximately 2537, 3650, 4057, 4358, 5461, 5770, and 5790 angstroms with the wavelength at 4358 being very intense and therefore the most appropriate. In order to provide a relatively mono-chromatic source, the other wavelengths are eliminated with appropriate filters as shown in Table 2.3.

Stoicheff[87] and Welsh et al.[88] have summarized recent advances in the development of Raman sources. Welsh[88] has stated that to operate a mercury lamp at high currents with a corresponding high intensity in the visible region, the electrode pools must be cooled. With such cooling the arc current may be 15 amperes without darkening of the lamp envelopes. In addition, by cooling the body of the lamp by passing cooling solution through the jackets surrounding the lamp, the current could be increased to about 30 amperes.

The type, number, size, and shape of the mercury lamps vary widely in instruments which are custom built. In regard to commercial units one type of mercury lamp is a straight tube as used in the Hilger source unit. This source has four such lamps spaced evenly around the Raman tube. By

[85] E. J. Ambrose, A. Elliott, and R. B. Temple, *Nature* **163**, 859 (1949).

[86] A. Elliott, *J. Appl. Chem.* **6**, 341 (1956).

[87] B. P. Stoicheff, *Can. J. Phys.* **32**, 330 (1954).

[88] H. L. Welsh, E. J. Stansbury, J. Romanko, and T. Feldman, *J. Opt. Soc. Am.* **45**, 338 (1955).

TABLE 2.3

APPROPRIATE FILTERS FOR MERCURY SOURCE

Exciting line	Filter
2537	Mercury vapor (or a mercury resonance lamp as a source).
3650	Corning glass 7-51 or Eastman Kodak Glass Filter 18A.
4047	To remove 3650 line: Corning glass 5-58, sodium nitrite solution or Eastman Kodak Wratten 2B filter.
	To remove 4358 line: Iodine in carbon tetrachloride or 0.003 M potassium ferricyanide.
4358	Du Pont dye Rhodamine 5GDN Extra to remove higher wavelengths. Praseodymium chloride.
	See above for removal of 3650 line.
5461	Basic sodium chromate (pH 8.7) for lines below 5461. Cupric nitrate solution.
	Saturated solution of neodymium chloride.

placing a magnesium oxide reflector around the lamp the efficiency is improved 98%.

The other type lamp of major importance was first developed by Welsh et al.[89] at the University of Toronto and hence is called the Toronto type lamp. This lamp consists of a 4-turn helix of Pyrex tubing and is a more intense source than the Hilger type. In the Toronto type lamp both electrodes are cooled and in addition a cooling coil passes through the center of the helix.

This type of lamp with both electrode cooling and cooling of the helix was used by Janz and James[90] for high temperature Raman work on molten salts and is shown in Fig. 2.19. In order to start the lamp, water at 98° C was passed through the helix and at the moment of discharge a solution at 37° C was transferred through the helix. This lamp was also surrounded by a large reflector of magnesium oxide.

A new type of Raman source consisting of an annular electrodeless lamp powered by microwaves at 2450 Mc has been discussed by Ham and Walsh.[91] These authors initially described the construction of helium, mercury and sodium lamps and illustrated their performance with Raman spectra excited by the following lines; He (5876 Å), Hg (4358) and Na (5889 and 5896). Recently potassium and rubidium lamps have been constructed and their resonance lines (K, 7665, 7699; and Rb, 7800, 7948) used to excite the Raman spectrum of liquid bromine.[92]

[89] H. L. Welsh, M. F. Crawford, T. R. Thomas, and G. R. Love, *Can. J. Phys.* 30, 577 (1952).

[90] G. J. Janz, Y. Mikawa and D. W. James, *Appl. Spectry.* 15, No. 2, 47 (1961).

[91] N. S. Ham and A. Walsh, *Spectrochim. Acta* 12, 88 (1958).

[92] N. S. Ham and A. Walsh, *J. Chem. Phys.* 36, 1096 (1962).

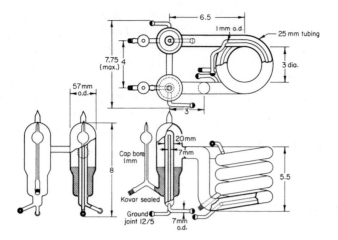

FIG. 2.19.   Toronto type Raman lamp. [Reprinted by courtesy of *Appl. Spectry.*
15, No. 2, 47 (1961).]

The helium annulus has a 15-mm inside diameter and 30-mm external
diameter with a length of 45 mm. After degassing for 24 hr at 200° C, the lamp
was operated for half an hour and then re-evacuated and finally filled with helium
at 4 mm pressure. The mercury and alkali lamps are similar in construction (see
Fig. 2.20).

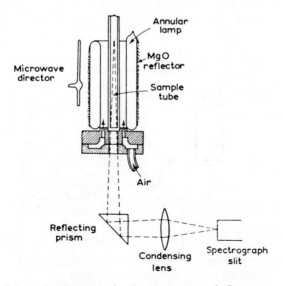

FIG. 2.20.   Schematic diagram of microwave-powered Raman source assembly.
(Redrawn from Ham and Walsh.[91])

The annulus is coated with magnesium oxide to act as a reflector and is cooled by forced air. The Raman tube is located in the center of the annulus and a conventional spectrograph may be used for detection. The microwave generator is a Raytheon Microtherm Model CDM4 which is rated at 125 watts at a frequency of 2450 Mc/sec ($\lambda = 12.25$ cm).

The experiments done by Ham and Walsh showed that microwave-powered lamps provide a simple and successful means of exciting Raman spectra. The wide choice in exciting frequency coupled with ease of interchange are the outstanding features of this novel Raman source.

2.10   Raman Spectrographs

There have been a number of custom-built Raman spectrographs described in the literature. However, in this section only two commercial units; namely, the Hilger E 612 and the Cary Model 81 Raman Spectrophotometer, will be briefly described.

The Hilger E 612 is a two-prism spectrograph which can be operated as a photographic or photoelectric recording instrument. A brief schematic design of the instrument is shown in Fig. 2.21. This instrument has a collimator, with a symmetrical slit and glass lens, a rigid metal base with the two glass prisms in their mounts and a rotatable mount holding the camera and scanning attachment.

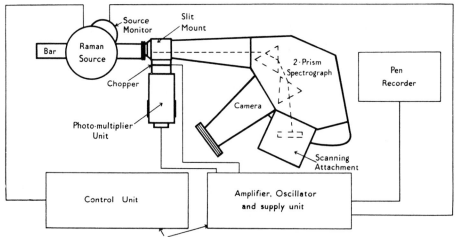

FIG. 2.21.   Diagram of the Hilger E 612 Raman Spectrometer (courtesy Hilger and Watts Ltd., London, England).

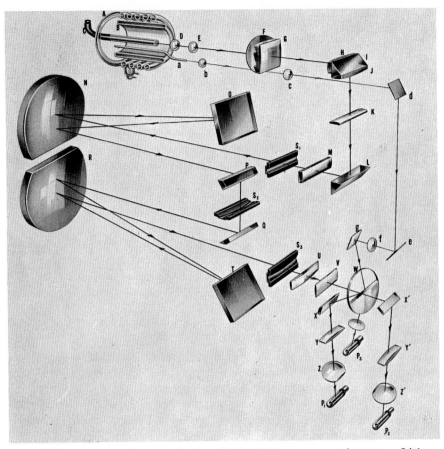

Fig. 2.22. Optical diagram of the Cary Model 81 Raman spectrophotometer. Light from Toronto-type arc lamp A is filtered by fluid in jacket B so that only energy of 4358 Å wavelength illuminates the sample contained in cell C. Raman light from the end of the sample cell is directed by lenses D and E through collimating lens F to the first image-slicer G. This image-slicer divides the beam into 20 images. These are directed into the 10 sections of the second image-slicer H, each section receiving two images. The second image-slicer, with the aid of lenses J, K, and M, superimposes images of the elements of G into two narrow strips of light in the plane of double entrance slit S_1. Prisms I and L serve only to change the direction of the light. From collimating mirror N the beam is reflected to grating O, then reflected by mirror P through double intermediate slit S_2 to the second monochromator. From S_2 it is reflected by mirror Q and the second collimator R to the second grating T, and then directed through double exit slit S_3. Lens U and V direct the beam to rotating mirror W which alternately directs it to phototubes P_1, and P_2 by means of lenses X, Y, Z and X′, Y′, Z′. The two phototube signals are combined and compared to the reference signal developed by phototube P_3.

Concurrently, part of the filtered lamp radiation is directed by glass light pipe a into an auxiliary optical train (elements b, c, d, e, f, g) to rotating mirror W. It is then directed through lens h to reference phototube P_3 which develops a signal for comparison to the Raman signals from phototubes P_1, P_2 (courtesy Applied Physics Corporation, Monrovia, California).

The collimator has a lens aperture of 86 mm and a focal length of approximately 23 in. The slit has adjustable stainless steel jaws and a reducing and three-aperture wedge in front with a shutter in back. The glass prisms have a refracting angle of 63° and are 86 mm high × 130 mm, and 164 mm face length respectively. The camera has a relative aperture of $f/5.7$ and holds a $4\frac{1}{4} \times 3\frac{1}{4}$ in. plate, and has a spectrum length of 86 mm from 3900 to 6300 Å. This light is passed once through the prisms, which gives inverse dispersion on the plate of 16 Å/mm at 4358 Å. When a photomultiplier tube is the detector, the light is dispersed in the first pass through the prisms and reflected at a tilting mirror to obtain double dispersion. The mirror is rotated automatically at one of four selected speeds, and may be set to a calibrated scale. With this mirror assembly the dispersion at the photomultiplier is equivalent to 6.8 cm^{-1}/mm at 4358 Å.

Photographic emulsions which are most suitable for instruments such as the Hilger E 612 are Eastman Kodak Type 103a-O for the Raman lines near the exciting line and Type 103a-J for the higher Raman frequencies (i.e., near 3000 cm^{-1}). The a stands for antihalation backing which eliminates the halo around the 4358 exciting line.

The Cary Model 81 Raman Spectrophotometer has a 3-kw Toronto-type mercury arc similar to that shown in Fig. 2.19. The lamp is started by two Tesla spark coils and is cooled with air from two blowers. A cylindrical glass filter jacket is located between the lamp and the sample cell. The monochromator is a dual grating, twin slit, double monochromator and has a focal length of 1000 mm. The entrance, intermediate and exit slits are simultaneously variable over the range 0–30 cm^{-1}. The gratings are ruled 1200 lines/mm and are blazed for 4500 Å in the first order. The double monochromator is an important feature of the optical design since it permits a large slit-height to focal-length ratio and reduces the effects of Tyndall and Rayleigh scattering. Chopping the beam does not reduce the light intensity at the receptor since two phototubes alternately monitor the signal which is combined and compared to a reference signal developed by a phototube which monitors the background radiation. A more elaborate description of the Model 81 optical diagram accompanies Fig. 2.22.

2.11 Raman Measurements

(a) SAMPLE TECHNIQUES

Gases, liquids, and solids can be studied by Raman spectroscopy with liquids being the easiest to handle.

With the Cary Model 81 Raman Spectrophotometer liquid sample holders of 2 mm o.d. with 0.2-ml or 0.6-ml volume, 7 mm o.d. with a 5-ml volume and

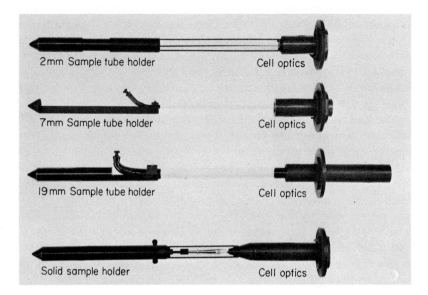

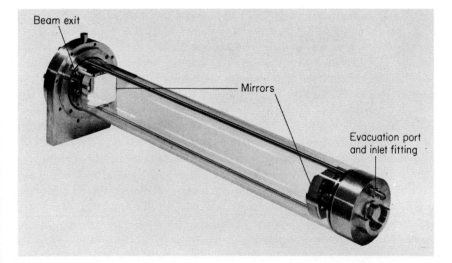

FIG. 2.23. Sample holders for measuring the Raman spectra of gases, liquids, and solids (courtesy Applied Physics Corporation, Monrovia, California).

19 mm o.d. with 65-ml volume are available. Selection of cell size is important in eliminating cell fluorescence. With the larger size 19-mm cell the light from the cell walls does not enter the monochromator whereas the 2- and 7-mm cells require internal reflection from the outside surface. Axial and crossed polarizers can be placed in the cell optics if desired (see Fig. 2.23).

Solids can be measured with a special holder and optics assembly which allow the solid samples to be suspended in the center of the lamp. The beam size in the sample space is approximately 4 mm in diameter at the smallest point.

Solids can be dissolved in suitable solvents and handled in the same manner as liquids. Water, which transmits so poorly in the infrared region, is an ideal solvent for inorganic compounds. The selection of an organic solvent is dependent upon its solvent power, its Raman spectrum and possible chemical interaction with the solute.

The gas cell shown in Fig. 2.23 has a volume of 3500 ml and is of the multiple reflection type. Light can pass as many as 44 times through the 20-in. path length of the cell. The pressure can be adjusted from low pressures up to 10 atm. The gas cell is housed in a special compartment holding two extra large Toronto-type mercury arc lamps.

(b) DETERMINATION OF DEPOLARIZATION RATIO

It has been pointed out that the determination of the depolarization ratio, ρ_n is an important aid in the assignment of Raman lines to certain vibrations (see Section 1.7). For example, totally symmetrical vibrations yield polarized Raman lines (i.e., with values of ρ_n less than $\frac{6}{7}$) and unsymmetrical vibrations yield unpolarized Raman lines. For example, as shown in the Raman spectrum of carbon tetrachloride in Fig. 2.24 the Raman band at 459 cm^{-1} is polarized and therefore corresponds to the totally symmetrical vibration, ν_1. In contrast, the Raman bands at 218, 314, 762, and 791 cm^{-1} are depolarized and assigned to unsymmetrical vibrations.

Two methods for the qualitative determination of the state of polarization of Raman lines were initially developed by Edsall and Wilson.[93] Cleveland and Murray[94] found these methods inadequate for quantitative measurements of depolarization ratio. They suggested a method in which a Polaroid disk, so oriented that it passes light whose electric vector is horizontal, is placed between the Raman tube and the lens which condenses the scattered light on the slit of the spectrograph. Two exposures of equal duration are made, one with the arc below, the other with the arc at the side, of the horizontal Raman tube. The ratio of the intensities in the two exposures was determined by comparison with the lines of

[93] J. T. Edsall and E. B. Wilson, Jr., *J. Chem. Phys.* **6**, 124 (1938).
[94] F. F. Cleveland and M. J. Murray, *J. Chem. Phys.* **7**, 396 (1939).

seven argon spectra produced by argon light of known intensity ratios. Crawford and Horwitz[95] subsequently described a modification of Edsall and Wilson's method using appropriately oriented polaroid cylinders for both exposures. With the Hilger E 612 Spectrometer depolarization measurements can be made by a similar two-exposure method. Two polaroid cylinders, one passing the parallel component and the other the perpendicular component, can be constructed from sheets of Polaroid. Two exposures for identical times are made on the same plate with one exposure being made with each polaroid sheet wrapped around the Raman tube. The intensities on the photographic plate can be

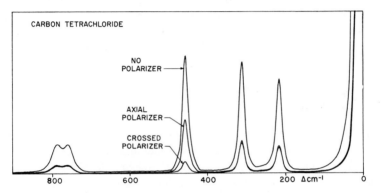

Fig. 2.24. Recorded Raman spectrum of carbon tetrachloride measured with axial and crossed polarizers. The unpolarized spectrum is also shown for comparison (courtesy Applied Physics Corporation Monrovia, California).

measured with a suitable microphotometer and the ratios determined. Another photographic method involves placing a polarizer in the beam of Raman scattered light. A polarizer can be made by cutting two semicircles from the same piece of Polaroid in such a manner that upon cementing the two pieces to form a circle the plane of polarization of one-half is 90° from the plane of polarization of the other. The upper half of the split-field Polaroid disk allows only the vertical component of the scattered light to pass and the lower half passes only the horizontal component.

Fenske et al.[96] have described the measurement of depolarization ratios when a recording Raman spectrometer is used. With a Toronto source and photoelectric recording techniques Stamm, Solzman, and Mariner[97] have reported

[95] B. L. Crawford, Jr., and W. Horwitz, J. Chem Phys. 15, 268 (1947).
[96] M. R. Fenske, W. G. Braun, R. V. Wiegand, D. Quiggle, R. H. McCormick, and D. H. Rank, Anal. Chem. 19, 700 (1947).
[97] R. F. Stamm, C. F. Salzman, Jr. and T. Mariner, J. Opt. Soc. Am. 43, 119 (1953).

depolarization measurements. As previously discussed, the polarization ratio is defined as the ratio of the intensity of the scattered light polarized perpendicular to the xy plane, $I_\perp$, to that polarized parallel to this plane $I_\parallel$, with the z axis being taken in the direction of the propagation of the incident light. With the Toronto source the incident beam is no longer parallel to the z axis but is principally in the xy plane with some component in the x direction. In the procedure of Stamm *et al.* two Polaroid cylinders were oriented so that the transmitted electric vector **E** was either perpendicular or parallel to the axis of the Raman sample tube. From line intensities depolarization ratios were calculated for chloroform and found to be incorrect and on the high side because of the convergence associated with the Toronto arc. By plotting the observed depolarization ratio as a function of the known depolarization ratio a correction curve was obtained which permitted ratios of unknown substances to be determined with an average deviation of $\pm 2\%$.

(c) INTENSITY MEASUREMENTS

The determination of the absolute intensities of Raman lines is even more difficult than the determination of the absolute intensity of infrared absorption bands. Bernstein and Allen[98] as well as Rea[99] have considered the variables which affect observed Raman intensities. Variables dependent upon the nature of the sample are the refractive index of the sample and the absorption of both the exciting and scattered radiation by the sample. Variables independent of the sample include the spectral variation in the transmittance of the instrument and in the frequency response of the detector, the variation caused by the convergence of the exciting and Raman radiation, and such instrumental conditions as slit width, scanning speed and time constant.

For these reasons the intensity of a Raman line is usually measured in terms of the arbitrarily chosen 459 cm^{-1} line of carbon tetrachloride (see Figs. 1.17 and 2.24). This ratio has been called the scattering coefficient.

A reasonably satisfactory standard intensity scale for the interchange of intensity data has been defined by Danti[100] as follows:

$$I(\text{std}) = \frac{100I(\text{obs})}{I_{459}} \times \frac{G_{459}}{G} \times R(n) \times T(A) \times \sigma(\Delta \nu) \tag{2.29}$$

[98] H. J. Bernstein and G. Allen, *J. Opt. Soc. Am.* **45**, 237 (1955).

[99] D. G. Rea, *J. Opt. Soc. Am.* **49**, 90 (1959).

[100] A. Danti, "Information for Contributors to the Catalogs of Raman Spectral Data," Chemical Thermodynamic Properties Center, Agricultural and Mechanical College of Texas, College Station, Texas.

where

I(obs) = observed intensity of the Raman line;

I_{459} = observed intensity of the 459 cm^{-1} line of carbon tetrachloride under the same instrumental conditions;

G = amplifier sensitivity for the Raman line;

G_{459} = amplifier sensitivity for the 459 cm^{-1} line of carbon tetrachloride (generally taken as unit sensitivity);

$R(n)$ = correction factor for the refractive index of the sample relative to that of carbon tetrachloride;

$T(A)$ = correction factor for absorbance of sample relative to carbon tetrachloride;

$\sigma(\Delta\nu)$ = factor for correcting the spectral sensitivity of the instrument at the wavenumber of the Raman line to that at 459 cm^{-1};

In applying this equation, the Raman line and the 459 cm^{-1} line of carbon tetrachloride must be scanned under identical operating conditions such as slit width, scanning speed etc.

The correction factor $R(n)$ for the optical effect of the refractive index and the correction factor $T(A)$ may be determined by the method described by Rea.[99] For colorless compounds $T(A)$ is zero but for substances absorbing the exciting radiation at 4358 Å, the absorbance should be measured at this wavelength and the correction applied.

The final factor $\sigma(\Delta\nu)$, the spectral variation in photosensitivity of the spectrophotometer and the photomultiplier tube can be determined by the method described by Rosenbaum, Cerato, and Lauer.[101] These authors used a lamp calibrated by the National Bureau of Standards for evaluation of $\sigma(\Delta\nu)$.

(d) HIGH AND LOW TEMPERATURE METHODS

Several authors have discussed the measurement of Raman spectra at elevated temperatures but in general the experimental details reported did not contain sufficient information. Bues[102] used a large crucible as a sample container in an electric furnace. The incident mercury radiation from a U-shaped low pressure mercury arc was reflected into the melt by two well formed silicon carbide crystals placed in a second inverted crucible with a slit in the bottom. The scattered radiation passing up through the slit was focussed on the slit of the spectrograph by a lens and a prism.

[101] E. J. Rosenbaum, C. C. Cerato and J. L. Lauer, *J. Opt. Soc. Am.* **42**, 670 (1952).
[102] W. Bues, *Z. Anorg. Allgem. Chem.* **279**, 104 (1955).

The high temperature Raman cell used by Janz and James[103] for fused salt studies is shown in Fig. 2.25. The description of this cell given by James[104] is as follows:

"The Raman tube A (10 mm o.d.) is wound with Kanthal, B and S No. 24 resistance wire platinized to reduce reflectance. This is prewound on an 8 mm o.d. mandrel, then this coil is forced on the Raman tube to give 27 turns of wire. The principle of prewinding the wire on a slightly smaller mandrel eliminates the need to attach the wire to the Raman tube. The natural spring of the wire prevents the coils from sagging even after the wire has been heated. A steel wire clip holds the wound Raman tube in a 20 mm o.d. silica tube, B. The two tubes are positioned at the base, by a tapered cylindrical brass sleeve

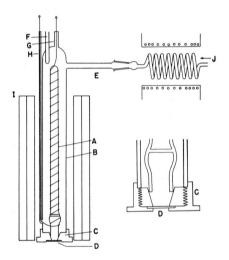

FIG. 2.25.   High temperature Raman cell assembly. (A) Raman tube; (B) silica furnace tube; (C) brass sleeve; (D) removable glass window; (E) preheated air inlet; (F) thermo-couple well; (G) entrance tube for resistance windings; (H) exit tube for gas and resistance windings; (I) double-compartment glass jacket; (J) silica coil in preheating furnace. Insert gives detail of brass sleeve and base of Raman tube.

C. A removable glass window D, prevents escape of hot air over the surface of the reflecting prism. The diameter of the tube B was found to be quite critical in the removal of the temperature gradients. With a 20 mm o.d. silica tube, temperatures up to 600° C could be maintained with a maximum 10° C gradient. However, if a 25 mm o.d. silica tube was used, all other

[103] G. J. Janz and D. W. James, *J. Chem. Phys.* **35**, 739 (1961).

[104] D. W. James, Ph. D. Thesis, Rensselaer Polytechnic Institute, Troy, New York, 1960.

factors remaining constant, a maximum of 400° C was attained with gradients up to 50° C. The top of the silica tube is fitted with a gas inlet tube E, a thermocouple well F, and an opening for one lead to the resistance windings G. The side arm tube H, from the base of the silica tube, is the gas outlet and the exit for one of the electrical leads. The part of the silica tube extending above the mercury arc, and the gas inlet tube, are insulated with a $\frac{1}{4}$-inch layer of asbestos.

"Surrounding the two tubes, but separated from them by an air gap, is a two-compartment Pyrex jacket, I. The inner compartment is evacuated, while the outer compartment is a filter jacket. Through this a filter solution (normally saturated sodium nitrite), thermostatted to any desired temperature, is circulated. If depolarization data are required, two Polaroid cylinders with axes at right angles, may be alternately slipped over the outside of the filter jacket.

"Connected to the gas inlet E, by a ground glass joint, is a coil of 6 mm o.d. silica tubing J. This coil has 15 turns and a total length of 60 inches and is situated in a furnace. An air stream, which is passed at monitored flow rates over the Raman cell in the assembly, is preheated by passing through the coil."

Low temperature measurements do not present as many experimental problems as the high temperature measurements. Rice, Barredo, and Young[105] have described a relatively simple low temperature procedure. A copper rod was drilled to fit the Raman tube closely and kept immersed in a Dewar flask containing liquid nitrogen or a Dry Ice-acetone mixture. The exciting light reached the Raman tube through two large windows cut into the copper jacket. The formation of interfering layers of condensed atmospheric moisture on the Raman tube was prevented by a jet of either nitrogen gas or cold alcohol.

Hisatsune and Fitzsimmons[106] modified a Hilger Raman Source Unit for low temperature work by enlarging the housing so that the Raman tube could be placed inside an unsilvered Dewar flask. The bottom of this Dewar was optically flat with a vacuum space of about 2 cm. The Raman tube in the Dewar could be cooled either by a flow of cold gas or by a liquid refrigerant.

[105] B. Rice, J. M. González Barredo, and T. F. Young, *J. Am. Chem. Soc.* **73**, 2306 (1951).
[106] I. C. Hisatsune and R. V. Fitzsimmons, *Spectrochim. Acta* **15**, 206 (1959).

CHAPTER 3

CLASSIFICATION OF MOLECULES

3.1 Symmetry Properties

Symmetry plays an important role in the structure of molecules: some are highly symmetrical, some less so, and many have no symmetry at all. It would thus seem reasonable to set up some system whereby molecules could be classified by their symmetry characteristics. Crystallographers were the first to study symmetry properties in connection with crystal structure studies. When spectroscopists realized that the symmetry of a molecule played an important role in what vibrations were permitted and which excluded, they also became concerned with symmetry properties and the establishment of a convenient reference system.

In this chapter symmetry will be discussed from the standpoint of the spectroscopist rather than the crystallographer. For a more general and detailed treatment of this subject the reader should consult additional references.[1,2]

From the standpoint of infrared and Raman spectroscopy molecules can be conveniently classified using the following five symmetry elements:

(1) A center of symmetry designated by i.
(2) A p-fold rotation axis of symmetry designated by C_p where C stands for cyclic and rotation through $2\pi/p$ or $360°/p$ produces an orientation indistinguishable from the original molecule.
(3) Planes of symmetry usually designated by σ with subscripts v, h, or d depending upon whether the plane is a vertical, horizontal, or diagonal plane of symmetry.
(4) A p-fold rotation-reflection axis of symmetry designated by S_p where rotation through $2\pi/p$ or $360°/p$ followed by a reflection at a plane perpendicular to the axis of rotation produces an orientation indistinguishable from the original molecule.

[1] P. J. Wheatley, "The Determination of Molecular Structure." Oxford Univ. Press, London and New York, 1959.
[2] J. C. D. Brand and J. C. Speakman, "Molecular Structure." Edward Arnold, London, 1960.

(5) The identity, I, a trivial symmetry element possessed by all molecules and introduced for the purposes of mathematical group theory.

Each of these symmetry elements will now be examined in more detail.

(a) CENTER OF SYMMETRY

A molecule has a center of symmetry, i, if by reflection at the center (inversion) the molecule is transformed into itself. For every atom with x, y, z coordinates from the center there must be an identical atom with $-x$, $-y$, and $-z$ coordinates. Some examples of molecules possessing a center of symmetry are shown in Fig. 3.1(a, b, c). In the case of carbon dioxide there is an atom located at the center. However, dibromodichloroethane and benzene do not have an atom located at the center. In the case of dibromodichloroethane only the *trans* isomer has a center of symmetry. If one hydrogen atom has the coordinates x, y, and z from the center, then the other hydrogen atom has the coordinates $-x$, $-y$, and $-z$ and similar conditions apply to the bromine and chlorine atoms. However, for the *cis*-isomer such conditions would not be fulfilled. It should also be quite obvious that a molecule may only possess one center of symmetry.

(b) ROTATION AXIS OF SYMMETRY

A molecule has a rotation axis of symmetry, C_p, if rotation by $360°/p$ yields a molecular configuration indistinguishable from the original one. Again referring to Fig. 3.1(d) rotation about the axis shown through 180° yields a water molecule indistinguishable from the molecule upon which the rotation has been performed. In this case $p = 2$ and the axis is designated a C_2 axis and often spoken of as a twofold or diad axis. In the case of boron trichloride [Fig. 3.1(e)] rotation through 120° or $360°/3$ yields a similar result. Likewise chloroform shown in Fig. 3.2(b) has a C_3 axis of rotation. For $n = 3, 4, \ldots$ the axes are designated as threefold, fourfold ... or triad, tetrad ... axes. In the case of benzene shown in Fig. 3.1(f) there is a sixfold axis of rotation passing through the center of symmetry. In addition, coincident with this axis there are a C_2 axis and a C_3 axis since rotation through 180° or 120° will also yield a benzene molecule indistinguishable from the original one on which the rotation has been performed. Perpendicular to this sixfold axis of rotation are six C_2 axes three of which pass through the carbon atoms and three of which pass through the carbon—carbon bonds. Rotation about each of these axes through 180° yields an indistinguishable benzene molecule.

(c) PLANES OF SYMMETRY

A molecule has a plane of symmetry, σ, if by reflection at the plane the molecule is transformed into itself. In other words, a plane of symmetry bisects the mole-

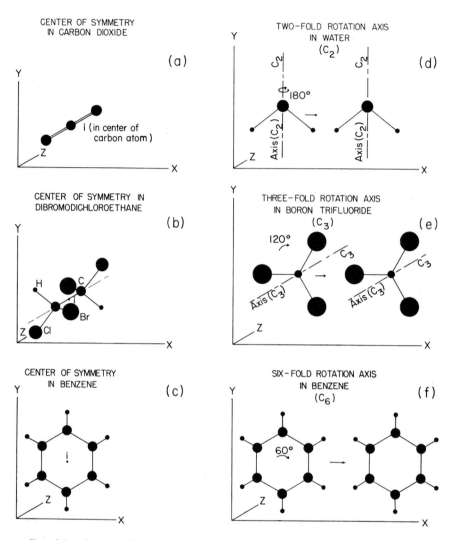

FIG. 3.1.   Centers of symmetry and rotation axes in various compounds.

cule into two equivalent parts, one part being the mirror image of the other. For instance, consider the water molecule shown in Fig. 3.2(a). A plane is shown which bisects the HOH angle of 105°. If every portion of the water molecule on the left-hand side of this plane were translated across the plane to the right-hand side to a new position equidistant from the plane and vice versa (i.e., the right-hand portion translated to the left) the resulting figure could not be distinguished from the original one. The water molecule, therefore, has a plane of symmetry bisecting the 105° angle. It is evident that this is a special plane in the yz dimension. For any other planes parallel to this particular plane a corresponding operation of reflection similar to that just described would not yield the same water molecule. The plane bisecting the 105° angle is spoken of as a symmetry element and should not be confused with the symmetry operation which is performed to demonstrate that the molecule does possess a plane of symmetry. It should be clear then that for every symmetry element there is a corresponding symmetry operation, that is, a coordinate transformation (in this case a reflection) which produces a configuration of atoms indistinguishable from the original molecule. It has already been shown in the previous section that a coordinate transformation by rotation as well as by reflection can likewise yield a similar result.

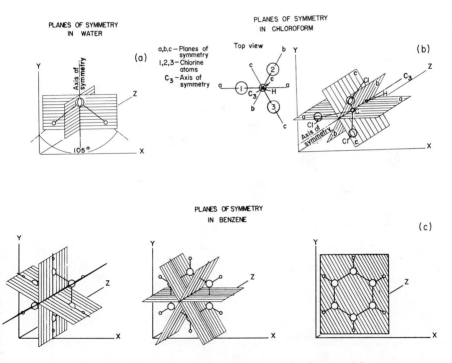

FIG. 3.2. Planes of symmetry in water, chloroform, and benzene.

It might be well to point out that if the hydrogen atom on the left-hand side had been labeled 1 and the one on the right-hand side labeled 2 then after performing the symmetry operation the final molecule would have been distinguishable from the starting molecule. However, such a procedure imposes a restriction that does not apply in the usual symmetry considerations. It is not

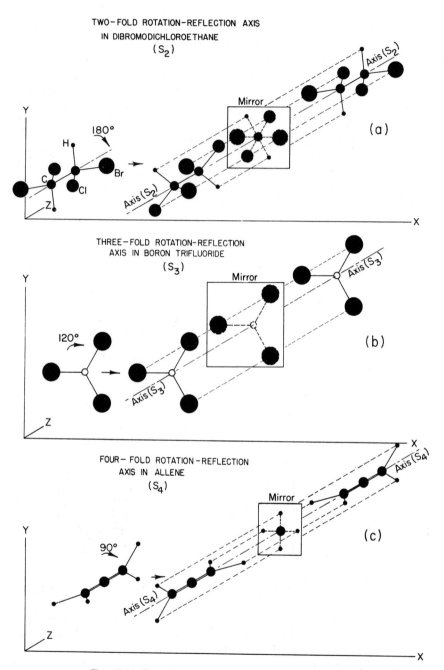

FIG. 3.3. Rotation-reflection axes in various compounds.

necessary that each atom or nucleus end up after the symmetry operation in its exact original position but only that the resulting total molecule be indistinguishable from the original molecule.

Again considering Fig. 3.2(a) it is quite apparent that the plane in which the water molecule lies is also a plane of symmetry in the xy dimension. Both planes of symmetry are designated as σ_v because they are both vertical to the major symmetry axis, i.e., the C_2 axis shown in Fig. 3.2(a) in the y direction. To distinguish the two planes, one is designated as σ_v' (the choice is arbitrary). Likewise the chloroform molecule shown in Fig. 3.2(b) has three planes of symmetry vertical to the threefold rotation axis. However, in the case of benzene the plane in which the carbon and hydrogen atoms lie [Fig. 3.2(c)] is horizontal to the major symmetry axis, i.e., the C_6 axis [refer to Fig. 3.1(f)]. The remaining six planes of symmetry [Fig. 3.1(d) and (e)] are vertical to the C_6 axis. Hence, benzene has one horizontal plane (σ_h) and six vertical planes $(6\sigma_v)$ of symmetry.

(d) P-Fold Rotation-Reflection Axis of Symmetry

A molecule has a p-fold rotation-reflection axis of symmetry, S_p, if rotation through $360°/p$ followed by reflection at a plane perpendicular to the axis of rotation yields a configuration indistinguishable from the starting molecule. This is the most difficult symmetry operation to vizualize but with the aid of Fig. 3.3 perhaps it can be made clear. In the case of dibromodichloroethane rotation through $180°$ does not yield the original configuration. However, by reflection at a plane perpendicular to the axis of rotation [see Fig. 3.3(a)] the original structure is obtained. Such an axis is designated as an S_2 axis. Likewise boron trifluoride has an S_3 and allene an S_4 rotation-reflection axis [see Fig. 3.3(b) and (c)]. It may be interesting to compare boron trifluoride with chloroform. Boron trifluoride has a C_3 axis coincident with the S_3 axis. However, chloroform being nonplanar has only a C_3 axis. Hence, boron trifluoride is a molecule of higher symmetry. In the case of benzene [see Fig. 3.1(f)] there is an S_6 axis coincident with the C_6 axis previously discussed.

(e) The Identity, I

The fifth and last symmetry element is the identity, I, sometimes designated in the literature by the symbol E. All molecules possess the identity even if they possess none of the other four symmetry elements. The symmetry operation corresponding to this symmetry element involves leaving the molecule unaltered. Hence, the resulting molecule can not be distinguished from the original. This symmetry element is introduced for mathematical reasons which will become apparent in the following sections.

3.2 Point Groups

In the previous section it was mentioned that all molecules possess the symmetry element, the identity. Also it was shown that a large number of molecules have additional symmetry elements. For example, the water molecule has two vertical planes of symmetry and a twofold rotation axis of symmetry. With a little thought it will be realized that any molecule which has two vertical planes must of necessity have a twofold rotation axis. However, the reverse is not true for a molecule may possess a twofold rotation axis and not the two mirror planes of symmetry. Likewise in the case of either chloroform or boron trifluoride the three vertical planes of symmetry require that there be a threefold rotation axis of symmetry in each of these molecules. Hence, it can be seen that the presence of certain symmetry elements means that others are of necessity required. In the case of benzene the symmetry can be adequately described by the following elements, a sixfold axis, a plane of symmetry in the rotation axis and a plane of symmetry perpendicular to this axis. Yet as was shown in the previous section benzene has additional symmetry elements, namely, a center of symmetry, and (coincident with the sixfold axis) a sixfold rotation-reflection axis and a twofold and threefold axis as well as a two- three-and sixfold rotation-reflection axis, six twofold axes, and seven planes of symmetry. Thus, the existence of certain symmetry elements requires per se the presence of others. It might be assumed that any possible combination of symmetry elements is permitted. However, such an assumption can be readily proved false. For example, a molecule cannot possess a threefold and fourfold axis in the same direction. Likewise it can be proved by mathematical group theory that only certain combinations of symmetry elements are possible. Such a restricted combination of symmetry elements that leaves at least one point unchanged is called a *point group*. A point group is also a group in a mathematical sense as will be demonstrated in detail in the next section. For the present the main concern will be with the classification of molecules into distinct point groups and the shorthand notations describing these groups. Point groups can be classified by either the Hermann-Mauguin or the Schoenflies notation.[1] In this text the Schoenflies notation has been employed in the previous section and will be naturally continued here.

In principle molecules may belong to any of the possible point groups permitted by mathematical group theory. In reality, however, the actual chemical examples of specific point groups are somewhat restricted. In dealing with crystals only one-, two-, three-, four-, and sixfold axes are permissible. With such a restriction, there are only thirty-two possible combinations of symmetry elements yielding the thirty-two crystal point groups.

Table 3.1 lists these thirty-two point groups plus four additional point groups (marked with a superscript "^{a}") for which there are actual molecular examples.

In the following discussion all of the individual point groups will not be considered. Rather the comments will be restricted to those particular point groups where it is felt some questions regarding the symmetry elements might arise.

Point group, C_p. A molecule possessing only a C_p rotation axis of symmetry falls in this group. Those molecules with no symmetry at all except for the identity, I, fall in group C_1. A molecule with only a twofold axis of symmetry would be a member of the C_2 point group, etc.

Point group S_p. A molecule having only a p-fold rotation reflection axis of symmetry belongs to the S_p point group. This point group is designated also by C_i for those molecules with a center of symmetry, such as the *trans*-form of dibromodichloroethane [see Figs. 3.1(b) and 3.3(a)], and having as a necessary consequence an S_2 axis.

Point group C_{pv}. Since in the Schoenflies notation, rotation axes are designated as being vertical, the point group C_{pv} includes those molecules with a vertical rotation axis of order p with p vertical planes of symmetry lying in the rotation axis. The water molecule belongs to the C_{2v} point group while chloroform belongs to the C_{3v} point group (see Fig. 3.2). Boron trifluoride, however, does not belong to the C_{3v} group because it possesses an S_3 element and therefore has higher symmetry [see Fig. 3.1(e)]. The point group C_{1v} is usually designated by C_s and can just as logically be designated by C_{1h} since the Schoenflies notation of designating the rotation axis as being vertical is an arbitrary one. Linear heteronuclear diatomic molecules belong to the point group $C_{\infty v}$ since they possess an infinitefold axis and an infinite number of planes through the axis.

Point group C_{ph}. Molecules belonging to this point group have a rotation axis of order p and a horizontal plane of symmetry perpendicular to the axis. As mentioned C_{1h} is equivalent to C_{1v} or C_s. The point group C_{2h} has an S_2 axis coincident with the C_2 axis.

Point group D_p. The D stands for dihedral. Molecules belonging to this point group have a p-fold axis, C_p, and perpendicular to this axis p-twofold axes at equal angles to each other. No D_1 group is listed in Table 3.1 since such a group is identical with C_2.

Point group D_{pd}. Similar to the point group D_p, molecules in this group have a p-fold axis, C_p, and perpendicular to this axis p-twofold axes plus p-planes of symmetry (σ_d) passing through the p-fold axis and bisecting the angles between the two consecutive twofold axes. The point group D_{2d} has three mutually perpendicular C_2 axes and one S_4 axis coincident with one of the C_2 axes and two

TABLE 3.1

IMPORTANT POINT GROUPS AND THEIR SYMMETRY ELEMENTS

Symbol (General)	Symbol (Specific)	Center i	C_2	C_3	C_4	C_5	C_6	S_2	S_4	S_6	S_8	σ_v	σ_h	σ_a
C_p	C_1													
	C_2		1											
	C_3			1										
	C_4				1									
	C_6						1							
S_p	S_2	1						1						
	S_4		1						1					
	S_6	1		1						1				
C_{pv}	C_{1v}		(equivalent to C_s or C_{1h})									1		
	C_{2v}		1									2		
	C_{3v}			1								3		
	C_{4v}				1							4		
	C_{6v}						1					6		
	[a]$C_{\infty v}$		(C_∞; any C_p)									∞		
C_{ph}	C_{2h}	1	1					1					1	
	C_{3h}			1									1	
	C_{4h}	1			1				1				1	
	C_{6h}	1					1			1			1	
D_p	D_2		3											
	D_3		3	1										
	D_4		4		1									
	D_6		6				1							
D_{pd}	D_{2d}		3						1					2
	D_{3d}	1	3	1						1				3
	[a]D_{4d}		4	1							1			4
D_{ph}	D_{2h}	1	3									(3 undesignated planes)		
	D_{3h}		3	1								3	1	
	D_{4h}	1	4		1				1			4	1	
	[a]D_{5h}		5			1						5	1	
	D_{6h}	1	6				1			1		6	1	
	[a]$D_{\infty h}$	1	∞; (C_∞)									∞	1	
T	T		3	4										
	T_d		3	4					3			(6 undesignated planes)		
	T_h	1	3	4						4		(3 undesignated planes)		
O	O		6	4	3									
	O_h	1	6	4	3				3	4		(9 undesignated planes)		

[a] See text preceding table.

diagonal planes of symmetry passing through the S_4 axis. Allene shown in Fig. 3.3(c) belongs to the point group D_{2d}.

In the point group D_{3d} the S_6 axis is coincident with the C_3 axis.

The point group D_{4d} has one C_4 axis (coincident with one C_2 and one S_8 axis), four C_2 axes and four diagonal planes of symmetry. In Table 3.1 the coincident C_2 axis is not listed.

Point group D_{ph}. Molecules with a p-fold axis and p-vertical planes of symmetry lying in the rotation axis plus a horizontal plane of symmetry perpendicular to the C_p axis fall in this point group. The D_{1h} group is identical with C_{2v} and therefore not listed as such. Boron trichloride [Fig. 3.1(e)] is an example of the D_{3h} point group.

In the point group D_{4h} the S_4 axis is coincident with the C_4 axis. On this same axis there is a coincident C_2 axis which is not included in Table 3.1. The four C_2 axes which are perpendicular to the C_4 axis are of course listed.

In the point group D_{6h} the S_6 axis which is coincident with the C_6 axis is listed but not the C_2 and C_3 or S_2 and S_3 axes which are also coincident with the C_6 axis. Benzene shown in Fig. 3.1(c) and (f) and in Fig. 3.2(c) is the only known example of this group.

Point group T. The T stands for tetrahedral. Molecules belong to this group if they have four threefold axes and three mutually perpendicular twofold axes. The T_h group has the same symmetry elements plus a center of symmetry.

Point group T_d. The classic example of this point group is methane shown in Fig. 3.4. Methane has four threefold axes, three mutually perpendicular twofold axes (coincident with S_4 axes), and two mutually perpendicular planes of symmetry through each twofold axis, or a total of six planes of symmetry.

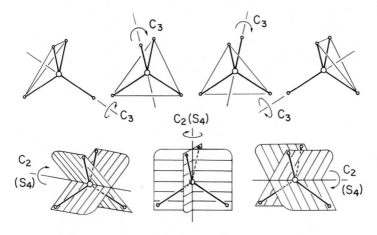

FIG. 3.4. Symmetry elements of methane (point group T_d).

Point group O. The O stands for octahedral. Molecules in this group have three mutually perpendicular fourfold axes and four threefold axes.

Point group O_h. This group has the same symmetry elements as point group O plus a center of symmetry and nine planes of symmetry. As a consequence of this center of symmetry there are also three S_4 axes coincident with the three C_4 axes.

3.3 Group Theory

The important point groups to which most molecules can be assigned have been discussed; so it is now pertinent to consider how mathematical group theory is involved in the treatment of point groups.

A set of so-called elements I, A, B, C, ..., is said to be a group if the following four conditions apply:

(1) There is an identity element, I, for which $AI = IA = A$ where A represents any element in the group.
(2) The elements obey a law of combination which states that the product of any two elements of the group is also an element of the group, i.e., $AB = C$.
(3) The elements obey a law of association, e.g., $A(BC) = (AB)C$.
(4) Every element in the group has an inverse in the group, i.e., for every element A there is an inverse A^{-1} such that $A \times A^{-1} = I = A^{-1} \times A$ and $B \times B^{-1} = I = B^{-1} \times B$, etc. In other words the product of the element and its inverse yields the identity element.

As a concrete example, consider the four elements 1, -1, i, and $-i$, where $i = \sqrt{-1}$, and apply the above four conditions assuming that $I = 1$, $A = -1$, $B = i$ and $C = -i$. It can be seen that these conditions can be more readily checked if a multiplication table is arranged as follows. Each element is arranged in a horizontal column and in a vertical column. By cross multiplication the table can be completed; thus for the first vertical column, $1 \times 1 = 1$, $-1 \times 1 = -1$, $i \times 1 = i$, and $-i \times 1 = -i$.

TABLE 3.2

MULTIPLICATION TABLE FOR A GROUP OF FOUR ELEMENTS

	1	-1	i	$-i$
1	1	-1	i	$-i$
-1	-1	1	$-i$	i
i	i	$-i$	-1	1
$-i$	$-i$	i	1	-1

The remaining columns can be completed in a similar manner. Now the table can be examined to see if the four requirements of a group are fulfilled.

(1) Since the identity is 1 and A is -1 then $-1 \times 1 = 1 \times -1 = -1$. For the element B, $i \times 1 = 1 \times i = i$ and for the element C, $-i \times 1 = 1 \times -i = -i$ and the first condition holds for all elements.

(2) Simple inspection of Table 3.2 shows that the product of any two elements of the group is also an element. In mathematical terms the elements of the group constitute a set; so it would be stated that the set is closed with respect to the binary operation.

(3) To obey the law of association $A(BC) = AB(C)$ or in this example $-1 \times (i \times -i) = -1 \times i(-i)$ and hence this condition is satisfied.

(4) Examination of the elements with respect to the inverse requirement reveals that this condition is fulfilled since the inverse of 1 is 1, the inverse of -1 is -1, the inverse of $+i$ is $-i$ and the inverse of $-i$ is $+i$. Also substitution into $A \cdot A^{-1} = I = A^{-1} \cdot A$ yields $(-1)(-1) = 1 = (-1)(-1)$ and into $B \cdot B^{-1} = I = B^{-1} \cdot B$ yields $(i)(-i) = 1 = (-i)(i)$ etc. Thus, it has been shown explicitly that the four elements I, A, B, and C do constitute a group in a mathematical sense.

3.4 Group Theory Applied to Point Groups

In dealing with a given molecule or, to be more general, a given point group the elements of the group are the symmetry operations or so-called *covering operations*. As discussed earlier a covering or symmetry operation is an operation performed on the molecule so that equivalent nuclei occupy the same points in space as in the originally assumed equilibrium configuration. It should be mentioned at this point that chloroform will be the specific example which will be treated in this text. Other texts have dealt with the water molecule in some detail and it is felt that chloroform being a molecule of five atoms is of the proper degree of complexity for detailed treatment in this text. Chloroform then being a member of the C_{3v} point group will be the representative molecule considered. The covering operations for the chloroform molecule are:

(1) Rotation through $360°/3$ or $2\pi/3$ radians and designated by C_3. There are two such elements: C_3^+ and C_3^-.*

* A clockwise rotation through $120°$ is designated C_3^+. If this operation is performed twice ($C_3^+ \times C_3^+$ or C_3^2) a clockwise rotation of $240°$ results which is equivalent to a counterclockwise rotation of $-120°$ which is designated C_3^-. For every symmetry operation there is a corresponding one which will return the molecule to its original configuration. This corresponding operation is termed the inverse of the first. Thus, C_3^- is the inverse of C_3^+, σ_{v_1} is the inverse of σ_{v_1}, etc.

(2) Reflection in a plane through the rotation axis and one of chlorine atoms and designated by σ_v. Since there are three such planes, there are three elements, σ_{v_1}, σ_{v_2}, and σ_{v_3}.

(3) Rotation of zero degrees about the C_3 axis and designated by I. The I stands for the identity operation and there is only one such element.

It can be seen that there are a total of six elements for any molecule belonging to the C_{3v} point group. By preparing a multiplication table (Table 3.3) similar to Table 3.2, it can be shown that these elements also fulfill the requirements for a group in a mathematical sense.

TABLE 3.3

MULTIPLICATION TABLE FOR C_{3v} SYMMETRY OPERATIONS[a]

	I	C_3^+	C_3^-	σ_{v_1}	σ_{v_2}	σ_{v_3}
I	I	C_3^+	C_3^-	σ_{v_1}	σ_{v_2}	σ_{v_3}
C_3^+	C_3^+	C_3^-	I	σ_{v_3}	σ_{v_1}	σ_{v_2}
C_3^-	C_3^-	I	C_3^+	σ_{v_2}	σ_{v_3}	σ_{v_1}
σ_{v_1}	σ_{v_1}	σ_{v_2}	σ_{v_3}	I	C_3^+	C_3^-
σ_{v_2}	σ_{v_2}	σ_{v_3}	σ_{v_1}	C_3^-	I	C_3^+
σ_{v_3}	σ_{v_3}	σ_{v_1}	σ_{v_2}	C_3^+	C_3^-	I

[a] In using such a table it is important to note that the operation performed first is at the top and the operation performed second is at the left.

If this table is examined for the four requirements for a group, it is seen that the first requirement is fulfilled because there is an identity element.

The second requirement regarding the law of combination is obeyed because the product of any two elements of the group is also an element of the group. For example, consider the multiplication of σ_{v_3} (side row) by σ_{v_1} (top row) to yield C_3^+. The product $\sigma_{v_3}\sigma_{v_1}$ means that the symmetry operation σ_{v_1} should be carried out first and then followed by σ_{v_3}. (The convention is similar to algebraic operations; the operation applied first is written on the right.) The result of carrying out these two operations should be the same as performing the single operation C_3^+. Figure 3.5(a) demonstrates that such a result is obtained. Starting with the configuration shown, reflection in the σ_{v_1} plane interchanges atoms 2 and 3. Reflection in the σ_{v_3} plane then interchanges atoms 1 and 3. As shown, the single operation of rotation through 120° yields the same result. Hence, σ_{v_3} $\sigma_{v_1} = C_3^+$. Again, considering another example, Fig. 3.5(b) demonstrates that rotation through 120° followed by a reflection in the σ_{v_2} plane equals the single operation of reflection in the σ_{v_3} plane. It can be readily demonstrated in a similar fashion that the product of any two of the six elements yields an element of the group.

The third requirement is that the law of association must be obeyed, i.e., $A(BC) = AB(C)$ etc. For example, consider the case of

$$\sigma_{v_1}(\sigma_{v_2}\sigma_{v_3}) = (\sigma_{v_1}\sigma_{v_2})\,\sigma_{v_3} \tag{3.1}$$

Application of Table 3.3 yields

$$(\sigma_{v_2}\sigma_{v_3}) = C_3^+$$

and

$$(\sigma_{v_1}\sigma_{v_2}) = C_3^+$$

and substituting into Eq. (3.1)

$$\sigma_{v_1}C_3^+ = C_3^+\sigma_{v_3}$$

but from Table 3.3

$$\sigma_{v_1}C_3^+ = \sigma_{v_2}$$

and

$$C_3^+\sigma_{v_3} = \sigma_{v_2}$$

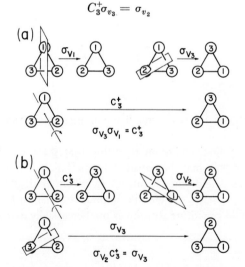

FIG. 3.5. Examples of multiplication of symmetry elements. It is important to note that the planes are numbered with the molecule in the equilibrium position, i.e., with atom 1 at the top, followed by atom 2 on the right and atom 3 on the left. Thus, in the equilibrium position the plane bisecting atom 1 is σ_{v_1} and that bisecting atom 2 is σ_{v_2} etc. These planes remain fixed and do *not* change with the symmetry operation. Note that in example (a), after the σ_{v_1} operation, the σ_{v_3} plane now bisects atom 2. Atoms 3 and 2 have been interchanged by σ_{v_1} but the σ_{v_3} plane is unaltered.

Hence

$$\sigma_{v_2} = \sigma_{v_2}. \tag{3.2}$$

Note that the order of performing the operation must be consistent. The σ_{v_3} is taken from the top and the σ_{v_2} from the side row thereby yielding C_3^+. If the reverse procedure had been followed, the σ_{v_2} being taken from the top row and the σ_{v_3} from the side row, the result would have been C_3^-.

As a second example, consider the case of

$$C_3^-(\sigma_{v_2} C_3^+) = (C_3^- \sigma_{v_2}) C_3^+. \tag{3.3}$$

Again from Table 3.3

$$(\sigma_{v_2} C_3^+) = \sigma_{v_3}$$

and

$$(C_3^- \sigma_{v_2}) = \sigma_{v_3}$$

and substituting into Eq. (3.3)

$$C_3^- \sigma_{v_3} = \sigma_{v_3} C_3^+$$

but from Table 3.3

$$C_3^- \sigma_{v_3} = \sigma_{v_1}$$

and

$$\sigma_{v_3} C_3^+ = \sigma_{v_1}.$$

Hence,

$$\sigma_{v_1} = \sigma_{v_1}.$$

It can also be shown for any other like combination of elements that the law of association holds.

The fourth and final condition requiring that there be an inverse of each element in the group may be satisfied by noting in Table 3.3 the pairs of operations which yield the identity, I, when multiplied together, e.g., $\sigma_{v_1} \times \sigma_{v_1} = I$, $C_3^+ \times C_3^- = I$, etc. To summarize, then, it has been shown that the six elements do constitute a group as mathematically defined.

3.5 Characters and Representations of Groups

It will now be shown that a symmetry operation can be characterized by a matrix. For the sake of simplicity the water molecule (point group C_{2v}) rather than chloroform will be considered. The treatment which follows is similar to that given in a previously cited reference.[2] The circles shown in Fig. 3.6(a) represent the equilibrium positions of the atoms. Three coordinates are shown for each atom with solid arrows representing arbitrary *displacements* of the atoms before the symmetry operation, σ'_v (reflection in the plane of the page) is performed. Displacements which are usually designated by Δx, Δy, Δz will here be called simply x, y, and z. The primed coordinates represent the displacement coordinates after the σ'_v operation. From Fig. 3.6(a) it can be seen that the set of primed displacement coordinates is related to the original coordinates by the following linear equations,

$$X_1 = -X'_1 \qquad X_2 = -X'_2 \qquad X_3 = -X'_3$$

$$Y_1 = Y'_1 \qquad Y_2 = Y'_2 \qquad Y_3 = Y'_3 \qquad (3.4)$$

$$Z_1 = Z'_1 \qquad Z_2 = Z'_2 \qquad Z_3 = Z'_3$$

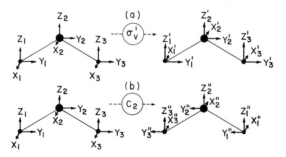

FIG. 3.6   The effect of symmetry operations on cartesian displacement coordinates for the water molecule. In (a) reflection in the σ'_v plane (the YZ plane of the page) is performed. In (b) C_2 rotation (about the Z axis) is performed.

The nine equations of this set can be written as nine by nine matrix as follows,

$$
\begin{Vmatrix} X'_1 \\ Y'_1 \\ Z'_1 \\ X'_2 \\ Y'_2 \\ Z'_2 \\ X'_3 \\ Y'_3 \\ Z'_3 \end{Vmatrix}
=
\begin{Vmatrix}
-1 & 0 & 0 & 0 & 0 & 0 & 0 & 0 & 0 \\
0 & 1 & 0 & 0 & 0 & 0 & 0 & 0 & 0 \\
0 & 0 & 1 & 0 & 0 & 0 & 0 & 0 & 0 \\
0 & 0 & 0 & -1 & 0 & 0 & 0 & 0 & 0 \\
0 & 0 & 0 & 0 & 1 & 0 & 0 & 0 & 0 \\
0 & 0 & 0 & 0 & 0 & 1 & 0 & 0 & 0 \\
0 & 0 & 0 & 0 & 0 & 0 & -1 & 0 & 0 \\
0 & 0 & 0 & 0 & 0 & 0 & 0 & 1 & 0 \\
0 & 0 & 0 & 0 & 0 & 0 & 0 & 0 & 1
\end{Vmatrix}
\times
\begin{Vmatrix} X_1 \\ Y_1 \\ Z_1 \\ X_2 \\ Y_2 \\ Z_2 \\ X_3 \\ Y_3 \\ Z_3 \end{Vmatrix}
\qquad (3.5)
$$

This result can be verified by following the usual rule for matrix multiplication (see also Chapter 14, page 428), i.e.,

$$X_1' = (-1)(X_1) + (0)(Y_1) + (0)(Z_1) + (0)(X_2) + (0)(Y_2)$$
$$+ (0)(Z_2) + (0)(X_3) + (0)(Y_3) + (0)(Z_3)$$

(3.6)

or

$$X_1' = -X_1 \text{ etc.}$$

This matrix is an example of a diagonal matrix in which the elements are zero except along the leading diagonal. The *character* of the matrix symbolized by χ is the sum of the diagonal elements and in this example is equal to,

$$-1 + 1 + 1 - 1 + 1 + 1 - 1 + 1 + 1 = +3.$$

(3.7)

A transformation matrix such as the one just shown may be established for all the covering (i.e., symmetry operations of the group. For example, for the C_2 symmetry operation it can be seen from Fig. 3.6(b) that the linear equations are as follows,

$$X_1'' = -X_3 \qquad X_2'' = -X_2 \qquad X_3'' = -X_1$$
$$Y_1'' = -Y_3 \qquad Y_2'' = -Y_2 \qquad Y_3'' = -Y_1$$
$$Z_1'' = \ \ Z_3 \qquad Z_2'' = \ \ Z_2 \qquad Z_3'' = \ \ Z_1$$

(3.8)

and the resulting matrix is,

$$
\begin{Vmatrix} X_1'' \\ Y_1'' \\ Z_1'' \\ X_2'' \\ Y_2'' \\ Z_2'' \\ X_3'' \\ Y_3'' \\ Z_3'' \end{Vmatrix}
=
\begin{Vmatrix}
0 & 0 & 0 & 0 & 0 & 0 & -1 & 0 & 0 \\
0 & 0 & 0 & 0 & 0 & 0 & 0 & -1 & 0 \\
0 & 0 & 0 & 0 & 0 & 0 & 0 & 0 & 1 \\
0 & 0 & 0 & -1 & 0 & 0 & 0 & 0 & 0 \\
0 & 0 & 0 & 0 & -1 & 0 & 0 & 0 & 0 \\
0 & 0 & 0 & 0 & 0 & 1 & 0 & 0 & 0 \\
-1 & 0 & 0 & 0 & 0 & 0 & 0 & 0 & 0 \\
0 & -1 & 0 & 0 & 0 & 0 & 0 & 0 & 0 \\
0 & 0 & 1 & 0 & 0 & 0 & 0 & 0 & 0
\end{Vmatrix}
\times
\begin{Vmatrix} X_1 \\ Y_1 \\ Z_1 \\ X_2 \\ Y_2 \\ Z_2 \\ X_3 \\ Y_3 \\ Z_3 \end{Vmatrix}
$$

(3.9)

Again this result can be verified, i.e.,

$$X_1'' = (0)(X_1) + (0)(Y_1) + (0)(Z_1) + (0)(X_2) + (0)(Y_2)$$
$$+ (0)(Z_2) + (-1)(X_3) + (0)(Y_3) + (0)(Z_3).$$

(3.10)

or

$$X_1'' = -X_3 \text{ etc.}$$

The character of this square matrix is the sum of the diagonal elements $-1 - 1 + 1 = -1$ and hence $\chi(C_2) = -1$. In like manner it may be shown from the transformation of the displacement coordinates under the remaining pair of operations I and σ_v that $\chi(I) = 9$ and $\chi(\sigma_v) = 1$.

The matrices of a group of operations form a so called representation Γ of the group. In the C_{2v} case the matrices characterizing symmetry operations I, C_2 [Eq. (3.9)], σ_v and σ_v' [Eq. (3.5)] form the representation of the C_{2v} group. The representation Γ_{3N} of the cartesian displacements of water may be summarized by,

Γ_{3N}	I	C_2	σ_v	σ_v'
	$+9$	-1	$+1$	$+3$

where $+9$, -1, $+1$, and $+3$ are the characters of the matrices.

It may be possible to find a transformation of coordinates so that a matrix with off diagonal terms [such as Eq. (3.9)] can be transformed into a matrix of the general type.

$$\begin{Vmatrix} A_1 & A_2 & . & 0 & 0 \\ A_3 & A_4 & : & 0 & 0 \\ \cdots & \cdots & \cdots & \cdots \\ 0 & 0 & . & B_1 & B_2 \\ 0 & 0 & : & B_3 & B_4 \end{Vmatrix}$$

where $\mathbf{A}$ and $\mathbf{B}$ are square submatrices along the diagonal of the main matrix and where terms outside $\mathbf{A}$ and $\mathbf{B}$ are zero. The character of the new main matrix remains unchanged. If a transformation of coordinates can be found which will put all the matrices of a given representation in this general form, the representation is said to be *reducible*.[3] If no transformation can further diagonalize all submatrices $\mathbf{A}$ or $\mathbf{B}$ then the set of matrices of a given representation is said to be completely reduced and the sets of submatrices ($\mathbf{A}$ and $\mathbf{B}$) for each operation are called the *irreducible representations*.

A new coordinate system called normal coordinates can be used which are linear combinations of cartesian displacement coordinates. For each normal coordinate each cartesian displacement coordinate is multiplied by an appropriate coefficient. These coefficients define the amplitudes and directions of atomic displacements so that in nonlinear molecules with N atoms, $3N - 6$ normal coordinates describe the normal modes of vibrations and 6 normal

---

[3] J. E. Rosenthal and G. M. Murphy, *Rev. Med. Phys.* **8**, 317 (1936).

coordinates describe molecular translation and rotation. It can be demonstrated[2] that a representation of a symmetry operation in cartesian displacement coordinates is equivalent to the representation in normal coordinates or,

$$
\begin{array}{c|cccc}
 & I & C_2 & \sigma_v & \sigma_v' \\
\Gamma_{Q,T,R} & +9 & -1 & +1 & +3
\end{array}
$$

where $\Gamma_{Q,T,R}$ is the representation which has the normal coordinates Q_1, Q_2, Q_3, R_x, R_y, R_z, T_x, T_y, and T_z describing the vibration, rotation and translation of the molecule.

For example, if the symmetry operation is decribed with normal coordinates instead of cartesian displacement coordinates, then by an analogous treatment (see Fig. 3.7) the matrix characterizing C_2 is given by

$$
\begin{Vmatrix} Q_1' \\ Q_2' \\ Q_3' \\ R_x' \\ R_y' \\ R_z' \\ T_x' \\ T_y' \\ T_z' \end{Vmatrix} =
\begin{Vmatrix}
1 & 0 & 0 & 0 & 0 & 0 & 0 & 0 & 0 \\
0 & 1 & 0 & 0 & 0 & 0 & 0 & 0 & 0 \\
0 & 0 & -1 & 0 & 0 & 0 & 0 & 0 & 0 \\
0 & 0 & 0 & -1 & 0 & 0 & 0 & 0 & 0 \\
0 & 0 & 0 & 0 & -1 & 0 & 0 & 0 & 0 \\
0 & 0 & 0 & 0 & 0 & 1 & 0 & 0 & 0 \\
0 & 0 & 0 & 0 & 0 & 0 & -1 & 0 & 0 \\
0 & 0 & 0 & 0 & 0 & 0 & 0 & -1 & 0 \\
0 & 0 & 0 & 0 & 0 & 0 & 0 & 0 & 1
\end{Vmatrix} \times
\begin{Vmatrix} Q_1 \\ Q_2 \\ Q_3 \\ R_x \\ R_y \\ R_z \\ T_x \\ T_y \\ T_z \end{Vmatrix} \qquad (3.11)
$$

If this matrix characterizing C_2 is compared with that obtained for the C_2 operation in the cartesian displacement coordinates [Eq. (3.9)] it can be seen that the character is -1 as before but now there are no off-diagonal elements. In cartesian displacement coordinates the symmetry operation exchanges or "mixes" coordinates belonging to the symmetrically equivalent hydrogen atoms. In normal coordinates no mixing occurs. The symmetry operations merely transform a nondegenerate normal coordinate into some multiple of itself. Thus the use of normal coordinates leads to a reduced representation of the group. The coordinates used are said to form the *basis* of the representation.

For a group with a finite number of elements there are as many different irreducible representations as there are classes of operations. There are the same number of vibrational types or species as there are different irreducible representations. Each of the elements (1 or -1) on the diagonal of the matrix in Eq. (3.11) is a one by one matrix which is part of an irreducible representation. However, all one by one matrices which pertain to vibrations, rotations, or

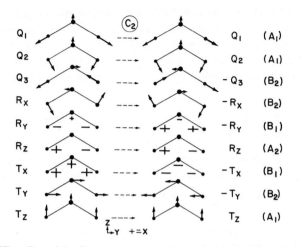

FIG. 3.7   The effect of the C_2 symmetry operation on the normal coordinates (schematic) for water. The vibration types of the normal coordinates are indicated in parentheses. A or B mean that the normal coordinate is symmetric or antisymmetric to the twofold axis, the subscripts 1 or 2 mean that the normal coordinate is symmetric or antisymmetric to the XZ plane of symmetry bisecting the $H-O-H$ angle. The C_2 operation alters B type coordinates and leaves A type coordinates unchanged.

translations of the *same vibrational type* or species are identical for each operation. In Table 3.4 the characters of the four possible *different* irreducible representations Γ_1, Γ_2, Γ_3, and Γ_4 of the C_{2v} point group are listed.

TABLE 3.4

CHARACTERS OF THE IRREDUCIBLE REPRESENTATIONS OF THE C_{2v} POINT GROUP

	I	$C_2(z)$	$\sigma_v(xz)$	$\sigma_v'(yz)$		
$(\Gamma_1)\ A_1$	1	1	1	1	T_z	
$(\Gamma_2)\ A_2$	1	1	-1	-1	R_z	
$(\Gamma_3)\ B_1$	1	-1	1	-1	T_x,	R_y
$(\Gamma_4)\ B_2$	1	-1	-1	1	T_y,	R_x

Table 3.4 is called a character table for the C_{2v} group. Along the top are given the classes of operations. Along the left are the vibration types which correspond to the irreducible representations. The numbers are the characters of the matrices which form the irreducible representation. The number under the class symbol I gives the degeneracy of the vibration, 1 for singly degenerate, 2 for doubly degenerate (see Table 3.5, for example). The characters under the other classes are $+1$ for symmetrical vibrations and -1 for antisymmetrical

vibrations. The final column of Table 3.4 contains the normal coordinate for translation or rotation. Since cartesian coordinates are specified for these, cartesian planes and axes are specified (in parenthesis) after the class symbols.

In Fig. 3.7 Q_1 and Q_2 are A_1 types, and Q_3 is a B_2 type. The vibration types or species are designated according to the symmetry operations which they represent as follows:

A		symmetric with respect to the principal axis of symmetry
B		antisymmetric with respect to the principal axis of symmetry
E		doubly degenerate vibrations, the irreducible representation is two dimensional, i.e., a 2×2 matrix (see Section 1.4)
F		triply degenerate vibrations, i.e., a three-dimensional representation
g and u (subscripts)		symmetric or antisymmetric with respect to a center of symmetry*
1 and 2 (subscripts)		symmetric or antisymmetric with respect to a rotation axis (C_p) or rotation-reflection axis (S_p) other than the principal axis or in those point groups with only one symmetry axis with respect to a plane of symmetry
prime and double prime (superscript)		symmetric or antisymmetric with respect to a plane of symmetry

These abbreviations are used except for linear molecules belonging to the point groups $C_{\infty v}$ and $D_{\infty h}$. For these two point groups the designations chosen are the same as for the electronic states of homonuclear diatomic molecules. Large Greek letters are used as follows:

Σ^+	symmetric with respect to a plane of symmetry through the molecular axis
Σ^-	antisymmetric with respect to a plane of symmetry through the molecular axis
π, Δ, ϕ	degenerate vibrations with a degree of degeneracy increasing in this order.

In designating symmetry species the order just listed is followed. For example, in the case of the C_{2v} point group the designations are A_1, A_2, B_1 and B_2 rather than A', A'', B', and B''.

---

* g and u are taken from the German words gerade and ungerade meaning even and uneven respectively.

In the case of the point group C_{3v} the characters of the irreducible representations can be shown[2,4,5] to be those given in Table 3.5.

TABLE 3.5

CHARACTERS OF THE IRREDUCIBLE REPRESENTATIONS OF THE C_{3v} POINT GROUP

C_{3v}	I	$C_3^+(z)$	$C_3^-(z)$	σ_{v_1}	σ_{v_2}	σ_{v_3}		
$(\Gamma_1)\,A_1$	1	1	1	1	1	1	T_z	
$(\Gamma_2)\,A_2$	1	1	1	-1	-1	-1	R_z	
$(\Gamma_3)\,E$	2	-1	-1	0	0	0	T_x,	T_y
							R_x,	R_y

As in the C_{2v} case a given symmetry operation changes a nondegenerate normal coordinate into $+1$ times itself (symmetrical) or -1 times itself (antisymmetrical). In the CH stretching vibration of chloroform (C_{3v}) the carbon and hydrogen move along the symmetry axis which is coincident with the CH bond. This normal coordinate (A_1) is symmetrical with respect to all the symmetry elements and is unchanged by all the symmetry operations.

A normal coordinate which is a member of a degenerate set is transformed by a symmetry operation into a linear combination of the members of the set. In the doubly degenerate CH bending vibrations (E) in chloroform the hydrogen motion has two mutually perpendicular components (x and y) at right angles to the CH bond or symmetry axis (z). The C_3^+ operation, for example, rotates each component 120° thus transforming each component into a linear combination of both components so that

$$x \overset{C_3^+}{\to} x' = x \cos\phi - y \sin\phi \qquad (\cos\phi = -1/2)$$

$$y \to y' = x \sin\phi + y \cos\phi \qquad (\sin\phi = \sqrt{3}/2)$$

Carbon and chlorine atom displacements transform in the same manner and therefore so do the whole CH bending normal coordinates Q_{4a} and Q_{4b} so that

$$Q_{4a} \overset{C_3^+}{\to} Q'_{4a} = Q_{4a} \cos\phi - Q_{4b} \sin\phi$$

$$Q_{4b} \to Q'_{4b} = Q_{4a} \sin\phi + Q_{4b} \cos\phi$$

[4] R. P. Bauman, "Absorption Spectroscopy." Wiley, New York, 1962.
[5] K. Nakamoto, "Infrared Spectra of Inorganic and Coordination Compounds." Wiley New York, 1963.

See Fig. 3.8 for a similar treatment for the CCl_3 bending coordinates. A two-by-two matrix is needed to characterize the transformation of pairs of E type normal coordinates for the C_3^+ and other operations.

$$
\begin{Vmatrix} Q_a' \\ Q_b' \end{Vmatrix} = \overset{C_3^+}{\begin{Vmatrix} -1/2 - \sqrt{3}/2 \\ +\sqrt{3}/2 - 1/2 \end{Vmatrix}} \times \begin{Vmatrix} Q_a \\ Q_b \end{Vmatrix}
$$

The complete set of matrices is the irreducible representation for E type normal coordinates for the C_{3v} group and is given by,

$$
\overset{I}{\begin{Vmatrix} 1 & 0 \\ 0 & 1 \end{Vmatrix}} \qquad \overset{C_3^+}{\begin{Vmatrix} -1/2 - \sqrt{3}/2 \\ +\sqrt{3}/2 - 1/2 \end{Vmatrix}} \qquad \overset{C_3^-}{\begin{Vmatrix} -1/2 + \sqrt{3}/2 \\ -\sqrt{3}/2 - 1/2 \end{Vmatrix}}
$$

$$
\overset{\sigma_{v1}}{\begin{Vmatrix} 1 & 0 \\ 0 & -1 \end{Vmatrix}} \qquad \overset{\sigma_{v2}}{\begin{Vmatrix} -1/2 + \sqrt{3}/2 \\ +\sqrt{3}/2 + 1/2 \end{Vmatrix}} \qquad \overset{\sigma_{v3}}{\begin{Vmatrix} -1/2 - \sqrt{3}/2 \\ -\sqrt{3}/2 + 1/2 \end{Vmatrix}}
$$

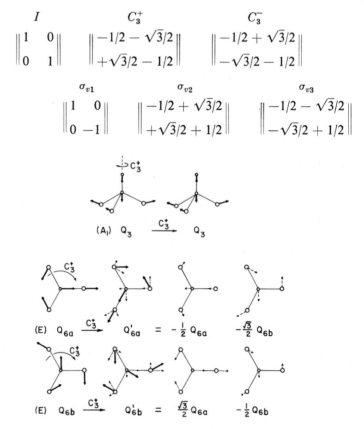

FIG. 3.8. CCl_3 bending normal coordinates (schematic) for chloroform transformed by the C_3^+ operation. The A_1 bending coordinate Q_3 is transformed into $+1$ times itself by the C_3^+ operation. Each of the doubly degenerate E bending coordinates, Q_{6a} and Q_{6b}, is transformed by the C_3^+ operation into a linear combination of both coordinates. Top views of the doubly degenerate coordinates are illustrated where the central arrow represents both carbon and hydrogen displacements.

The group character Table 3.5 can be simplified further. For example the *character* of the matrix for the operation C_3^+ is always the same as C_3^-. In like manner the character of σ_{v_1}, σ_{v_2}, and σ_{v_3} are always the same. Operations of this sort are said to belong to the same class. Finally, the identity operation, I is representative of a third class of operations. Thus, a further simplification of the group character table for the point group C_{3v} is possible. The first three rows of Table 3.6 show this simplification.

TABLE 3.6

CHARACTER AND CALCULATION TABLE FOR THE C_{3v} POINT GROUP

C_{3v}	(1) I	(2) C_3	(3) σ_v	
A_1	1	1	1	T_z
A_2	1	1	-1	R_z
E	2	-1	0	$(T_x, T_y); (R_x, R_y)$
ϕ	$0°$	$120°$	$0°$	
$2\cos\phi$	2	-1	2	
$\pm 1 + 2\cos\phi$	3	0	1	$\chi_M(R)$
2ϕ	$0°$	$240°$	$0°$	
$2\cos2\phi$	2	-1	2	
$2 \pm 2\cos\phi + 2\cos2\phi$	6	0	2	$\chi_\alpha(R)$
U_R	5	2	3	
$\varXi(R)$	9	0	3	

In Table 3.6 the first row contains the symbols (I, C_3 and σ_v) for the three classes and the number in parenthesis gives the number of elements in that class. As has been shown there is one identity, two C_3 and three σ_v. A_1, A_2, and E represent the possible vibrational types or irreducible representations for the C_{3v} point group.

In Table 3.6 ϕ is the angle of rotation for the symmetry operations of which there are two basic types, proper and improper rotations. A proper rotation is a rotation through angle $\pm\phi$ about a symmetry axis. (The identity operation is a rotation through zero degrees.) An improper rotation is a rotation followed by a reflection in a plane perpendicular to the axis of rotation. (A reflection such as σ_v is an improper rotation through an angle of zero degrees.) The values in the rows involving ϕ have been calculated since they will be used and discussed shortly.

3.6   The Number of Fundamentals of Each Type

For the nonlinear molecule $CHCl_3$ there are $3N - 6$ or 9 fundamentals. The number of fundamentals belonging to each vibration type (i.e., A_1, A_2, or E) can be calculated using the character table and the following equation,[6]

$$N_i = \frac{1}{N_g} \sum n_e \, \Xi(R) \, \chi_i(R) \tag{3.12}$$

where N_i is the number of fundamentals of vibration type i, n_e is the number of elements in each class (the number in parenthesis in the first row of Table 3.6), N_g is the number of elements in the group, i.e., the sum of the n_e values and $\chi_i(R)$ is the character in the character table for vibration type i and operation R. $\Xi(R)$ is given by

$$\Xi(R) = (U_R - 2)(1 + 2 \cos \phi) \tag{3.13}$$

for proper rotations and

$$\Xi(R) = (U_R)(-1 + 2 \cos \phi) \tag{3.14}$$

for improper rotations. The number of atoms that remain unchanged by the symmetry operation is given by U_R. In $CHCl_3$, for example, the identity operation leaves all five atoms unchanged. The C_3 operation changes three chlorine atoms and leaves two atoms unchanged. The σ_v operation changes two chlorine atoms and leaves three atoms unchanged. The values for U_R and $\Xi(R)$ for $CHCl_3$ are given in the last two rows of Table 3.6. Substituting these values into Eq. (3.12) in which the summation extends over all the classes of the group we obtain,

$$N_{A_1} = \tfrac{1}{6}\{(1) \cdot 9 \cdot 1 + (2) \cdot 0 \cdot 1 + (3) \cdot 3 \cdot 1\} = 3$$

$$N_{A_2} = \tfrac{1}{6}\{(1) \cdot 9 \cdot 1 + (2) \cdot 0 \cdot 1 + (3) \cdot 3 \cdot -1\} = 0$$

$$N_E = \tfrac{1}{6}\{(1) \cdot 9 \cdot 2 + (2) \cdot 0 \cdot -1 + (3) \cdot 3 \cdot 0\} = 3$$

The $CHCl_3$ molecule, therefore, has three A_1 vibrations, no A_2 vibrations and three doubly degenerate E vibrations giving a total of nine fundamentals.

[6] A. G. Meister, F. F. Cleveland and M. J. Murray, *Am. J. Phys.* 11, 239 (1943).

3.7 Infrared Activity

The vibration types which contribute to a change in dipole moment and are therefore infrared active can be determined by the following reduction formula,[6]

$$N_i(M) = \frac{1}{N_g} \sum n_e \, \chi_M(R) \, \chi_i(R) \tag{3.15}$$

where $\chi_M(R)$ is the character of the dipole moment for the operation R which is always given by,

$$\chi_M(R) = \pm 1 + 2\cos\phi \tag{3.16}$$

where ϕ is the angle of rotation during operation R. The plus sign is for proper rotations and the minus sign for improper rotations. The character $\chi_M(R)$ for a given class is always a linear combination of the characters of the vibration types for that class. $N_i(M)$ is the number of times the character $\chi_i(R)$ of the vibration type appears in $\chi_M(R)$. In the C_{3v} case for example,

$$\chi_M(R) = N_{A_1}(M)\,\chi_{A_1}(R) + N_{A_2}(M)\,\chi_{A_2}(R) + N_E(M)\,\chi_E(R)$$

Using Eq. (3.15) and Table 3.6 we obtain,

$$N_{A_1}(M) = \tfrac{1}{6}\{(1)\cdot 3\cdot 1 + (2)\cdot 0\cdot 1 + (3)\cdot 1\cdot 1\} = 1$$

$$N_{A_2}(M) = \tfrac{1}{6}\{(1)\cdot 3\cdot 1 + (2)\cdot 0\cdot 1 + (3)\cdot 1\cdot -1\} = 0$$

$$N_E(M) = \tfrac{1}{6}\{(1)\cdot 3\cdot 2 + (2)\cdot 0\cdot -1 + (3)\cdot 1\cdot 0\} = 1$$

Making the appropriate substitution we obtain,

$$\chi_M(R) = \chi_{A_1}(R) + \chi_E(R)$$

or simply

$$M = A_1 + E$$

Only those vibration types whose characters are contained in $\chi_M(R)$ are infrared active. Thus, fundamental vibrations of type A_1 and E are allowed and type A_2 is forbidden in the infrared spectrum.

3.8 Raman Activity

The vibration types which contribute to a change in polarizability of the molecule and are therefore Raman active are determined with the following equation,[6]

$$N_i(\alpha) = \frac{1}{N_g} \sum n_e \, \chi_\alpha(R) \, \chi_i(R) \tag{3.17}$$

Equation (3.17) is like Eq. (3.15) except that $\chi_M(R)$ has been replaced by $\chi_\alpha(R)$ the character of the polarizability which is given by,

$$\chi_\alpha(R) = 2 \pm 2 \cos \phi + 2 \cos 2\phi \tag{3.18}$$

where the plus sign is used for proper rotation and the minus sign for improper rotations. Like the infrared case the character $\chi_\alpha(R)$ is a linear combination of the $\chi_i(R)$ values. $N_i(\alpha)$ is the number of times the character of the vibration type appears in $\chi_\alpha(R)$ so that in the C_{3v} case,

$$\chi_\alpha(R) = N_{A_1}(\alpha) \, \chi_{A_1}(R) + N_{A_2}(\alpha) \, \chi_{A_2}(R) + N_E(\alpha) \, \chi_E(R)$$

From Eq. (3.17) and Table 3.6 one obtains,

$$N_{A_1}(\alpha) = \tfrac{1}{6}\{(1) \cdot 6 \cdot 1 + (2) \cdot 0 \cdot 1 + (3) \cdot 2 \cdot 1\} = 2$$
$$N_{A_2}(\alpha) = \tfrac{1}{6}\{(1) \cdot 6 \cdot 1 + (2) \cdot 0 \cdot 1 + (3) \cdot 2 \cdot - 1\} = 0$$
$$N_E(\alpha) = \tfrac{1}{6}\{(1) \cdot 6 \cdot 2 + (2) \cdot 0 \cdot -1 + (3) \cdot 2 \cdot 0\} = 2$$

Making appropriate substitution we obtain,

$$\chi_\alpha(R) = 2\chi_{A_1}(R) + 2\chi_E(R)$$

Only those vibration types whose characters are contained in $\chi_\alpha(R)$ are active in the Raman effect. Thus, fundamental vibrations of type A_1 and E are allowed and type A_2 is forbidden in the Raman effect.

3.9 Overtone and Combination Bands

Both the infrared and the Raman spectrum may contain overtone and combination bands. In general, the overtone and combination bands are of weaker intensity than the fundamentals and in the Raman spectrum they are usually few in number.

To obtain the activity of combination bands, the *direct products* of the characters of the vibration types to which ν_i and ν_j belong must be evaluated as follows[6]

	E	C_3	σ_v	
$\chi A_1(R)$	1	1	1	
$\chi E(R)$	2	-1	0	
$\chi_{A_1 \times E}(R)$	2	-1	0	(multiply)

Hence, the character of the direct product is the same as $\chi_E(R)$. Whenever an E type vibration is allowed in the infrared and Raman spectrum then the combination frequency $\nu_{i_{A_1}} \pm \nu_{j_E}$ will also be allowed.

The selection rules for the remaining binary combinations may be obtained in a similar manner except for $E \times E$. In this case

	E	C_3	σ_v	
$\chi_E(R)$	2	-1	0	
$\chi_E(R)$	2	-1	0	
$\chi_{E \times E}(R)$	4	1	0	(multiply)

Since $\chi_{E \times E}$ does not have the character of A_1, A_2, or E, it contains more than one component and the reduction formula of Eq. (3.15) is used with the character of the direct product replacing $\chi_M(R)$. $N_{i(EE)}$ which replaces $N_i(M)$ is the number of times $\chi_i(R)$ appears in $\chi_{E \times E}(R)$.

$$N_{A_1}(EE) = \tfrac{1}{6}\{(1) \cdot 4 \cdot 1 + (2) \cdot 1 \cdot 1 + (3) \cdot 0 \cdot 1\} = 1$$

$$N_{A_2}(EE) = \tfrac{1}{6}\{(1) \cdot 4 \cdot 1 + (2) \cdot 1 \cdot 1 + (3) \cdot 0 \cdot 1\} = 1$$

$$N_E(EE) = \tfrac{1}{6}\{(1) \cdot 4 \cdot 2 + (2) \cdot 1 \cdot -1 + (3) \cdot 0 \cdot 0\} = 1$$

It can be verified that the sum of the characters of each class in Table 3.6 equals $\chi_{E \times E}(R)$. Thus, $E \times E = A_1 + A_2 + E$. If any of the three components A_1, A_2, or E is allowed, the combination frequency $E \times E$ is allowed. In this case then, the $E \times E$ combination is allowed in both the infrared and Raman. The possible binary combination for the C_{3v} point group are summarized in Table 3.7.

In calculating the selection rules for overtones the method varies for degenerate and nondegenerate vibrations. For nondegenerate vibrations the character of the $(n - 1)$th overtone is determined by,

$$\chi_i^n(R) = [\chi_i(R)]^n \tag{3.19}$$

Again the direct product is used to obtain the first and second overtones of an A_2 vibration, thus,

	E	C_3	σ_v	
$\chi_{A_2}(R)$	1	1	−1	
$\chi_{A_2}(R)$	1	1	−1	
				multiply
$\chi_{A_2^2}(R)$	1	1	1	
$\chi_{A_2}(R)$	1	1	−1	
				multiply
$\chi_{A_2^3}(R)$	1	1	−1	

The character of the first overtone, $\chi_{A_2^2}(R)$ is the same as $\chi_{A_1}(R)$, hence this overtone is allowed since as has been previously shown the A_1 vibrations are allowed. However, the character of the second overtone is the same as $\chi_{A_2}(R)$ and hence this overtone is forbidden in both the infrared and Raman spectrum. The selection rules for the overtones of the type A_2 vibration can be summarized as

$$A_2^n = \begin{cases} n \text{ even—allowed} \\ n \text{ odd—forbidden} \end{cases}$$

In a similar manner it is obvious that the A_1 overtones are allowed for both even and odd values of n.

For doubly-degenerate vibrations, the following equation is applied,

$$\chi_E^n(R) = \tfrac{1}{2} [\chi_E^{n-1}(R) \chi_E(R) + \chi_E(R^n)] \tag{3.20}$$

where $\chi_E(R^n)$ is the character corresponding to the operation R performed n times in succession. One must determine $\chi_E(E)^2$, $\chi_E(C_3^2)$ and $\chi_E(\sigma_v^2)$. $\chi_E(E)^2$ is the same as $\chi_E(E)$ and therefore equals 2. Carrying out the operation $C_3(\pm 120°)$ twice is the same as only carrying it out once, hence $\chi_E(C_3^2) = \chi_E(C_3) = -1$. The operation σ_v performed twice is the same as performing the identity operation and therefore $\chi_E(\sigma_v^2) = \chi_E(E) = 2$. The values of $\chi_E(R)^n$ up to $n = 5$ are as follows,

	E	C_3	σ_v
$\chi_E(R)^2$	2	−1	2
$\chi_E(R)^3$	2	2	0
$\chi_E(R)^4$	2	−1	2
$\chi_E(R)^5$	2	−1	0

Using Eq. (3.20), the character of the first overtone $\chi_E^2(R)$ is obtained as follows,

	E	C_3	σ_v	
$\chi_E(R)$	2	−1	0	
$\chi_E(R)$	2	−1	0	
				multiply
$\chi_E(R)^2$	4	1	0	
$\chi_E(R^2)$	2	−1	2	
				add
	6	0	2	
				divide by 2
$\chi_E^2(R)$	3	0	1	

Since $\chi_E^2(R)$ does not have the character of A_1, A_2, or E, it contains more than a single component and the reduction formula of Eq. (3.15) is used with $\chi_E^2(R)$ replacing $\chi_M(R)$ and,

$$N_{A_1}(E^2) = \tfrac{1}{6}\{(1) \cdot 3 \cdot 1 + (2) \cdot 0 \cdot 1 + (3) \cdot 1 \cdot 1\} = 1$$

$$N_{A_2}(E^2) = \tfrac{1}{6}\{(1) \cdot 3 \cdot 1 + (2) \cdot 0 \cdot 1 + (3) \cdot 1 \cdot -1\} = 0$$

and

$$N_E(E^2) = \tfrac{1}{6}\{(1) \cdot 3 \cdot 2 + (2) \cdot 0 \cdot -1 + (3) \cdot 1 \cdot 0\} = 1$$

It can be seen that the sums of the A_1 and E characters in Table 3.6 yield $\chi_E^2(R)$. Hence, $E^2 = A_1 + E$ and since A_1 and E frequencies are allowed the first overtone of ν_{jE} is allowed. The selection rules which apply to any molecule belonging to the C_{3v} point group are summarized in Table 3.7.

TABLE 3.7

SELECTION RULES FOR C_{3v} MOLECULES

Vibration type	Infrared	Raman
A_1	a^a	a
A_2	f^b	f
E	a	a
$A_1 \times A_1$	a	a
$A_1 \times A_2$	f	f
$A_1 \times E$	a	a
$A_2 \times A_2$	a	a
$A_2 \times E$	a	a
$E \times E$	a	a
A_1^n	a	a
$A^n(n \text{ even})$	a	a
$A_2^n(n \text{ odd})$	f	f
E^n	a	a

[a] a = allowed.
[b] f = forbidden.

An alternate method for calculating the number of vibrations of each type is given by Herzberg[7] and also by Brugel.[8]

3.10 Selection Rules, Character Tables, and Chemical Examples

Using the approach outlined in considerable detail for the C_{3v} point group and the chloroform molecule as a particular example, the selection rules for the remaining groups can be derived with the exception of the $C_{\infty v}$ and $D_{\infty h}$ point groups. The equations applied to nonlinear polyatomic molecules must be modified in order to determine the selection rules for linear molecules because with linear molecules continuous groups are involved. There are an infinite number of symmetry operations which will yield an equivalent configuration of the molecule. For example, if the axis of rotation is chosen as the line on which the nuclei lie, there are an infinite number of rotations about this axis which yield an equivalent configuration of the molecule. Since the determination of the selection rules is based on the application of a reduction formula which for non-linear molecules involves a summation over all the elements of a finite group, it is not possible to make these calculations in the same way for linear molecules because one would have to sum over an infinite number of elements. Hence, for continuous groups such as $C_{\infty v}$ and $D_{\infty h}$ it is necessary to replace the summation [Eq. (3.15) or (3.17)] with an integral as follows,

$$N_i = \int \chi(R)\, \chi_i(R)\, dR \Big/ \int dR \qquad (3.21)$$

where $\chi(R)$ represents either $\chi_M(R)$ or $\chi_\alpha(R)$ and the integration is taken over the range of the continuously changing parameter R (in this case ϕ) to cover all the operations of the group, and the other symbols are as defined previously. Ferigle and Meister[9] have outlined these calculations in detail for the $C_{\infty v}$ and $D_{\infty h}$ point groups and they will not be repeated in this text.

The character table, selection rules and a large number of examples of each point group taken from the recent literature* are summarized in Table 3.8.

[7] G. Herzberg, "Infrared and Raman Spectra of Polyatomic Molecules." Van Nostrand, New York, 1945.

[8] W. Brugel, "An Introduction to Infrared Spectroscopy." Wiley, New York, 1962.

[9] S. M. Ferigle and A. G. Meister, *Am. J. Phys.* 20, 421 (1952).

* This literature survey which is by no means complete covers most of the compounds reported in the interval 1945-1960 in the following journals, *J. Am. Chem. Soc.*, *J. Chem. Phys.*, *J. Chem. Soc.*, *J. Mol. Spectr.*, and *Trans. Faraday Soc.* Herzberg's text[7] has a complete listing of compounds studied prior to 1945. These compounds are also included in this Table.

TABLE 3.8

SYMMETRY ELEMENTS, SYMMETRY TYPES (OR SPECIES), AND CHARACTERS, SELECTION
RULES, AND CHEMICAL EXAMPLES OF IMPORTANT POINT GROUPS

(The vibrations belonging to the totally symmetric species give rise to polarized Raman
bands. E = doubly degenerate; F = triply degenerate)

Point Group C_1

Symmetry elements

  I

Symmetry types and characters

C_1	I
A	1

Selection rules (forbidden vibrations)

  Infrared, none
  Raman, none

Chemical examples

Point group	Number of atoms	Compounds	References
C_1	5	CHFClBr	G. Herzberg, Molecular Spectra and Molecular Structure, Vol. II, "Infrared and Raman Spectra of Polyatomic Molecules," p. 322. Van Nostrand, New York, 1945.
	6	N_2H_4, $SO_2 \cdot OH \cdot Cl$	G. Herzberg, *Ibid.* p. 336.
	8	(Gauche forms) C_2F_4HCl,[a] C_2H_4ClI,[a] CF_2Cl-$CFCl_2$,[a] CH_2DCH_2Br;[a] CCl_3CHFCl, C_2H_3FClBr, $CF_2ClCHFCl$, $CF_2BrCFClBr$, $CHCl_2COOH$	G. Herzberg, *Ibid.*, p. 350.
		(Gauche form) C_2H_4ClBr[a]	*Ibid*; J. K. Brown and N. Sheppard, *Trans. Faraday Soc.* **48**, 128 (1952).
		N_2H_5Cl, N_2D_5Cl N_2H_5Br, N_2D_5Br	J. C. Decius, and D. P. Pearson, *J. Am. Chem. Soc.* **75**, 2436 (1953).
C_1 (? or C_s)		CH_3NO_3	J. C. D. Brand, and T. M. Cawthon, *J. Am. Chem. Soc.* **77**, 319 (1955).
	11	C_2H_5COOH (Gauche form) C_3H_7Cl,[a] C_3H_7Br,[a] C_3H_7I[a](n-propyl)	G. Herzberg, *op. cit.*, p. 362. J. K. Brown, and N. Sheppard, *Trans. Faraday Soc.* **50**, 1164 (1954).

[a] Isomeric modification belongs to point group C_s.

TABLE 3.8 (*continued*)

Point Group C_2

Symmetry elements

$I, C_2(z)$

Symmetry types and characters

C_2	I	$C_2(z)$		
A	1	1	T_z, R_z	$\alpha_{xx}, \alpha_{yy}, \alpha_{zz}, \alpha_{xy}$
B	1	-1	$T_x, T_y; R_x, R_y$	α_{yz}, α_{xz}

Selection rules (forbidden vibrations)

Infrared, none
Raman, none

Chemical examples

Point group	Number of atoms	Compounds	References
C_2	4	H_2O_2 S_2Cl_2	G. Herzberg, *op. cit.*, p. 301. *Ibid.*, p. 302.
$C_2(?)$	5	B_2S_5	F. T. Greene, and J. L. Margrave, *J. Am. Chem. Soc.* 81, 5555 (1959).
	8	(Gauche form) CH_2ClCH_2Cl,[a]	J. K. Brown and N. Sheppard, *Trans. Faraday Soc.* 48, 128 (1952).
		CH_2BrCH_2Br,[a] CH_2ICH_2I,[a] $C_2F_4Cl_2$,[a] $C_2F_4Br_2$,[a] $C_2H_2Br_4$,[a] $CFCl_2CFCl_2$,[a] $CHCl_2CHCl_2$,[a] $CHBr_2CHBr_2$.[a]	*Ibid.*, G. Herzberg, *op. cit.*, p. 350. R. E. Kagarise and D. H. Rank, *Trans. Faraday Soc.* 48, 394 (1952).
	16	C_6H_{10}(cyclohexene)	C. W. Beckett, N. K. Freeman, and K. S. Pitzer, *J. Am. Chem. Soc.* 70, 4227 (1948).
	18	(*Trans* form) $C_6H_{10}Cl_2$ $C_6H_{10}Br_2$(1, 2 dichloro and dibromo) cyclohexane	K. Kozima, K. Sakashita, and S. Maeda, *J. Am. Chem. Soc.* 76, 1965 (1954).

[a] Isomeric modification belongs to point group C_{2h}.

TABLE 3.8 (*continued*)

Point Group C_{1v}, C_{1h}, or C_s

Symmetry elements

 I, $\sigma(xy)$

Symmetry types and characters

$C_{1v} \equiv C_{1h} \equiv C_s$	I	$\sigma(xy)$		
A'	1	1	T_x, T_y; R_z	α_{xx}, α_{yy}, α_{zz}, α_{xy}
A''	1	-1	T_z; R_x, R_y	α_{yz}, α_{xz}

Selection rules (forbidden vibrations)

 Infrared, none

 Raman, none

Chemical examples

Point group	Number of atoms	Compounds	References
C_{1v},	3	NOCl	G. Herzberg, *op. cit.*, p. 287.
C_{1h},	4	N_3H, HNCO	G. Herzberg, *op. cit.*, p. 302.
or		FClCO	A. H. Nielsen, T. G. Burke, P. J. H. Woltz, and E. A. Jones, *J. Chem. Phys.* **20**, 596 (1952).
C_s		$SOCl_2$	C. A. McDowell, *Trans. Faraday Soc.* **49**, 371 (1953). D. E. Martz and R. T. Lagemann, *J. Chem. Phys.* **22**, 1193 (1954).
		HDCO	D. W. Davidson, B. P. Stoicheff, and H. J., Bernstein, *J. Chem. Phys.* **22**, 289 (1954).
		SOF_2	P. Bender and J. M. Wood, Jr., *J. Chem. Phys.* **23**, 1316 (1955).
		HFCO	H. W. Morgan, P. A. Staats, and J. H. Goldstein, *J. Chem. Phys.* **25**, 337 (1956).
	5	$CHCl_2Br$	G. Herzberg, *op. cit.*, p. 320.
		$CHClBr_2$, $CDClBr_2$	*Ibid.*; D. A. Pontarelli *et al.*, *J. Chem. Phys.* **20**, 1949 (1952).
		CH_2ClF, CH_2ClBr, CH_2ClI, CH_2BrI, $CHFCl_2$, $CHClF_2$, $CHBrF_2$, $CHFBr_2$, H_2NCN	G. Herzberg, *op. cit.*, p. 322.
$C_s(?)$	6	CF_2ClCN, CCl_2FCN	S. C. Wait, Jr. and G. J. Janz, *J. Chem. Phys.* **26**, 1554 (1957).
		CH_3OH, CH_3OD	G. Herzberg, *op. cit.*, p. 334.

TABLE 3.8 (*continued*)

Chemical examples (continued)

Point group	Number of atoms	Compounds	References
C_{1v}, C_{1h}, or C_s	6	C_2HCl_3, NH_2COH, ClH_2CCN, Cl_2HCCN, CH_3SH, $HClO_4$, H_2CNOH, C_2H_3I C_2H_3Cl, C_2H_3Br	G. Herzberg, *op. cit.*, p. 336. *Ibid.*; C. W. Gullikson and J. R. Nielsen, *J. Mol. Spectry.* 1, 158 (1957).
C_s(?)		CF_3OF	R. T. Lagemann, *et al.*, *J. Chem. Phys.* 20, 1768 (1952).
		F_2CCFH, F_2CCFD	D. E. Mann, N. Acquista, and E. K. Plyler, *J. Chem. Phys.* 22, 1586 (1954).
		F_2CCHD	W. F. Edgell and C. J. Ultee, *J. Chem. Phys.* 22, 1983 (1954).
		F_2CCFCl	J. A. Rolfe and L. A. Woodward, *Trans. Faraday Soc.* 50, 1030 (1954).
		Cl_2CCClF	J. R. Nielsen, C. W. Gullikson and A. H. Woollett, *J. Chem. Phys.* 23, 1994 (1955).
C_{1v},	6	$FClCCH_2$	D. E. Mann, N. Aquista, and E. K. Plyer, *J. Chem. Phys.* 23, 2122 (1955).
C_{1h}, or C_s		CF_3NO	J. Mason and J. Dunderdale, *J. Chem. Soc.* 1956, p. 754.
		F_2CCHBr	R. Theimer and J. R. Nielsen, *J. Chem. Phys.* 27, 264 (1957).
		$F_2CCClBr$	*Ibid.*, 30, 98 (1959).
		$HC{\equiv}CCHO$	J. C. D. Brand and J. K. G. Watson, *Trans. Faraday Soc.* 56, 1582 (1960).
	7	CH_3NH_2, CH_3NO_2, CH_3NO_2, CD_3NO_2, CH_3N_3, CCl_3NO_2, CBr_3NO_2, $CCl_3CO_2^-$, CH_3COH, CD_3COH, CH_3COCl, CH_3COBr, $^+H_3N-NH_2$, $^+D_3N-NH_2$, $HC{\equiv}C-COOH$, $^+H_3N-NH_2$, C_2H_3CN, CH_3NCO	G. Herzberg, *op. cit.*, p. 342.
C_s(?)		CF_3CHO	R. E. Dodd, H. L. Roberts and L. A. Woodward, *J. Chem. Soc.* 1957, p. 2783.
		CH_3HgOH	P. L. Goggin and L. A. Woodward, *Trans. Faraday Soc.* 56, 1591 (1960).

TABLE 3.8 (*continued*)

Chemical examples (continued)

Point group	Number of atoms	Compounds	References
C_{1v}, C_{1h}, or C_s	8	CH_3CHCl_2, CH_3CHBr_2, CH_3CHI_2, C_2F_4HCl,[a] C_2H_4ClI[a]	G. Herzberg, *op. cit.*, p. 350.
		(*trans* form) CH_2ClCH_2Br[a]	*Ibid.*; J. K. Brown and N. Sheppard, *Trans. Faraday Soc.* **48**, 128 (1952).
		C_2H_5Cl	G. Herzberg, *op. cit.*, p. 350.
		C_2H_5Br, C_2H_5I, C_2HCl_5, CH_2DCH_2Br,[a] C_2H_4NH, $CF_2ClCFCl_2$,[a]	
$C_s(?)$		CH_3COOH, CCl_3COOH	
C_s (? or C_1)		CH_3NO_3	*Ibid.*; J. C. D. Brand and T. M. Cawthon, *J. Am. Chem. Soc.* **77**, 319 (1955).
		CH_3COSH	N. Sheppard, *Trans. Faraday Soc.* **45**, 693 (1949).
		C_2H_5D	L. R. Posey, Jr. and E. F. Barker, *J. Chem. Phys.* **17**, 182 (1949).
		$(CH_2)_2NH$	H. W. Thompson and W. T. Cave, *Trans. Faraday Soc.* **47**, 951 (1951).
		F_3CCF_2Cl	J. R. Nielsen, C. Y. Liang, R. M. Smith, and D. C. Smith, *J. Chem. Phys.* **21**, 383 (1953).
		F_3CCH_2Cl, F_3CCHCl_2	J. R. Nielsen, C. Y. Liang and D. C. Smith, *J. Chem. Phys.* **21**, 1060 (1953).
C_{1v},	8	$F_2ClCCCl_3$, FCl_2CCCl_3	J. R. Nielsen, C. Y. Liang, D. C. Smith, and M. Alpert, *J. Chem. Phys.* **21**, 1070 (1953).
C_{1h},		H_3CCHCl_2	L. W. Daasch, C. Y. Liang, and J. R. Nielsen, *J. Chem. Phys.* **22**, 1293 (1954).
or C_s		$ClCH_2COOH$	J. D. Barceló, M. P. Jorge, and C. Otero, *J. Chem. Phys.* **28** 1230 (1958).
	9	$CH_3CH=CH_2$	G. Herzberg, *op. cit.*, p. 354.
		C_2H_5OH, C_2H_5SH, C_2H_5SeH, C_2H_5CN, C_2H_5NC, CH_3CONH_2, CH_3CSNH_2, CCl_3CONH_2, CH_2ClCH_2OH, $CNCH_2COOH$	*Ibid.*, p. 356.

TABLE 3.8 (continued)

Chemical examples (continued)

Point group	Number of atoms	Compounds	References
C_{1v}, C_{1h}, or C_s	9	C_2H_5CN	N. E. Duncan and G. J. Janz, *J. Chem. Phys.* **23**, 434 (1955).
		F_3CCF_2H	J. R. Nielsen, H. H. Claassen, and N. B. Moran, *J. Chem. Phys.* **23**, 329 (1955).
		$CH_2CHSiCl_3$	E. R. Shull, R. A. Thursack, and C. M. Birdsall, *J. Chem. Phys.* **24**, 147 (1956).
		Cl_3CCHCH_2	E. R. Shull, *J. Chem. Phys.* **27**, 399 (1957).
	10	$C_2H_5NO_2$, C_2H_4OHCN, $(CH_3)_2NH$, $C_2H_5C\equiv CH$, $C_2H_5C\equiv CBr$, $C_2H_5C\equiv CI$, $H_2C=CCH_3CN$, $CNCH=CHCH_3$,	G. Herzberg, *op. cit.*, p. 360.
$C_s(?)$ $C_s(?)$ $C_s(?)$ $C_s(?)$		$C_2H_5NH_2$, C_2H_5CHO, C_2H_5COCl, C_2H_5COBr, C_2H_5NCO, C_2H_5SCN, C_2H_5NCS	
		C_3H_5CN(cyclopropyl cyanide)	L. H. Daly and S. E. Wiberley, *J. Mol. Spectry.* **2**, 177 (1958).
$C_s(?)$	11	$H_3CHC=CHCHO$	G. Herzberg, *op. cit.*, p. 362.
		$CH_3CHClCH_3$, $CH_3CHBrCH_3$, CH_3CHICH_3	N. Sheppard, *Trans. Faraday Soc.* **46**, 533 (1950).
		$CH_3B_2H_5$	W. J. Lehmann, C. O. Wilson and I. Shapiro, *J. Chem. Phys.* **32**, 1088 (1960).
		(n-propyl) C_3H_7Br, C_3H_7Cl, C_3H_7I[a]	J. K. Brown and N. Sheppard, *Trans. Faraday Soc.* **50**, 1164 (1954).
$C_s(?)$ $C_s(?)$	12	$C_2H_5C_2H_3$ (butene 1), C_3H_5COOH (cyclopropane carbonic acid)	G. Herzberg, *op. cit.*, p. 368.
C_{1v}, C_{1h}, or C_s	12	$m-C_6H_4FCl$	F. W. Harris, N. A. Narasimham, and J. R. Nielsen, *J. Chem. Phys.* **24**, 1232 (1956).

TABLE 3.8 (*continued*)

Point Group C_{2v}

Symmetry elements

$I,\ C_2(z),\ \sigma_v(xz),\ \sigma_v(yz)$

Symmetry types and characters

C_{2v}	I	$C_2(z)$	$\sigma_v(xz)$	$\sigma_v(yz)$		
A_1	1	1	1	1	T_z	$\alpha_{xx},\ \alpha_{yy},\ \alpha_{zz}$
A_2	1	1	-1	-1	R_z	α_{xy}
B_1	1	-1	1	-1	$T_x;\ R_y$	α_{xz}
B_2	1	-1	-1	1	$T_y;\ R_x$	α_{yz}

Selection rules (forbidden vibrations)

Infrared, A_2, $A_1 \times A_2$, $B_1 \times B_2$, $A_2{}^n$(n odd)
Raman, none

Chemical examples

Point group	Number of atoms	Compounds	References
C_{2v}	3	$H_2O,\ D_2O,\ H_2S,$ $NO_2{}^-,\ H_2Se,\ D_2Se,$ $(UO_2)^{2+}$	G. Herzberg, *op. cit.*, p. 280-282. *Ibid.*, p. 287.
		F_2O	G. Herzberg, *op. cit.*, p. 287; H. J. Bernstein and J. Powling, *J. Chem. Phys.* **18**, 685 (1950).
		NO_2	G. Herzberg, *op. cit.*, p. 284; R. E. Weston, Jr., *J. Chem. Phys.* **26**, 1248 (1957).
		O_3	M. J. S. Dewar, *J. Chem. Soc.* 1948, 1299.
		SO_2	G. Herzberg, *op. cit.*, p. 285.
	4	$H_2CO,\ D_2CO$	G. Herzberg, *op. cit.*, p. 300.
		$C_2I_2,\ Cl_2CS,\ (HCO_2)^-$	*Ibid.*, p. 302.
		Cl_2CO	*Ibid.*; A. H. Nielsen, T. G. Burke, P. J. H. Woltz, and E. A. Jones, *J. Chem. Phys.* **20**, 596 (1952).
		F_2CO	*Ibid.*
		S_2O_2	A. V. Jones, *J. Chem. Phys.* **18**, 1263 (1950).

TABLE 3.8 (*continued*)

Chemical examples (continued)

Point group	Number of atoms	Compounds	References
C_{2v}	4	NO_2Cl	R. Ryason and M. K. Wilson, *J. Chem. Phys.* **22**, 2000 (1954);
		NO_2F	R. E. Dodd, J. A. Rolfe, and L. A. Woodward, *Trans. Faraday Soc.* **52**, 145 (1956).
		$COBr_2$	J. Overend and J. C. Evans, *Trans. Faraday Soc.* **55**, 1817 (1959).
	4	ONO_2^-	C. C. Addison and B. M. Gatehouse, *J. Chem. Soc.* **1960**, 613.
	5	CH_2F_2 , CH_2Br_2 , CH_2I_2 , CF_2Br_2 , CCl_2Br_2	G. Herzberg, *op. cit.*, p. 322.
$C_{2v}(?)$		HNO_3 , DNO_3	
		$F_2C_2Cl_2$	*Ibid.*; H. W. Thompson and R. B. Temple, *J. Chem. Soc.* **1948**, 1422; H. H. Claassen, *J. Chem. Phys.* **22**, 50 (1954).
		CH_2Cl_2	G. Herzberg, *op. cit.*, p. 317.
		SO_2Cl_2	G. Herzberg, *op. cit.*, p. 322; D. E. Martz and R. T. Lagemann, *J. Chem. Phys.* **22**, 1193 (1954).
		$H_2C=C=O$	G. Herzberg, *op. cit.*, p. 322; F. Halverson and V. Z. Williams, *J. Chem. Phys.* **15**, 552 (1947).
		CH_2N_2 , CD_2N_2	B. L. Crawford, Jr., W. H. Fletcher, and D. A. Ramsay, *J. Chem. Phys.* **19**, 406 (1951).
		CBr_2Cl_2	A. Davis, F. F. Cleveland, and A. G. Meister, *J. Chem. Phys.* **20**, 454 (1952).
		SO_2F_2	W. D. Perkins and M. K. Wilson, *J. Chem. Phys.* **20**, 1791 (1952); D. W. A. Sharp, *J. Chem. Soc.* **1957**, 3761.
		SeF_4	J. A. Rolfe, L. A. Woodward, and D. A. Long, *Trans. Faraday Soc.* **49**, 1388 (1953).

TABLE 3.8 *(continued)*

Chemical examples (continued)

Point Group	Number of atoms	Compounds	References
C_{2v}	5	SF_4	R. E. Dodd, L. A. Woodward, and H. L. Roberts, *Trans. Faraday Soc.* **52**, 1052 (1956).
		$H_2PO_2^-$	M. Tsuboi, *J. Am. Chem. Soc.* **79**, 1351 (1957).
	5	B_2O_3	D. White, D. E. Mann, P. N. Walsh, and A. Sommer, *J. Chem. Phys.* **32**, 481 (1960).
	6	*cis*-$C_2H_2Br_2$, *cis*-$C_2H_2I_2$, CCl_2CF_2	G. Herzberg, *op. cit.*, p. 336.
		cis-$C_2H_2Cl_2$	*Ibid.*, p. 329.
		F_2CCH_2	W. F. Edgell and W. E. Byrd, *J. Chem. Phys.* **18**, 892 (1950); D. C. Smith, J. R. Nielsen, and H. H. Claassen, *J. Chem. Phys.* **18**, 326 (1950).
		F_2CCl_2	J. R. Nielsen, H. H. Claassen, and D. C. Smith, *J. Chem. Phys.* **18**, 485 (1950).
		F_2CCD_2	W. F. Edgell and C. J. Ultree, *J. Chem. Phys.* **22**, 1983 (1954).
	7	$H_2C{-}O{-}CH_2$, $H_2C{-}S{-}CH_2$	G. Herzberg, *op. cit.*, pp. 340-342; H. W. Thompson and W. T. Cave, *Trans. Faraday Soc.* **47**, 946 (1951).
		$H_2C(CN)_2$	F. Halverson and R. J. Francel, *J. Chem. Phys.* **17**, 694 (1949).
		$D_2C{=}C{=}CH_2$	W. E. Shuler and W. H. Fletcher, *J. Mol. Spectry.* **1**, 95 (1957).
	8	$(NH_2)_2CO$, $(ND_2)_2CO$	G. Herzberg, *op. cit.*, p. 350; R. B. Penland, S. Mizushima, C. Curran, and J. V. Quagliano, *J. Am. Chem. Soc.* **79**, 1575 (1957).
$C_{2v}(?)$		$(COOH)_2$, $(NH_2)_2CS$	G. Herzberg, *op. cit.*, p. 350.
		cis-$C_2H_4Cl_2$, *cis*-$C_2H_2Cl_4$	*Ibid.*, p. 346.
	9	$(CH_3)_2S$, $(CH_3)_2Se$	G. Herzberg, *op. cit.*, p. 356.
		$(CH_3)_2O$	G. Herzberg, *op. cit.*, p. 353.
	9	C_4H_4O (furan), C_4H_4S (thiophene)	G. Herzberg, *op. cit.*, p. 356; H. W. Thompson and R. B. Temple, *Trans. Faraday Soc.* **41**, 27 (1945).

TABLE 3.8 (*continued*)

Chemical examples (continued)

Point Group	Number of atoms	Compounds	References
C_{2v}	9	$(SiH_3)_2S$, $S(SiD_3)_2$	H. R. Linton and E. R. Nixon, *J. Chem. Phys.* **29**, 921 (1958); E. A. V. Ebsworth, R. Taylor and L. A. Woodward, *Trans. Faraday Soc.* **55**, 211 (1959).
		$(SiH_3)_2Se$, $(SiD_3)_2Se$	*Ibid.*
	10	$(CH_3)_2CO$,	G. Herzberg, *op. cit.*, p. 360.
		C_4H_6 (butadiene),[a]	
		C_4H_4NH (pyrrole),	
$C_{2v}(?)$		$C_2H_4(OH)_2$, $C_2H_4(CN)_2$	
		$C_4H_4N_2$ (pyrimidine)	L. N. Short and H. W. Thompson, *J. Chem. Soc.* **1952**, 168.
		C_4H_6 (cyclobutene)	R. C. Lord and D. G. Rea, *J. Am. Chem. Soc.* **79**, 2401 (1957).
		C_4D_6	
	11	$CH_3CH_2CH_3$	G. Herzberg, *op. cit.*, p. 359.
		C_5H_5N (pyridine)	G. Herzberg, *op. cit.*, p. 362; A. R. Katritzky, *J. Chem. Soc.* **1958**, 4162.
		C_5H_6 (cyclopentadiene)	G. Herzberg, *op. cit.*, p. 362.
$C_{2v}(?)$		C_4H_6O (cyclobutanone)	*Ibid.*; K. Frei and H. H. Gunthard, *J. Mol. Spectry.* **5**, 218 (1960).
		C_3F_8	W. F. Edgell, H. D. Mallory, and D. G. Weiblen, *J. Am. Chem. Soc.* **72**, 4856 (1950).
		$(CH_3)_2SiCl_2$	A. L. Smith, *J. Chem. Phys.* **21**, 1997 (1953).
		$(CH_3)_2SiH_2$	E. A. V. Ebsworth, M. Onyszchuk, and N. Sheppard, *J. Chem. Soc.* **1958**, 1453
	12	C_6HCl_5	G. Herzberg, *op. cit.*, p. 368.
C_{2v} (or D_{2h})		$C_6H_2Cl_4$	
C_{2v} (or D_{3h} or C_s)		$C_6H_4Br_2$, $C_6H_4Cl_2$	
$C_{2v}(?)$		*cis*-$CH_3C_2H_2CH_3$ (butene-2),	
$C_{2v}(?)$		$(CH_3CO)_2$, $(CH_3)_2C=NOH$,	
$C_{2v}(?)$		$C_2H_4(NH_2)_2$	
		C_6H_5F, C_6H_5Cl, C_6H_5Br, C_6H_5I	*Ibid.*; D. C. Smith, E. E. Ferguson, R. L. Hudson, and J. R. Nielsen, *J. Chem. Phys.* **21**, 1475 (1953); D. H. Whiffen, *J. Chem. Soc.* **1956**, 1350.

TABLE 3.8 *(continued)*

Chemical examples (continued)

Point Group	Number of atoms	Compounds	References
C_{2v}	12	m-$C_6H_4F_2$	G. Herzberg, *op. cit.*, p. 368; E. E. Ferguson, R. L. Collins, J. R. Nielsen, and D. C. Smith, *J. Chem. Phys.* **21**, 1470 (1953).
		p-C_6H_4FCl	G. Herzberg, *op. cit.*, p. 368; N. A. Narasimham, M. Z. El-Sabban, and J. R. Nielsen, *J. Chem. Phys.* **24**, 420 (1956).
		p-C_6H_4FBr, p-C_6H_4FI	*Ibid.*
		C_6H_5D, C_6HD_5	C. R. Bailey, C. K. Ingold, H. G. Poole, and C. L. Wilson, *J. Chem. Soc.* **1946**, 222.
		C_5H_5NO (pyridine 1-oxide)	A. R. Katritzky, *J. Chem. Soc.* **1958**, 4162.
$C_{2v}(?)$	13	C_5H_8 (cyclopentene)	C. W. Beckett, N. K. Freeman, and K. S. Pitzer, *J. Am. Chem. Soc.* **70**, 4227 (1948).
C_{2v}	15	$(CH_3)_2C_3H_4$ (1, 1-dimethyl-cyclopropane)	F. F. Cleveland, M. J. Murray, and W. S. Gallaway, *J. Chem. Phys.* **15**, 742 (1947).
		$C_5H_5NBCl_3$ (pyridine boron trichloride)	A. R. Katritzky, *J. Chem. Soc.* **1958**, 4162.
$C_{2v}(?)$		C_7H_8 (tropilidene)	M. V. Evans and R. C. Lord, *J. Am. Chem. Soc.* **82**, 1876 (1960).
	16	$(CH_3)_2NB_2H_5$, $(CH_3)_2HB_2D_5$	D. E. Mann, *J. Chem. Phys.* **22**, 70 (1954).
	25	$(C_6H_5)_2SnCl_2$	V. S. Griffiths and G. A. W. Derwish, *J. Mol. Spectry.* **5**, 148 (1960).

[a] *(C_{2v} or C_{2h} group.)*

Point Group C_{3v}

Symmetry elements

I, $2C_3(z)$, $3\sigma_v$

Symmetry types and characters

C_{3v}	I	$2C_3(z)$	$3\sigma_v$		
A_1	1	1	1	T_z	$\alpha_{xx} + \alpha_{yy}$, α_{zz}
A_2	1	1	-1	R_z	
E	2	-1	0	(T_x, T_y); (R_x, R_y)	$(\alpha_{xx} - \alpha_{yy}, \alpha_{xy})$, $(\alpha_{yz}, \alpha_{xz})$

TABLE 3.8 (*continued*)

Selection Rules (forbidden vibrations)

Infrared, A_2, $A_1 \times A_2$, A^n, (n odd)
Raman, A_2, $A_1 \times A_2$, A_2^n, (n odd)

Chemical examples

Point Group	Number of atoms	Compounds	References
C_{3v}	4	NH_3, ND_3	G. Herzberg, *op. cit.*, p. 294.
		PF_3, PBr_3, PCl_3, AsF_3, $AsBr_3$, $AsCl_3$, $SbCl_3$	*Ibid., p.* 297.
		PH_3, PD_3, AsH_3, AsD_3, ClO_3^-, BrO_3^-	*Ibid.,* p. 302.
		IO_3^-	*Ibid.*; W. E. Dasent and T. C. Waddington, *J. Chem. Soc.* **1960**, 2429.
		NF_3	G. Herzberg, *op. cit.*, p. 302; E. L. Pace and L. Pierce, *J. Chem. Phys.* **23**, 1248 (1955).
		$SbBr_3$	J. C. Evans, *J. Mol. Spectry.* **4**, 435 (1960).
	5	CH_3Cl	G. Herzberg, *op. cit.*, p. 312.
		CH_3Br, CH_3F, CH_3I, CD_3Cl, CD_3Br	G. Herzberg, *op. cit.*, p. 314.
		$CHCl_3$, $CDCl_3$	*Ibid.*, p. 316; T. G. Gibian and D. S. McKinney, *J. Am. Chem. Soc.* **73**, 1431 (1951).
		$HSiCl_3$	*Ibid.*
		$CHBr_3$, $CDBr_3$, CHI_3, $HSiBr_3$, $HGeCl_3$, $HGeBr_3$, $HSnCl_3$, $HSnBr_3$, $ClCBr_3$, $BrCCl_3$, $FCCl_3$, $BrSiCl_3$, $OPCl_3$	G. Herzberg, *op. cit.* p. 322.
		$ClCF_3$	*Ibid.*; H. W. Thompson and R. B. Temple, *J. Chem. Soc.* **1948**, 1422; H. H. Claassen, *J. Chem. Phys.* **22**, 50 (1954).
	5	CHF_3	*Ibid.*; G. Herzberg, *op. cit.*, p. 322.
		$CBrF_3$, CIF_3	*Ibid.*; W. F. Edgell and C. E. May, *J. Chem. Phys.* **22**, 1808 (1954).

TABLE 3.8 (*continued*)

Chemical examples (continued)

Point group	Number of atoms	Compounds	References
C_{3v}	5	$PSCl_3$	G. Herzberg, *op. cit.*, p. 322; G. Cilento, D. A. Ramsay, and R. N. Jones, *J. Am. Chem. Soc.* **71**, 2753 (1949).
		GeH_3Cl	R. C. Lord and C. M. Steese, *J. Chem. Phys.* **22**, 542 (1954).
		ClO_3F	D. R. Lide, Jr. and D. E. Mann, *J. Chem. Phys.* **25**, 1128 (1956).
		HPO_3^-	M. Tsuboi, *J. Am. Chem. Soc.* **79**, 1351 (1957).
		SO_3F^-	D. W. A. Sharp, *J. Chem. Soc.* **1957**, 3761.
		$VOCl_3$	F. A. Miller and L. R. Cousins, *J. Chem. Phys.* **26**, 329 (1957).
		OsO_3N^-	L. A. Woodward, J. A. Creighton, and K. A. Taylor, *Trans. Faraday Soc.* **56**, 1267 (1960).
		SO_3Cl^-, BF_3Cl^-	T. C. Waddington and F. Klanberg, *J. Chem. Soc.* **1960**, 2339.
	6	CCl_3CN	G. Herzberg, *op. cit.*, p. 336; W. F. Edgell and C. J. Ultee, *J. Chem. Phys.* **27**, 543 (1957); S. C. Wait, Jr. and G. J. Janz, *ibid.* **26**, 1555 (1957).
		CF_3CN	*Ibid.*
		CH_3CN, CH_3NC	H. W. Thompson and R. L. Williams, *Trans. Faraday Soc.* **48**, 502 (1952).
	6	H_3BCO	R. D. Cowan, *J. Chem. Phys.* **18**, 1101 (1950); G. W. Bethke and M. K. Wilson, *ibid.* **26**, 1118 (1957); R. C. Taylor, *ibid.* **26**, 1131 (1957).
	7	$CH_3C \equiv CCl$, $CH_3C \equiv CBr$, $CH_3C \equiv CI$	G. Herzberg, *op. cit.*, p. 342.
	8	CH_3-CCl_3, CH_3-CF_3	G. Herzberg, *op. cit.*, p. 350.
		CCl_3-CF_3	*Ibid.*; J. R. Nielsen, C. Y. Liang, R. M. Smith, and D. C. Smith, *J. Chem. Phys.* **21**, 383 (1953).
		CH_3SiCl_3	A. L. Smith, *J. Phys. Chem.* **21**, 1997 (1953).

TABLE 3.8 *(continued)*

Chemical examples (continued)

Point group	Number of atoms	Compounds	References
C_{3v}	8	CH_3SiF_3	R. L. Collins and J. R. Nielsen, *J. Chem. Phys.* **23**, 351 (1955).
	13	$N(CH_3)_3$	S. H. Bauer and M. Blander, *J. Mol. Spectry.* **3**, 132 (1959).
	14	$(CH_3)_3CCl$, $(CH_3)_3CBr$, $(CH_3)_3CI$	N. Sheppard, *Trans. Faraday Soc.* **46**, 527 (1950).
		$(CH_3)_3SiCl$	A. L. Smith, *J. Phys. Chem.* **21**, 1997 (1953).
	15	$(C_6H_5)SnCl_3$	V. S. Griffiths and G. A. W. Derwish, *J. Mol. Spectry.* **5**, 148 (1960).
	16	$CH_3C(CH_3)_2CCH$	N. Sheppard, *J. Chem. Phys.* **17**, 455 (1949).
	17	C_7H_{10} (nortricyclene)	E. R. Lippincott, *J. Am. Chem. Soc.* **73**, 2001 (1951).
$C_{3v}(?)$	31	$[Co(NH_3)_5SO_4]Br$	K. Nakamoto, J. Fujita, S. Tanaka, and M. Kobayashi, *J. Am. Chem. Soc.* **79**. 4904 (1957).
	35	$(C_6H_5)_3SnCl$	V. S. Griffiths and G. A. W. Derwish, *J. Mol. Spectry.* **5**, 148 (1960).

Point Group C_{4v}

Symmetry elements

I, $2C_4(z)$, $C_4^2 \equiv C_2''$, $2\sigma_v$, $2\sigma_d$

Symmetry types and characters

C_{4v}	I	$2C_4(z)$	$C_4^2 \equiv C_2''$	$2\sigma_v$	$2\sigma_d$		
A_1	1	1	1	1	1	T_z	$\alpha_{xx} + \alpha_{yy}$, α_{zz}
A_2	1	1	1	−1	−1	R_z	
B_1	1	−1	1	1	−1		$\alpha_{xx} - \alpha_{yy}$
B_2	1	−1	1	−1	1		α_{xy}
E	2	0	−2	0	0	(T_x, T_y); (R_x, R_y),	$(\alpha_{yz}, \alpha_{xz})$

TABLE 3.8 (*continued*)

Selection rules (forbidden vibrations)

Infrared	Raman
A_2, B_1, B_2, $A_1 \times A_2$, $A_1 \times B_1$, $A_1 \times B_2$, $A_2 \times B_1$, $A_2 \times B_2$, $B_1 \times B_2$, $A_2^n(n$ odd$)$, B_1^n (n odd), $B_n(n$ odd$)$	A_2, $A_1 \times A_2$, $B_1 \times B_2$, $A_2^n(n$ odd$)$

Chemical examples

Point group	Number of atoms	Compounds	References
$C_{4v}($?$)$ ($?$)	6	$SbCl_5$ IF_5	G. Herzberg, *op. cit.*, p. 336. R. C. Lord, M. A. Lynch, Jr., W. C. Schumb, and E. J. Slowinski, Jr., *J. Am. Chem. Soc.* **72**, 522 (1950).
		BrF_5	C. V. Stephenson and E. A. Jones, *J. Chem. Phys.* **20**, 1830 (1952).
	7	SF_5Cl	L. H. Cross, H. L. Roberts, P. Goggin, and L. A. Woodward, *Trans. Faraday Soc.* **56**, 945 (1960).
	11	$Fe(CO)_5$	M. F. O'Dwyer, *J. Mol. Spectry.* **2**, 144 (1958).
	14	B_5H_9, B_5D_9	H. J. Hrostowski and G. C. Pimentel, *J. Am. Chem. Soc.* **76**, 998 (1954).

TABLE 3.8 (continued)

Point Group $C_{\infty v}$

Symmetry elements

$I,\ 2C_{\infty}^{\varphi},\ 2C_{\infty}^{2\varphi},\ 2C_{\infty}^{3\varphi},\ \cdots \infty\sigma_v$

Symmetry types and characters

$C_{\infty v}$	I	$2C_{\infty}^{\varphi}$	$2C_{\infty}^{2\varphi}$	$2C_{\infty}^{3\varphi}$	$\cdots$	$\infty\sigma_v$		
$A_1 \equiv \Sigma^+$	1	1	1	1	$\cdots$	1	T_z	$\alpha_{xx}+\alpha_{yy},\ \alpha_{zz}$
$A_2 \equiv \Sigma^-$	1	1	1	1	$\cdots$	-1	R_z	
$E_1 \equiv \Pi$	2	$2\cos\varphi$	$2\cos 2\varphi$	$2\cos 3\varphi$	$\cdots$	0	$(T_x, T_y);$ (R_x, R_y)	$(\alpha_{yz},\ \alpha_{xz})$
$E_2 \equiv \Delta$	2	$2\cos 2\varphi$	$2\cos 2\cdot 2\varphi$	$2\cos 3\cdot 2\varphi$	$\cdots$	0		$(\alpha_{xx}-\alpha_{yy},\ \alpha_{xy})$
$E_3 \equiv \Phi$	2	$2\cos 3\varphi$	$2\cos 2\cdot 3\varphi$	$2\cos 3\cdot 3\varphi$	$\cdots$	0		
$\cdots$			$\cdots$	$\cdots$		$\cdots$		

Selection rules (forbidden vibrations) (See reference 9 for selection rules for combination bands and overtones)

Infrared, $\Sigma^-,\ \Delta,\ \Phi$

Raman, $\Sigma^-,\ \Phi$

Chemical examples

Point group	Number of atoms	Compounds	References
$C_{\infty v}$	3	HCN, DCN OCS, ClCN, BrCN, ICN, OCN⁻, SCN⁻, SeCN⁻, HgClBr, HgClI, HgBrI (HF₂)⁻ HC≡CCN	G. Herzberg, *op. cit.*, p. 279. Ibid., p. 287.
$C_{\infty v}(?)$			*Ibid.* G. C. Turrell W. D. Jones, and A. Maki, *J. Chem. Phys.* **26**, 1544 (1957).

TABLE 3.8 (*continued*)

Point Group C_{2h}

Symmetry elements

I, $C_2(z)$, $\sigma_h(xy)$, i

Symmetry types and characters

C_{2h}	I	$C_2(z)$	$\sigma_h(xy)$	i		
A_g	1	1	1	1	R_z	α_{xx}, α_{yy}, α_{zz}, α_{xy}
A_u	1	1	-1	-1	T_z	
B_g	1	-1	-1	1	R_x ; R_y	α_{yz}, α_{zx}
B_u	1	-1	1	-1	T_x ; T_y	

Selection rules (forbidden vibrations)

Infrared	Raman
A_g, B_g, $A_g \times A_g$, $A_g \times B_g$, $B_g \times B_g$, $A_u \times A_u$, $A_u \times B_u$, $B_u \times B_u$, A_g^n, B_g^n, A_u^n, (n even), B_u^n, (n even)	A_u, B_u, $A_g \times A_u$, $A_g \times B_u$, $B_g \times A_u$, $B_g \times B_u$, A_u^n, (n odd), B_u^n, (n odd)

Chemical examples

Point group	Number of atoms	Compounds	References
C_{2h}	4	$(HF)_2$	G. E. Evans and G. Glockler, *J. Chem. Phys.* **16**, 324 (1948).
	5	C_3O_2 (carbon suboxide)	G. Herzberg, *op. cit.*, p. 303; H. D. Rix, *J. Chem. Phys.*, **22**, 429 (1954).
$C_{2h}(?)$	6	$C_2H_2O_2$ (glyoxal), $C_2O_2Cl_2$ (oxalyl chloride), *trans*-$C_2H_2Br_2$, $C_2H_2I_2$	G. Herzberg, *op. cit.*, p. 336.
	8	*trans*-CH_2Br-CH_2Br	*Ibid.*, p. 350; J. K. Brown and N. Sheppard, *Trans. Faraday Soc.* **48**, 128 (1952).
		trans-CH_2Cl-CH_2Cl	*Ibid.*; G. Herzberg, *op. cit.*, p. 346.
		trans-CH_2I-CH_2I, *trans*-$C_2F_4Cl_2$, $C_2F_4Br_2$,	G. Herzberg, *op. cit.*, p. 350.
C_{2h} (and C_2 ?)		$CFCl_2CFCl_2$, $NCHC=CHCN$ *trans*-$Br_2CHCHBr_2$	*Ibid.*; R. E. Kagarise and D. H. Rank, *Trans. Faraday Soc.* **48**, 394 (1952).
		trans-$Cl_2CHCHCl_2$	*Ibid.*

TABLE 3.8 (*continued*)

Chemical examples (continued)

Point group	Number of atoms	compounds	References
		trans-F_2HCCHF_2	P. Klaboe and J. R. Nielsen, *J. Chem. Phys.* **32**, 899 (1960).
		trans-FH_2CCH_2F	*Ibid.* **33**, 1764 (1960).
C_{2h}	10	*trans*-$C_4H_4Cl_2$ (2,3-dichloro-1, 3-butadiene)	G. J. Szasz and N. Sheppard, *Trans. Faraday Soc.* **49**, 358 (1953).
		trans-$NCCH_2CH_2CN$	W. E. Fitzgerald and G. J. Janz, *J. Mol. Spectry.* **1**, 49 (1957).
C_{2h} (or C_{2v}?)	12	*trans*-$CH_3C_2H_2CH_3$ (butene−2)	G. Herzberg, *op. cit.*, p. 368.
	14	$\overline{OCH_2CH_2OCH_2CH_2}$ (*p*-dioxane)	F. E. Malherbe and H. J. Bernstein, *J. Am. Chem. Soc.* **74**, 4408 (1952).
	18	*trans*-$C_6H_{10}Br_2$ (1,4-dibromocyclohexane), *trans*-$C_6H_{10}Cl_2$	K. Kozima and T. Yoshino, *J. Am. Chem. Soc.* **75**, 166 (1953).
		trans-C_8H_{10} (1, 3, 5, 7-octatetraene)	E. R. Lippincott, W. R. Feairheller, Jr. and C. E. White, *J. Am. Chem. Soc.* **81**, 1316 (1959).

Point Group C_{3h}

Symmetry elements

I, C_3, σ_h, S_3

Symmetry types and characters

C_{3h}	I	C_3	σ_h	S_3		
A'	1	1	1	1	R_z	$\alpha_{xx} + \alpha_{yy}, \ \alpha_{zz}$
A''	1	1	−1	−1	T_z	
E'	2	−1	2	−1	T_x, T_y	$(\alpha_{xx} - \alpha_{yy}, \alpha_{xy})$
E''	2	−1	−2	1	R_x, R_y	$(\alpha_{yz}, \alpha_{xz})$

Selection rules (Forbidden vibrations)

Infrared	Raman
$A', E'', A' \times A', A' \times E'',$ $A'' \times A'', A'' \times E', A'^n, A''^n$ (*n* even)	$A'', A' \times A'', A''^n$ (*n* odd)

TABLE 3.8 (continued)

Chemical examples

Point group	Number of atoms	Compounds	References
C_{3h}	7	H_3BO_3	G. Herzberg, *op. cit.*, p. 342; D. E. Bethell and N. Sheppard, *Trans. Faraday Soc.* **51**, 9 (1955); R. R. Servoss and H. M. Clark, *J. Chem. Phys.* **26**, 1175 (1950).
	12	$(HBO_2)_3$	D. White, D. E. Mann, P. N. Walsh, and A. Sommer, *J. Chem. Phys.* **32**, 488 (1960).
	16	$B(OCH_3)_3$	R. R. Servoss and H. M. Clark, *J. Chem. Phys.* **26**, 1179 (1957).

Point Group D_{2d} or V_d

Symmetry elements

$$I,\ 2S_4(z),\ S_4^2 \equiv C_2'',\ 2C_2,\ 2\sigma_d$$

Symmetry types and characters

$D_{2d} \equiv V_d$	I	$2S_4(z)$	$S_4^2 \equiv C_2''$	$2C_2$	$2\sigma_d$		
A_1	1	1	1	1	1		$\alpha_{xx} + \alpha_{yy},\ \alpha_{zz}$
A_2	1	1	1	-1	-1	R_z	
B_1	1	-1	1	1	-1		$\alpha_{xx} - \alpha_{yy}$
B_2	1	-1	1	-1	1	T_z	α_{xy}
E	2	0	-2	0	0	$(T_x, T_y); (R_x, R_y)$	$(\alpha_{yz}, \alpha_{xz})$

Selection rules (forbidden vibrations)

Infrared	Raman
A_1, A_2, B_1, $A_1 \times A_1$, $A_1 \times A_2$, $A_1 \times B_1$, $A_2 \times A_2$, $A_2 \times B_2$, $B_1 \times B_1$, $B_1 \times B_2$, $B_2 \times B_2$, A_1^n, A_2^n, B_1^n, B_2^n, (n even)	A_2, $A_1 \times A_2$, $B_1 \times B_2$, A_2^n, (n odd)

Chemical examples

Point group	Number of atoms	Compounds	References
D_{2d} (V_d)	6	B_2Cl_4	D. E. Mann and L. Fano, *J. Chem. Phys.* **26**. 1665 (1957).

TABLE 3.8 (continued)

Chemical examples

Point group	Number of atoms	Compounds	References
D_{2d} (V_d)	7	$H_2C=C=CH_2$	R. C. Lord and P. Venkateswarlu, *J. Chem. Phys.* **20**, 1237 (1952).
	8	N_4S_4	E. R. Lippincott and M. C. Tobin, *J. Chem. Phys.* **21**, 1559 (1953).
D_{2d} (or D_{4h})	12	C_4H_8 (cyclobutane)	G. Herzberg, *op. cit.*, p. 368; G. W. Rathjens, Jr., N. K. Freeman, W. D. Gwinn, and K. S. Pitzer, *J. Am. Chem. Soc.* **75**, 5634 (1953).
	13	C_5H_8 (spiropentane)	F. F. Cleveland, M. J. Murray, and W. S. Gallaway, *J. Chem. Phys.* **15**, 742 (1947).
	15	(see structure below) (2,6-dioxaspiro [3.3] heptane)	S. C. Sirkar, F. L. Voelz, and F. F. Cleveland, *J. Chem. Phys.* **23**, 1684 (1955).
D_{2d} (or D_{4h})	16	C_8H_8 (cyclo-octatetraene)	W. B. Person, G. C. Pimentel, and K. S. Pitzer, *J. Am. Chem. Soc.* **74**, 3437 (1952).
D_{2d} (or D_{4h})		$(PNCl_2)_4$	L. W. Daasch, *J. Am. Chem. Soc.* **76**, 3403 (1954).
	27	$Fe_3(CO)_{12}$	R. K. Sheline, *J. Am. Chem. Soc.* **73**, 1615 (1951).

Structure for atom 15:

$$
\begin{array}{ccc}
& CH_2 \qquad CH_2 & \\
& \diagup \quad \diagdown \diagup \quad \diagdown & \\
O & \qquad C \qquad & O \\
& \diagdown \quad \diagup \diagdown \quad \diagup & \\
& CH_2 \qquad CH_2 &
\end{array}
$$

Point Group D_{3d} or S_{6v}

Symmetry elements

$$I,\ 2S_6(z),\ 2S_6^2 \equiv 2C_3,\ S_6^3 \equiv S_2 \equiv i,\ 3C_2,\ 3\sigma_d$$

Symmetry types and characters

$D_{3d} \equiv S_{6v}$	I	$2S_6(z)$	$2S_6^2 \equiv 2C_3$	$S_6^3 \equiv S_2 \equiv i$	$3C_2$	$3\sigma_d$		
A_{1g}*	1	1	1	1	1	1		$\alpha_{xx} + \alpha_{yy}, \alpha_{zz}$
A_{1u}	1	−1	1	−1	1	−1		
A_{2g}	1	1	1	1	−1	−1	R_z	
A_{2u}	1	−1	1	−1	−1	1	T_z	
E_g	2	−1	−1	2	0	0	(R_x, R_y)	$(\alpha_{xx} - \alpha_{yy}, \alpha_{xy})$,
E_u	2	1	−1	−2	0	0	(T_x, T_y)	$(\alpha_{yz}, \alpha_{xz})$

TABLE 3.8 (*continued*)

Selection rules (forbidden vibrations)

Infrared	Raman
A_{1g}, A_{1u}, A_{2g}, E_g, $A_{1g} \times A_{1g}$, $A_{1g} \times A_{1u}$, $A_{1g} \times A_{2g}$, $A_{1g} \times E_g$, $A_{1u} \times A_{1u}$, $A_{1u} \times A_{2u}$, $A_{1u} \times E_u$, $A_{2g} \times A_{2g}$, $A_{2g} \times A_{2u}$, $A_{2g} \times E_g$, $A_{2u} \times A_{2u}$, $A_{2u} \times E_u$, $E_g \times E_g$, $E_u \times E_u$, A_{1g}^n, A_{1u}^n, A_{2g}^n, A_{2u}^n (n even), E_g^n, E_u^2, E_u^4, ...	A_{1u}, A_{2g}, A_{2u}, E_u, $A_{1g} \times A_{1u}$, $A_{1g} \times A_{2g}$, $A_{1g} \times A_{2u}$, $A_{1g} \times E_u$, $A_{1u} \times A_{2g}$, $A_{1u} \times A_{2u}$, $A_{1u} \times E_g$, $A_{2g} \times A_{2u}$, $A_{2g} \times E_u$, $A_{2u} \times E_g$, $E_g \times E_u$, A_{1u}^n, (n odd), A_{2g}^n (n odd), A_{2u}^n (n odd), E_u^3, E_u^5, ...

Chemical examples

Point group	Number of atoms	Compounds	References
D_{3d} (or D_{3h})	8	C_2D_6	G. Herzberg, *op. cit.*, p. 342.
		C_2H_6	*Ibid.*; L. G. Smith, *J. Chem. Phys.* 17, 139 (1949); D. C. Smith, R. A. Saunders, J. R. Nielsen, and E. E. Ferguson, *ibid.* 20, 847 (1952).
		Si_2H_6, Si_2D_6	G. Herzberg, *op. cit.*, p. 350; G.W. Bethke and M.K. Wilson, *J. Chem. Phys.* 26, 1107 (1957).
D_{3d} (or D_{3h})		C_2Cl_6, C_2Br_6, Si_2Cl_6, B_2H_6, $CH_3NH_3^+$, $CH_3ND_3^+$, $^+H_3N-NH_3^+$, $^+D_3N-ND_3^+$	G. Herzberg, *op. cit.*, p. 350.
	9	$(SiD_3)_2O$	R. C. Lord, D. W. Robinson, and W. C. Schumb, *J. Am. Chem. Soc.* 78, 1327 (1956).
		$(SiH_3)_2O$	*Ibid.*; J. R. Aronson, R. C. Lord, and D. W. Robinson, *J. Chem. Phys.* 33, 1004 (1960).
	10	$CH_3C \equiv CCH_3$ $CF_3C \equiv CCF_3$	R. P. Bauman, *J. Chem. Phys.* 24, 13 (1956).
		$F_3C-C \equiv C-CF_3$	F. A. Miller and R. P. Bauman, *J. Chem. Phys.* 22, 1544 (1954).
	18	C_6H_{12} (cyclohexane)	C. W. Beckett, K. S. Pitzer, and R. Spitzer, *J. Am. Chem. Soc.* 69, 2488 (1947).

TABLE 3.8 (continued)

Point Group D_{4d} or S_{8v}

Symmetry elements

$I,\ 2S_8(z),\ 2S_8^2 \equiv 2C_4,\ 2S_8^3,\ S_8^4 \equiv C_2'',\ 4C_2,\ 4\sigma_d$

Symmetry types and characters

$D_{4d} \equiv S_{8v}$	I	$2S_8(z)$	$2S_8^2 \equiv 2C_4$	$2S_8^3$	$S_8^4 \equiv C_2$	$4C_2$	$4\sigma_d$		
A_1	1	1	1	1	1	1	1		$\alpha_{xx} + \alpha_{yy},\ \alpha_{zz}$
A_2	1	1	1	1	1	-1	-1	R_z	
B_1	1	-1	1	-1	1	1	-1		
B_2	1	-1	1	-1	1	-1	1	T_z	
E_1	2	$\sqrt{2}$	0	$-\sqrt{2}$	-2	0	0	(T_x, T_y)	
E_2	2	0	-2	0	2	0	0		$(\alpha_{xx} - \alpha_{yy},\ \alpha_{xy})$
E_3	2	$-\sqrt{2}$	0	$\sqrt{2}$	-2	0	0	(R_x, R_y)	$(\alpha_{yz},\ \alpha_{zz})$

Selection rules (forbidden vibrations)

Infrared

$A_1,\ A_2,\ B_1,\ E_2,\ E_3,\ A_1 \times A_2,\ A_1 \times B_1,\ A_1 \times E_2,\ A_1 \times E_3,$
$A_2 \times B_2,\ A_2 \times E_2,\ A_2 \times E_3,\ B_1 \times B_2,\ B_1 \times E_1,\ B_1 \times E_2,$
$B_2 \times E_1,\ B_2 \times E_2,\ A_1^n\ (n\ \text{even}),\ A_2^n\ (n\ \text{even}),\ B_1^n\ (n\ \text{even}),$
$B_2^n\ (n\ \text{even}),\ E_1^n\ (n\ \text{even}),\ E_3^n\ (n\ \text{even})$

Raman

$A_2,\ B_1,\ B_2,\ E_1,\ A_1 \times B_1,\ A_1 \times B_2,\ E_1,\ A_1 \times E_1,\ A_2 \times B_1,\ A_2 \times E_1,\ A_2 \times B_2,\ A_1 \times E_1,\ A_2 \times B_1,$
$A_2 \times B_2,\ A_2 \times E_1,\ B_1 \times B_2,\ B_1 \times E_3,\ B_2 \times E_3,\ A_2^n\ (n\ \text{odd}),\ A_2^n\ (n\ \text{odd}),$
$B_1^n\ (n\ \text{odd}),\ B_2^n\ (n\ \text{odd}),\ E_1^n\ (n\ \text{odd})$

Chemical examples

Point group	Number of atoms	Compounds	References
D_{4d}	8	S_8	G. Herzberg, *op. cit.*, p. 350.
	12	$S_2F_{10},\ Te_2F_{10}$	R.E. Dodd, L. A. Woodward, and H. L. Roberts, *Trans. Faraday Soc.* **53**, 1545 (1957).

TABLE 3.8 *(continued)*

Point Group D_{2h} or V_h

Symmetry elements

I, $\sigma(xy)$, $\sigma(xz)$, $\sigma(yz)$, i, $C_2(z)$, $C_2(y)$, $C_2(x)$

Symmetry types and characters

$D_{2h} \equiv V_h$	I	$\sigma(xy)$	$\sigma(xz)$	$\sigma(yz)$	i	$C_2(z)$	$C_2(y)$	$C_2(x)$		
A_g	1	1	1	1	1	1	1	1		$\alpha_{xx}, \alpha_{yy}, \alpha_{zz}$
A_u	1	-1	-1	-1	-1	1	1	1		
B_{1g}	1	1	-1	-1	1	1	-1	-1	R_z	α_{xy}
B_{1u}	1	-1	1	1	-1	1	-1	-1	T_z	
B_{2g}	1	-1	1	-1	1	-1	1	-1	R_y	α_{xz}
B_{2u}	1	1	-1	1	-1	-1	1	-1	T_y	
B_{3g}	1	-1	-1	1	1	-1	-1	1	R_x	α_{yz}
B_{3u}	1	1	1	-1	-1	-1	-1	1	T_x	

Selection rules (forbidden vibrations)

<table>
<tr><th>Infrared</th><th>Raman</th></tr>
<tr><td>

A_{1g}, A_{1u}, B_{1g}, B_{2g}, B_{3g}, $A_{1g} \times A_{1g}$,
$A_{1g} \times A_{1u}$, $A_{1g} \times B_{1g}$, $A_{1g} \times B_{2g}$,
$A_{1g} \times B_{3g}$, $A_{1u} \times A_{1u}$, $A_{1u} \times B_{1g}$,
$A_{1u} \times B_{1u}$, $A_{1u} \times B_{2u}$, $A_{1u} \times B_{3u}$,
$B_{1g} \times B_{1g}$, $B_{1g} \times B_{1u}$, $B_{1g} \times B_{2g}$,
$B_{1g} \times B_{2u}$, $B_{1g} \times B_{3g}$, $B_{1u} \times B_{1u}$,
$B_{1u} \times B_{2u}$, $B_{1u} \times B_{3u}$, $B_{2g} \times B_{2g}$,
$B_{2g} \times B_{3g}$, $B_{2u} \times B_{2u}$, $B_{2u} \times B_{3u}$,
$B_{3g} \times B_{3g}$, $B_{3u} \times B_{3u}$, A_{1g}^n, A_{1u}^n,
B_{1g}^n, B_{1u}^n (n even), B_{2g}^n, B_{2u}^n (n even),
B_{3g}^n, B_{3u}^n (n even)

</td><td>

A_{1u}, B_{1u}, B_{2u}, B_{3u}, $A_{1g} \times A_{1u}$,
$A_{1g} \times B_{1u}$, $A_{1g} \times B_{2u}$, $A_{1g} \times B_{3u}$,
$A_{1u} \times B_{1g}$, $A_{1u} \times B_{2g}$, $A_{1u} \times B_{3g}$,
$B_{1g} \times B_{1u}$, $B_{1g} \times B_{2u}$, $B_{1g} \times B_{3u}$,
$B_{1u} \times B_{2g}$, $B_{1u} \times B_{3g}$, $B_{2g} \times B_{2u}$,
$B_{2g} \times B_{3u}$, $B_{2u} \times B_{3g}$, $B_{3g} \times B_{3u}$,
A_{1u}^n (n odd), B_{1u}^n (n odd), B_{2u}^n (n odd),
B_{3u}^n (n odd)

</td></tr>
</table>

Chemical examples

Point group	Number of atoms	Compounds	References
D_{2h} (V_h)	6	$F_2C = CF_2$	J. R. Nielsen, H. H. Claassen, and D. C. Smith, *J. Chem. Phys.* **18**, 812 (1950).
		$Br_2C = CBr_2$	D. E. Mann, J. H. Meal, and E. K. Plyler, *J. Chem. Phys.* **24**, 1018 (1956).
$D_{2h}(?)$	8	B_2H_6	W. E. Anderson and E. F. Barker, *J. Chem. Phys.* **18**, 698 (1950).
	12	$1,4\text{-}C_6H_4D_2$, $1,2,4,5\text{-}C_6H_2D_4$	C. R. Bailey, C. K. Ingold, H. G. Poole, and C. L. Wilson, *J. Chem. Soc.* **1946**, 222.
		$1,4\text{-}C_6H_4F_2$	E. E. Ferguson, R. L. Hudson, J. R. Nielsen, and D. C. Smith, *J. Chem. Phys.* **21**, 1457 (1953).

TABLE 3.8 (*continued*)

Chemical examples (continued)

Point group	Number of atoms	Compounds	References
D_{2h}	15	p-$FC_6H_4CH_3$	*Ibid.*, 1736 (1953).
		$1,4$-$C_6H_4(CF_3)_2$	E. E. Ferguson, L. Mikkelson, J. R. Nielsen, and D. C. Smith, *J. Chem. Phys.* **21**, 1731 (1953),
	20	$C_{12}H_8$ (naphthalene) $C_{12}D_8$	E. R. Lippincott and E. J, O'Reilly, Jr., *J. Chem. Phys.* **23**, 238 (1955).

Point Group D_{3h}

Symmetry elements

I, $2C_3(z)$, $3C_2$, σ_h, $2S_3$, $3\sigma_v$

Symmetry types and characters[a]

D_{3h}	I	$2C_3(z)$	$3C_2$	σ_h	$2S_3$	$3\sigma_v$		
A_1'	1	1	1	1	1	1		$\alpha_{xx} + \alpha_{yy}$, α_{zz}
A_1''	1	1	1	-1	-1	-1		
A_2'	1	1	-1	1	1	-1	R_z	
A_2''	1	1	-1	-1	-1	1	T_z	
E'	2	-1	0	2	-1	0	(T_x, T_y)	$(\alpha_{xx} - \alpha_{yy}, \alpha_{xy})$
E''	2	-1	0	-2	1	0	(R_x, R_y)	$(\alpha_{yz}, \alpha_{xz})$

[a] For D_{3h}' (free rotation), A_1', A_1'', A_2', A_2'', E', and E'' are replaced by A_1, $\bar{A}_1$, A_2, $\bar{A}_2$, E, and $\bar{E}$, respectively. The selection rules are the same.

Selection rules (forbidden vibrations)

Infrared	Raman
A_1', A_2', A_1'', E'', $A_1' \times A_1'$, $A_1' \times A_2'$, $A_1' \times A_1''$, $A_1' \times E''$, $A_2' \times A_2'$, $A_2' \times A_2''$, $A_2' \times E''$, $A_1'' \times A_1''$, $A_1'' \times A_2''$, $A_1'' \times E'$, $A_2'' \times A_2''$, $A_2'' \times E'$, $(A_1')^n$, $(A_2')^n$, $(A_1'')^n$, $(A_2'')^n$ (n even)	A_2', A_1'', A_2'', $A_1' \times A_2'$, $A_1' \times A_1''$, $A_1' \times A_2''$, $A_2' \times A_1''$, $A_2' \times A_2''$, $A_1'' \times A_2''$, $(A_2')^n$ (n odd), $(A_1'')^n$ (n odd), $(A_2'')^n$ (n odd)

TABLE 3.8 (*continued*)

Chemical examples

Point group	Number of atoms	Compounds	References
D_{3h}	4	BF_3	G. Herzberg, *op. cit.*, p. 298.
		BCl_3, BBr_3, SO_3, NO_3^-	*Ibid.*, p. 302.
		$CO_3^=$	*Ibid.*; B. M. Gatehouse, S. E. Livingstone, and R. S. Nyholm, *J. Chem. Soc.* **1958**, 3137.
	6	PCl_5	G. Herzberg, *op. cit.*, p. 336; J. K. Wilmshurst and H. J. Bernstein, *J. Chem. Phys.* **27**, 661 (1957).
		$SbCl_5$	J. K. Wilmshurst, *J. Mol. Spectry.* **5**, 343 (1960).
D_{3h} (or D_{3d})	8	C_2H_6,[a] C_2D_6	G. Herzberg, *op. cit.*, p. 342.
D_{3h} (or D_{3d})		C_2Cl_6, C_2Br_6, Si_2H_6,[a] Si_2Cl_6, B_2H_6, $CH_3NH_3^+$, $CH_3ND_3^+$, $^+H_3N-NH_3^+$, $^+D_3N-ND_3^+$	*Ibid.*, p. 350.
$D_{3h}(?)$	9	$(CH_3)_2Zn$, $(CH_3)_2Hg^a$	*Ibid.*, p. 356.
		C_3H_6 (cyclopropane) C_3D_6	*Ibid.*, p. 352; A. W. Baker and R. C. Lord, *J. Chem. Phys.* **23**, 1636 (1955).
$D_{3h}(?)$	10	$C(NH_2)_3^+$, $C(ND_2)_3^+$	G. Herzberg, *op. cit.*, p. 360; C. L. Angell, N. Sheppard, A. Yamaguchi, T. Shimanouchi, T. Miyazawa, and S. Mizushima, *Trans. Faraday Soc.* **53**, 589 (1957).
$D_{3h}(?)$	11	$Fe(CO)_5$	R. K. Sheline and K. S. Pitzer, *J. Am. Chem. Soc.* **72**, 1107 (1950).
	12	$B_3N_3H_6$	G. Herzberg, *op. cit.*, p. 368.
D_{3h} (or C_{2v} or C_s)		$C_6H_3Cl_3$, $C_6H_3Br_3$, etc.	*Ibid.*
		$1,3,5-C_6H_3D_3$	C. R. Bailey, C. K. Ingold, H. G. Poole, and C. L. Wilson, *J. Chem. Soc.* **1946**, 222.
$D_{3h}(?)$	12	$(PNCl_2)_3$	G. Herzberg, *op. cit.*, p. 368; L. W. Daasch, *J. Am. Chem. Soc.* **76**, 3403 (1954).

TABLE 3.8 (*continued*)

Chemical examples (continued)

Point group	Number of atoms	Compounds	References
D_{3h} (cont'd)	15	$C_3N_6H_6$ (melamine), $C_3N_6D_6$	W. J. Jones and W. J. Orville-Thomas, *Trans. Faraday Soc.* **55**, 203 (1959).
	16	$Al(BH_4)_3$	W. C. Price, *J. Chem. Phys.* **17**, 1044 (1949).
	20	$Fe_2(CO)_9$	R. K. Sheline and K. S. Pitzer, *J. Am. Chem. Soc.* **72**, 1107 (1950).
	22	C_8H_{14} [bicyclo-(2,2,2)-octane]	J. J. Macfarlane and I. G. Ross, *J. Chem. Soc.* **1960**, 4169.
D_{3h}'	8	$Cl_3Si-SiCl_3$	M. Katayama, T. Simanouti, Y. Morino, and S. Mizushima, *J. Chem. Phys.* **18**, 506 (1950).
	9	H_3CHgCH_3 , H_3CZnCH_3	H. S. Gutowsky, *J. Chem. Phys.* **17**, 128 (1949).
		H_3CCdCH_3	H. S. Gutowsky, *J. Am. Chem. Soc.* **71**, 3194 (1949).
	12	$H_3C-C\equiv C-C\equiv C-CH_3$	F. F. Cleveland, K. W. Greenlee, and E. E. Bell, *J. Chem. Phys.* **18**, 355 (1950); S. M. Ferigle, F. F. Cleveland, and A. G. Meister, *J. Chem. Phys.* **20**, 1928 (1952).

[a] See point group D_{3d} for additional references.

Point Group D_{4h}

Symmetry elements

I, $2C_4(z)$, $C_4^2\,C_2''$, $2C_2$, $2C_2'$, σ_h , $2\sigma_v$, $2\sigma_d$, $2S_4$, S_2 , i

Symmetry types and characters

D_{4h}	I	$2C_4(z)$	C_2''	$2C_2$	$2C_2'$	σ_h	$2\sigma_v$	$2\sigma_d$	$2S_4$	i		
A_{1g}	1	1	1	1	1	1	1	1	1	1		$\alpha_{xx}+\alpha_{yy}$, α_{zz}
A_{1u}	1	1	1	1	1	−1	−1	−1	−1	−1		
A_{2g}	1	1	1	−1	−1	1	−1	−1	1	1	R_z	
A_{2u}	1	1	1	−1	−1	−1	1	1	−1	−1	T_z	
B_{1g}	1	−1	1	1	−1	1	1	−1	−1	1		$\alpha_{xx}-\alpha_{yy}$
B_{1u}	1	−1	1	1	−1	−1	−1	1	1	−1		
B_{2g}	1	−1	1	−1	1	1	−1	1	−1	1		α_{xy}
B_{2u}	1	−1	1	−1	1	−1	1	−1	1	−1		
E_g	2	0	−2	0	0	−2	0	0	0	2	(R_x , R_y)	$(\alpha_{yz} , \alpha_{xz})$
E_u	2	0	−2	0	0	2	0	0	0	−2	(T_x , T_y)	

TABLE 3.8 (*continued*)

Selection rules (forbidden vibrations)

Infrared	Raman

A_{1g}, A_{1u}, A_{2g}, B_{1g}, B_{1u}, B_{2g}, B_{2u}, E_g, $A_{1g} \times A_{1g}$, $A_{1g} \times A_{1u}$, $A_{1g} \times A_{2g}$, $A_{1g} \times B_{1g}$, $A_{1g} \times B_{1u}$, $A_{1g} \times B_{2g}$, $A_{1g} \times B_{2u}$, $A_{1g} \times E_g$, $A_{1u} \times A_{1u}$, $A_{1u} \times A_{2u}$, $A_{1u} \times B_{1g}$, $A_{1u} \times B_{1u}$, $A_{1u} \times B_{2g}$, $A_{1u} \times E_u$, $A_{2g} \times A_{2g}$, $A_{2g} \times A_{2u}$, $A_{2g} \times B_{1u}$, $A_{2g} \times B_{2g}$, $A_{2g} \times B_{2u}$, $A_{2g} \times E_g$, $A_{2u} \times A_{2u}$, $A_{2u} \times B_{1g}$, $A_{2u} \times B_{1u}$, $A_{2u} \times B_{2g}$, $A_{2u} \times B_{2u}$, $A_{2u} \times E_u$, $B_{1g} \times B_{1g}$, $B_{1g} \times B_{1u}$, $B_{1g} \times B_{2g}$, $B_{1g} \times E_g$, $B_{1u} \times B_{1u}$, $B_{1u} \times B_{2u}$, $B_{1u} \times E_u$, $B_{2g} \times B_{2g}$, $B_{2g} \times B_{2u}$, $B_{2g} \times E_g$, $B_{2u} \times B_{2u}$, $B_{2u} \times E_u$, $E_g \times E_g$, $E_u \times E_u$, $A_{2g} \times B_{1g}$, $A_{1u} \times B_{2u}$, A_{1g}^n, A_{1u}^n, A_{2g}^n, A_{2u}^n (n even), B_{1g}^n, B_{1u}^n, B_{2g}^n, B_{2u}^n, E_g^n, E_u^n (n even)

A_{1u}, A_{2g}, A_{2u}, B_{1u}, B_{2u}, E_u, $A_{1g} \times A_{1u}$, $A_{1g} \times A_{2g}$, $A_{1g} \times B_{1u}$, $A_{1g} \times B_{2u}$, $A_{1g} \times A_{2u}$, $A_{1u} \times B_{1g}$, $A_{1u} \times B_{2g}$, $A_{2g} \times A_{2u}$, $A_{2g} + B_{1u}$, $A_{2g} \times B_{2u}$, $A_{2u} \times B_{1g}$, $A_{2u} \times B_{2g}$, $B_{1g} \times B_{1u}$, $B_{1g} \times B_{2g}$, $B_{1u} \times B_{2g}$, $B_{2g} \times B_{2u}$, $A_{1g} \times E_u$, $A_{2g} \times A_{1u}$, $A_{2g} \times E_u$, $B_{1g} \times B_{2u}$, $B_{1g} \times E_u$, $B_{2g} \times E_u$, $E_g \times A_{1u}$, $E_g \times A_{2u}$, $E_g \times B_{1u}$, $E_g \times B_{2u}$, $E_g \times E_u$, A_{1u}^n (n odd), A_{2g}^n (n odd), B_{1u}^n (n odd), B_{2u}^n (n odd), E_u^n (n odd)

Chemical examples

Point group	Number of atoms	Compounds	References
D_{4h}	6	NH_4Br, ND_4Br	E. L. Wagner and D. F. Hornig, *J. Chem. Phys.* **18**, 305 (1950).
D_{4h} (?)	7	$SnBr_6^{2-}$	G. Herzberg, *op. cit.*, p. 342.
	9	$Pt(CN)_4^{2-}$	D. M. Sweeny, I. Nakagawa, S. Mizushima, and J. V. Quagliano, *J. Am. Chem. Soc.* **78**, 889 (1956).
D_{4h} (or D_{2d})	12	C_4H_8 (cyclobutane)	G. Herzberg, *op. cit.*, p. 368; G. W. Rathjens, Jr., N. K. Freeman, W. D. Gwinn, and K. S. Pitzer, *J. Am. Chem. Soc.* **75**, 5634 (1953).
		C_4F_8 (perfluorocyclobutane)	W. F. Edgell, *J. Am. Chem. Soc.* **69**, 660 (1947)
D_{4h} (or D_{2d})	16	$(PNCl_2)_4$	L. W. Daasch, *J. Am. Chem. Soc.* **76**, 3403 (1954).

TABLE 3.8 (continued)

Point Group D_{6h}

Symmetry elements

I, $2C_6(z)$, $2C_6^2 = 2C_3$, $C_6^3 = C_2''$, $3C_2$, $3C_2'$, σ_h, $3\sigma_v$, $3\sigma_d$, $2S_6$, $2S_3$, $S_6^3 = S_2 = i$

Symmetry types (or species)

D_{6h}	I	$2C_6(z)$	$2C_6^2=2C_3$	$C_6^3=C_2''$	$3C_2$	$3C_2'$	σ_h	$3\sigma_v$	$3\sigma_d$	$2S_6$	$2S_3$	$S_6^3=S_2=i$		
A_{1g}	1	1	1	1	1	1	1	1	1	1	1	1		$\alpha_{xx}+\alpha_{yy},\ \alpha_{zz}$
A_{1u}	1	1	1	1	1	1	−1	−1	−1	−1	−1	−1		
A_{2g}	1	1	1	1	−1	−1	1	−1	−1	1	1	1	R_z	
A_{2u}	1	1	1	1	−1	−1	−1	1	1	−1	−1	−1	T_z	
B_{1g}	1	−1	1	−1	1	−1	−1	−1	1	1	−1	1		
B_{1u}	1	−1	1	−1	1	−1	1	1	−1	−1	1	−1		
B_{2g}	1	−1	1	−1	−1	1	−1	1	−1	1	−1	1		
B_{2u}	1	−1	1	−1	−1	1	1	−1	1	−1	1	−1		
E_{1g}	2	1	−1	−2	0	0	−2	0	0	−1	1	2	(R_x, R_y)	$(\alpha_{yz}, \alpha_{xz})$
E_{1u}	2	1	−1	−2	0	0	2	0	0	1	−1	−2	(T_x, T_y)	
E_{2g}	2	−1	−1	2	0	0	2	0	0	−1	−1	2		$(\alpha_{xx}-\alpha_{yy}, \alpha_{xy})$
E_{2u}	2	−1	−1	2	0	0	−2	0	0	1	1	−2		

TABLE 3.8 (*continued*)

Selection rules (forbidden vibrations)

Infrared	Raman
$A_{1g}, A_{1u}, A_{2g}, B_{1g}, B_{1u}, B_{2g}, B_{2u}, E_{1g}, E_{2g}, E_{2u}, A_{1g} \times A_{1g}$,	$A_{1u}, A_{2g}, A_{2u}, B_{1g}, B_{1u}, B_{2g}, B_{2u}, E_{1u}, E_{2u}, A_{1g} \times A_{1u}$,
$A_{1g} \times A_{2g}, A_{1g} \times B_{1g}, A_{1g} \times E_{2g}, A_{1u} \times E_{2u}, A_{1u} \times A_{1u}$,	$A_{1u} \times A_{2g}, A_{1g} \times A_{2u}, A_{1g} \times B_{1u}, A_{1g} \times B_{2u}, A_{1u} \times A_{1u}$,
$A_{1g} \times E_{1g}, A_{1g} \times E_{2g}, A_{1g} \times E_{2u}, A_{1u} \times B_{1u}, A_{1u} \times A_{1u}$,	$A_{1g} \times B_{2u}, A_{1g} \times E_{1u}, A_{1u} \times B_{1g}, A_{1u} \times E_{2g}, A_{1u} \times A_{2u}$,
$A_{1u} \times A_{1u}, A_{1u} \times B_{2u}, A_{1u} \times E_{1u}, A_{1u} \times B_{1u}, A_{1u} \times B_{2u}$,	$A_{1u} \times B_{1u}, A_{1u} \times B_{2u}, A_{1u} \times E_{2g}, A_{1u} \times B_{2g}, A_{1u} \times E_{1g}$,
$A_{1u} \times B_{2u}, A_{1u} \times E_{1u}, A_{1u} \times E_{2g}, A_{1u} \times E_{2u}, A_{2g} \times E_{2u}$,	$A_{2g} \times E_{1u}, A_{2g} \times A_{2u}, A_{2g} \times B_{1u}, A_{2g} \times B_{2u}, A_{2g} \times B_{2g}$,
$A_{2g} \times A_{2g}, A_{2g} \times E_{1u}, A_{2g} \times B_{1u}, A_{2g} \times B_{2g}, B_{1g} \times B_{2g}$,	$A_{2g} \times E_{1u}, A_{2g} \times E_{1u}, A_{2g} \times B_{2u}, B_{1g} \times E_{2u}, B_{1g} \times B_{2g}$,
$A_{2g} \times B_{2u}, B_{1g} \times E_{1g}, A_{2g} \times B_{1u}, A_{2g} \times E_{2g}, B_{1g} \times E_{2u}$,	$B_{1g} \times E_{1u}, B_{1g} \times B_{2u}, A_{2g} \times E_{1u}, A_{2g} \times E_{2u}, B_{1g} \times B_{1u}$,
$B_{1g} \times B_{1u}, B_{1g} \times E_{1u}, A_{2u} \times E_{1u}, A_{2u} \times B_{2g}, B_{1g} \times E_{2u}$,	$A_{2u} \times B_{2u}, B_{1g} \times E_{1g}, A_{2u} \times E_{1g}, A_{2u} \times E_{2g}, B_{1g} \times B_{2g}$,
$B_{1g} \times E_{2g}, A_{2u} \times A_{2u}, A_{2u} \times E_{2g}, A_{2u} \times B_{1u}, B_{1g} \times E_{1u}$,	$A_{2u} \times B_{2u}, B_{2g} \times B_{2u}, A_{2u} \times E_{1g}, A_{2u} \times E_{2g}, B_{1u} \times B_{2g}$,
$B_{1u} \times E_{2g}, A_{2u} \times E_{1u}, B_{1u} \times E_{1u}, B_{2g} \times B_{2g}, B_{2u} \times B_{1u}$,	$B_{2g} \times E_{2g}, B_{1u} \times E_{1u}, B_{2u} \times E_{1u}, E_{1g} \times E_{1u}, B_{2g} \times E_{2u}$,
$B_{1u} \times B_{2u}, B_{2g} \times E_{1u}, B_{1u} \times E_{1u}, B_{2g} \times B_{2g}, B_{2u} \times B_{2u}$,	$B_{2u} \times E_{2g}, E_{1g} \times E_{2u}, B_{2u} \times E_{1g}, E_{1u} \times E_{1u}, E_{2g} \times E_{2u}$,
$B_{2u} \times B_{2u}, B_{2u} \times E_{1u}, B_{2g} \times E_{2g}, B_{2u} \times E_{2u}, E_{1g} \times E_{2g}$,	$E_{1u} \times E_{2g}, E_{2g} \times E_{2u}, E_{2g} \times E_{1u}, E_{1g} \times E_{1u}, E_{2u} \times E_{2u}$,
$E_{2g} \times E_{1u}, E_{1g} \times E_{2u}, E_{2g} \times E_{2u}, E_{1g} \times E_{2g}, E_{2g} \times E_{2g}$,	$E_{1u} \times E_{2g}, E_{2g} \times E_{2g}, E_{2u} \times E_{2u}, A_{1u}^n (n \text{ odd}), A_{2u}^n (n \text{ odd})$,
$E_{2u} \times E_{1u}, E_{2u} \times E_{2u}, E_{1g} \times E_{1u}, A_{1g}^n, A_{1u}^n$,	$B_{1u}^n (n \text{ odd}), B_{2u}^n (n \text{ odd}), E_{1u}^n (n \text{ odd})$,
$A_{2g}^n, A_{2u}^n (n \text{ even}), B_{1g}^n, B_{1u}^n, B_{2g}^n, B_{2u}^n, E_{1g}^n, E_{1u}^n (n \text{ even}), E_{2g}^n$,	
$E_{2u}^n (n \text{ even})$	

Chemical examples

Point group	Number of atoms	Compounds	References
$D_{6h}(?)$	12	C_6Cl_6 C_6H_6, C_6D_6	G. Herzberg, *op. cit.*, p. 368. *Ibid.*, p. 362; C. R. Bailey, C. K. Ingold, H. G. Poole, and C. L. Wilson, *J. Chem. Soc.* **1946**, 222.

TABLE 3.8 *(continued)*

Point Group $D_{\infty h}$

Symmetry elements

$I, 2C_\infty^\varphi, 2C_\infty^{2\varphi}, 2C_\infty^{3\varphi}, \cdots, \sigma_h, \infty C_2, \infty \sigma_v, 2S_\infty^\varphi, 2S_\infty^{2\varphi}, \cdots, S_2 \equiv i$

Symmetry types and characters

$D_{\infty h}$	I	$2C_\infty^\varphi$	$2C_\infty^{2\varphi}$	$2C_\infty^{3\varphi}$	$\cdots$	σ_h	∞C_2	$\infty \sigma_v$	$2S_\infty^\varphi$	$2S_\infty^{2\varphi}$	$\cdots$	$S_2 \equiv i$		
$A_{1g} \equiv \Sigma_g^+$	1	1	1	1	$\cdots$	1	1	1	1	1	$\cdots$	1		$\alpha_{xx}+\alpha_{yy},\ \alpha_{zz}$
$A_{1u} \equiv \Sigma_u^+$	1	1	1	1	$\cdots$	-1	-1	1	-1	-1	$\cdots$	-1	T_z	
$A_{2g} \equiv \Sigma_g^-$	1	1	1	1	$\cdots$	1	-1	-1	1	1	$\cdots$	1	R_z	
$A_{2u} \equiv \Sigma_u^-$	1	1	1	1	$\cdots$	-1	1	-1	-1	-1	$\cdots$	-1		
$E_{1g} \equiv \Pi_g$	2	$2\cos\varphi$	$2\cos 2\varphi$	$2\cos 3\varphi$	$\cdots$	-2	0	0	$-2\cos\varphi$	$-2\cos 2\varphi$	$\cdots$	2	(R_x, R_y)	$(\alpha_{xz},\ \alpha_{yz})$
$E_{1u} \equiv \Pi_u$	2	$2\cos\varphi$	$2\cos 2\varphi$	$2\cos 3\varphi$	$\cdots$	2	0	0	$2\cos\varphi$	$2\cos 2\varphi$	$\cdots$	-2	(T_x, T_y)	
$E_{2g} \equiv \Delta_g$	2	$2\cos 2\varphi$	$2\cos 4\varphi$	$2\cos 6\varphi$	$\cdots$	2	0	0	$2\cos 2\varphi$	$2\cos 4\varphi$	$\cdots$	2		$(\alpha_{xx}-\alpha_{yy},\ \alpha_{xy})$
$E_{2u} \equiv \Delta_u$	2	$2\cos 2\varphi$	$2\cos 4\varphi$	$2\cos 6\varphi$	$\cdots$	-2	0	0	$-2\cos 2\varphi$	$-2\cos 4\varphi$	$\cdots$	-2		
$E_{3g} \equiv \Phi_g$	2	$2\cos 3\varphi$	$2\cos 6\varphi$	$2\cos 9\varphi$	$\cdots$	-2	0	0	$-2\cos 3\varphi$	$-2\cos 6\varphi$	$\cdots$	2		
$E_{3u} \equiv \Phi_u$	2	$2\cos 3\varphi$	$2\cos 6\varphi$	$2\cos 9\varphi$	$\cdots$	2	0	0	$2\cos 3\varphi$	$2\cos 6\varphi$	$\cdots$	-2		
$\cdots$					$\cdots$						$\cdots$			

Selection rules (forbidden vibrations) (See reference 9 for selection rules for combinations and overtone bands)

Infrared	Raman
$\Sigma_g^+, \Sigma_g^-, \Sigma_u^-, \Pi_g, \Delta_g, \Delta_u, \Phi_g, \Phi_u$	$\Sigma_u^+, \Sigma_g^-, \Sigma_u^-, \Pi_u, \Delta_u, \Phi_g, \Phi_u$

Chemical examples

Point group	Number of atoms	Compounds	References
$D_{\infty h}$	3	CO_2	G. Herzberg, *op. cit.*, p. 272.
		CS_2	*Ibid.*, p. 276.
		$N_3^-, BO_2^-, HgCl_2, HgBr_2, HgI_2, CdCl_2,$ $CdBr_2, CdI_2, ZnCl_2, ZnBr_2$	*Ibid.*, p. 287.
	4	C_2H_2, C_2D_2	*Ibid.*, pp. 288–289.
		C_2N_2	*Ibid.*, p. 293.
		B_2O_2	D. White, D. E. Mann, P. N. Walsh, and A. Sommer, *J. Chem. Phys.* 32, 481 (1960).
$D_{\infty h}$ (or C_{2v} or C_{2h})	5	C_3O_2	G. Herzberg, *op. cit.*, p. 303.
	6	$NCC{\equiv}CCN$	F. A. Miller and R. B. Hannan, Jr., *J. Chem.*

TABLE 3.8 (*continued*)

Point Group T_d

Symmetry elements

I, $8C_3$, $6\sigma_d$, $6S_4$, $3S_4^2 \equiv 3C_2$

Symmetry types and characters

T_d	I	$8C_3$	$6\sigma_d$	$6S_4$	$3S_4^2 \equiv 3C_2$		
A_1	1	1	1	1	1		$\alpha_{xx} + \alpha_{yy} + \alpha_{zz}$
A_2	1	1	−1	−1	1		
E	2	−1	0	0	2		$\alpha_{xx} + \alpha_{yy} - 2\alpha_{zz}$, $\alpha_{xx} - \alpha_{yy}$
F_1	3	0	−1	1	−1	R_x , R_y , R_z	
F_2	3	0	1	−1	−1	T_x , T_y , T_z	α_{xy} , α_{yz} , α_{xz}

Selection Rules (forbidden vibrations)

Infrared	Raman
A_1 , A_2 , E, F_1 , $A_1 \times A_1$, $A_1 \times A_2$, $A_1 \times E$, $A_1 \times F_1$, $A_2 \times A_2$, $A_2 \times E$, $A_2 \times F_2$, $E \times E$, A_1^n , A_2^n , E^n	A_2 , F_1 , $A_1 \times A_2$, $A_1 \times F_1$, $A_2 \times F_2$, A_2^n (n odd)

Chemical examples

Point group	Number of atoms	Compounds	References
T_d	4	P_4	G. Herzberg, *op. cit.*, p. 299; H. J. Bernstein and J. Powling, *J. Chem. Phys.* **18**, 1018 (1950); H. S. Gutowsky and C. J. Hoffman, *J. Am. Chem. Soc.* **72**, 5751 (1950).
	5	CH_4 , CD_4	G. Herzberg, *op. cit.*, p. 306.
		CCl_4	*Ibid.*, p. 310; H. H. Claassen, *J. Chem. Phys.* **22**, 50 (1954).
		CF_4	*Ibid.*; G. Herzberg, *op. cit.*, p. 322.
		$SiCl_4$	*Ibid.*; A. L. Smith, *J. Chem. Phys.* **21**, 1997 (1953).

160 3. CLASSIFICATION OF MOLECULES

TABLE 3.8 (*continued*)

Chemical examples (continued)

Point group	Number of atoms	Compounds	References
		SO_4^-	G. Herzberg, *op. cit.*, p. 322; D. W. A. Sharp, *J. Chem. Soc.* 1950, 3761; K. Nakamoto, J. Fujita, S. Tanaka, and M. Kobayashi, *J. Am. Chem. Soc.* 79, 4904 (1957).
		SiH_4, SiF_4, $TiCl_4$, GeH_4, $GeBr_4$, $GeCl_4$, $SnCl_4$, CBr_4, $SiBr_4$, $SnBr_4$, SeO_4^{2-}, SiO_4^{4-}, ClO_4^-, IO_4^-, CrO_4^{2-}, MoO_4^{2-}, WoO_4^{2-}, PO_4^{3-}, AsO_4^{3-}	G. Herzberg, *op. cit.*, p. 322.
$T_d(?)$		$CdBr_4^-$, NH_4^+	
		$GaBr_4^-$, GaI_4^-	L.A. Woodward and G.H. Singer, *J. Chem. Soc.* 1958, 716.
		$ZrCl_4$	J. K. Wilmshurst, *J. Mol. Spectry.* 5, 343 (1960).
		OsO_4	L. A. Woodward, L. A. Creighton, and K. A. Taylor, *Trans. Faraday Soc.* 56, 1267 (1960).
	6	NH_4Cl, ND_4Cl	E. L. Wagner and D. F. Hornig, *J. Chem. Phys.* 18, 296 (1950).
		NH_4F	R. C. Plumb and D. F. Hornig, *J. Chem. Phys.* 23, 947 (1955).
	9	$Ni(CO)_4$	G. Herzberg, *op. cit.*, p. 356.
	17	$(CH_3)_4C$, $(CH_3)_4Ge$, $(CH_3)_4Si$	C. W. Young, J. S. Koehler, and D. S. McKinney, *J. Am. Chem. Soc.* 69, 1410 (1947).
		$(CH_3)_4Pb$	*Ibid.*; R. K. Sheline and K. S. Pitzer, *J. Chem. Phys.* 18, 595 (1950).
		$(CH_3)_4Sn$	W. F. Edgell and H. W. Curtis, *J. Am. Chem. Soc.* 77, 6486 (1955); E. R. Lippincott and M. C. Tobin, *J. Am. Chem. Soc.* 75, 4141 (1953).
		$(CH_3)_4Si$	*Ibid.*; K. Shimizu and H. Murata, *J. Mol. Spectry.* 5, 44 (1960).
		$Ni(PF_3)_4$	L. A. Woodward and J. R. Hall, *Nature* 181, 831 (1958).

TABLE 3.8 *(continued)*

Point Group O_h

Symmetry elements

$I, 8C_3, 6C_2, 6C_4, 3C_4^2, 3C_2'', S_2\, i, 6S_4, 8S_6, 3\sigma_h, 6\sigma_d$

Symmetry types and characters

O_h	I	$8C_3$	$6C_2$	$6C_4$	$3C_4^2$	i	$6S_4$	$8S_6$	$3\sigma_h$	$6\sigma_d$		
A_{1g}	1	1	1	1	1	1	1	1	1	1		$\alpha_{xx}+\alpha_{yy}+\alpha_{zz}$
A_{1u}	1	1	1	1	1	-1	-1	-1	-1	-1		
A_{2g}	1	1	-1	-1	1	1	-1	1	1	-1		
A_{2u}	1	1	-1	-1	1	-1	1	-1	-1	1		
E_g	2	-1	0	0	2	2	0	-1	2	0		$(\alpha_{xx}+\alpha_{yy}-2\alpha_{zz}, \alpha_{zz}-\alpha_{yy})$
E_u	2	-1	0	0	2	-2	0	-1	-2	0		
F_{1g}	3	0	-1	1	-1	3	1	0	-1	-1	R_x, R_y, R_z	
F_{1u}	3	0	-1	1	-1	-3	-1	0	1	1	T_x, T_y, T_z	
F_{2g}	3	0	1	-1	-1	3	-1	0	-1	1		$(\alpha_{xy}, \alpha_{yz}, \alpha_{xz})$
F_{2u}	3	0	1	-1	-1	-3	1	0	1	-1		

Selection rules (forbidden vibrations)

Infrared

$A_{1g},\ A_{2g},\ A_{2u},\ E_g,\ E_u,\ F_{1g},\ F_{2g},\ F_{2u},\ A_{1g}\times A_{1g},$
$A_{1g}\times A_{2g},\ A_{1g}\times E_u,\ A_{1g}\times F_{1g},\ A_{1g}\times F_{1g},$
$A_{1g}\times F_{2g},\ A_{1u},\ A_{1u}\times A_{2g},\ A_{1u}\times E_g,\ A_{1u}\times E_g,$
$A_{1u}\times E_u,\ A_{1u}\times F_{1u},\ A_{1u}\times F_{2u},\ A_{2g}\times F_{2g},$
$A_{2g}\times E_u,\ A_{2g}\times E_u,\ E_g\times F_{1g},\ A_{2g}\times F_{2g},\ A_{2g}\times F_{2u},$
$E_g\times E_g,\ E_g\times E_u,\ E_g\times F_{1g},\ E_u\times E_u,\ E_u\times F_{1u},$
$E_u\times F_{2u},\ F_{1g}\times F_{1g},\ F_{1g}\times F_{1u},\ F_{1u}\times F_{1u},\ F_{1u}\times F_{2u},$
$F_{2u}\times F_{2u},\ A_{2u}\times E_g,\ A_{2u}\times E_g,\ A_{2u}\times E_u,\ A_{2u}\times A_{1u},$
$A_{2u}\times F_{1u},\ A_{2u}\times F_{2u},\ A_{2u}\times A_{2g},\ A_{2u}\times A_{1g},\ A_{2u}\times A_{1u},$
$F_{1g}\times F_{2g},\ F_{2g}\times F_{2g},\ A_{1u}^n,\ A_{2g}^n,\ A_{2u}^n,\ E_g^n,\ E_u^n,\ F_{1g}^n,$
$F_{2g}^n,\ F_{1u}^n\ (n>2),\ F_{2u}^n\ (n>2)$

Raman

$A_{1u},\ A_{2g},\ A_{2u},\ E_u,\ F_{1g},\ F_{2u},\ A_{1g}\times A_{1u},\ A_{1g}\times A_{2g},$
$A_{1g}\times E_u,\ A_{2u}\times E_u,\ A_{1g}\times F_{1g},\ A_{1g}\times F_{2g},\ A_{1u}\times A_{2g},$
$A_{1u}\times E_g,\ A_{1g}\times E_g,\ A_{1u}\times F_{1u},\ A_{1u}\times F_{2u},\ A_{2g}\times E_u,$
$A_{2g}\times F_{2u},\ E_u\times F_{1u},\ E_g\times F_{1u},\ E_g\times F_{2u},$
$E_u\times F_{1g},\ E_u\times F_{2g},\ F_{1g}\times F_{1u},\ F_{2g}\times F_{2u},$
$A_{2g}\times F_{2u},\ A_{2u}\times A_{1g},\ A_{2u}\times A_{2g},\ A_{2u}\times A_{2g},$
$A_{2u}\times E_g,\ A_{2u}\times F_{1g},\ A_{2u}\times F_{2g},\ A_{1u}^n\ (n\ \text{odd}),$
$A_{2g}^n\ (n\ \text{odd}),\ A_{2u}^n\ (n\ \text{odd}),\ E_u^n,\ F_{1u}^n,\ F_{2u}^n$

TABLE 3.8 (*continued*)

Chemical examples			
Point group	Number of atoms	Compounds	References
O_h	7	SeF_6, TeF_6	G. Herzberg, *op. cit.*, p. 342; J. Gaunt, *Trans. Faraday Soc.* **49**, 1122 (1953).
		SF_6	*Ibid.*; R. T. Lagemann and E. A. Jones, *J. Chem. Phys.* **19**, 534 (1951).
$O_h(?)$		$SnCl_6^{2-}$, $PbCl_6^{2-}$, $SbCl_6^-$	G. Herzberg, *op. cit.*, p. 342.
		MoF_6, WF_6, UF_6	T. G. Burke, D. F. Smith, and A. H. Nielsen, *J. Chem. Phys.* **20**, 447 (1952); J. Gaunt, *Trans. Faraday Soc.* **49**, 1122 (1953).
		OsF_6, PtF_6	B. Weinstock, H. H. Claassen, and J. G. Malm, *J. Chem. Phys.* **32**, 181 (1960).

The point groups are listed in an order corresponding to Table 3.1 for the sake of consistency. Not all the point groups of Table 3.1 are listed but only those for which actual chemical examples exist.

A vibrational species will be infrared active if one or more of the three components of translation (T_x, T_y, T_z) are listed in the row for that species in the character tables. This is because the dipole moment is a vector which is transformed by the symmetry operations the same way as is the translation which is also a vector. Furthermore, the direction of translation listed (T_x, for example) indicates the direction (x) of the change in dipole moment for that vibrational species. In a like manner the components of the polarizability (α_{xx}, α_{xy}, etc.) which change during a vibration are listed in the row for Raman active vibrational species in the character tables. The polarizability which is a tensor has six independent components. In character tables of groups with degenerate species linear combinations such as $\alpha_{xx} + \alpha_{yy}$ or $\alpha_{xx} - \alpha_{yy}$ may be listed as belonging to certain symmetry species. Degenerate pairs of translations, rotations, and polarizability components are enclosed in parentheses.

3.11 Techniques of Band Assignments

The problem of band assignments, that is, assignment of observed frequencies to fundamental modes of vibration and their allowed overtones and combinations, may be a very complex task. It quickly becomes more and more difficult as the number of vibrational modes increases. Several useful techniques such as selection rules, gas contours, and polarization studies have already been discussed and will be briefly mentioned in this section with application to band assignments. Isotope effects and the product rule will also be discussed.

(a) SELECTION RULES

These rules govern the appearance or nonappearance of a band in the spectrum but do not yield information regarding band intensities. The derivation and significance of the selection rules have been discussed in the preceding sections. Their usefulness in band assignments will vary with the symmetry involved but, in cases where there is a difference in the infrared and Raman activity, or inactive species, they may be very helpful. If the molecular structure (point group) is known, the number of fundamentals of each species expected in the infrared spectrum and in the Raman spectrum may be determined.

(b) GAS CONTOURS

A study of the contour of an infrared band measured in the gaseous phase can often reveal the direction of the change in dipole moment of the molecular vibration causing the band. The use of gas contours as an aid in band assignments has been discussed in some detail in Chapter 1 (see, for example, Figs. 1.13 and 1.14). To cite an illustration, a linear molecule may have vibrational modes which result in a change in the dipole moment along (parallel to) the molecular axis or perpendicular to it and are associated with characteristic "parallel" or "perpendicular" band contours respectively.

(c) DEPOLARIZATION RATIOS

The significance and determination of depolarization ratios have been discussed in Sections 1.19 and 2.11(b) respectively. It was pointed out that only totally symmetrical vibrations give polarized Raman lines, that is, a depolarization ratio less than 6/7. Depolarization ratios are thus useful in assigning observed polarized Raman lines to vibrations belonging to the totally symmetric species. In the case of chloroform, which has three A_1 vibrations and three E vibrations, all Raman active, the symmetric A_1 vibrations should be polarized and the E vibrations depolarized. Determination of the depolarization ratios will therefore aid in assigning observed Raman lines to A_1 and E vibrational species. The actual band assignments for chloroform are discussed in some detail in Chapter 14.

(d) POLARIZED INFRARED RADIATION

A study of the polarized infrared spectrum of an oriented solid can reveal information about the direction of the change in dipole moment of the unit cell as a result of a molecular vibration. The techniques and some of the applications of polarized infrared measurements were discussed in Section 2.8. If the molecular orientation in the solid sample is known, the polarized infrared spectrum can frequently be of help in making band assignments.

(e) ISOTOPE EFFECTS AND THE PRODUCT RULE

The relationship between nuclear mass and the frequency of vibration has been introduced in earlier sections. If we assume, as is generally possible, that the force constants are unaltered by isotope substitution, the shift in observed frequency can be attributed principally to mass effects. Qualitatively this shift will aid in the assignment of frequencies simply by observing what bands are altered, and to what extent they are altered by isotopic substitution. Vibrational modes which largely involve the substituted species, that is, the species having a large amplitude in the normal vibrational mode, will be expected to have appreciable shifts in frequency. The larger the mass difference, the larger the frequency difference and thus deuterium substitution, for example, gives a particularly large effect because of the large difference in relative mass. In the simple case of diatomic molecules, such as HCl and DCl, the observed frequencies are approximately 2990 and 2091 cm^{-1} respectively. Here the ratio 2091/2990 is 0.70 and the ratio predicted is $\sqrt{\mu/\mu'}$ where μ and μ' are the reduced masses of HCl and DCl. The predicted value is 0.72 and is in close agreement.

A general quantitative relation, involving the isotope effect, is the Teller-Redlich product rule. It is based on the assumption that the product of the zero order frequency ratios, ω'/ω,* for all vibrations of a given symmetry type is independent of the potential constants and depends only on the relative masses of the atoms and on the geometrical structure of the molecule. The general relation is:

$$\frac{\omega_1'\omega_2' \dots \omega_i'}{\omega_1\omega_2 \dots \omega_i} = \left[\left(\frac{M'}{M}\right)^t \left(\frac{I_x'}{I_x}\right)^{r_x} \left(\frac{I_y'}{I_y}\right)^{r_y} \left(\frac{I_z'}{I_z}\right)^{r_z} \prod_j \left(\frac{m_j}{m_j'}\right)^{N^j} \right]^{1/2} \quad (3.22)$$

where all factors pertaining to isotopic species are designated by the primes and ω_1, ω_2, ..., ω_i represent the i genuine vibrations of the symmetry type considered. M is the molecular weight and I_x, I_y, and I_z are the three moments of inertia† of

---

* Harmonic oscillator zero-order frequencies differ a little from experimental frequencies of slightly anharmonic vibrations.

† Note that I_x, I_y, and I_z are equivalent to I_a, I_b, and I_c used for the moments of inertia elsewhere in this book.

the molecule. The m_j values are the masses of the representative atoms, j, of each set. A set consists of equivalent atoms transformed into each other by the symmetry operations. The N^j exponents are the number of vibrations each set contributes to the vibration species considered. These factors will be explained below in the example considered. The t and r_x, r_y, and r_z values are the number of nongenuine vibrations (translations and rotations respectively) which belong to the vibration species.

The N^j, t, r_x, r_y, and r_z values may be obtained from the character table for the point group. The necessary data, using the C_{3v} molecule, chloroform, as an example, is shown in Table 3.9. The values for t and r come directly from the

TABLE 3.9

C_{3v} CHARACTER TABLE AND RELATED DATA FOR ISOTOPE EFFECT

C_{3v}	I	$2C_3$	$3\sigma_v$	
A_1	1	1	1	T_z
A_2	1	1	-1	R_z
E	2	-1	0	R_x, R_y, T_x, T_y
ϕ	0	120	0	
$\cos \phi$	1	$-\frac{1}{2}$	1	
$U^C(R)$	1	1	1	
$U^H(R)$	1	1	1	
$U^{Cl}(R)$	3	0	1	
$X^C(R)$	3	0	1	
$X^H(R)$	3	0	1	
$X^{Cl}(R)$	9	0	1	

table. The value for t is the number of times T_x, T_y, or T_z appear for each species and is 1 for A_1 and 1 for the E species. Note that in the E species T_x and T_y have been considered as *one* degenerate pair. The r values are either 0 or 1 depending on whether R_x, R_y, or R_z belong to the vibration species. It can be seen from the character table that no R values belong to the A_1 species and thus all r values for A_1 are 0. Both R_x and R_y belong to the E type but again form a degenerate pair and only one moment of inertia ratio, $(I'/I) = (I'_x/I_x) = (I'_y/I_y)$, is used. The N^j values are given by an equation (similar to 3.15 and 3.17) as follows,

$$N^j = \frac{1}{Ng} \sum_R \eta_e \chi^j(R) \, \chi(R) \tag{3.23}$$

where Ng is the total number of symmetry operations (or elements) in the point group, η_e is the number of operations (or elements) in each class, and

$\chi(R)$ is the character (from character table) for the symmetry species and class. As previously shown, for the C_{3v} point group N_g is 6, consisting of one identity, I, two rotations, $\pm C_3$, and three reflections, $3\sigma_v$. Thus, the η_e values are 1, 2, and 3 respectively. The $\chi^j(R)$ values are given by:

$$\chi^j(R) = U^j(R)(1 + 2 \cos \phi) \qquad (3.24)$$

for proper rotations and for improper rotations by:

$$\chi^j(R) = U^j(R)(-1 + 2 \cos \phi) \qquad (3.25)$$

where $U^j(R)$ is the number of atoms of each set left unchanged by each operation, R, and ϕ is the angle of proper or improper rotation. The values for $U^j(R)$ and the resulting values calculated for $\chi^j(R)$ are included in Table 3.9. The N^j values can now be obtained from Eq. (3.23). For the carbon atom, the only one in the set, the N^j value for the A_1 species is:

$$N^C = \tfrac{1}{6}[(1)(3)(1) + (2)(0)(1) + (3)(1)(1)] = 1 \qquad (3.26)$$

and in the same way, the other N^j values are:

$$N^H = 1 \quad \text{and} \quad N^{Cl} = 2 \qquad (3.27)$$

for the A_1 species. The corresponding values for the E species, again using Eq. (3.23) and Table 3.9, are:

$$N^C = 1, \quad N^H = 1, \quad \text{and} \quad N^{Cl} = 3 \qquad (3.28)$$

which completes the N^j values required for both vibration species.

The product rule can now be applied to the three A_1 vibrations and to the three E vibrations of chloroform. The three A_1 vibrations are 3033, 667, and 364 for $CHCl_3$ and 2256, 651, and 366 for $CDCl_3$. Equation (3.22) is then:

$$\frac{v_1'v_2'v_3'}{v_1v_2v_3} = \frac{(2256)(651)(366)}{(3033)(667)(364)} = 0.727 = \left[\left(\frac{M'}{M}\right)\left(\frac{m_H}{m_H'}\right)\right]^{1/2} \qquad (3.29)$$

or

$$0.727 = \left[\left(\frac{120.4}{119.4}\right)\left(\frac{1.008}{2.015}\right)\right]^{1/2} = (0.505)^{1/2} = 0.711 \qquad (3.30)$$

where no I'/I ratios appear since all r values are zero and the only atomic mass ratio included is that for hydrogen and deuterium, since the others are invariant. The agreement is not exact, which might be expected, since the observed frequencies, v, have been used rather than the zero order frequencies, ω, which are actually required. Consideration of anharmonicity would predict the ratio $\nu_1'\nu_2' .../\nu_1\nu_2 ...$ somewhat larger than the ratio of zero order frequencies, as is observed. For the E vibrations, Eq. (3.22) becomes:

$$\frac{\nu_4'\nu_5'\nu_6'}{\nu_4\nu_5\nu_6} = \frac{(908)\,(738)\,(262)}{(1216)\,(761)\,(262)} = 0.724 = \left[\left(\frac{M'}{M}\right)\left(\frac{I'}{I}\right)\left(\frac{m_H}{m_H'}\right)\right]^{1/2} \quad (3.31)$$

or

$$0.724 = \left[\left(\frac{120.4}{119.4}\right)\left(\frac{265.7}{262.1}\right)\left(\frac{1.008}{2.015}\right)\right]^{1/2} = (0.511)^{1/2} = 0.715 \quad (3.32)$$

where 265.7 and 262.1 (both time 10^{-40}) are one of the equal moments of inertia for $CDCl_3$ and $CHCl_3$ respectively. The good agreement in both cases helps confirm the given assignment for the six fundamental vibrations.

CHAPTER 4

THE ORIGIN OF GROUP FREQUENCIES

4.1 Introduction

When relatively simple molecules are to be studied, complete mathematical procedures exist for calculating the vibrational frequencies. As increasingly more complex molecules are studied, the difficulty of the mathematical treatment increases enormously so empirical methods must be resorted to. These use as their backbone, the available literature on the simpler molecules which have been analyzed mathematically.

In the mathematical treatment, the molecule as a whole is considered, and the vibrations are rigorously calculated. In the empirical approach, various subparts of the molecule are studied separately. It is found empirically that certain submolecular groups when present in a molecule, consistently give rise to absorption bands in the same spectral regions. These are the characteristic group frequencies.

Spectra-structure relationships may be better understood if several of the complications, such as the interaction of vibrations, are considered in a simplified manner. This approach is necessarily more qualitative and less rigorous than the mathematical treatment, but has proved quite useful in practice. Specific examples discussed here will also be discussed and referenced individually in later sections on group frequencies.

4.2 Introduction to Mass and Force Constant Effects

If a diatomic molecule is considered to be two weights (nuclei) connected by a helical spring (interatomic bond), the vibrational frequency will be a direct function of the force constant of the spring and an inverse function of the masses involved.

It is found that a $C \equiv N$ group absorbs near 2250 cm^{-1}, a $C = N$ group absorbs

168

near 1650 cm^{-1}, and a C—N group absorbs near 1050 cm^{-1}. These wavenumber changes are, of course, due to the change in force constant of the bond, as the atomic weights are unchanged.

It is also found that a C—H group absorbs near 3000 cm^{-1}, a C—C group near 1000 cm^{-1}, and a C—I group near 500 cm^{-1}. These wavenumber changes are mainly due to the changes in mass of one of the atoms of the group, as the bond strength remains nearly unchanged (for a first approximation).

For the diatomic case the above values can be roughly approximated by an expression derived from Hooke's Law.

$$\nu = \frac{1}{2\pi c} \sqrt{k \left(\frac{1}{m_1} + \frac{1}{m_2} \right)}$$

Here, ν is the frequency in cm^{-1}, c is the velocity of light, k is the force constant of the bond in dynes per centimeter, and m_1 and m_2 are the masses in grams. This equation is equivalent to the following equation where M_1 and M_2 are the atomic weights of the two atoms and K is the actual $k \times 10^{-5}$.

$$\nu = 1303 \sqrt{K \left(\frac{1}{M_1} + \frac{1}{M_2} \right)}$$

[$1303 = (1/2\pi c) \sqrt{N \times 10^5}$, where N is Avogadro's number (6.02×10^{23})].

Single bonds have a value of k mainly between 4 and 6×10^5 dyn/cm, double bonds between 8 and 12×10^5, and triple bonds between 12 and 18×10^5 dyn/cm.

4.3 Interaction and Coupling Effects

As we have seen above, the three hypothetical diatomic molecules C—H, C—C, and C—I would each have a single frequency near 3000, 1000, and 500 cm^{-1} respectively. If we were to combine these into three more hypothetical triatomic molecules C—C—H, C—C—C, and C—C—I, each would have one bending and two stretching frequencies, as each "molecule" has one bond angle and two bonds. In the case of C—C—H, one stretching frequency would be near the frequency of the hypothetical C—H molecule at 3000 cm^{-1} and the second, near the C—C molecule at 1000 cm^{-1} (see Fig. 4.1). Similarly the stretching frequencies of C—C—I would be near those of C—C at 1000 cm^{-1} and C—I at 500 cm^{-1}. Upon analysis we would find that these two molecules vibrate so that when either bond stretches and contracts, the other bond remains nearly unchanged in length. This is because the individual bond oscillators have frequencies quite different from each other. For the C—C—C molecules, however, the individual bond oscillators (C—C) have frequencies exactly the same, and they are coupled together because of an atom common to both bonds. They interact, with the result that the two stretching frequencies involve *both* C—C bonds for both vibrations. In one, both bonds stretch symmetrically and in the other, one stretches while the other contracts. These frequencies are displaced above and below the original C—C frequency (see Fig. 4.1).

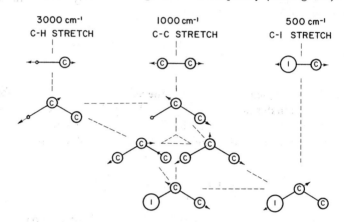

FIG. 4.1.   Stretching vibrations of the CCH, CCC, and CCI "molecules" compared with the CH, CC, and CI "diatomic" vibrations. The higher of the two stretching frequencies in the CCX case is predominantly CH stretching when X=H and gradually becomes predominantly CC stretching as the mass of X increases. The lower stretching frequency is predominantly CC stretch when X=H and gradually becomes predominantly CX as X increases to the mass of iodine. In the CCC case both oscillators are equally involved, in and out of phase. The frequencies for the CCC case are found above and below the CC diatomic frequency. Actual examples are: ethane, 992 cm⁻¹ (C—C); ethyl iodide, 951 cm⁻¹ (C—C), 500 cm⁻¹ (C—I); propane, 1054 cm⁻¹ (asymmetric C—C—C), 867 cm⁻¹ (symmetric C—C—C).

In the same way the vibrations of hypothetical molecules N≡C—N, N=C=N, C=N—C, and C—N—C are compared with the vibrations of hypothetical molecules C≡N, C=N, and C—N (see Fig. 4.2). It is seen that the vibrations of N=C=N are displaced from the frequency of the C=N molecule, and the vibrations of C—N—C are displaced from the frequency of the C—N molecule, since both of these molecules have coupled oscillators with exactly the same frequency and so interact symmetrically and asymmetrically. For the molecules N≡C—N and C=N—C however, the multiple bonds vibrate with much less interaction, and so their frequencies are found near the frequencies for the C≡N and C=N molecules.

Thus, it is seen that when a bond oscillator is directly coupled (because of an atom common to both) with another bond oscillator having nearly the *same* individual frequency, they interact nearly completely. The resultant two frequencies (both involving both oscillators) are displaced from their original positions by an amount depending on the phasing and coupling of the oscillators. However, if the frequencies of the oscillators are sufficiently *different*, the interaction will be very much smaller. The vibration of the individual oscillator will be mechanically *independent* of the rest of the molecule to a large degree and may have correlatable frequencies when this group is present in different molecules.

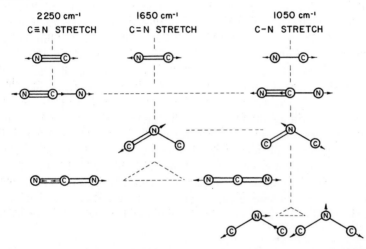

FIG. 4.2. Stretching vibrations of the $N \equiv C - N$, $C = N - C$, $N = C = N$, and $C - N - C$ "molecules" compared with the $C \equiv N$, $C = N$, and $C - N$ "diatomic" vibrations. The $N = C = N$ and $C - N - C$ frequencies diverge from the $C = N$ and $C - N$ "diatomic" frequencies. The $N \equiv C - N$ and $C = N - C$ "molecules" have their highest frequency near the $C \equiv N$ and $C = N$ "diatomic" frequency.

Interaction is used here in the sense that two interacting oscillators in one molecule do not vibrate individually, but both vibrations involve both oscillators in and out of phase. In the case of complete interaction, the two frequencies, in and out of phase, may be widely separated or may be practically identical. The *separation* of the frequencies in this case, depends on the effectiveness of the *coupling* of the two oscillators. The degree of coupling may be loosely described as the degree to which the vibration of one individual oscillator "disturbs" the other oscillator. In the usual stretching case, the coupling is very strong if the two oscillators have a common atom. When one bond is caused to vibrate, the other bond is "disturbed" or altered in length because of the common atom.

If the compound is considered with two carbonyl groups, one on each end of a hydrocarbon chain, there will be interaction in the sense that in one of the two $C=O$ vibrations, one $C=O$ will stretch while the other contracts, and in the other vibration both $C=O$ bonds will stretch together. Both of these $C=O$ vibrations, in and out of phase, will absorb near 1715 cm^{-1} near the absorption position of a single carbonyl, due to very weak coupling between the $C=O$ groups. Carbon dioxide (two carbonyls back to back) will have two stretching vibrations also. The first where one $C=O$ stretches while the other contracts appears at 2350 cm^{-1}, the other where both $C=O$ bonds stretch together appears in the region about 1340 cm^{-1}. This divergence of stretching frequencies is a result of the strong coupling of the two $C=O$ bonds in CO_2, due to the common carbon atom. Figure 4.3 illustrates some of these frequency relationships.

Actually, some interaction occurs in all vibrations, the only limit being that the interacting vibrations must be of the same symmetry species. For instance, it is impossible for the molecule to perform some stretching vibrations without bending bond angles. Consider a planar molecule such as vinyl chloride with no other symmetry element except the plane of symmetry. In plane and out of plane vibrations will not interact at all with each other since they are of different symmetry species. All in plane vibrations will interact to some extent and all out of plane vibrations will interact to some extent. However, not all interaction effects are of the same magnitude for some are quite small. In this discussion which is on group frequencies, we are only emphasizing the more important interaction effects. Suitable group frequencies usually result when interaction effects are small or constant between the group and the rest of the molecule.

4.4 Individual Oscillator Groups

Groups such as $C \equiv N$ and $C=O$ which have relatively high vibrational frequencies are attached to the rest of the molecules by single bonds which have relatively low frequencies. The interaction is weak as a result, and therefore $C \equiv N$ and $C=O$ frequencies are mechanically relatively independent of the rest of the molecule. However, mesomeric and inductive effects involving the rest of the molecule can alter the stiffness of these bonds and therefore alter their frequencies somewhat.

Groups such as $O-H$ and $N-H$ have high stretching frequencies relative to the $C-O$ and $C-N$ bonds to which they are attached, and therefore the two vibrate relatively independently. These groups are particularly sensitive to hydrogen bonding effects, however, so that the frequencies and intensities of the bands are quite sensitive to intermolecular environment.

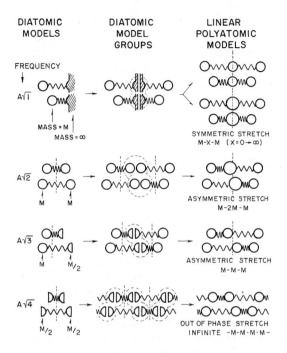

FIG. 4.3. Frequency relationships between diatomic models and certain polyatomic models.

The vibrating diatomic molecular models on the left have masses equal to M, $M/2$, or infinity (spring attached to a wall). The force constants of all the "bond springs" are the same and equal to K.

In the middle group, two unconnected models side by side are set in vibration with the phases shown. It is noticed that the middle two atoms (circled) remain the same distance apart during all phases of the vibration, each performing a simple harmonic motion. Therefore, it makes no difference if they are unconnected as shown in the middle group or are connected to make the vibrating polyatomic models on the right which have the *same frequencies as the models on their left*. In the triatomic symmetrical vibration at the top right, the center atom does not move. The frequency of this vibration is, therefore, independent of the mass of the middle atom which may have any value from zero to infinity. The centers of gravity which are always motionless are indicated by dotted line intersections with molecular axes.

The diatomic frequencies $\nu'(\sec^{-1})$ are calculated by the formula

$$\nu' = \frac{1}{2\pi} \sqrt{k \left(\frac{1}{m_1} + \frac{1}{m_2} \right)}$$

In the solved equations, the common factor A equals $(1/2\pi) \sqrt{K/M}$.

The diatomic model $M-M$ has a frequency $A\sqrt{2}$. The triatomic linear model $M-M-M$ has stretching frequencies below and above this at $A\sqrt{1}$ and $A\sqrt{3}$. These are approximately analogous to $CH_2 = CH_2$ (1623 cm^{-1}) and $CH_2 = C = CH_2$ (1071 and 1980 cm^{-1}).

The groups just mentioned, $C \equiv N$, $C = O$, $O - H$, and $N - H$, are examples of individual oscillators which have correlatable stretching frequencies due to their mechanical independence from the rest of the molecule.

Some difficulties might be expected with the $C = S$ group in a thio amide, as the $C = S$ bond and $C - N$ bond are expected to have similar individual frequencies and being coupled would interact.

4.5   Multiple Oscillator Groups

Groups containing multiple oscillators can also be correlated and are considered next.

In a group such as CH_2, the vibrating carbon-hydrogen bonds will not interact greatly with the $C - C$ bonds to which they are attached, but they will completely interact with each other as the individual CH bonds have the same frequencies, and they are intimately coupled because of the common atom. The resulting two frequencies, CH_2 asymmetric and symmetric stretch, will both be mechanically independent to a large degree of the rest of the molecule, however, so both bands may be correlated for the group as a whole. It is also found that attaching additional CH_2 groups to make a normal aliphatic chain does not affect the vibrational frequencies greatly even though all the CH_2 bonds vibrate for each frequency. This is because the separate CH_2 groups are not as strongly coupled to each other as the two CH's in each CH_2 group are. The effectiveness of the coupling of two oscillators which have the same individual frequency has been described above as how much one vibrating oscillator "disturbs" the other. As one CH of a CH_2 group vibrates, it moves the carbon atom which is common to both CH's. Thus, one CH vibrating disturbs the other CH, and this causes the two frequencies to diverge noticeably as a result of $CH - CH$ interaction. However, as one CH_2 group stretches in and out of phase, it "disturbs" the carbon of the next CH_2 very little because of the "insulating effect" of the low frequency $C - C$. Therefore, the frequencies as a result of $CH_2 - CH_2$ interaction diverge only slightly because of the weaker coupling.

Specifically, the group $-CH_2 - CH_2-$ has four $C - H$ bonds and will have four $C - H$ stretching vibrations (see Fig. 4.4). In vibrations (a) and (b), each CH_2 group is stretching symmetrically, and these vibrations have almost the same frequency. In vibrations (c) and (d), each CH_2 group is stretching asymmetrically, and these vibrations have almost the same frequency. A group of four CH_2's will have eight $C - H$ stretching vibrations concentrated in two main bands. In one band all the CH_2's stretch symmetrically but with four different phasings (usually unresolved), and in the other all the CH_2's stretch asymmetrically but with four different phasings (usually unresolved). Thus, in spite of interactions, we can correlate CH_2 groups regardless of the chain length.

As was mentioned before, double and triple bonds are usually attached to single bonds. Multiple double and triple bonds in one molecule are usually isolated from each other by single bonds. Thus two similar double bonds separated by a single bond will give rise to two bands due to symmetric and asymmetric double bond stretching vibrations, but the bands will not be far apart as the coupling is relatively weak, and they will be in the vicinity of the band for a molecule with one double bond.

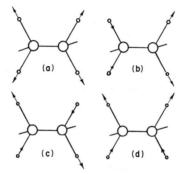

FIG. 4.4. Illustration of the four CH stretching vibrations of the $CH_2 - CH_2$ group. Vibrations (a) and (b) are found at nearly the same frequency. Vibrations (c) and (d) are also found at nearly the same frequency which is somewhat higher than the (a) and (b) frequencies.

The picture is completely different if we directly couple two double bonds by having one carbon atom common to both double bonds, as in carbon dioxide, allene, ketene, iso-cyanates, etc. Here the symmetric and asymmetric stretching frequencies are far removed from the double bond region. The asymmetric frequency occurs near the triple bond region and the symmetric frequency occurs near the single bond region. The spread is in part caused by the linearity of this type of group, as we shall see later. Both bands are correlatable for the group as a whole.

In the approximate "bond-and-a-half"* category are found nitro and ionized carboxyl groups and aromatic rings.

---

* The motions of electrons are so much faster than molecular vibrations that it is useful to think of a pi electron pair equally distributed around three atoms as approximately two "half-bonds," which, with the two sigma bonds, make two approximate "bonds-and-a-half."

Nitro and ionized carboxyl groups consist of two coupled "bond-and-a-half" bonds and have correlatable symmetric and asymmetric stretching frequencies found between the double and single bond regions. A benzene ring consists

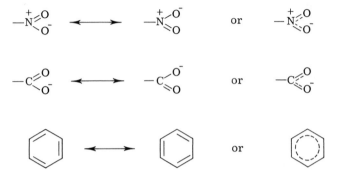

of six equal, intimately coupled, "bond-and-a-half" bonds which result in six stretching frequencies, each involving all the bonds. These range all the way from the double bond region to the single bond region.

4.6 Single Bond Interactions

As shown above, groups containing multiple, coupled oscillators with nearly the same individual frequencies must be considered as a whole. This is particularly true when the skeletal single bond stretching region is studied, for here, there are usually a number of single bonds all directly coupled to other single bonds, with the result that it is usually meaningless to talk about an individual single bond stretching frequency. For example in n-octane there are seven $C-C$ bonds which will result in seven $C-C$ stretching frequencies, but all the bonds will stretch and contract in various phases for all the vibrations (see Fig. 4.5). In practice, however, it is found that certain single bound vibrations have correlatable frequencies. When hydrocarbon chains of moderate lengths are studied, it is found from the infrared and Raman literature that the highest $C-C$ stretching frequency consists of every other bond stretching while the intervening bonds contract (see Fig. 4.6 a,b,c). The highest frequency becomes slightly higher as the chain length increases but this change is small from the two bond case of $C-C-C$ on up (see Fig. 4.5). In the related cases of unbranched aliphatic ethers, $C-O-C$, and secondary amines, $C-N-C$, the highest asymmetric skeletal stretching frequencies also give rise to correlatable infrared bands from the two bond case on up, and these have considerably more intensity in the infrared than the comparable hydrocarbon frequencies.

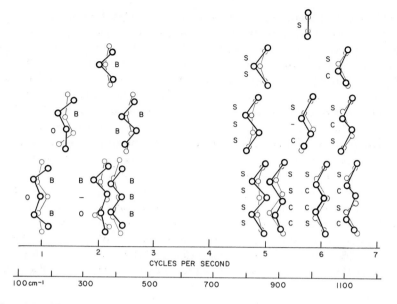

FIG. 4.5. Vibrations of ball and spring models representing the planar skeletal vibrations of some normal hydrocarbons. The extremes of the vibrations are illustrated. For one of these extremes, bonds which are stretched are labeled S and those which are contracted, C. Those angles which become smaller are labeled B for "bend" and those which become larger, O for "open." A dash (—) means no change. Nonplanar skeletal vibrations are not shown. The butane model has one nonplanar vibration, the torsion of the middle bond, and the pentane model has two, the in- and out-of-phase torsion of the two middle bonds. Model construction: 7/16-in. diameter ball bearings, 16 mil helical spring, 9 coils 11/16 in. diameter, 2 in. between atoms, supporting threads 8 ft long.

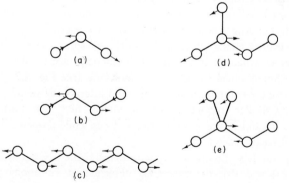

FIG. 4.6. Vibrations (a), (b), and (c) represent the highest single bond stretching frequencies for unbranched chains which do not differ a great deal in frequency with changes in chain length. Vibrations (d) and (e) represent the comparable vibrations of branched chains.

The effect of branching is best seen in the alcohols. Coupled $C-C$, $C-O$, or $C-N$ bonds are expected to interact almost completely since they have nearly the same individual frequencies. As in the above cases, the highest skeletal stretching frequencies in a straight chain primary alcohol which involve the asymmetric (or out of phase) stretching of the $O-C-C$ group give rise to correlatable bands regardless of chain length. The middle carbon of the $O-C-C$ group moves to the right as the two attached atoms move to the left. Thus as the carbon moves away from the attached oxygen, it must distort two bonds. In an aliphatic secondary alcohol, $O-C-C_2$, the comparable vibration consists of the branched carbon moving to the right while the three attached atoms have components of motion to the left. Motion of the branched carbon distorts three bonds (see Fig. 4.6 d, e). In tertiary alcohols, $O-C-C_3$ the branched carbon moves to the right while the four attached atoms have components of motion to the left. The branched carbon must distort four bonds in order to move. This extra resistance to the motion of the branched carbon atom in this type of vibration raises the frequency somewhat, enabling us to distinguish primary, secondary, and tertiary alcohols by vibrations which involve $C-O$ stretching.

4.7   Bending Interaction

Bond angle bending vibrations are found to behave in a manner similar to the stretching vibrations. In the stretching case it was found that the most important mechanical effect was the similarity of frequencies of two co-attached bond oscillators strongly coupled by having a *common atom*. In the bending case, a bond angle bending between two bonds is coupled most strongly to another bond angle bending when they both move a *common bond*, since in this case, one angle cannot change without "disturbing" some atoms of the other angle. They interact when their individual frequencies are similar. An example of this is the hypothetical $C-C-C-C$ molecule (see Fig. 4.7). The two angles α and β share the common middle bond and interact completely when they have individually similar frequencies so that in the first case, both α and β open symmetrically and in the second case, α closes while β opens. These are found at different frequencies.

This is further illustrated by considering the $-CH_2-CH_2-$ group. In Fig. 4.8 (a) and (b), the two CH_2 deformation vibrations (deforming the $H-C-H$ angle), in phase and out of phase, have almost the same frequency, as they do not strongly involve a movement of a common bond (the $C-C$ bond) and so are weakly coupled. The motion of each hydrogen is directly opposed by the motion of the other hydrogen within the CH_2 group, and the carbon of the next CH_2 is hardly moved at all. Thus, one deforming CH_2 group does not appreciably "disturb" its neighbor, so in spite of interaction, all the phasings of multiple CH_2 deformations usually give frequencies which are practically identical.

Other bendings of the CH_2 group are called wag, twist, and rock (see CH_2 discussion). In none of these does the $H-C-H$ angle change appreciably, so, the motions of the hydrogens must be directly opposed by the motion of the carbon of the next CH_2 group. These may be described as $C-C-H$ bendings, since they require a distinct motion of the $C-C$ bond to oppose the motion of the $C-H$ bond. In Fig. 4.8 (c) and (d), the two CH_2 wags (bending

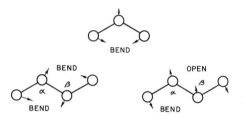

FIG. 4.7. Bending-bending interaction. The bending vibrations of the angles α and β interact resulting in two vibrations involving both α and β for each. In the bending vibration on the left as α bends it moves the middle atoms common to α and β so that the common bond rotates clockwise. As β bends it also rotates this bond clockwise. Thus these two bending oscillators *cooperate* in moving the common atoms in roughly the same direction. This effectively decreases the mass of the common atoms that one oscillator must move, which raises the frequency above the frequency for the single uncoupled oscillator. In the bending vibration on the right, as α bends it attempts to move the common bond clockwise but as β opens it attempts to move the common bond counter clockwise. This *opposition* effectively increases the mass of the common atoms that one oscillator must move which lowers the frequency below that for the single uncoupled oscillator.

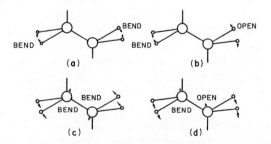

FIG. 4.8. CH_2 deformation and wagging interaction. The in- and out-of-phase CH_2 deformation vibrations (a) and (b) are found at nearly the same frequencies due to weak coupling. The in and out of phase CH_2 wagging vibrations (c) and (d) are found at somewhat different frequencies due to somewhat stronger coupling.

of the C—C—H angle as shown) both bend against a common C—C bond and are found at different frequencies because of the strong coupling. Thus while a CH_2 deformation frequency is more or less mechanically independent of the rest of the molecule and is correlatable, a CH_2 wag frequency is dependent to a much greater extent on the rest of the molecule, since one CH_2 wagging "disturbs" the carbon of the next CH_2 group. The same is true for CH_2 twist and rock.

Hydrogen wagging vibrations (out of plane) on a benzene ring give rise to useful infrared bands (see Fig. 4.9). The lone hydrogen wag on a penta substi-

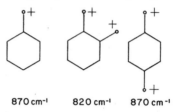

870 cm⁻¹   820 cm⁻¹   870 cm⁻¹

FIG. 4.9. Aromatic hydrogen wagging interaction. The in-phase, out-of-plane hydrogen wagging vibration of two adjacent hydrogens on a benzene ring is lower in frequency than the vibrational frequency of two isolated hydrogens due to coupling. The "plus" sign means motion up out of the plane of the page.

tuted benzene ring absorbs near 870 cm⁻¹. The two adjacent hydrogens in a vicinal tetrasubstituted benzene are coupled, since an individual CH wagging motion must be locally opposed by out of plane motions of the adjacent carbons which "disturb" the adjacent CH. Since the two CH groups have the same individual wagging frequencies and are coupled by being adjacent, they interact, and the two frequencies diverge. The in phase frequency where both hydrogens move out of plane in the same direction, gives rise to a strong infrared band near 820 cm⁻¹, lower than the frequency of the penta substituted benzene. Symmetrical tetra substituted benzenes have two isolated hydrogens para to each other, and while they interact, the coupling is weak. The in phase wagging absorbs at 870 cm⁻¹ not too different from penta substituted benzene. In 1,2,4 trisubstitution, the two adjacent hydrogens are coupled to each other but are only weakly coupled to the isolated hydrogen. An absorption which appears near 820 cm⁻¹ arises predominately from the in phase wagging of the two adjacent hydrogens, and an absorption near 870 cm⁻¹ arises predominately from the wagging of the isolated CH. While all the hydrogens move somewhat for each of these vibrations, the in phase wagging frequencies of adjacent hydrogens between substituting groups are not much affected by the presence or absence of other weakly coupled hydrogens. Thus, coupling makes it possible to distinguish an isolated hydrogen (870 cm⁻¹) from two adjacent hydrogens (820 cm⁻¹), 3(780 cm⁻¹), 4(750 cm⁻¹), or 5(740 cm⁻¹) adjacent hydrogens regardless of other hydrogens not immediately adjacent on the ring.

4.8   Bending-Stretching Interaction

When a bond stretching frequency and a bond angle bending frequency are nearly the same and are strongly coupled by having a common atom (at the "hinge" of the bond angle), they will strongly interact too. The best example of this is in monosubstituted amides (see section on amides) where the C—N—H bending frequency comes near the C—N stretching frequency and complete interaction results. In Fig. 4.10, vibration (a) appears at higher and (b) appears

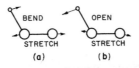

FIG. 4.10. Bending-stretching interaction. When interaction occurs between a hydrogen bending vibration and a skeletal stretching vibration, two vibrations result, each involving both bending and stretching. In this figure the hydrogen atom is represented by a small circle and the skeletal atoms X and Y by large circles. During the bending of the HXY angle (110°) the H—X bond and X—Y bond rotate in opposite directions. The rotation of the X—Y bond has little effect on the stretching of the X—Y bond since the two act at right angles to each other. The rotation of the H—X bond tends to move the X atom in such a way as to oppose or cooperate with the X—Y stretching vibration depending on the phasing. Cooperation (a) will effectively lighten the mass of the X atom which the X—Y stretching oscillator must move and will raise the frequency. Opposition (b) will lower the frequency by effectively increasing the mass of the X atom.

at lower wavenumbers than either the unmixed NH bend or C—N stretch would appear because of this interaction.

Other examples occur in phenols and carboxylic acids where similar interactions occur between the OH deformation and the C—O stretching vibrations.

4.9   Overtone-Fundamental Interaction

When an overtone of a vibration (or combination band of two vibrations) accidently occurs near the frequency of a fundamental of another vibration belonging to the same symmetry class, an interaction known as Fermi resonance can occur. The result is the same as in previous examples of interaction, namely, two frequencies result which are higher and lower than either the unmixed overtone or fundamental. Both frequencies are made up of both the overtone and the fundamental which has the apparent effect of increasing the intensity of overtones which fall near fundamentals.

An example of this is seen in many aldehydes. The aldehyde CH bending frequency occurs at just about half the frequency of the unmixed CH stretch, so that the first overtone of the CH bending coincides in frequency with the unmixed CH stretch. These two interact and two frequencies result, both of which involve both CH stretch and the overtone of CH bend.

The classic case is carbon dioxide[1] where the symmetric stretch appears in the Raman effect as two bands at 1286 and 1388 cm^{-1} due to an accidental coincidence of the unmixed symmetrical stretch with the first overtone of the bending vibration at 667 cm^{-1} ($2 \times 667 = 1334$ cm^{-1}) resulting in Fermi resonance.

4.10   The Effect of Bond Angle

In molecules, most bond angles are found to be in two main categories, the linear or 180° bond angle and the bond angle in the neighborhood of 120° to 110°. The linear case includes the triple bond-single bond angle as in nitriles and acetylenes and the double bond-double bond angle as in carbon dioxide, allenes, isocyanates, etc. The majority of other cases fall into the second category which includes aromatic and olefinic bond angles of approximately 120° to the tetrahedral CH_2 angle of approximately 109°. The main class of compounds that depart from these two categories are cyclic ring compounds.

If we consider a simplified triatomic case where the two end atoms are the same and are bound to the middle atom by two equal bonds, the approximate stretching frequencies are given by the following equations derived from Herzberg's equations for the XY_2 molecule.[1] For the symmetric case, a bending force constant of zero is assumed for simplicity. This causes a small error in the calculated symmetric stretching frequency which can be tolerated in the present discussion.

$$\nu_{sym.} \simeq \frac{1}{2\pi c} \sqrt{k \left(\frac{1}{m_{end}} + \frac{1 + \cos\alpha}{m_{mid.}} \right)}$$

$$\nu_{asym.} = \frac{1}{2\pi c} \sqrt{k \left(\frac{1}{m_{end}} + \frac{1 - \cos\alpha}{m_{mid.}} \right)}$$

[1] G. Herzberg, "Infrared and Raman Spectra of Polyatomic Molecules." Van Nostrand, New York, 1945.

Here ν is the frequency in cm^{-1}, c is the velocity of light, k is the force constant in dynes per centimeter, m_{end} is the mass in grams of one end atom, $m_{mid.}$ is the mass of the middle atom, and α is the bond angle.

The equations with ν in wavenumbers where M_{end} and $M_{mid.}$ are atomic weights and K is the actual $k \times 10^{-5}$ are given below.

$$\nu_{sym.} \simeq 1303 \sqrt{K \left(\frac{1}{M_{end}} + \frac{1 + \cos \alpha}{M_{mid.}} \right)}$$

$$\nu_{asym.} = 1303 \sqrt{K \left(\frac{1}{M_{end}} + \frac{1 - \cos \alpha}{M_{mid.}} \right)}$$

Sample calculations for the specific case where all atomic weights are 14 (approximately the values for carbon, nitrogen and oxygen) yield the results seen below for various bond angles, where K is the force constant.

α	Symmetric in cm^{-1}	Asymmetric in cm^{-1}
180°	349 $\sqrt{K}$	604 $\sqrt{K}$
120°	428 $\sqrt{K}$	552 $\sqrt{K}$
90°	493 $\sqrt{K}$	493 $\sqrt{K}$
60°	552 $\sqrt{K}$	428 $\sqrt{K}$

It is seen that the maximum spread between the symmetric and asymmetric stretching frequencies occurs for the 180° case, the separation becoming smaller as the angle decreases, the two frequencies becoming equal at 90°, and the symmetric becoming higher in frequency than the asymmetric for the 60° case. These changes are all a necessary result of the geometry change and are not caused by changes in the force constant K (see Fig. 4.11). These calculations are not to be taken too exactly but are for purposes of demonstration only.

When saturated heterocyclic rings are considered we cannot, of course, use this triatomic equation, as all the skeletal bonds are involved in all the skeletal vibrations. It has, however, served its purpose in demonstrating the effects that can result in changing bond angle.

Saturated heterocyclic rings containing one or two nitrogens or oxygens have as many skeletal stretching vibrations as there are skeletal bonds but of the two extreme frequencies, one involves the totally symmetric or ring "breathing" vibration which is usually a strong Raman band, and the other involves among other things, the asymmetric stretching of the C—O—C or C—N—C which is usually a strong infrared band.

Six-membered rings of the above type have bands close to the positions of the bands of noncyclic ethers or secondary amines, namely, the highest asymmetric stretch near 1125 cm⁻¹ and the totally symmetric stretch near 825 cm⁻¹.

In five-membered rings the extremes move closer together, the asymmetric coming near 1060 cm⁻¹ and the symmetric near 920 cm⁻¹.

In four-membered rings, both bands are near 1000 cm⁻¹.

In the three-membered rings the asymmetric stretch is near 820 cm⁻¹ and the symmetric stretch is near 1250 cm⁻¹.

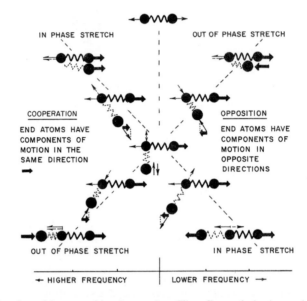

FIG. 4.11. Stretching-stretching interaction. The effects of phasing and bond angles on coupled stretching oscillators. An additional oscillator (spring represented by dotted lines) is added to an identical "diatomic" oscillator (heavy line spring) in the manner shown. Depending on the phasing and bond angle the added oscillator will tend to oppose or cooperate with the original oscillator in moving the common middle atom. This effectively increases or decreases the middle atom mass moved by the original oscillator. Opposition will lower the frequency and cooperation will raise it. At 90° the added spring has no effect on the frequency which is the same as that of the original "diatomic" oscillator. (Bending interactions are neglected here.)

This can be carried on further to consider a carbonyl to be a two-membered ring where the symmetric stretching of both bonds absorbs near 1700 cm⁻¹. Most of this effect in rings is due to a change in bond angle rather than to a change in force constant.

In olefinic or carbonyl compounds the double bond stretching vibration is not entirely mechanically independent of the rest of the molecule as has been assumed for a first approximation. During this vibration the carbon atoms directly attached to the double bond carbon usually remain nearly stationary thereby localizing the vibration to the double-bond area of the molecule. However, it is apparent that as the double bond stretches the attached single bonds will be altered in length to some degree and some bending occurs (see Fig. 4.12). This interaction has some effect on the double-bond frequency, the

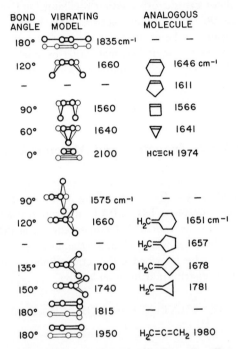

BOND ANGLE	VIBRATING MODEL		ANALOGOUS MOLECULE	
180°		1835 cm⁻¹	—	—
120°		1660		1646 cm⁻¹
—	—	—		1611
90°		1560		1566
60°		1640		1641
0°		2100	HC≡CH	1974
90°		1575 cm⁻¹	—	—
120°		1660	H₂C=	1651 cm⁻¹
—	—	—	H₂C=	1657
135°		1700	H₂C=	1678
150°		1740	H₂C=	1781
180°		1815	—	—
180°		1950	H₂C=C=CH₂	1980

FIG. 4.12. Vibrating mechanical model study showing the effect of geometry change on double bond stretching frequencies. In these models, masses and springs are unchanged. Only the angles are altered. The model wavenumbers are proportional to the model frequencies obtained. In these schematic representations of the vibrations it can be seen that in the 90° angle case, each single bond remains the same length in the two extremes of the vibration illustrated. As the angles become increasingly larger or smaller than 90°, the single bond lengths are increasingly altered during these vibrations when the double bond is stretching. This added resistance to double bond stretching raises the frequency by an amount dependent on the angle.

The reasonably good match between the model frequencies and the analogous molecular frequencies[2] implies that most of the spectral shift of double bonds in strained rings can be explained by mechanical effects with little change in force constant (spring stiffness) required.

The lower set of models (with a different proportionality constant) also serves reasonably well for cyclic carbonyl frequency shifts. The models yield 1728, 1770, and 2030 cm⁻¹ for cyclohexanone, cyclobutanone, and ketene (O=C=CH₂). Actual values are respectively 1717, 1782, and 2153 cm⁻¹.

effect varying with bond angle.[2] In noncyclic compounds the angle is usually not a variable (ca. 120°) so the effect of double-bond–single-bond interaction is unchanging. In cyclic double bond compounds however, the angle may be altered and this alters the degree of double-bond–single-bond interaction which alters the frequency to some extent. (See chapters on olefins and carbonyls.)

Thus it is seen that a bond angle change can affect the coupling, or the degree to which one oscillator can disturb another oscillator, and can therefore affect the frequencies. At 90° the coupling between two bonds is at a minimum, since the stretching of one bond does not contract or stretch the other bond but merely bends it. As the angle becomes larger or smaller, the stretching of one bond necessarily alters the other bond somewhat, and the coupling strength increases.

4.11   Introduction to Inductive and Mesomeric Effects

A phosphine oxide has a $P{=}O$ stretching vibration which absorbs near 1160 cm^{-1}. A trialkyl phosphate has its $P{=}O$ absorption near 1270 cm^{-1}. This difference, which cannot be explained by mass effects, is due to a change in distribution of the electrons which changes the force constant of the bond. The inductive effect may be described as the action of one group to affect electrostatically this electron distribution in other groups.

$$(-CH_2-CH_2)_3\,P{=}O \longleftrightarrow (-CH_2-CH_2)_3\,\overset{+}{P}-O^-$$
$$[1] \qquad\qquad\qquad\qquad [2]$$

$$(-CH_2-O-)_3\,P{=}O \longleftrightarrow (-CH_2-O-)_3\,\overset{+}{P}-O^-$$
$$[3] \qquad\qquad\qquad\qquad [4]$$

A phosphine oxide has a contribution from resonance form no. [2] which weakens the $P{=}O$ bond. In the trialkyl phosphates, the tendency for the double bonded oxygen atom to withdraw electrons from the phosphorus (no. [4]) is in competition with the tendency for the other oxygens to draw electrons from the phosphorus. Therefore resonance form no. [4] is less important, resulting in a stiffer $P{=}O$ bond for the trialkyl phosphates relative to the phosphine oxides.

The frequency of the $P{=}O$ absorption has been correlated with the sum of the electronegativities of the other attached atoms, each of which does its part in pulling electrons to compete with the $\overset{+}{P}-O^-$ resonance contribution (see $P{=}O$ discussion).

[2] N. B. Colthup, *J. Chem. Educ.* **38**, 394 (1961).

The same things happens in the case of sulfur. A dialkyl sulfoxide has an $S=O$ stretching vibration which absorbs near 1050 cm^{-1}. A dialkyl sulfite has its $S=O$ absorption near 1200 cm^{-1}. This again is due to the relative contribution of resonance forms no. [2] and no. [4].

$$(-CH_2-CH_2)_3\,S=O \longleftrightarrow (-CH_2-CH_2)_2\,\overset{+}{S}-O^-$$
$$\qquad [1] \qquad\qquad\qquad\qquad [2]$$

$$(-CH_2-O-)_2\,S=O \longleftrightarrow (-CH_2-O-)_2\,\overset{+}{S}-O^-$$
$$\qquad [3] \qquad\qquad\qquad\qquad [4]$$

When an electron attracting atom such as oxygen is attached to the sulfur, it reduces the contribution of resonance form no. [4] which results in a stiffer $S=O$ bond and absorption at higher wavenumbers.

In an SO_2 group the two coupled SO bonds have the same force constant, any change in which will affect both the symmetric and asymmetric stretching frequencies of the SO_2 group. Dialkyl sulfones $(-CH_2-CH_2)_2SO_2$ absorb near 1310 cm^{-1} and 1130 cm^{-1}. Dialkyl sulfates $(-CH_2-O)_2SO_2$ absorb near 1400 cm^{-1} and 1200 cm^{-1}. This increase is again due to the electron attracting ability of the attached atoms.

In the sulfur and phosphorus compounds mentioned above, the inductive or electrostatic effect alone explains most of the spectral shifts.

In the carbonyl case the inductive effect alone is insufficient to explain the spectral shifts. In addition to the inductive effect, we must also consider the mesomeric effect or changes in distribution of pi electrons. In the carbonyl compounds below, varying contributions from resonance forms no. [2] and no. [3] will alter the $C=O$ stretching frequency.

[1] $C-\overset{\displaystyle O}{\overset{\|}{C}}-Cl$	[2] $C-\overset{\displaystyle O^-}{\overset{\|}{\underset{+}{C}}}-Cl$	[3] $C-\overset{\displaystyle O^-}{\overset{\|}{C}}=\overset{+}{Cl}$	1800 cm^{-1}
$C-\overset{\displaystyle O}{\overset{\|}{C}}-O-C$	$C-\overset{\displaystyle O^-}{\overset{\|}{\underset{+}{C}}}-O-C$	$C-\overset{\displaystyle O^-}{\overset{\|}{C}}=\overset{+}{O}-C$	1740 cm^{-1}
$C-\overset{\displaystyle O}{\overset{\|}{C}}-CH_2$	$C-\overset{\displaystyle O^-}{\overset{\|}{\underset{+}{C}}}-CH_2$	$C-\overset{\displaystyle O^-}{\overset{\|}{C}}=\overset{+}{CH_2}$	1715 cm^{-1}
$C-\overset{\displaystyle O}{\overset{\|}{C}}-C=C$	$C-\overset{\displaystyle O^-}{\overset{\|}{\underset{+}{C}}}-C=C$	$C-\overset{\displaystyle O^-}{\overset{\|}{C}}=C-\overset{+}{C}$	1685 cm^{-1}
$C-\overset{\displaystyle O}{\overset{\|}{C}}-N$	$C-\overset{\displaystyle O^-}{\overset{\|}{\underset{+}{C}}}-N$	$C-\overset{\displaystyle O}{\overset{\|}{C}}=N^+$	1670 cm^{-1}

As in the previous cases, adjacent electronegative groups such as chlorine, oxygen, or nitrogen should raise the frequency of the $C=O$ vibration relative to ketones due to the inductive effect which reduces the contribution from resonance form no. [2]. The mesomeric effect, however, will lower the frequency, as it weakens the C=O bond as seen in resonance form no. [3]. In amides there is a large mesomeric effect which lowers the carbonyl frequency below that of ketones. An acid chloride has little mesomeric effect. Its high frequency is due to the inductive effect. In esters, both the inductive and mesomeric effect play a part. The carbonyl frequency is intermediate between amide and acid chlorides, and is somewhat higher than ketones. Conjugation with a double bond or aromatic ring weakens the carbonyl force constant by resonance (no. [3]) resulting in a lower frequency.

Both groups on the carbonyl affect its frequency. A urethane $C-O-CO-N$ is intermediate in frequency between an amide and an ester. The compound $Cl-CO-NR_2$ is intermediate in frequency between an amide and an acid chloride.

Electrostatic effects do not necessarily have to act through the bond. If a negative charge could be brought near the oxygen of the carbonyl, it would repel negative charges on the oxygen. The $C^+_-O^-$ resonance contribution would be reduced, resulting in a stiffer bond and a higher frequency. In α-chloro acetone, there are two rotational isomers. The carbonyl absorption in the isomer where the chlorine is near the oxygen is 20 cm⁻¹ higher than the isomer where the chlorine is not near the oxygen. Since both isomers should have similar inductive effects through the bond, this 20 cm⁻¹ difference is due to a "field effect" due to the concentration of electrons around the chlorine electrostatically repelling a negative charge on the oxygen atom and therefore stiffening the C=O bond (see ketones).

In substituted anilines, the effect of electron repelling or electron attracting groups may be seen in changes in the strong $C-N$ absorption near 1300 cm⁻¹.

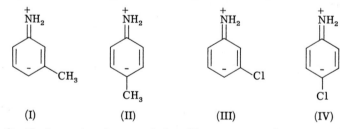

(I)   (II)   (III)   (IV)

The $C-N$ absorption in p-methyl aniline occurs at lower wavenumbers than the *meta* isomer, because the electron repelling character of the methyl partially interferes with the $C-N$ stiffening resonance no. [2] which concentrates negative charges near the methyl. In the same manner, p-chloro aniline enhances the $C-N$ stiffening resonance no. [4] due to the electron attracting characteristics of the chlorine, and therefore the $C-N$ absorbs at higher wavenumbers than the *meta* isomer.

There are many other examples of mesomeric and inductive effects where one group changes the electron distribution of another group. When the vibrational frequency of the affected group is unaffected by mass changes or geometry changes, the frequency of the group may be directly correlated with other physical properties such as Hammett σ values, electronegativities, o, p directing ability, etc., many examples of which exist in the literature. These will be discussed individually in later sections.

4.12 Hydrogen Bonding

Hydrogen bonding[3-5] has long been recognized as an interaction between an X—H group of a molecule with a Y atom, usually of another molecule. The X—H group is described as a proton donor and the Y atom as the proton acceptor. The atoms usually involved in strong hydrogen bond formation are N, O, and F.

Since the force field around the hydrogen atom is modified as a result of the formation of the X—H $\cdots$ Y bond, the X—H vibrational bands are altered. The X—H stretching band, which is usually sharp in the unbonded state in dilute solution in CCl_4 or in the vapor state, usually becomes broader and more intense and is shifted to lower frequencies upon the formation of a hydrogen bond (see Fig. 4.13).

Vibrations involving X—H bending usually increase in frequency upon the formation of a hydrogen bond, the shift being the reverse of the shift in the stretching vibration. Vibrations involving the Y atom may also be altered since the force field around Y is altered as a result of the hydrogen bond.

The amount of the X—H frequency shift upon formation of the X—H $\cdots$ Y bond has been correlated with the X $\cdots$ Y distance, the smaller the distance, the larger the shift.[6,7]

It has also been observed that the lower the ionization potential (higher acidity) of the X—H bond and the higher the electron affinity (higher basicity) of Y, the stronger is the hydrogen bond X—H $\cdots$ Y, and the shorter the X $\cdots$ Y distance[3] (see Fig. 4.13).

The criteria for hydrogen bond formation is as follows.[3]

[3] C. G. Cannon, *Spectrochim. Acta* 10, 341 (1958).
[4] C. A. Coulson, *Research* 10, 149 (1957).
[5] L. Kellner, *Rept. Progr. Phys.* 15, 1 (1952).
[6] R. C. Lord and R. E. Merrifield, *J. Chem. Phys.* 21, 166 (1953).
[7] K. Nakamoto, M. Margoshes, and R. E. Rundle, *J. Am. Chem. Soc.* 77, 6480 (1955)

(a) The X—H bond must have a tendency to be partially ionic in character, the X atom being of high electronegativity. This leads to an X—H bond where the $1s$ orbital of the hydrogen atom is not fully used and is available for overlap with the lone pair orbital of Y. ($\overline{X}$—H$^+$)

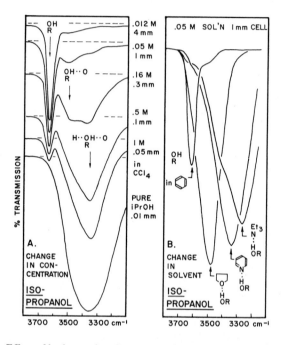

FIG. 4.13.   Effect of hydrogen bonding on the OH stretching vibration of isopropanol.
A. Shows the effect of changing the isopropanol concentration in CCl$_4$ (M = molar) and compensating for dilution by increasing the cell thickness (given in mm). The number of isopropanol molecules in the spectrometer beam remains constant. The background level is adjusted to prevent overlap.
B. Shows the effect of changing the solvent (benzene, tetrahydrofuran, pyridine, and triethyl amine) while leaving the isopropanol concentration (0.05 M) and the cell thickness (1 mm) unchanged.

(b) The Y atom must have lone pair electrons in a nonspherical orbital such as sp hybrid orbitals.

(c) For maximum hydrogen bond energy the X—H bond and the axis of the lone pair orbital must be collinear.

CHAPTER 5

ALIPHATIC GROUPS

In this and in the following chapters spectra-structure correlations will be discussed in detail. These will be infrared correlations unless they are specifically labeled as Raman correlations. For many groups such as $C \equiv N$, $C = O$, $C = C$, etc., frequency correlations will be the same for both techniques.

5.1 Methyl Groups

The vibrations of the CH_3 group are listed in Fig. 5.1.[1,2]

There are three CH bonds in a methyl group so there will be three CH stretching vibrations. In the symmetric stretching vibration, all three hydrogens move out together away from the carbon. The two asymmetric CH_3 stretching vibrations are usually very similar in frequency. One of these can be approximately described as two hydrogens moving out and the third hydrogen in.

The two asymmetric CH_3 deformations are also very similar in frequency. One of these can be approximately described as two hydrogens move toward each other, as in a CH_2 scissors bending, while the other moves away from both. The symmetric CH_3 deformation has been described as an "umbrella" vibration where all three hydrogens move towards each other together.

The stretchings and deformations are all more or less localized in the CH_3 group and have frequencies in correlatable regions of the spectrum. If the CH_3 group is compared with NH_3, these frequencies correspond to NH_3 vibrations. The CH_3 rocking and torsion vibrations in which the CH_3 group does not internally deform but moves as a whole unit, correspond to NH_3 rotations which in the CH_3 case, must be compensated for by motions of the rest of the molecule. Because the rest of the molecule is mechanically involved in these vibrations, the CH_3 rocking vibration is quite variable in its frequency.

The spectral regions for the CH_3 group are listed in Table 5.1.

[1] N. Sheppard and D. M. Simpson, Quart. Rev. (London) 7, 19 (1953).
[2] N. Sheppard, Trans. Faraday Soc. 51, 1465 (1955).

The asymmetric CH_3 stretching vibration for an aliphatic CH_3 group absorbs[3] near 2960 ± 10 cm^{-1} and in a hydrocarbon chain, can be differentiated from the CH_2 absorption near 2930 cm^{-1}. The symmetric CH_3 stretch absorbs at 2870 ± 10 cm^{-1},[3] while additional bands due to the CH_3 groups occur in some compounds at 2934 cm^{-1} and 2912 cm^{-1}.[3] Methyl groups on aromatic rings usually have prominent bands near 2925 and 2865 cm^{-1} with variable intensity bands near 2975 and 2945 cm^{-1}.[4] Methyl groups[5-7] on oxygen, sulfur[6], and on nitrogen[8,9] in amines have been studied. The methyl amine

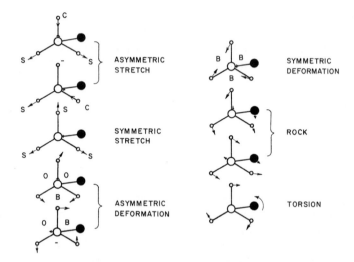

FIG. 5.1.   Vibrations of the CH_3 group. Those CH bonds which are stretching are ,abeled S and those contracting C. Those HCH angles which become smaller are labeled B for bend, and those which become larger, O for open. A dash means no change. In the first asymmetric stretching vibration the top half of the methyl group stretches while the bottom half contracts and in the second, the left half stretches while the right half contracts. In the first asymmetric deformation the bottom half bends while the top half opens and in the second, the right half bends while the left half opens. In the symmetric stretching and deformation vibrations all the CH bonds stretch in phase and all the HCH angles bend in phase. In the rock and torsion vibrations, the CH_3 group does not deform internally but rotates as a whole unit in three different directions.

[3] J. J. Fox and A. E. Martin, *Proc. Roy. Soc. (London)* **A167**, 257 (1938).

[4] G. M. Badger and A. G. Moritz, *Spectrochim. Acta* **15**, 672 (1959).

[5] S. E. Wiberley, S. C. Bunce, and W. H. Bauer, *Anal. Chem.* **32**, 217 (1960).

[6] A. Pozefsky and N. D. Coggeshall, *Anal. Chem.* **23**, 1611 (1951).

[7] H. B. Henbest, G. D. Meakins, B. Nicholls, and A. A. Wagland, *J. Chem. Soc.* **1957**, 1462.

[8] R. D. Hill and G. D. Meakins, *J. Chem. Soc.* **1958**, 760.

[9] W. B. Wright, Jr., *J. Org. Chem.* **24**, 1362 (1959).

TABLE 5.1

SPECTRAL BANDS FOR THE CH_3 GROUP GIVEN IN CM^{-1}

(aliphatic) $-CH_3$	2972–2952 strong (asymmetric stretch)
	2882–2862 weaker than 2960 (symmetric stretch)
	1475–1450 medium (asymmetric deformation)
	1383–1377 medium (symmetric deformation)
(aromatic) $-CH_3$	2930–2920 medium
	2870–2860 medium
CH_3 | $-CH_2-CH-CH_2-$	1159–1151 medium

$\quad\quad CH_3$
   /
(R)CH
   \\
$\quad\quad CH_3$
(R = hydrocarbon group)
	1389–1381 medium

	1372–1368 equal to the 1385 intensity
	1171–1168 medium
	1150–1130 variable

CH_3
  |
$(R)-C-(R)$
  |
CH_3
	1391–1381 medium

	1368–1366 intensity 5/4 1385
	1221–1206 weak
	1191–1185 medium

CH_3
  |
$(R)-C-CH_3$
  |
CH_3
	1401–1393 medium

	1374–1366 about twice the 1390 intensity
	1253–1235 medium
	1208–1163 medium
$CH_3-(C=O)$	3000–2900 much weaker than hydrocarbons
	1440–1405 medium
	1375–1350 stronger than hydrocarbons
(aliphatic) $-N-CH_3$ (amine)	2805–2780 strong
(aromatic) $-N-CH_3$	2820–2810
(aliphatic) $-N-(CH_3)_2$	2825–2810 2775–2765
(aromatic) $-N-(CH_3)_2$	2810–2790
$(RO)CH_3$	2992–2955 strong (asymmetric stretch)
	2897–2867 strong (symmetric stretch)
	2832–2815 variable (deformation overtone)
	1470–1440 medium (asymmetric and symmetric deformation)
$(RS)CH_3$ $(R-S-S)CH_3$	2992–2955 medium (asymmetric stretch)
	2897–2867 medium (symmetric stretch)
	1440–1415 medium (asymmetric deformation)
	1330–1290 weaker (symmetric deformation)
$Si-CH_3$	1440–1410 weak (asymmetric deformation)
	1270–1255 strong (symmetric deformation)
$P-CH_3$	1330–1280 weak (symmetric deformation)

group absorbs near 2800 cm^{-1}. The CH stretching region is sometimes complicated by CH deformation overtones or combination bands intensified by Fermi resonance.

In aliphatic compounds the asymmetric CH_3 deformation absorbs near 1465 cm^{-1} and the symmetric deformation near 1375 cm^{-1}.[10] When there are two methyls on one aliphatic carbon atom, two bands with nearly equal intensity appear near 1385 and 1370 cm^{-1} due to in phase and out of phase interaction of the two symmetrical CH_3 deformations.[10] A t-butyl group has a strong band near 1365 cm^{-1} and a weaker one near 1390 cm^{-1} [10] from the same cause. When the methyl is next to a carbonyl, an intensified symmetric CH_3 deformation appears at 1375–1350 cm^{-1}.[11] The above methyl frequencies show some sensitivity to the electronegativity of the attached atom,[2,12,13] the symmetric deformation being particularly sensitive. See Table 5.2 which is arranged according to the periodic chart of elements. These changes are largely due to changes in the HCX bending force constant.[2]

TABLE 5.2

SYMMETRIC CH_3 DEFORMATION

(2)			(4)		
$F-CH_3$	1475	cm^{-1}	$Br-CH_3$	1305	cm^{-1}
$O-CH_3$	1460–1440		$Se-CH_3$	1282	
$N-CH_3$	1440–1410		$As-CH_3$	1263–1242	
$C-CH_3$	1385–1370		$Ge-CH_3$	1240–1230	
$B-CH_3$	1330–1280				
			(5)		
(3)			$I-CH_3$	1252	
$Cl-CH_3$	1355		$Sb-CH_3$	1213–1194	
$S-CH_3$	1330–1290		$Sn-CH_3$	1200–1180	
$P-CH_3$	1310–1280				
$Si-CH_3$	1280–1255		(6)		
			$Bi-CH_3$	1165–1147	
			$Pb-CH_3$	1170–1154	

For the symmetric CH_3 deformation there is little overlap of position for different types of methyls. For example, a band at 1375 cm^{-1} is due only to a methyl on a carbon atom.

[10] H. L. McMurry and V. Thornton, *Anal. Chem.* 24, 318 (1952).
[11] N. B. Colthup, *J. Opt. Soc. Am.* 40, 397 (1950).
[12] L. J. Bellamy and R. L. Williams, *J. Chem. Soc.* 1956, 2753.
[13] J. K. Wilmshurst, *J. Chem. Phys.* 26, 426 (1957).

The asymmetric deformation is less variable, ranging from 1471 to 1410 cm⁻¹. The asymmetric XCH_3 deformation and the XCH_2 scissors deformation are usually found in about the same region.

Methyl rocking frequencies are mass sensitive and variable in position due to interaction with skeletal stretching modes. While they are not as reliable as the stretching and deformation bands, a few remarks may be made. In normal hydrocarbons, the CH_3 rock absorbs weakly at 1150–1120 cm⁻¹ and at 900–890 cm⁻¹.[14,15] In isopropyl groups in hydrocarbons, a band involving CH_3 rock usually occurs[10] at 922–919 cm⁻¹ and in t-butyl groups in hydrocarbons, at 932–926 cm⁻¹.[10] In nonhydrocarbons, the regions are wider, at 950–875 cm⁻¹ and 935–810 cm⁻¹ respectively. A CH_3 on an aromatic ring usually absorbs near 1040 cm⁻¹. An $S—CH_3$ has a rocking frequency near 960 cm⁻¹, a $P—CH_3$ near 880, and an $Si—CH_3$ near 800 cm⁻¹ (see sections on phosphorus and silicon).

Branching of the skeletal chain causes absorption due to the asymmetric motion of the branched carbon against its neighbors. Secondary branching causes absorption bands near 1150 cm⁻¹ and tertiary branching, near 1200 cm⁻¹.[10] Certain $C—C$ stretching vibrations such as the above can interact with methyl rocking vibrations of the same symmetry class, the resultant mixing making exact nomenclature distinction difficult. In the branched case it is likely that both the 920 and 1150 cm⁻¹ bands involve both asymmetric $C—C—C$ stretching and methyl rocking.

For hydrocarbon intensity measurements, see McMurry and Thornton,[10] Jones,[15] Francis,[16] and Egorov et al.[17]

5.2 Methylene Groups

The vibrations of the CH_2 group are illustrated in Fig. 5.2.[1]

In the first three vibrations (asymmetric and symmetric stretch and deformation) the vibration is more or less completely localized within the CH_2 group and results in correlatable absorption frequencies. If this group is compared with the H_2O molecule, the first three vibrations correspond to H_2O vibrations, but the last three (wag, twist, and rock) correspond to H_2O rotations. In the CH_2 group, these "rotations" are opposed by motions of the carbon atoms attached to the CH_2 group, and therefore these attached atoms are definitely

[14] J. K. Brown, N. Sheppard, and D. M. Simpson, *Phil. Trans.* **A247**, 35 (1954).

[15] R. N. Jones, *Spectrochim. Acta* **9**, 235 (1957).

[16] S. A. Francis, *Anal. Chem.* **25**, 1466 (1953).

[17] Y. P. Egorov, V. V. Shlyapochnikov, and A. D. Petrov, *J. Anal. Chem.* (USSR) **14**, 617 (1959).

mechanically involved in the vibrations. This causes among other things, a coupling between adjacent CH_2 groups and, as a result, in a chain of CH_2 groups, the wag, twist, and rock frequencies are each spread out over a region. In the asymmetric and symmetric stretching frequencies and the deformation frequencies, the coupling between adjacent CH_2 groups is weak, so each of these frequencies falls in a narrow correlatable region of the spectrum.

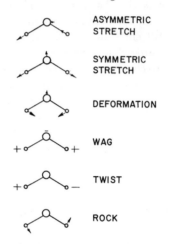

ASYMMETRIC STRETCH

SYMMETRIC STRETCH

DEFORMATION

WAG

TWIST

ROCK

FIG. 5.2.   Vibrations of the CH_2 group. The symbols $+$ and $-$ mean motion out of the plane of the page.

In the case of the CH_2 rocking frequencies which are spread over a region, the lowest and most intense rocking frequency, where all the CH_2 groups rock in phase, does fall in a correlatable region near 724 cm^{-1} when there are 4 or more CH_2 groups in a noncyclic hydrocarbon chain.[10] The CH_2 spectral regions are listed in Table 5.3.

In most hydrocarbons, the CH_2 asymmetric stretch is near 2930 cm^{-1}, the symmetric stretch[3,5] near 2850 cm^{-1} and the deformation near 1465 cm^{-1}. Unsaturation (double or triple bond) next to the CH_2 lowers its deformation to about 1440 cm^{-1}. A carbonyl, nitrile, or nitro group lowers the deformation frequency of the adjacent CH_2 group to about 1425 cm^{-1} and intensifies it. Sulfur, phosphorus, silicon, chlorine, bromine, and iodine all lower the deformation frequency of the adjacent CH_2 group to 1450–1405 cm^{-1}.

In ethers, alcohols, and amines, the absorption of the symmetrical CH_2 stretch of the adjacent CH_2 group usually becomes about the same intensity as the asymmetric and so stands out from other CH_2 groups. In secondary and tertiary amines (but not in amides), the symmetrical CH_2 stretching frequency of the CH_2 group next to the nitrogen atom, in addition to being intensified, becomes lower in frequency, appearing near 2800 cm^{-1}.[9] The same

TABLE 5.3

SPECTRAL BANDS FOR THE CH_2 GROUP

$(R)-CH_2-(R)$ $(R = $ hydrocarbon group$)$	2936–2916 strong (asymmetric stretch) 2863–2843 weaker than 2930 (symmetric stretch) 1475–1450 medium (deformation)
$-(CH_2)_6-(CH_3)$	724– 722 weak (CH_2 rock)
$-(CH_2)_5-(CH_3)$	724– 723
$-(CH_2)_4-(CH_3)$	726– 724
$-(CH_2)_3-(CH_3)$	729– 726
$-(CH_2)_2-(CH_3)$ (4th carbon branched)	743– 734
$-CH_2-(CH_3)$ (3rd carbon branched)	785– 770
$(R)-CH_2-(CH=CH_2)$ $(R)-CH_2-(C\equiv CH)$	2936–2916 strong 2863–2843 weaker than 2930 1455–1435 medium
$(R)-CH_2-(C=O)$ $(R)-CH_2-(C\equiv N)$ $(R)-CH_2-(NO_2)$	3000–2900 medium (stretch) 1445–1405 stronger than in hydrocarbons (deformation)
$(R)-CH_2-(O-R)$ $(R)-CH_2-(OH)$ $(R)-CH_2-(NH_2)$	2955–2922 strong 2878–2835 as strong as 2930 1475–1445 medium
$(R)-CH_2-(NHR)$ $(R)-CH_2-(NR_2)$	2960–2920 strong 2820–2760 as strong as 2930 1475–1445 medium
$(R)-CH_2-(SH)$ $(R)-CH_2-(S-C)$ $(R)-CH_2-(S-S)$	2948–2922 strong 2878–2846 weaker than 2930 1440–1415 medium (deformation) 1270–1220 strong (CH_2 wag)
$(R)-CH_2(Cl)$	3000–2950 weak 1460–1430 medium (deformation) 1300–1240 strong (CH_2 wag)
$(R)-CH_2(P)$	1445–1405 medium
CH_2 in cyclopropanes	3100–3072 (asymmetric stretch) 3033–2995 (symmetric stretch) 1050–1000
CH_2 in cyclobutanes	2999–2977 (asymmetric stretch) 2924–2875 (symmetric stretch)
CH_2 in cyclopentanes	2959–2952 (asymmetric stretch) 2866–2853 (symmetric stretch)
CH_2 in cyclohexanes	ca. 2927 (asymmetric stretch) ca. 2854 (symmetric stretch)
Epoxy	3058–3029 3004–2990 (usually one band only)

is true of an $N-CH_3$ group, (see Table 5.1). This effect in amines is completely eliminated when the nitrogen acquires a positive charge in amine salts.

Overtones and combination bands of CH bending vibrations intensified by Fermi resonance appear in the CH stretching region. These can usually be seen on the low frequency side of the main CH stretching bands. A particularly distinct band is usually seen in cyclohexanes near 2700 cm^{-1}.

In cyclic rings, there is a steady increase in the CH_2 asymmetric stretching frequency from the normal 6-membered ring near 2930 cm^{-1} to the strained 3-membered ring near 3080 cm^{-1}.[5,18-21] The CH_2 and CH groups in a cyclopropane ring absorb at 3100-2990 cm^{-1}.[5,19,21] A band at 1050-1000 cm^{-1} is characteristic for most cyclopropyl rings.[21,22] Bands for monoalkyl substituted cyclopropanes appear near 3080, 1020-1000, and 820-810 cm^{-1}.[23] Bands for 1,1 dialkyl cyclopropanes appear near 3080, 1020-1000, and 880-840 cm^{-1}.[23] Highly substituted cyclopropyl rings may be difficult to characterize. Monoalkyl cyclobutanes absorb at 920-910 cm^{-1}.[22]

The in phase CH_2 rock of four or more adjacent CH_2 groups in a chain absorbs at 724 cm^{-1}. The frequency increases as there are fewer adjacent CH_2 groups.[10]

The CH_2 wagging frequencies can be most clearly seen in the solid phase spectra of long straight chain compounds such as acids and soaps. A series of sharp bands between 1347 and 1182 cm^{-1} can be seen whose complexity increases with the number of CH_2 groups in the chain (see acids). In liquid normal hydrocarbons, a CH_2 wagging vibration absorbs weakly at 1307-1304 cm^{-1}.[15] The CH_2 wag bands are intensified in CH_2Cl (ca. 1275 $\pm$ 25 cm^{-1}), CH_2S (ca. 1250 cm^{-1}), CH_2Br (ca. 1230 cm^{-1}), and CH_2I (ca. 1170 cm^{-1}). The CH_2 wagging vibration is mechanically related to CH_3 symmetrical deformation vibration. The frequencies show the same sensitivity to substituent electronegativity. The CH_2 wagging frequencies in $C-CH_2-X$ compounds are about 50-75 cm^{-1} lower than the CH_3 symmetrical deformation frequencies in comparable X-CH_3 compounds.

The CH_2 twisting vibrations usually are quite weak and are therefore of little use. They usually appear at a little lower frequency than the CH_2 wagging frequencies.

[18] S. H. Hastings, A. T. Watson, R. B. Williams, and J. A. Anderson, Jr., *Anal. Chem.* 24, 612 (1952).

[19] E. K. Plyler and N. Acquista, *J. Res. Natl. Bur. Standards* 43, 37 (1949).

[20] H. B. Henbest, G. D. Meakins, B. Nicholls, and K. J. Taylor, *J. Chem. Soc.* 1957, 1459.

[21] S. A. Liebman and B. J. Gudzinowicz, *Anal. Chem.* 33, 931 (1961).

[22] J. M. Derfer, E. E. Pickett, and C. E. Boord, *J. Am. Chem. Soc.* 71, 2482 (1949).

[23] L. M. Sverdlov and E. P. Krainov, *Opt. i Spektroskopiya* 7, 460 (1959).

5.3   Carbon-Hydrogen Group

In Table 5.4 are listed correlations for the CH group.

TABLE 5.4

SPECTRAL REGIONS FOR THE CH GROUP

−O−CH	Orthoformates	
	Acetals, *Sec*-peroxides	1350–1315 cm⁻¹ medium
−N−CH	Substituted amine	
HO−CH	*Sec*-alcohol free	1410–1350 1300–1200
	Sec-alcohol bonded	1440–1400 1350–1285
−CHO	Aldehyde	2900–2800 2775–2695 1420–1370

The hydrocarbon CH stretch occurs[3] near 2900 cm^{-1} and is usually lost among other aliphatic absorptions. The CH deformation absorbs weakly in hydrocarbons at 1350–1315 cm^{-1} in the infrared. This vibration is more distinctive in the Raman effect. In nonhydrocarbons such as orthoformates, acetals, secondary peroxides, or α-substituted amines, the CH deformation at 1350–1315 cm^{-1} is intensified in the infrared.[11] In secondary alcohols, the CH and OH deformation interact to give two bands sensitive to hydrogen bonding at 1440–1350 and 1350–1200 cm^{-1} (see alcohols). A chlorine next to the CH will raise the stretching (ca. 3000 cm^{-1}) and lower and intensify the bending frequency (1250–1200 cm^{-1}).

When the CH is attached to a carbonyl, as in the formates and formamides, the stretching and bending frequencies are about 2930–2900 and 1400 cm^{-1} respectively but are not very useful for correlation purposes.

In aldehydes, the CH in plane deformation absorbs at 1410–1370 cm^{-1}. Two aldehyde bands are usually observed in the CH stretch region[5,24] at 2900–2800 cm^{-1} and 2775–2695 which are probably due to an interaction between the CH stretch and the overtone of the CH deformation. The few aldehydes which do not show this doubling (e.g., chloral) have a larger discrepancy between the overtone and the fundamental, so that interaction does not occur (see aldehydes).

[24] S. Pinchas, *Anal. Chem.* **27**, 2 (1955).

CHAPTER 6

TRIPLE BONDS AND CUMULATED DOUBLE BONDS

6.1 Introduction

Triple bonds (X≡Y) absorb in the region 2300–2000 cm⁻¹ due to the triple bond stretching vibration. Cumulated double bonds, or two double bonds on the same atom (X = Y = Z), absorb in roughly the same region 2275–1900 cm⁻¹, due to the asymmetric stretching of the X = Y = Z bonds.* The symmetric X = Y = Z stretching band occurs usually at 1400–1100 cm⁻¹ but on the whole is too weak or indistinct to be generally useful. The wide displacement of the symmetric and asymmetric X = Y = Z vibrations from the X = Y region (1800–1600 cm⁻¹) is due to the linearity of the group. For a 180° bond angle, the separation of the two frequencies is at a maximum. Many of the compounds of these types are actually resonance hybrids of triple and cumulated double bond forms, so that nomenclature distinction is difficult in some cases. In general, compounds which are predominantly X = Y = Z absorb considerably more strongly than compounds which are predominantly X≡Y. Since this region of the spectrum is relatively absorption free, even weak X = Y absorption can be distinctive and reliable. Table 6.1 lists the spectral regions for these types of groups.

6.2 Monosubstituted Acetylenes

The ≡CH stretching band near 3300 cm⁻¹ has a narrower half intensity band width than the usual bonded NH or OH bands which appear in this region.

---

* If the M≡M oscillator frequency and the linear M=M=M asymmetric stretching frequency are calculated by the equations in Sections 4.2 and 4.10 the results will be identical if k for M=M is 2/3 k for M≡M.

TABLE 6.1

THE 2300–1900 CM^{-1} REGION

$-C\equiv C-H$	2140–2100 cm^{-1}	weak-variable
$-C\equiv C-$	2260–2190	very weak-variable
$C=C=CH_2$	2000–1900	strong
$CH_2-C\equiv N$	2260–2240	medium weak
$C=C-C\equiv N$	2235–2215	medium
aryl-$C\equiv N$	2240–2220	variable
$-C\equiv N\rightarrow O$	2304–2288	strong
$-N=C=O$	2275–2263	very strong
$-S-C\equiv N$	2170–2135	medium strong
$-N=C=S$	2150–2050	very strong
$>N-C\equiv N$	2225–2175	strong
$-N=C=N-$	2150–2100	very strong
$>C=C=N-$	2050–2000	very strong
$-CH=\overset{+}{N}=\overset{-}{N}$	2132–2012	very strong
$-N=\overset{+}{N}=\overset{-}{N}$	2170–2080	very strong
aryl-$\overset{+}{N}\equiv N$	2309–2136	medium
$-\overset{+}{N}\equiv\overset{-}{C}$	2165–2110	strong
$>C=C=O$	2159–2127	very strong
$[C\equiv N]^-$	2200–2070	medium
$[Fe(C\equiv N)_6]^{4-}$	2010	medium
$[Fe(C\equiv N)_6]^{3-}$	2100	medium
$[N=C=O]^-$	2220–2130	strong
$[N=C=S]^-$	2090–2020	strong
metal(CO)	2170–1900	strong

The $C\equiv C$ stretching frequency absorbs weakly but clearly in alkyl acetylenes near 2120 cm^{-1}. Conjugation with a carbonyl increases the intensity of this band. The broad strong band due to $\equiv$CH wag is usually prominent at 700–610 cm^{-1} and has a broad weak overtone at 1375–1225 cm^{-1}. The regions for the $C\equiv CH$ group are summarized in Table 6.2.[1,2,2a]

TABLE 6.2

$\equiv C-H$ stretch	3340–3267 cm^{-1}	strong
$C\equiv C$ stretch	2140–2100	weak in hydrocarbons
overtone CH wag	1375–1225	weak-broad
$\equiv C-H$ wag	700– 610	strong-broad

[1] R. A. Nyquist and W. J. Potts, *Spectrochim. Acta* **16**, 419 (1960).

[2] J. H. Wotiz and F. A. Miller, *J. Am. Chem. Soc.* **71**, 3441 (1949).

[2a] N. Sheppard and D. M. Simpson, *Quart. Rev. (London)* **6**, 1 (1952).

6.3 Disubstituted Acetylenes

The $C-C{\equiv}C-C$ stretching frequency appears near 2260–2190 cm^{-1} in hydrocarbons,[2,3] but because of symmetry, when the substituents are similar in mass and inductive and mesomeric properties, the intensity may be very weak or zero in the infrared. This vibration is far better studied in the Raman effect where it shows up strongly. In the Raman spectra of dialkyl acetylenes two bands appear near 2300 and 2235 cm^{-1}, probably due to Fermi-resonance doubling.[2,2a,3] When the two substituents are sufficiently different in their properties, the bond is made more polar and a strong band may result in the infrared.

A CH_2 wagging band in the narrow range 1336–1325 cm^{-1} is characteristic for most molecules containing the group $-C{\equiv}C-CH_2-CH_2-$.[4]

6.4 Allenes

Allenes ($C{=}C{=}CH_2$) absorb strongly at 2000–1900 cm^{-1} due to the asymmetric CCC stretch. The band is sometimes double. The terminal $=CH_2$ wagging vibration gives rise to a strong band near 850 cm^{-1} with its overtone near 1700 cm^{-1}.[5]

6.5 Nitriles

Nitriles are characterized by the $C{\equiv}N$ stretching frequency which occurs[6] at 2260–2240 cm^{-1} in aliphatic nitriles. This medium intensity band is weakened in intensity when an electron attracting atom such as oxygen or chlorine is placed on the α carbon, whereas the same group on the β carbon has less effect.[6,7] A CH_2 group next to the nitrile absorbs near 1425 cm^{-1}.

[3] M J. Murray and F. F. Cleveland, *J. Am. Chem. Soc.* **63**, 1718 (1941).

[4] J. J. Mannion and T. S. Wang, *Spectrochim. Acta* **17**, 990 (1961).

[5] J. H. Wotiz and D. E. Mancuso, *J. Org. Chem.* **22**, 207 (1957).

[6] R. E. Kitson and N. E. Griffith, *Anal. Chem.* **24**, 334 (1952).

[7] J. P. Jesson and H. W. Thompson, *Spectrochim. Acta* **13**, 217 (1958).

Conjugation lowers the nitrile frequency, due to resonance, to 2235–2215 cm^{-1} in most cases.[6]

The β amino acrylonitriles appear lower still and absorb strongly at 2210–2185 cm^{-1} due to resonance[7a]

$$(> \overset{+}{N} = CH - CH = C = \overset{-}{N}).$$

Benzonitriles absorb at 2240–2220 cm^{-1}. The intensity of this band is quite variable and depends on the nature of substituents. Electron attracting groups such as nitro groups decrease the band intensity and increase the frequency, whereas electron donating groups such as amino groups increase the intensity and decrease the frequency.[8] The frequencies and the log of the intensity A have been correlated with Hammett σ values.[8]

6.6 Nitrile N-oxides

Aryl nitrile N-oxides (aryl $-C\equiv N \rightarrow O$) absorb strongly at 2304–2288 cm^{-1} ($C\equiv N$ stretch) and strongly at 1393–1365 cm^{-1} (N—O stretch).[9]

6.7 Isocyanates

Compounds containing the isocyanate group (R—N=C=O) absorb very strongly at 2275–2263 cm^{-1} due to the asymmetric stretching of the N=C=O bonds.[10–13] This band is relatively unaffected by conjugation. The molar absorptivity measured with a LiF prism in the spectrometer is $\epsilon \sim 2000$ compared to $\epsilon \sim 13$ for unconjugated nitriles at 2260–2240 cm^{-1}. The symmetric N=C=O stretch band is too weak in infrared absorption to be of value. It is thought to absorb very weakly at 1395–1375 cm^{-1}.

[7a] S. Baldwin, *J. Org. Chem.* **26**, 3288 (1961).

[8] H. W. Thompson and G. Steel, *Trans. Faraday Soc.* **52**, 1451 (1956).

[9] R. H. Wiley and B. J. Wakefield, *J. Org. Chem.* **25**, 546 (1960).

[10] H. Hoyer, *Chem. Ber.* **89**, 2677 (1956).

[11] W. H. T. Davison, *J. Chem. Soc.* **1953**, 3712.

[12] N. Bortnick, L. S. Luskin, M. D. Hurowitz, and A. W. Rytina, *J. Am. Chem. Soc.* **78**, 4358 (1956).

[13] G. L. Caldow and H. W. Thompson, *Spectrochim. Acta* **13**, 212 (1958).

6.8   Thiocyanates

Organic thiocyanates ($-S-C\equiv N$) show a medium strong sharp peak at 2170–2135 cm^{-1} due to the C$\equiv$N stretching vibration.[13,14]

6.9   Isothiocyanates

Aliphatic and aromatic isothiocyanates ($-N=C=S$) give rise to a very strong band at 2150–2050 cm^{-1} due to the asymmetric stretching of the NCS bonds.[14–17] A shoulder usually appears at 2221–2150 cm^{-1}. In compounds with an adjacent CH$_2$ or CH group, ($R-CH_2-N=C=S$), the CH$_2$ or CH wagging gives rise to a strong band at 1347–1318 cm^{-1}.[16] The symmetric NCS vibration absorbs at 945–925 cm^{-1} in aryl isothiocyanates and 700–650 cm^{-1} in alkyl isothiocyanates.[15]

6.10   Nitriles on a Nitrogen Atom

Cyanamides absorb strongly at 2225–2210 cm^{-1}.[7] This low wavenumber and high intensity is due to resonance which weakens the C$\equiv$N bond

$$(> N-C\equiv N \longleftrightarrow > \overset{+}{N}=C=\overset{-}{N}).$$

Cyanoguanidines $[(N_2)-C=N-C\equiv N]$ absorb strongly at 2210–2175 cm^{-1} due also to resonance.

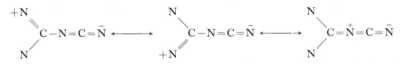

The band in cyanoguanidines is frequently multiple. Other nitrogen-nitrile compounds also absorb near here.

[14] E. Lieber, C. N. R. Rao, and J. Ramachandran, *Spectrochim. Acta* **13**, 296 (1959).
[15] N. S. Ham and J. B. Willis, *Spectrochim. Acta* **16**, 279 (1960).
[16] E. Svatek, R. Zahradnik, and A. Kjaer, *Acta Chem. Scand.* **13**, 442 (1959).
[17] L. S. Luskin, G. E. Gantert, and W. E. Craig, *J. Am. Chem. Soc.* **78**, 4965 (1956).

6.11 Carbodiimides

Disubstituted carbodiimides ($R-N=C=N-R$) have strong absorption at 2150–2100 cm^{-1} due to asymmetric NCN stretching.[18] This band is sometimes double.

6.12 Ketene Imines

Ketene imines ($>C=C=N-$) trisubstituted with aliphatic or aromatic groups absorb strongly at 2050–2000 cm^{-1}.[19] The unusual compound $(CH_3-SO_2)_2-C=C=N-CH_3$ absorbs at 2170 cm^{-1}.[20]

6.13 Diazo Compounds

Diazo compounds are resonance hybrides of resonance forms 1 and 2.

$$[1] \quad R-CH=\overset{+}{N}=\overset{-}{N} \quad \longleftrightarrow \quad [2] \quad R-\overset{-}{C}H-\overset{+}{N}\equiv N$$

They are characterized by a strong band[21] at 2132–2012 cm^{-1} best described as asymmetric CNN stretching. The compounds

$$R-CH=\overset{+}{N}=\overset{-}{N}$$

absorb at 2049–2036 cm^{-1}, and the compounds

$$RR'-C=\overset{+}{N}=\overset{-}{N}$$

absorb at 2032–2012 cm^{-1} where the R groups are either aliphatic or aromatic. No other correlatable bands are detected for the diazo group in these compounds.

[18] G. D. Meakins and R. J. Moss, *J. Chem. Soc.* **1957**, 993.
[19] C. L. Stevens and J. C. French, *J. Am. Chem. Soc.* **76**, 4398 (1954).
[20] R. Dijkstra and H. J. Backer, *Rec. Trav. Chim.* **73**, 575 (1954).
[21] P. Yates, B. L. Shapiro, N. Yoda, and J. Fugger, *J. Am. Chem. Soc.* **79**, 5756 (1957).

Diazo carbonyl compounds are found at somewhat higher wavenumbers due to resonance contribution no. [3].[21]

$$[3] \quad \overset{-}{O}-C=CH-\overset{+}{N}\equiv N$$

Diazo ketones such as

$$\overset{R\ \ H}{\underset{}{O=C-C}}=\overset{+}{N}=\overset{-}{N}$$

absorb at 2100–2087 cm^{-1}, and the compounds

$$\overset{R\ \ R'}{\underset{}{O=C-C}}=\overset{+}{N}=\overset{-}{N}$$

absorb at 2074–2057 cm^{-1}. The carbonyls are lowered around 60 cm^{-1} by the same resonance. When R is aliphatic the carbonyl absorbs at 1647–1644 cm^{-1}, and when R is aromatic the carbonyl absorbs at 1628–1605 cm^{-1}.[21]

In addition to the band at 2100–2057 cm^{-1} diazo carbonyl compounds have a second strong band at 1388–1333 cm^{-1} which is probably the symmetric CNN stretch. This does not appear in the aliphatic or aromatic diazo compounds.[21]

The quinone diazides or diazooxides seem to be resonance hybrids also.

Compounds have been studied having 1,2 and 1,4 benzo and naphthoquinone diazide groups.[22,23] They absorb at 2173–2014 cm^{-1} and 1642–1562 cm^{-1}, due to the asymmetric CNN stretch and the C=O stretch respectively.

6.14   Azides

Organic azides

$$(-N=\overset{+}{N}=\overset{-}{N} \longleftrightarrow -\overset{-}{N}-\overset{+}{N}\equiv N)$$

are characterized by a strong band[24-27] at 2170–2080 cm^{-1} due to the vibration

[22] R. J. W. Le Fèvre, J. B. Sousa, and R. L. Werner, J. Chem. Soc. 1954, 4686.
[23] K. B. Whetsel, G. F. Hawkins and F. E. Johnson, J. Am. Chem. Soc. 78, 3360 (1956).
[24] E. Lieber, C. N. R. Rao, T. S. Chao and C. W. W. Hoffman, Anal. Chem. 29, 916 (1957).
[25] Y. N. Sheinker, Y. K. Syrkin, Izvest. Akad. Nauk SSSR, Ser. Fiz. 14, 478 (1950).
[26] J. H. Boyer, J. Am. Chem. Soc. 73, 5248 (1951).
[27] E. Lieber, D. R. Levering, L. J. Patterson, Anal. Chem. 23, 1594 (1951).

best described as an asymmetric NNN stretch. The band is relatively insensitive to conjugation effects or to changes in electronegativities of the substituent.

The symmetric NNN stretch gives rise to a weaker band at 1343–1177 cm^{-1} not so useful for identification.

In acid azides, the asymmetric N_3 stretch which is usually a singlet appears as a doublet in $C_6H_5C(O)-N_3$ and compounds where the aromatic ring is substituted with nitro groups. For these compounds the following strong bands are observed.[28]

2237–2179 and 2155–2141 cm^{-1}	N_3 asymmetric stretch
1258–1238	N_3 symmetric stretch
1709–1692	C=O stretch

6.15 Aryl Diazonium Salts

The diazonium group

$$(aryl -\overset{+}{N}\equiv N \; X^-)$$

is characterized by a medium intensity band at 2309–2136 cm^{-1}. The position of the band depends mainly on the identity of the diazonium cation. A shift of no more than 40 cm^{-1} occurs when the anion is changed.[23,29,30]

6.16 Isocyanides

Aliphatic isocyanides

$$(aliph -\overset{+}{N}\equiv\overset{-}{C})$$

absorb strongly at 2146–2134 cm^{-1}. Aromatic isocyanides

$$(arom -\overset{+}{N}\equiv\overset{-}{C})$$

absorb at 2125–2109 cm^{-1}.[31]

[28] E. Lieber and E. Oftedahl, *J. Org. Chem.* **24**, 1014 (1959).
[29] M. Aroney, R. J. W. Le Fèvre and R. L. Werner, *J. Chem. Soc.* **1955**, 276.
[30] R. H. Nuttall, E. R. Roberts and D. W. A. Sharp, *Spectrochim. Acta* **17**, 946 (1961).
[31] I. Ugi and R. Meyr, *Chem. Ber.* **93**, 239 (1960).

6.17   Ketenes

Ketene absorbs[32,33] at 2153 cm^{-1}, and diphenyl, ketene at 2130 cm^{-1}.[33]

6.18   Cyanide Ions

The cyanide ion in sodium and potassium and related simple cyanides absorbs at 2080–2070 cm^{-1}. Silver cyanide absorbs at 2178 cm^{-1} reflecting the more covalent character of the metalcarbon bond in this case. The ferrocyanide ion [Fe (C≡N)$_6$]$^{4-}$ absorbs near 2010 cm^{-1}, and the ferricyanide ion [Fe (C≡N)$_6$]$^{3-}$ near 2100 cm^{-1}.[34]

6.19   Cyanate Ions

Inorganic cyanate ions absorb at 2220–2130 cm^{-1} (asymmetric stretch), 1334–1292 cm^{-1} (symmetric stretch), 1293–1203 cm^{-1} (bending-overtone–Fermi-resonance with symmetric stretch), and 640–605 cm^{-1} (bending).[34,35]

6.20   Thiocyanate Ions

Inorganic thiocyanate ions absorb strongly at 2090–2020 cm^{-1} (asymmetric stretch) and weakly near 950 cm^{-1} (bending overtone) and 750 cm^{-1} (symmetric stretch). The bending frequency is near 470 cm^{-1}.[34,36] In thiocyanate ion coordination a distinction can be made between M←NCS, 860–780 cm^{-1} and M←SCN, 720–690 cm^{-1}.[37]

[32] D. H. Whiffen and H. W. Thompson, *J. Chem. Soc.* **1946**, 1005.
[33] F. Halverson and V. Z. Williams, *J. Chem. Phys.* **15**, 552 (1947).
[34] F. A. Miller and C. H. Wilkins, *Anal. Chem.* **24**, 1253 (1952).
[35] T. C. Waddington, *J. Chem. Soc.* **1959**, 2499.
[36] P. Kinell and B. Strandberg, *Acta Chem. Scand.* **13**, 1607 (1959).
[37] A. Turco and C. Pecile, *Nature* **191**, 66 (1961).

6.21   Metal Carbonyls

Metal carbonyls absorb strongly at 2170–1700 cm^{-1}.[38] When the carbon of the carbon monoxide is associated with only one metal, absorption usually occurs at 2170–1900 cm^{-1}. The CO frequency shows variation with the number and availability of electrons in the rest of the molecule. The CO frequency and bond order are lowered when the ligand is an electron donor. In complexes with strong electron donors the frequency may fall below 1900 cm^{-1}.

Bridging carbonyl compounds, where the carbon is associated with two metal atoms, usually absorb at 1900–1700 cm^{-1}.[38]

[38] J. Chatt, P. L. Pauson, and L. M. Venanzi, *in* "Organometallic Chemistry," (H. Zeiss, ed.), p. 477. Reinhold, New York, 1960.

CHAPTER 7

OLEFIN GROUPS

7.1 Noncyclic Olefins

In addition to the C=C bond, a vinyl group has three carbon-hydrogen bonds and so will have three CH stretching vibrations, three in plane CH bending and three out of plane CH bending vibrations. These vibrations each interact to give the modes illustrated in Fig. 7.1.[1-3] Also illustrated are the in phase, out of plane CH wagging vibrations for *trans* and *cis* disubstituted olefins, 1,1 disubstituted ethylene, and trisubstituted ethylene. The spectral regions for the alkyl substituted olefins are given in Table 7.1.[1-6]

Olefinic carbon-hydrogen stretching frequencies occur at 3100–3000 cm^{-1}. There is a tendency for the asymmetric =CH$_2$ stretch of the vinyl and vinylidine groups (3092–3077 cm^{-1})[4] to absorb at a higher frequency than =CH vibrations (3050–3000 cm^{-1}) in hydrocarbons.[4]

The C=C stretching frequency near 1640 cm^{-1} in vinyl hydrocarbons is a medium intensity band which becomes inactive in the infrared region in a symmetrical *trans* or symmetrical tetra substituted double bond compound, both of which have centers of symmetry. Even when the substituents are not exactly alike in *trans* and tetra substituted olefins, the infrared absorption may be quite weak.[5] These double bond vibrations all appear strongly in the Raman effect, however. *Trans*, tri, and tetra alkyl substituted olefins have somewhat higher C=C stretching frequencies than *cis*, vinylidine, or vinyl groups.[5] Conjugation, which weakens the C=C force constant, lowers the frequency 10–50 cm^{-1}. In 1,3 dienes the two double bonds interact to give two stretching bands. In both *cis* and *trans* 1,3 pentadiene in phase stretching bands occur

[1] N. Sheppard and D. M. Simpson, *Quart. Rev. (London)* 6, 1 (1952).
[2] W. J. Potts and R. A. Nyquist, *Spectrochim. Acta* 15, 679 (1959).
[3] J. R. Scherer and W. J. Potts, *J. Chem. Phys.* 30, 1527 (1959).
[4] S. E. Wiberley, S. C. Bunce, and W. H. Bauer, *Anal. Chem.* 32, 217 (1960).
[5] H. L. McMurry and V. Thornton, *Anal. Chem.* 24, 318 (1952).
[6] W. H. Tallent and I. J. Siewers, *Anal. Chem.* 28, 953 (1956).

at 1658 cm^{-1} and out of phase at 1605 cm^{-1}.[7] In 1,3 butadiene only the out of phase (asymmetric) stretch is infrared active, absorbing at 1603 cm^{-1}.[7] Fluorinated olefins have an unusually high $C=C$ frequency[8] at 1755–1735 cm^{-1} for the group $C=CF_2$ and 1800–1780 cm^{-1} for the group $CF=CF_2$. Other noncyclic, nonhydrocarbon double bond bands are usually found at 1680–1570 cm^{-1}.

The $C=C$ frequency is usually lowered if an aliphatic group substituent is replaced by a heavy atom such as chlorine or sulfur. The $C=C$ vibration interacts to some extent with $=CH_2$ deformation vibration and to some extent with the attached single bond stretching vibration since nonhydrogen substituent atoms remain nearly motionless for this mode. The $C=C$ stretching frequency

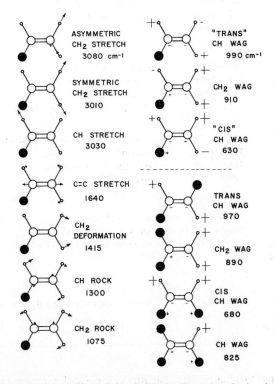

FIG. 7.1.   Olefinic vibrations. The left hand column illustrates the in plane vibrations of the vinyl group. The right hand column illustrates the out of plane vibrations (+ and −) of the vinyl group and for comparison, the in phase, out of plane hydrogen wagging vibrations of *trans*, *cis*, and 1,1 disubstituted olefins and trisubstituted olefins. The approximate frequencies are given for hydrocarbon substituted olefins.

[7] R. S. Rasmussen and R. R. Brattain, *J. Chem. Phys.* 15, 120, 131 (1947).

[8] L. J. Bellamy, *Spectrochim. Acta* 13, 60 (1958).

TABLE 7.1

SPECTRAL REGIONS FOR THE ALKYL SUBSTITUTED OLEFINS

Structure		
H H \ / C=C / \ C H vinyl	$3092-3077$ cm^{-1} $3025-3012$ cm^{-1} $1840-1805$ $1648-1638$ $1420-1412$ $995-\ \ 985$ $910-\ \ 905$	medium CH_2 asymmetric stretch medium CH stretch, CH_2 symmetric stretch medium $2 \times CH_2$ wag medium C=C stretch medium CH_2 deformation strong *trans* CH wag strong CH_2 wag
H C \ / C=C / \ C H *trans*	$3050-3000$ $1678-1668$ $980-\ \ 965$	medium CH stretch weak or absent (strong Raman band) C=C stretch strong *trans* CH wag
H H \ / C=C / \ C C *cis*	$3050-3000$ $1662-1631$ $1429-1397$ $730-\ \ 650$	medium CH stretch medium C=C stretch medium CH rock medium to strong *cis* CH wag
C H \ / C=C / \ C H vinylidine	$3100-3077$ $1792-1775$ $1661-1639$ $895-\ \ 885$	medium CH_2 asymmetric stretch medium $2 \times CH_2$ wag medium C=C stretch strong CH_2 wag
C H \ / C=C / \ C C trisubstituted	$3050-2990$ $1692-1667$ $840-\ \ 790$	weak CH stretch weak C=C stretch medium to strong CH wag
C C \ / C=C / \ C C tetrasubstituted	$1680-1665$	weak or absent (strong Raman band) C=C stretch

will be affected by changes in these interactions and by mesomeric and inductive effects which alter the strength of the C=C and attached C—X bonds.

The CH_2 "scissors" deformation of the vinyl and vinylidine groups gives rise to a medium intensity band near 1420 cm^{-1} [5] where the CH rocking vibration (in plane) of the *cis* alkyl disubstituted olefins also absorbs.

The CH rock of vinyl, *trans*, and trisubstituted double bonds is a less useful or reliable weak band somewhere near 1300 cm^{-1}. The CH_2 rock of vinyl and vinylidine groups gives rise to a weak unreliable band somewhere near 1075 cm^{-1}.

7.2 Olefinic Hydrogen Wagging Vibrations

The strongest bands in olefins arise from the hydrogen wag vibrations (out of plane).[1,2,5,7,9,10] See Fig. 7.1.

The lone CH of a trisubstituted olefin has its wagging (out of plane) frequency near 825 cm^{-1} in hydrocarbons, but this medium intensity band is not always easy to pick out among other bands.[2]

The CH_2 in phase, out of plane wagging vibration in a hydrocarbon vinylidine compound absorbs strongly near 890 cm^{-1} and is closely related to the 910 cm^{-1} vibration in the hydrocarbon vinyl group[2,3,5,9] which we shall also call CH_2 wag. Both have an unusually strong first overtone, useful as a check.

The in phase, out of plane CH wagging vibration of trans disubstituted hydrocarbon olefins absorbs strongly near 970 cm^{-1} and is closely related to the 990 cm^{-1} vibrations in the hydrocarbon vinyl group [2,3,5,9] which we shall call in both groups, trans CH wag. This band has no prominent overtone.

The in phase, out of plane CH wagging of the cis disubstituted hydrocarbon olefins gives rise to a more variable, less reliable, weaker band near 730–650 cm^{-1} in hydrocarbons.[2,5] This band is related to the variable vinyl vibration somewhere near 530 cm^{-1} in hydrocarbons[3,9] which we shall also call *cis* CH wag.

In the hydrogen wagging vibrations of *trans* and vinylidine disubstituted olefins and in the comparable vibrations of the vinyl olefins, the motions of the hydrogens are balanced by motions of the carbons within the group. The rest of the molecule is relatively uninvolved mechanically in these vibrations. In the hydrogen wagging vibration of the *cis* disubstituted olefin and the lowest vinyl olefin wagging vibration, the motions of the hydrogens are partially balanced by motions of the attached groups. These groups are thus more mechanically involved in the vibrations which makes the vibrational frequency of the *cis* disubstituted olefin more variable than the *trans* or vinylidine vibrations, or the comparable vinyl vibrations.

The out of phase, out of plane CH vibrations of the *cis*, *trans*, or vinylidine hydrocarbon olefins do not usually result in useful infrared bands.[2,9]

The most reliable of these bands mentioned above are the CH_2 wag of vinyl and vinylidine groups and the *trans* CH wag of vinyl and *trans* disubstituted olefins. When nonhydrocarbon olefins are considered, the CH_2 wagging frequency is not mass sensitive but is quite sensitive to mesomeric effects.[2] Those groups which mesomerically withdraw electrons from the CH_2 group

$$
\begin{matrix} O & & & O^- \\ \| & & & | \\ (C-O-C & \!\!\!\!\!\!\text{------} & CH{=}CH_2 & \leftrightarrow & C-O-C{=}CH{-}CH_2^+) \end{matrix}
$$

[9] J. K. Brown and N. Sheppard, *Trans. Faraday Soc.* **51**, 1611 (1955).
[10] H. W. Thompson and P. Torkington, *Trans. Faraday Soc.* **41**, 246 (1945).

TABLE 7.2
CH$_2$ WAGGING FREQUENCIES

R−O−CO−CH=CH$_2$	961 cm^{-1}
N≡C−CH−CH$_2$	960
R−CH=CH$_2$	910
Cl−CH=CH$_2$	894
R−CO−O−CH=CH$_2$	870
R−CO−N−CH=CH$_2$	840
R−O−CH=CH$_2$	813

$$\begin{matrix} N\equiv C \\ \diagdown \\ C=CH_2 \\ \diagup \\ N\equiv C \end{matrix} \qquad 985$$

$$\begin{matrix} R \\ \diagdown \\ C=CH_2 \\ \diagup \\ R-O-CO \end{matrix} \qquad 939$$

$$\begin{matrix} N\equiv C \\ \diagdown \\ C=CH_2 \\ \diagup \\ Cl \end{matrix} \qquad 916$$

$$\begin{matrix} R \\ \diagdown \\ C=CH_2 \\ \diagup \\ R \end{matrix} \qquad 890$$

$$\begin{matrix} Cl \\ \diagdown \\ C=CH_2 \\ \diagup \\ Cl \end{matrix} \qquad 867$$

$$\begin{matrix} R \\ \diagdown \\ C=CH_2 \\ \diagup \\ R-O \end{matrix} \qquad 795$$

$$\begin{matrix} R-O \\ \diagdown \\ C=CH_2 \\ \diagup \\ R-O \end{matrix} \qquad 711$$

raise the frequency, and those groups which mesomerically donate electrons

$$(C-O-CH=CH_2 \longleftrightarrow C-\overset{+}{O}=CH-\overset{-}{C}H_2)$$

lower the frequency relative to hydrocarbon olefins. In vinylidines, both groups shift the CH$_2$ frequency additively. For example, CH$_2$=CH−CN absorbs 50 cm^{-1} higher than CH$_2$=CH−R, and CH$_2$=C(CN)$_2$ absorbs about 100 cm^{-1} higher than CH$_2$=CR$_2$. The CH$_2$ wagging frequency has been correlated with the *ortho-para* directing ability of the group.[2] See Table 7.2 for representative compounds.[2]

The *trans* CH wagging vibration of the vinyl and *trans* disubstituted olefins is relatively insensitive to mass or mesomeric effects but shows some sensitivity to the inductive power of the group. Electronegative groups tend to lower this frequency relative to hydrocarbons.[2] In *trans* disubstitution, both groups shift the frequency. See Table 7.3.[2]

TABLE 7.3

TRANS CH WAGGING FREQUENCIES

$(CH_3)_3Si-CH=CH_2$	1009 cm^{-1}
$R-CH=CH_2$	990
$R-O-CO-CH=CH_2$	982
$R-CO-N-CH=CH_2$	972
$R-O-CH=CH_2$	960
$R-CO-O-CH=CH_2$	950
$Cl-CH=CH_2$	938

$$\begin{array}{cc} R-O-CO & H \\ \diagdown & \diagup \\ C=C & \\ \diagup & \diagdown \\ H & CO-O-R \end{array} \qquad 976$$

$$\begin{array}{cc} CH_3 & H \\ \diagdown & \diagup \\ C=C & \\ \diagup & \diagdown \\ H & CO-O-R \end{array} \qquad 968$$

$$\begin{array}{cc} R & H \\ \diagdown & \diagup \\ C=C & \\ \diagup & \diagdown \\ H & R \end{array} \qquad 964$$

$$\begin{array}{cc} CH_3 & H \\ \diagdown & \diagup \\ C=C & \\ \diagup & \diagdown \\ H & C\equiv N \end{array} \qquad 953$$

$$\begin{array}{cc} CH_3 & H \\ \diagdown & \diagup \\ C=C & \\ \diagup & \diagdown \\ H & Cl \end{array} \qquad 926$$

$$\begin{array}{cc} Cl & H \\ \diagdown & \diagup \\ C=C & \\ \diagup & \diagdown \\ H & C\equiv N \end{array} \qquad 920$$

$$\begin{array}{cc} Cl & H \\ \diagdown & \diagup \\ C=C & \\ \diagup & \diagdown \\ H & Cl \end{array} \qquad 892$$

7.3   Cyclic C=C

An external $C=CH_2$ on an otherwise saturated 6 membered ring is not noticeable different from its noncyclic vinylidine counterparts. As the ring gets smaller, the double bond-single bond angle increases due to strain. There is a steady increase in the $C=C$ stretching frequency[11] due predominantly to an increasing interaction with the $C-C$ bonds directly attached.[12] (See Fig. 4.12.) As the double bond stretches, the attached single bonds must be contracted, the amount of this interaction varying with the double bond-single bond angle.[12] See Table 7.4.

TABLE 7.4

$H_2C=C$ EXTERNAL CYCLIC DOUBLE BOND STRETCHING FREQUENCIES

6 membered ring	methylene cyclohexane	1651 cm^{-1} [11]
5 membered ring	methylene cyclopentane	1657 cm^{-1} [11]
4 membered ring	methylene cyclobutane	1678 cm^{-1} [11]
3 membered ring	methylene cyclopropane	1781 cm^{-1} [13]
(2 membered ring)	(allene)	1980 cm^{-1} [14]

Substitution of the hydrogens of the $C=CH_2$ group with methyl groups increases the frequency,[15] due in part to out of phase interaction with the attached $C-C$ bonds.

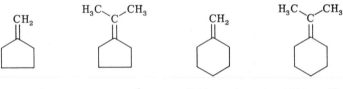

1657 cm^{-1}	1687 cm^{-1}	1651 cm^{-1}	1668 cm^{-1}

An unsubstituted $C=CH_2$ group on a bridged 5 membered ring is under more strain than methylene cyclopentane and resembles methylene cyclobutane.[15]

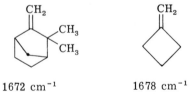

1672 cm^{-1}	1678 cm^{-1}

[11] R. C. Lord and F. A. Miller, *Appl. Spectry.* **10**, 115 (1956).
[12] N. B. Colthup, *J. Chem. Educ.* **38**, 394 (1961).
[13] E. J. Blau, *Dissertation Abstr.* **18**, 1628 (1958).
[14] G. Herzberg, "Infrared and Raman Spectra of Polyatomic Molecules." Van Nostrand, New York, 1945.
[15] G. Chiurdoglu, J. Laune, and M. Poelmans, *Bull. Soc. Chim. Belges* **65**, 257 (1956).

An internal $-CH=CH-$ in an otherwise saturated 6 membered ring is not noticeable different from its noncyclic *cis* counterpart. As the ring gets smaller, the $C=C$ stretching frequency decreases from the 6 to the 4 membered ring case as the double-bond–single-bond angle decreases to $90°$.[11,16] This is due predominantly to changes in the interaction with the $C-C$ bonds directly attached, which are altered in length as the double bond vibrates. (See Fig. 5.12.) This interaction is at a minimum at $90°$ and increases as the angle gets larger or smaller than $90°$.[12] The $=CH$ stretching frequency is also sensitive to ring size.[11] See Table 7.5.

TABLE 7.5

CH=CH INTERNAL CYCLIC DOUBLE BOND AND CH BOND STRETCHING FREQUENCIES

6 membered ring	cyclohexene	1646 cm^{-1}	3017 cm^{-1} [11]
5 membered ring	cyclopentene	1611 cm^{-1}	3045 cm^{-1} [11]
4 membered ring	cyclobutene	1566 cm^{-1}	3060 cm^{-1} [11]
3 membered ring	cyclopropene	1641 cm^{-1}	3076 cm^{-1} [17]
(2 membered ring)	(acetylene)	1974 cm^{-1}	3374 cm^{-1} [14]

Substitution of the remaining hydrogens with carbons will change the interaction.

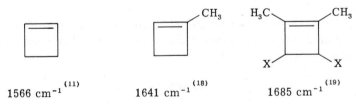

1566 cm^{-1} [11] 1641 cm^{-1} [18] 1685 cm^{-1} [19]

All of the above cyclobutene double bonds are equally strained, but the added out of phase interaction with the noncyclic $C-C$ bonds increases the frequency.[12] The same thing occurs in alkyl substituted cyclopentenes[20] and cyclohexenes.[18] As seen above, the frequencies for the 1,2 dialkyl cyclo-enes are nearly the same from the six to the four membered ring ($1690-1670 \text{ cm}^{-1}$). This is markedly different from the unsubstituted case ($1646 \rightarrow 1611 \rightarrow 1566 \text{ cm}^{-1}$). The decrease in the cyclic single-bond–double-bond angle as the ring gets smaller which reduces interaction and frequency, is compensated for by an increase in the

[16] R. C. Lord and R. W. Walker, *J. Am. Chem. Soc.* **76**, 2518 (1954).

[17] K. B. Wiberg, B. J. Nist, and D. F. Eggers, Jr., private communication (1961).

[18] Landolt-Börnstein, Band 1, Molekeln, Teil 2, pp. 480-510, 6th Ed., Springer, Berlin (1951).

[19] R. Criegee and G. Louis, *Chem. Ber.* **90**, 417 (1957).

[20] L. M. Sverdlov and E. P. Krainov, *Opt. Spectry.* (*USSR*) (*English Transl.*) **6**, 214 (1959).

noncyclic single-bond–double-bond angle which increases interaction and frequency. The effect of interaction is to leave the frequencies nearly unchanged even though the strain is altered.[12] The 1,2 dialkyl cyclopropenes have a ring angle much less than 90° where interaction again increases the frequency, and

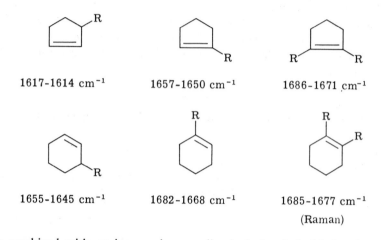

| 1617-1614 cm⁻¹ | 1657-1650 cm⁻¹ | 1686-1671 cm⁻¹ |

$$1617\text{-}1614 \text{ cm}^{-1} \qquad 1657\text{-}1650 \text{ cm}^{-1} \qquad 1686\text{-}1671 \text{ cm}^{-1}$$

$$1655\text{-}1645 \text{ cm}^{-1} \qquad 1682\text{-}1668 \text{ cm}^{-1} \qquad 1685\text{-}1677 \text{ cm}^{-1}$$
(Raman)

this combined with an increased noncyclic single-bond–double-bond angle[21] of about 150° markedly increases the frequency which occurs at 1900–1865 cm⁻¹.[22-24]

Table 7.6 lists double bond stretching frequencies (some from Raman data) of the 1,2 disubstituted cyclo-enes. Other positions as well as 1 and 2 may be substituted.

TABLE 7.6

INTERNAL CYCLIC DOUBLE BOND, 1,2 DISUBSTITUTED

six membered ring	cyclohexenes, 1,2 dialkyl	1685–1677 cm⁻¹ [18]
five membered ring	cyclopentenes, 1,2 dialkyl	1686–1671 [20]
four membered ring	cyclobutenes, 1,2 dimethyl	~1685 [19]
three membered ring	cyclopropenes, 1,2 dialkyl	1900–1865 [22-24]
(two membered ring)	(acetylene, 1,2 dimethyl)	2313 [14]

[21] P. H. Kasai, R. J. Myers, D. F. Eggers, Jr., and K. B. Wiberg, *J. Chem. Phys.* 30, 512 (1959).

[22] W. E. Doering and T. Mole, *Tetrahedron* 10, 65 (1960).

[23] R. Breslow and H. Höver, *J. Am. Chem. Soc.* 82, 2644 (1960).

[24] K. Faure and J. C. Smith, *J. Chem. Soc.* 1956, 1818.

Bridged rings with unsubstituted internal double bonds such as in dicyclopentadiene have extra strain resulting in smaller bond angles than in unbridged rings of the same size resulting in absorption at lower frequencies for these double bonds (ca. 1570 cm^{-1} for a bridged five membered ring and ca. 1615 cm^{-1} for a bridged six membered ring[11,16]).

1568 cm^{-1} 1566 cm^{-1} 1614 cm^{-1} 1611 cm^{-1}

CHAPTER 8

AROMATIC AND HETEROAROMATIC RINGS

8.1 Benzene Rings

When the modes of vibrations of the aromatic ring are studied, a fair amount of interaction between CC and CH vibrations is observed. When there is in plane interaction above about 1200 cm^{-1}, a carbon and its hydrogen usually move oppositely while below about 1200 cm^{-1} they usually move in the same direction. In out of plane interaction above about 720 cm^{-1} a carbon and its hydrogen usually move oppositely while below about 720 cm^{-1} they usually move in the same direction.

However, as in all group frequency work, simplifications are desirable. It is convenient for correlation purposes to separate the vibrations of the benzene rings into modes which are predominantly CH vibrations (small carbon amplitudes, large hydrogen amplitudes) and modes which predominantly involve CC vibrations (large carbon amplitudes). This separation is moderately justifiable on the basis of substitution studies but it is a simplification.

8.2 The Carbon-Carbon Vibrations

The benzene ring modes[1-5] which predominantly involve C$\dddot{}$C bonds are illustrated in Fig. 8.1.

[1] A. R. Katritzky, *Quart. Rev.* **13**, 353 (1959).

[2] R. R. Randle and D. H. Whiffen, Report Conf. Mol. Spectroscopy, 1954, Inst. Petroleum Paper No. 12.

[3] K. S. Pitzer and D. W. Scott, *J. Am. Chem. Soc.* **65**, 803 (1943).

[4] A. M. Bogomolov, *Opt. Spectry.* (*USSR*) (*English Transl.*) **9**, 162 (1960); *ibid.* **10**, 162 (1961).

[5] E. W. Schmid, J. Brandmuller, and G. Nonnenmacher, *Z. Elektrochem.* **64**, 726; 940 (1960).

There are six equal $C\dot{-}C$ bonds and so there will be six $C\dot{-}C$ stretching vibrations. If for description's sake, the ring is thought of as a continuous helical spring in the form of a doughnut, the two components of the 1588 cm^{-1} vibration may each be described as opposite quadrants of the ring stretching while the intervening quadrants contract. The two components of the 1486 cm^{-1} vibration may be described as one semicircle stretching while the other contracts. Other vibrations of these types where the quadrants or semicircles have intermediate orientations to those illustrated can be described as mixtures of the two fundamental components of each type. The 710 cm^{-1} vibration is described as every other sextant going up out of the plane while the intervening sextants

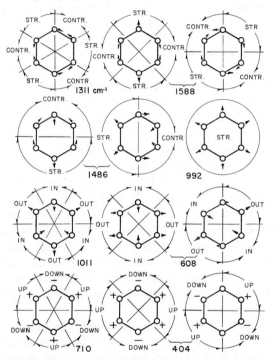

FIG. 8.1. Benzene ring carbon-carbon vibrations. The benzene ring modes which predominantly involve CC vibrations are schematically illustrated. The 1588, 1486, 608, and 404 cm^{-1} modes are doubly degenerate in benzene. For descriptive purposes the stretching vibrations are described as whole ring stretching, semicircle stretching, quadrant stretching, and sextant stretching. The in-plane and out-of-plane bendings are described as quadrant and sextant bending. The frequencies in wavenumbers for benzene are from reference 5.

The most important infrared vibrations in substituted benzenes are the quadrant and semicircle stretching vibrations and the out-of-plane bending vibrations by sextants and quadrants. These vibrations occur in substituted benzenes at about 1600–1585, 1500–1430, 700, and 450 cm^{-1}.

go down. The two components of the 404 cm^{-1} vibration may be described as opposite quadrants going up while the intervening quadrants go down.

In substituted benzenes these vibrations absorbing near 1600–1585, 1500–1430, 700, and 450 cm^{-1} are the most useful ones in the infrared spectrum. These modes, particularly the first three, have frequencies which are moderately insensitive to changes in ring substituents. These will be discussed later.

In the whole ring stretching and in plane ring bending modes in benzene (992, 1011, and the 608 cm^{-1} modes) the ring carbons move "radially" or nearly so. These "radial" modes can interact with the attached single bond stretching vibrations of substituents. These interactions give rise to substituent sensitive vibrations in the Raman or infrared spectrum about 1300–1040, 850–620, and 580–200 cm^{-1}.[2, 4–7] Examples of these mass sensitive frequencies in monosubstituted benzenes are: toluene, 1211, 786, and 520 cm^{-1},[4,5] fluorobenzene, 1219, 806, and 515 cm^{-1}, chlorobenzene, 1086, 702, and 414 cm^{-1}, bromobenzene, 1068, 672, and 315 cm^{-1}, and iodobenzene, 1063, 654, and 268 cm^{-1}.[5,6] These modes of vibration can be described, respectively, as (1) ring carbons 1, 3, and 5 which move radially in phase while the substituent on carbon 1 moves radially out of phase; (2) a quadrant in plane bending where the C–X distance increases as the distance between carbons 1 and 4 decreases; and (3) the C–X and carbons 1 and 4 distances both increase.

Substituent insensitive Raman bands occur near 1000 cm^{-1} in mono and *meta* isomers only (unsubstituted carbons 2, 4, and 6 move radially in phase) and near 625 cm^{-1} in mono and *para* isomers only (quadrant in plane bending where substituted carbons 1 and 4 move at right angles to the C–X bonds). These arise from these same "radial: modes but for the stated isomers only, the substituent atoms are nearly stationary. Thus in monosubstituted benzenes the four "radial" modes and the substituent single bond stretching vibration interact to give three substituent sensitive modes and two substituent insensitive modes.

The forms of the normal modes are not exactly the same in the substituted benzenes as they are in benzene itself due to substituent interaction, hydrogen interaction, (neglected in the first approximation), and mixing of the parent benzene modes when the lower symmetry permits it. This is particularly true of the "radial" modes. For example, the 992 and 1011 cm^{-1} parent modes mix in mono and *meta* isomers where they belong to the same symmetry type, but cannot mix in *ortho* and *para* isomers with identical substituents as here they are of different symmetry types. Complete normal coordinate treatments can be found in the literature.[4,5]

[6] D. H. Whiffen, *J. Chem. Soc.* **1956**, 1350.

[7] K. W. F. Kohlrausch, "Ramanspektren." Akademische Verlagsges., Leipzig, 1943.

8.3 Symmetry Considerations

Due to the high symmetry of benzene many modes are infrared inactive. The effect of symmetry on the infrared activity of the 1600–1585, 1500–1430, 700, and 450 cm^{-1} modes of vibrations in substituted benzenes will be discussed.

Of all the modes illustrated in Fig. 8.1 only the 1486 cm^{-1} doubly degenerate mode is infrared active in benzene. Both components of this "semicircle stretching" vibration remain infrared active in substituted benzenes absorbing near 1500–1430 cm^{-1}.

In the benzene vibrations at 710 cm^{-1} (out of plane ring bending by sextants) and 1588 cm^{-1} ("quadrant stretching"—2 components) the atoms *para* to each other move in opposite directions thus retaining the center of symmetry. These types of vibrations are infrared inactive as they cause no change in dipole moment. In substituted benzenes which have identical groups (including hydrogen) on all the *para* pairs of ring carbons which include *para*, symmetrical tetra- and hexasubstituted benzenes (and of course, benzene itself), the 1600–1585 cm^{-1} and 700 cm^{-1} vibrations are forbidden in the infrared spectrum as they all have centers of symmetry. When the groups on the para pairs are different, they of course destroy the symmetry and the vibrations are allowed in the infrared, the intensity being dependent on the nature of the groups. In *para* compounds where one group is *ortho-para* directing and the other is *meta* directing, the 1600–1585 cm^{-1} bands can be quite intense due to the dipole moment change provided by the different groups.

In mono, *meta,* and symmetrical trisubstituted benzenes, the center of symmetry is destroyed as each substituting group has a hydrogen atom *para* to it. The 700 cm^{-1} and 1600–1585 cm^{-1} bands are usually strong as the 1, 3, and 5 carbons which have one or more substituents move approximately in an opposite direction to the 2, 4, and 6 unsubstituted carbons for both of these vibrations, causing a large change in dipole moment.

An *ortho* disubstituted benzene ring does not have a center of symmetry, but its particular symmetry when the substituents are identical, makes the 700 cm^{-1} vibration infrared inactive while the 1600-1585 cm^{-1} remains active.

The 404 cm^{-1} quadrant out of plane bending doubly degenerate mode in benzene is infrared inactive. In mono and disubstituted benzenes the less symmetrical component is always infrared active absorbing near 450 cm^{-1}. In the disubstituted case ring carbons which have substituents move in the same direction out of plane. The other component usually retains a twofold axis of symmetry going through the substituents in *para* and mono and between identical substituents in *ortho* and *meta* isomers. This component is infrared inactive but becomes infrared active (but not necessarily a strong band) when the twofold axis is destroyed by unsimilar *ortho* or *meta* substituents or by unsymmetrical mono and *para* substituents.

8.4 The 1600 cm⁻¹ Region

The 1600 cm⁻¹ vibration ("quadrant stretching") has two components which can sometimes be resolved in substituted benzenes.[1,2] When the substituents are conjugated C, N, or O, there is absorption between 1620 and 1575 cm⁻¹ which sometimes consists of a doublet. When the substituents are C=O, C=N, C=C, or NO_2 conjugated with the ring, or when a substituent is a heavy element such as Cl, S, P, or Si, the 1600 cm⁻¹ absorption is usually a doublet at 1620–1585 cm⁻¹ and 1590–1565 cm⁻¹. The 1600 cm⁻¹ doublet is not very frequency sensitive to changes in *o*, *m*, or *p* substitution.

The intensities of the 1600 cm⁻¹ band and its relatively weaker companion near 1585 cm⁻¹ in monosubstituted benzene rings are high for electron donor or acceptor groups and low for weakly interacting groups.[1] *Meta* disubstituted rings have 1600–1585 cm⁻¹ band intensities which vary as the algebraic sum of the electronic effects of the substituents and *para* disubstituted benzenes, as the algebraic difference.[1] *Ortho* disubstituted aromatics are intermediate.[1] As was mentioned above, these bands are infrared inactive when the molecule has a center of symmetry in the ring center.*

These vibrations interact a little with CH in plane bending, a hydrogen and its carbon moving oppositely. The substituents are nearly motionless.

8.5 The 1500 cm⁻¹ Region

The 1500 cm⁻¹ vibration ("semicircle stretching") also has two components of which there is usually only one above 1470 cm⁻¹. The other component is lower in wavenumbers (1420–1400 cm⁻¹ for *para*, 1465–1430 cm⁻¹ for other substitutions[1,2]) in the hydrogen deformation region. For *mono, ortho,* and *meta* substitution, absorption occurs at 1510–1470 cm⁻¹. For *para* substitution, absorption occurs at 1525–1480 cm⁻¹. The absorption for *para* here is almost

---

* A molecule such as diphenyl acetylene has a center of symmetry but not in the ring center.

always 10–20 cm^{-1} higher than the other substitutions and so stands out in a mixture of isomers. For some rings conjugated with carbonyls, the intensity of the component near 1500 cm^{-1} may be very weak. The intensity of the 1500 cm^{-1} band is strong for electron donor groups and weak or absent when these are not present.[1] The intensity of the band near 1430 cm^{-1} is relatively independent of the nature of the substituent.[1]

The 1500 cm^{-1} aromatic band unlike the 1600 cm^{-1} bands can not be misinterpreted as an olefinic C=C band.

These vibrations interact with the in-plane CH bending vibrations to a greater extent than those near 1600 cm^{-1}. A hydrogen and its carbon move oppositely but the substituents are nearly motionless.

Table 8.1 gives ring stretching spectral regions for substituted benzenes. The symbol 1510→1480 cm^{-1} indicates election donor substituents cause absorption near 1510 cm^{-1} while electron acceptors cause absorption near 1480 cm^{-1}. Arithmetic means and standard deviations of band position in cm^{-1} are indicated otherwise.[1,2]

TABLE 8.1

BENZENE RING STRETCHING FREQUENCIES

monosubstituted benzene	1604 ± 3	1585 ± 3	1510 → 1480	1452 ± 4
o-disubstituted benzene	1607 ± 9	1577 ± 4	1510 → 1460	1447 ± 10
m-disubstitutted benzene	1600 → 1620	1586 ± 5	1495 → 1470	1465 → 1430
p-disubstituted benzene	1606 ± 6	1579 ± 6	1520 → 1480	1409 ± 8
1, 2, 4 trisubstituted benzenes	1616 ± 8	1577 ± 8	1510 ± 8	1456 ± 1

8.6 The 700 cm^{-1} Region

The 700 cm^{-1} absorption (out of plane ring bending by sextants) is a strong band in mono, *meta*, di, and symmetrical trisubstituted isomers occurring usually at 710-675 cm^{-1}.[1,2] There is interaction with CH out of plane bending as the 2, 4, and 6 hydrogens have considerable amplitudes in the same direction as the 2, 4, and 6 carbons in these isomers but the 1, 3, and 5 substitutents and hydrogens are nearly motionless.[4,5]

In vicinal and unsymmetrical trisubstitution the band is usually weaker and higher usually at 730–690 cm^{-1}. *Ortho* and *para* isomers also absorb weakly here when the two substituents differ. When the substituents are identical in *ortho* and *para* isomers, this band is infrared inactive.

8.7   The 450 cm⁻¹ Region

The 450 cm^{-1} band (out of plane ring bending by quadrants) is somewhat variable in frequency due to interaction with out of plane substituent bending. Monosubstituted benzenes absorb at 580–450 cm^{-1}, *ortho* at 490–430 cm^{-1}, *meta* at 470–430 cm^{-1}, and *para* at 580–470 cm^{-1}.[8]

8.8   Carbon-Hydrogen Vibrations

When the hydrogen vibrations are considered separately for correlation purposes benzene itself (which has six hydrogen atoms) will have six hydrogen stretching vibrations, six in plane hydrogen bendings, and six out of plane hydrogen bendings. In substituted benzene rings, the hydrogen stretching vibrations give rise to bands at 3100–3000 cm^{-1}.[9-11] Bands involving the in plane hydrogen beding vibrations absorb at 1300–1000 cm^{-1}.[1,2] Bands involving the out of plane hydrogen bending vibrations absorb from 1000 cm^{-1} to 675 cm^{-1}.[1,2]

8.9   The 900-675 cm⁻¹ Region

Due to coupling between adjacent hydrogens and much weaker coupling between hydrogens separated by substituting groups, we find infrared correlations for out-of-plane hydrogen vibrations depending on the number of adjacent hydrogen atoms in the ring[1,2,12] (see Fig. 8.2).

Six adjacent hydrogens in benzene give rise to an in-phase out-of-plane vibration at 671 cm^{-1}. Five adjacent hydrogens in monosubstituted aromatic rings have an in-phase out-of-plane vibration which absorbs at 770–730 cm^{-1}. Four adjacent hydrogens in *ortho* absorb at 770–735 cm^{-1}. Three adjacent hydrogens in *meta* and vicinal tri have an in-phase out-of-plane vibration which absorbs

[8] F. F. Bentley and E. F. Wolfarth, *Spectrochim. Acta* 15, 165 (1959).
[9] M. L. Josien and J. M. Lebas, *Bull. Soc. Chim. France* 1956, 53; 57; 62.
[10] J. M. Lebas, C. Carrigou-Lagrange, and M. L. Josien, *Spectrochim. Acta* 15, 225 (1959).
[11] S. E. Wiberley, S. C. Bunce, and W. H. Bauer, *Anal. Chem.* 32, 217 (1960).
[12] N. B. Colthup, *J. Opt. Soc. Am.* 40, 397 (1950).

at 795–770 cm⁻¹. Two adjacent hydrogens in *para*, unsymmetric tri, and vicinal tetra absorb at 850–795 cm⁻¹. An isolated hydrogen in *meta*, unsymmetric tri, symmetric tetra, unsymmetric tetra, and penta gives rise to absorption at 890–835 cm⁻¹.

The strong aromatic bands in the 850–675 cm⁻¹ region are summarized in Table 8.2 where arithmetic means in cm⁻¹ and standard deviations are given.[1,2]

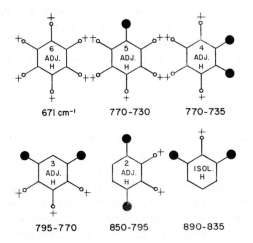

FIG. 8.2. In-phase, out-of-plane wagging vibrations of adjacent hydrogens on an aromatic ring.

TABLE 8.2

In Phase, Out of Plane Hydrogen Wagging and
Out of Plane Sextant Ring Bending Frequencies

monosubstituted benzene	751 ± 15	5 adjacent H wag	697 ± 11 ring bend
ortho disubstituted benzene	751 ± 7	4 adjacent H wag	
meta disubstituted benzene	782 ± 9	3 adjacent H wag	690 ± 15 ring bend
para disubstituted benzene	817 ± 13	2 adjacent H wag	

This correlation is useful for naphtalenes also.[12–15] In α substituted naphthaneles we have four adjacent hydrogens and three adjacent hydrogens. In β substituted naphtalenes we have four adjacent and two adjacent hydrogens and one isolated hydrogen. It also works for substituted pyridines[12,16,17] where the nitrogen (which has no hydrogen) is counted as a substituted carbon in a benzene ring. Thus a 4-alkyl pyridine compound which is a monosubstituted pyridine absorbs

[13] J. G. Hawkins, E. R. Ward, and D. H. Whiffen, *Spectrochim. Acta* 10, 105 (1957).
[14] R. L. Werner, W. Kennard and D. Rayson, *Australian J. Chem.* 8, 346 (1955).
[15] T. S. Wang and J. M. Sanders, *Spectrochim. Acta* 15, 1118 (1959).
[16] H. E. Podall, *Anal. Chem.* 29, 1423 (1957).
[17] G. L. Cook and F. M. Church, *J. Phys. Chem.* 61, 458 (1957).

like a *para* substituted benzene ring, because of the two adjacent hydrogens. The adjacent hydrogen classification is useful as a guide for many polycyclic benzenoid compounds and heteroaromatics, although the actual values may deviate from those for benzene substitution.[18,19]

There are a few substituents for which the above correlations do not work well. Nitro groups and carbonyl groups of carboxyl acids, esters, salts, or amides, directly on the ring alter the bands in this region and make interpretation difficult, probably due to interaction with out-of-plane vibrations of the group. Aromatics with these groups should be considered separately. Correlations have been made for aromatic rings substituted only with hydrocarbon substituents.[20]

8.10   The 1300-1000 cm⁻¹ Region

There are usually a number of medium-weak sharp bands in the 1300–1000 cm^{-1} region, many of which involve in plane hydrogen rocking vibrations.[1,2] These vibrations interact somewhat with C–C vibrations; below 1200 cm^{-1} a carbon tends to move in the same direction as its hydrogen moves. These bands are described in Table 8.3 as some hydrogens moving clockwise while others in opposition move counterclockwise. For example, monosubstituted aromatics usually have bands near 1027 cm^{-1} (2,3 hydrogens clockwise vs. 5,6 counterclockwise).

These sharp medium-weak bands are of variable intensity some being quite weak. Other vibrations occur here such as the "radial" modes interacting with substituent single bond stretching modes, methyl rocking modes of methyls on the ring (ca. 1040 cm^{-1}), and nonaryl single bond stretching modes. This region should be used with discretion.

A nonhydrogen vibration gives rise to a weak sharp band near 995 cm^{-1} in mono and *meta* isomers only.[1,2] In this vibration the 1, 3, and 5 ring carbons (with substituents) remain nearly stationary while the 2, 4, and 6 carbons move radially in phase.[4-6]

8.11   The 2000-1750 cm⁻¹ Region

In this region are a series of unusually intense overtones and combination bands which are different in their patterns for the various substituted benzenes and thus are very useful.[21,22] For them to be seen clearly the sample should be run thicker than normal. The patterns are shown in Fig. 8.3.

[18] C. G. Cannon and G. B. B. M. Sutherland, *Spectrochim. Acta* **4**, 373 (1951).
[19] M. P. Groenewege, *Spectrochim. Acta* **11**, 579 (1958).
[20] H. L. McMurry and V. Thornton, *Anal. Chem.* **24**, 318 (1952).

TABLE 8.3

APPROXIMATE FREQUENCIES FOR IN-PLANE HYDROGEN BENDING VIBRATIONS ON A BENZENE RING

Monosubstituted	Ortho-	Meta-	Para-
1027 ± 3 cm^{-1} (2,3 vs. 5,6)	1033 ± 11 cm^{-1} (3,4 vs. 5,6)	1076 ± 7 cm^{-1} (2 vs. 5)	1013 ± 5 cm^{-1} (2,3 vs. 5,6)
1073 ± 4 (2,6 vs. 3,4,5)	1125 ± 14 (3,6 vs. 4,5)	1096 ± 7 (4 vs. 6)	1117 ± 7 (2,6 vs. 3,5)
1156 ± 5 (3,5 vs. 4)	1160 ± 4 (3,5 vs. 4,6)	1157 ± 5 (2,5 vs. 4,6)	1175 ± 6 (2,5 vs. 3,6)
1177 ± 6 (2,5 vs. 3,6)	1269 ± 17 (all clockwise)	1278 ± 12 (all clockwise)	1258 ± 11 (all clockwise)
1240 ± 8 (all clockwise)			

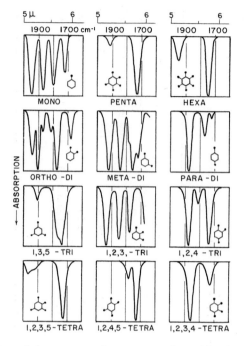

FIG. 8.3.   Characteristic patterns of overtone and combination bands for various substituted benzene rings.

8.12   The 3100-3000 cm⁻¹ Region

In this region are found multiple weak bands due to aromatic C—H stretching vibrations.[9-11]

8.13   Raman Correlations for Substituted Benzenes

In the Raman effect[7] most aromatics show bands at 1620–1565 cm⁻¹ (quadrant stretch) whether there is symmetry or not.

A very strong Raman band occurs at 1005—990 cm⁻¹ in the spectra of mono, *meta* di, and symmetrical trisubstituted benzenes which is absent in *ortho* and *para* isomers. In this vibration the 1, 3, and 5 ring carbons and substituents are nearly stationary while the 2, 4, and 6 carbons move radially in phase.[4,6] (This may be seen in the infrared spectrum as a weak sharp band in mono and *meta* isomers[1]).

Monosubstituted benzenes usually have a second Raman band at 1030–1015 cm[-1]. This is predominantly an in plane CH bend where the 2 and 3 hydrogens move clockwise while 5 and 6 move counterclockwise. *Ortho* substituted benzenes have a strong Raman band at 1045–1030 cm[-1] which is related to the mono band in that the 3 and 4 hydrogens move clockwise while the 5 and 6 hydrogens move counterclockwise. (Both of these are also infrared bands of medium-weak intensity[1]).

A depolarized Raman band occurs at 625–605 cm[-1] for mono and at 660-625 cm[-1] for *para* isomers which is due to one component of the in plane ring bending by quadrants (2, 5 carbons out, 3, 6 in) where the 1, and 4 ring carbons do not move radially and the substituents are nearly motionless. *Ortho* and *meta* isomers do not have a depolarized band here.

A very weak Raman band occurs in monosubstituted benzenes at 415–400 cm[-1] which is due to one component of the out-of-plane ring bending by quadrants (2, 5 carbons up, 3, 6 down) where the substituent does not move.

8.14 Condensed Ring Aromatic Compounds

In naphthalenes[12–15] and other condensed ring compounds[18] the classification of substitutions in terms of adjacent hydrogens[12] proves useful in interpreting the 900–700 cm[-1] region. Most α naphthalenes substituted only in the 1 position have infrared bands at 810–785 cm[-1] (3 adjacent hydrogens) and infrared bands at 780–760 cm[-1] (4 adjacent hydrogens)[14,15]. Most β naphthalenes substituted only in the 2 position absorb at 862–835 cm[-1] (isolated hydrogen), 835–805 cm[-1] (2 adjacent hydrogens) and 760–735 cm[-1] (4 adjacent hydrogens).[14,15] These and other out of plane vibrations for more highly substituted naphthalenes are summarized in Table 8.4.[13]

In this table the hydrogen pattern of each side of the naphthalene ring is considered separately. Hydrogen positions are given the lowest numbering which is not the case in conventional nomenclature. Regions are given in cm[-1] with average intensities indicated by m = medium, s = strong, vs = very strong. In the 3 and 4 adjacent hydrogen region two bands are usually seen but not always with the same intensity. One is probably a ring bending mode.[13]

[21] C. W. Young, R. B. DuVall, and N. Wright, *Anal. Chem.* **23**, 709 (1951).
[22] D. H. Whiffen, *Spectrochim. Acta* **7**, 253 (1955).

TABLE 8.4

CHARACTERISTIC BANDS FOR SUBSTITUTED NAPHTHALENES

Hydrogen pattern on one side	Isolated H	2 adjacent H	3 adjacent H	4 adjacent H
1 2 3 4				\800–761 s /770–726 s-vs
1 2 3			\820–776 s /774–730 s	
1 2 4	894–835 m-s	847–805 vs		
1 2		835–799 s		
2 3		834–812 s–vs		
1 3	\875–843 s /905–867 m-s			
1 4	889–870 s			
1 or 2	896–858 m			

Other naphthalene bands may be found in regions similar to those of benzene derivatives.[13,18] Bands for alkyl substituted naphthalenes have been found near 1600 cm^{-1} (a doublet), 1520–1505 cm^{-1} and 1400–1390 cm^{-1}.[18] There are many bands at 1400–1000 cm^{-1}.

In alkyl substituted anthracenes[18] bands appear at 1640–1620 cm^{-1}. A band is present near 1550 cm^{-1} which disappears with 9, 10 substitution. There is no 1500 cm^{-1} band. There are one or two strong bands at 900–650 cm^{-1}. The band near 900 cm^{-1} is associated with the 9, 10 isolated hydrogens and disappears when they are substituted.[18]

In alkyl substituted phenanthrenes[18] bands are found near 1600 cm^{-1} (often double on the high frequency side) and 1500 cm^{-1} which distinguishes it from anthracenes.

Tetralins[23] with 4 adjacent hydrogens on the aromatic ring absorb at 770–740 cm^{-1}, (H wag) with 3 adjacent hydrogens at 815–785 cm^{-1} (H wag) and 760–730 cm^{-1} (ring vibration), with two adjacent hydrogens at 850–810 cm^{-1} (H wag) and with isolated hydrogens at 835–773 cm^{-1} (ring vibration).

In the ring stretching region quinolines[1,24–26] show three bands near 1600 cm^{-1}

[23] T. Momose, Y. Ueda, and H. Yano, *Talanta* **3**, 65 (1959).
[24] H. Shindo and S. Tamura, *Pharm. Bull. (Tokyo)* **4**, 292 (1956).
[25] C. Karr, P. A. Estep, and A. J. Papa, *J. Am. Chem. Soc.* **81**, 152 (1959).
[26] J. T. Braunholtz and F. G. Mann, *J. Chem. Soc.* **1958**, 3368.

and 5 bands in the 1500–1300 cm^{-1} region. The 900–700 cm^{-1} region has adjacent hydrogen wagging bands similar to the corresponding naphthalenes.

Indoles[27] absorb near 1460, 1420, and 1350 cm^{-1}.

Quinazolines[28] absorb at 1628–1612, 1581–1566, and 1517-1478 cm^{-1}.

8.15 Pyridines

The characteristic bands for pyridine compounds[16–19] are listed in Tables 8.5 and 8.6. Table 8.5 is similar to the corresponding Table 8.1.

TABLE 8.5
PYRIDINE RING STRETCHING FREQUENCIES[1]

2 substituted pyridine	1615 → 1585	1572 ± 4	1471 ± 6	1433 ± 5
3 substituted pyridine	1595 ± 5	1577 ± 5	1485 → 1465	1421 ± 4
4 substituted pyridine	1603 ± 5	1561 ± 8	1520 → 1480	1415 ± 4
polysubstituted pyridine	1610 − 1597	1588 − 1564	1555 − 1490	
2 substituted pyridine N-oxides	1640 → 1600	1567 ± 10	1540 → 1480	1435 ± 10
3 substituted pyridine N-oxides	1605 ± 4	1563 ± 3	1480 ± 6	1434 ± 5
4 substituted pyridine N-oxides	1645 → 1610	—	1483 ± 6	1443 ± 7

TABLE 8.6
OUT OF PLANE VIBRATIONS[1]

2 substituted pyridine	780–740 4 adjacent H wag	
3 substituted pyridine	820–770 3 adjacent H wag	730–690 ring bend
4 substituted pyridine	850–790 2 adjacent H	
2 substituted pyridine N-oxides	790–750 4 adjacent H	
3 substituted pyridine N-oxides	820–760 3 adjacent H wag	680–660 ring bend
4 substituted pyridine N-oxides	855–820 2 adjacent H	

8.16 Pyridine N-oxides

Pyridine N-oxides[1,29] and the N-oxides of pyrimidine[29] and pyrazine[30,31] absorb strongly at 1320–1200 cm^{-1} due to the NO stretching frequency. A second band is found at 880–845 cm^{-1}.

[27] J. B. Brown, H. B. Henbest and E. R. H. Jones, *J. Chem. Soc.* **1952**, 3172.

[28] H. Culbertson, J. C. Decius, and B. E. Christensen, *J. Am. Chem. Soc.* **74**, 4834 (1952).

[29] R. H. Wiley and S. C. Slaymaker, *J. Am. Chem. Soc.* **79**, 2233 (1957).

[30] B. Klein and J. Berkowitz, *J. Am. Chem. Soc.* **81**, 5160 (1959).

[31] C. F. Koelsch and W. H. Grumprecht, *J. Org. Chem.* **23**, 1602 (1958).

8.17 Pyrimidines

Nontautomeric derivatives of pyrimidine[32] absorb strongly at 1580–1520 cm^{-1} and absorb near 990 cm^{-1} and 810 cm^{-1}. Amino substituted pyrimidines show NH$_2$ absorption bands at 3500–3100 and 1680–1635 cm^{-1}, in addition to the strong absorption at 1600–1500 cm^{-1}. Pyrimidines substituted with hydroxyl groups are generally in the "keto" form with C=O absorption near 1700 cm^{-1}.[32]

8.18 Triazines

The spectra of 1,3,5-*s*-triazines show absorption in three main regions, 1550 cm^{-1} ("quadrant stretching") 1420 cm^{-1} ("semicircle stretching") and 800 cm^{-1} (out of plane ring bending by "sextants").[33–38]

8.19 Alkyl or Aryl Substituted Triazines

Triazine rings, mono, di, or trisubstituted with an alkyl or aryl carbon directly attached to the ring have at least one strong band in the region 1580–1525 cm^{-1} (which may be double) and at least one weak band in the region 860–775 cm^{-1}. It does not seem to be possible to distinguish mono, di, or trisubstitution except possibly for ring CH stretch absorption for mono or di which can sometimes be seen in the 3100–3000 cm^{-1} region. There is usually at least one band in the 1450–1350 region.

[32] L. N. Short and H. W. Thompson, *J. Chem. Soc.* **1952**, 168.
[33] A. Roosens, *Bull. Soc. Chim. Belges* **59**, 377 (1950).
[34] J. Goubean, E. L. Jahn, A. Kreutzberger, and C. Grundmann, *J. Phys. Chem.* **58**, 1078 (1954).
[35] W. M. Padgett II and W. F. Hammer, *J. Am. Chem. Soc.* **80**, 803 (1958).
[36] J. E. Lancaster, R. F. Stamm and N. B. Colthup, *Spectrochim. Acta* **17**, 155 (1961).
[37] H. Schroeder, *J. Am. Chem. Soc.* **81**, 5658 (1959).
[38] Over 200 triazine spectra run by the author (1962).

8.20 Melamines and Guanamines

There is complicated absorption at 3500–3100 cm^{-1} (NH$_2$ stretch) and absorption at 1680–1640 cm^{-1} (NH$_2$ deformation) when there is an NH$_2$ group on the triazine ring. If the NH$_2$ groups are all mono or disubstituted, no absorption occurs at 1680–1640 cm^{-1}.

There is strong absorption in the 1600–1500 cm^{-1} region usually centering near 1550 cm^{-1} and multiple absorption in the 1450–1350 cm^{-1} region. In the 800 cm^{-1} region, a sharp medium intensity band occurs at 825–800 cm^{-1} which in most melamines is found in the narrow range 812 ± 5 cm^{-1}. This band falls in frequency to 795–750 cm^{-1} when the triazine is in the "*iso*" form with less than three double bonds in the ring and at least one double bond external to the ring. The ring N-alkyl *iso*-melamines and ammeline, both in the iso form,[39] exhibit a band here as does the HCl salt of melamine indicating protonation of a ring nitrogen.

8.21 Chloro, Oxy, and Thiosubstituted Triazines

Triazines with "hydroxyl" groups on the ring all exhibit strong C=O absorptions at 1775–1675 cm^{-1} indicating the presence of the "keto" form. Ammeline and ammelide exhibit broad absorption near 2650 cm^{-1} (not in melamine) due to the ring NH bonded to C=O oxygen, possibly in a dimer configuration. Absorption occurs at 795–750 cm^{-1} due to the ring in the iso form. The sodium salts of these compounds go back to the enol C—O$^-$Na$^+$ form,[39] as in tri sodium cyanurate which has no carbonyl and "normal" absorption at 820 cm^{-1}.

Trialkyl cyanurates absorb at 1600–1540 cm^{-1}, 1380–1320 cm^{-1}, 1160–1110 cm^{-1} (O—CH$_2$ stretch) and at 820–805 cm^{-1} (normal ring).

Thioammeline exhibits a broad band at 2900–2800 cm^{-1} (ring NH··S) and a band at 1200 cm^{-1} (C=S) not in S-alkyl thioammeline or the sodium salt of thioammeline. In addition thioammeline absorbs at 775 cm^{-1} (*iso* ring) where the S-alkyl and salt compounds absorb at 812 cm^{-1} (normal ring), all of which are consistent with the *iso* form for thioammeline.

In all these cases of hydroxy and mercaptan substituted heterocyclic rings, the tautomerization is best determined by comparison with alkylated compounds

[39] R. C. Hirt and R. G. Schmitt, *Spectrochim. Acta* **12**, 127 (1958).

where the form is fixed. For correlation purposes, the ring vibrations of *"iso"* or "keto" forms should be considered separately from "normal" or "enol" forms. The band near 800 cm^{-1} is usually quite reliable in telling a normal triazine ring (825–795 cm^{-1}) from an *iso* ring (795–750 cm^{-1}) in rings with any combination of nitrogen or oxygen substituents, or with two nitrogen substituents plus any third substituent. It fails to hold the same position in the trialkyl or aryl substituted triazines indicating some sensitivity to mechanical interaction here.

Dichlorotriazines absorb near 850 cm^{-1}.[40]

8.22   Tetrazines

Symmetrically substituted *s*-tetrazines have a center of symmetry, so the "quadrant" ring stretching band at 1600–1500 cm^{-1} is forbidden in the infrared. When the two substituents are electronically different, a strong band may result in this region. The "semicircle" ring stretching vibration (two components) remains active regardless of symmetry and results in absorption at 1495–1320 cm^{-1}. Another tetrazine band is found at 970–880 cm^{-1}.

8.23   Heteroaromatic Five Membered Ring Compounds

Five membered ring heteroaromatic compounds with two double bonds in the ring, generally show three ring stretching bands near 1590, 1490 and 1400 cm^{-1}.[1] Assignments for the skeletal vibrations in Fig. 8.4 are based upon those made for pyrrole[41,42] and furan.[43,44] Table 8.7 gives the regions for various types of rings.[1]

Most of these five membered heteroaromatics with a CH=CH group unsubstituted have strong hydrogen wag absorption at 800–700 cm^{-1}.

Compounds with hydroxyl or mercapto substituents can and usually do exist in the "keto" form. This is best determined by comparison with alkylated products where the structures are fixed.

[40] W. A. Heckle, H. A. Ory, and J. M. Talbert, *Spectrochim. Acta* **17**, 600 (1961).

[41] R. C. Lord and F. A. Miller, *J. Chem. Phys.* **10**, 328 (1942).

[42] P. Mirone, *Gazz. Chim. Ital.* **86**, 165 (1956).

[43] H. W. Thompson and R. B. Temple, *Trans. Faraday Soc.* **41**, 27 (1945).

[44] B. Bak, S. Brodersen and L. Hansen, *Acta Chem. Scand.* **9**, 749 (1955).

The NH stretch in pyrroles and indoles causes absorption at 3450-3400 cm^{-1} in dilute solution and at 3400–3100 cm^{-1} for hydrogen bonded solids. The bonded NH··N band in the solid state in most heteroaromatics with more than one nitrogen in the five membered ring results in broad absorption at 2800–2600 cm^{-1}.

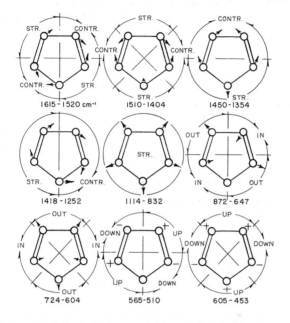

FIG. 8.4. Schematic skeletal vibrations of five membered ring compounds with two double bonds. For descriptive purposes the stretching vibrations may be described as whole ring, half ring, and quarter ring stretching. As the bonds are not all identical, the two highest frequencies consist predominantly of double bond stretching vibrations.

TABLE 8.7

HETEROAROMATIC FIVE MEMBERED RINGS[1]

2-substituted furans	1605–1570 cm^{-1}	1510–1475 cm^{-1}	1400–1380 cm^{-1}
polysubstituted furans	ca. 1560	ca. 1510	
2-substituted thiophenes	1534–1514	1454–1430	1361–1347
3-substituted thiophenes	ca. 1530	ca. 1410	ca. 1370
substituted pyrroles	1565	1500	
substituted thiazoles	1610	1500	1380
furoxans	1610	1460	1420
substituted isoxazoles	1600	1460	1380
substituted furazans	1570	1425	1380
1, 2, 4-oxadiazoles[45]	1590–1560	1470–1430	1390–1360

[45] J. Barrans, *Compt. rend.* **249**, 1096 (1959).

8.24 Cyclopentadienyl Ring-Metal Complexes

Metal complexes of the cyclopentadienyl ring with a large number of different metals have been studied.[46] The bands in Table 8.8 are observed for the cyclopentadienyl ring.

TABLE 8.8

CYCLOPENTADIENYL RING

3108–3027 cm^{-1}	CH stretch	medium
1443–1440	CC stretch	medium
1112–1090	CC stretch	medium-strong
1009– 990	CH deformation in plane	strong
830– 701	CH deformation out of plane	strong

[46] H. P. Fritz, *Chem. Ber.* **92**, 780 (1959).

CHAPTER 9

CARBONYL COMPOUNDS

9.1 Introduction

Carbonyl compounds give rise to a strong band at 1900–1550 cm^{-1} due to the stretching of the C=O bond. The carbonyl spectral regions are summarized in Table 9.1.

Factors which cause shifts in carbonyl frequencies are discussed below.

9.2 Mass Effects

The effect of replacing a carbon atom attached to a carbonyl group with a heavier atom is very small due to the mass effect alone.[1-5] The effect of replacing a carbon atom with a hydrogen atom has been calculated and would result in an aldehyde absorbing about 17 cm^{-1} lower than a ketone from the mass effect alone.[1]

The fact that aldehydes absorb about 15 cm^{-1} higher than ketones, and the fact that acid chlorides, esters, and amides are different from ketones are due therefore to changes in the force constant of the C=O bond.

9.3 Bond Angle Effects

During a carbonyl vibration, the atoms attached to the carbonyl do not move much when they have a mass equal to or greater than a carbon atom, hence the relatively small mass effect. However, since the attached atoms are nearly motionless, their single bonds must be contracted a little due to the motion

[1] S. Bratoz and S. Besnainou, *Compt. rend.* **248**, 546 (1959).
[2] K. Frei and H. H. Gunthard, *J. Mol. Spectry.* **5**, 218 (1960).
[3] J. O. Halford, *J. Chem. Phys.* **24**, 830 (1956).
[4] T. Miyazawa, *J. Chem. Soc. Japan, Pure Chem. Sect.* **77**, 366 (1956).
[5] J. K. Wilmshurst, *Can. J. Chem.* **37**, 1896 (1959).

TABLE 9.1

C=O SPECTRAL REGIONS

Dialkyl ketones	1725–1705 cm^{-1}
Singly conjugated ketones	1700–1670
Doubly conjugated ketones	1680–1640
α-Chloro ketone (Cl near O) (cyclic equatorial)	ca. 1745
α-Chloro ketone (Cl not near O) (cyclic axial)	ca. 1725
Ketone in five membered ring (unconjugated)	1750–1740
o-hydroxy aryl ketones	1670–1630
1,3 Diketones, enol form	1640–1580
Aliphatic aldehydes	1740–1720
Aromatic aldehydes	1710–1685
Formate esters	1725–1720
Other saturated esters	1750–1735
Conjugated esters (electron attracting groups on the oxygen raise the C=O frequency)	1735–1715
Lactones six membered ring	1750–1715
Lactones five membered ring	1795–1740
Carbonates noncyclic organic	1780–1740
Carbonates in five membered ring	1850–1790
Carboxylic acid dimer	1720–1680
Carboxylic acid monomer	1800–1740
Carboxylic acid salt	⎰1650–1550 ⎱1440–1370
Amides and ureas (electron attracting groups on the nitrogen raise the C=O frequency)	1695–1630
Lactams five membered ring	1750–1700
Lactams four membered ring	1780–1730
Carbamates	1740–1683
Anhydrides, noncyclic, unconjugated	⎰1825–1815⎰ higher band ⎱1755–1745⎱ stronger
Anhydrides, noncyclic, conjugated	⎰1780–1770⎰ higher band ⎱1725–1715⎱ stronger
Anhydrides, cyclic, unconjugated	⎰1870–1845⎰ lower band ⎱1800–1775⎱ stronger
Anhydrides, cyclic, conjugated	⎰1860–1850⎰ lower band ⎱1780–1760⎱ stronger
Acid chlorides, aliphatic	1810–1795
Acid chlorides, aromatic	⎰1785–1765 ⎱1750–1735
Chloroformates, aliphatic	1785–1775
Thiol esters, unconjugated	1710–1680
Thiol esters, conjugated	1700–1640

of the carbonyl carbon atom as it moves away from the oxygen. This additional resistance to the motion of the carbon atom raises the $C=O$ vibrational frequency and is a function of bond angle. In most carbonyl compounds, the bond angle is not a variable, but in compounds where the angles are different as in strained ring compounds, this effect should be considered. Here, the double bond-single bond interaction is altered, the interaction increasing as the double bond-single bond angle increases or as the $C-C-C$ angle decreases. Studies indicate that most of the frequency shifts in strained ring carbonyls are due to the geometry change rather than to a large change in force constant.[1,2]

The following equation, which gives the carbonyl frequency in wavenumbers, has been derived for saturated ketones,[3]

$$(cm^{-1}) = 1278 + 68K - 2.2\ \emptyset$$

The carbonyl wavenumber is dependent on K (force constant in practical units or actual $k \times 10^{-5}$) and $\emptyset$ (the $C-C-C$ angle in degrees). For unconjugated ketones, $K = 10.2 \pm 0.3$ ($\times 10^5$ dyn/cm).

The average difference between the frequencies of various types of cyclic carbonyl compounds and their acyclic analogues is given in cm^{-1} as follows[5a]: seven membered ring, -8 ± 3; six membered ring, $+7 \pm 14$; five membered ring, $+37 \pm 11$; and four membered ring, $+76 \pm 7$. Approximately the same relationships apply for carbonyls in bicyclic compounds when the smallest ring containing the $C=O$ is chosen.

9.4 Inductive Effects

The tendency of the carbonyl oxygen to attract electrons ($\overset{+}{C}-\overset{-}{O}$) results in a weakening of the $C=O$ force constant and a lowering of the $C=O$ frequency. Electron attracting groups attached to the carbon atom compete with the oxygen for electrons, resulting in less contribution from the polar form ($\overset{+}{C}-\overset{-}{O}$) and a higher frequency. As an example of this, ketones absorb near 1715 cm^{-1} whereas acid chlorides absorb near 1800 cm^{-1}. The carbonyl frequency has been correlated with the sum of the electronegativities of the attached atoms,[6] for cases where mesomerism is unimportant. A change in the carbonyl force constant due to a change in substituent electronegativity has the largest effect on the carbonyl stretching frequency but other force constants involved in the carbonyl

[5a] H. K. Hall, Jr. and R. Zbinden, *J. Am. Chem. Soc.* **80**, 6428 (1958); *ibid.* **82**, 1215 (1960).

[6] R. E. Kagarise, *J. Am. Chem. Soc.* **77**, 1377 (1955).

stretching vibration such as $C(O)-X$ stretching and $X-C(O)-Y$ bending also change with substituent electronegativities and have some effect on the carbonyl stretching frequency. Acid fluorides have carbonyl frequencies about 50 cm^{-1} higher than acid chlorides or bromides largely because of changes in these other force constants rather than in the carbonyl force constant.[7]

In α-chloro carbonyl compounds, a difference is observed between rotational isomers due to a field effect. When the chlorine is near the carbonyl oxygen in space, a higher frequency results relative to the isomer in which the chlorine is rotated away from the oxygen. The electron cloud of the chlorine atom near the oxygen electrostatically repels the tendency of oxygen to attract electrons ($\overset{+}{C}-\bar{O}$) resulting in an increase in the C=O frequency of about 20 cm^{-1}.[8,9]

9.5   Mesomeric Effects

Acid chlorides, esters, and amides have progressively decreasing carbonyl frequencies. This shift cannot be explained by inductive effects alone, particularly in amides where the nitrogen is more electronegative than a carbon atom, but an amide carbonyl has a lower frequency than a ketone. The dominant effect in amides is the mesomeric effect ($\bar{O}-C=\overset{+}{N}$), where the oxygen atom draws electrons and the nitrogen atom donates electrons, resulting in a weaker C=O bond but a stronger C—N bond. When an electron attracting group is placed on the nitrogen atom, it competes with the oxygen for electrons and a stiffer C=O bond and a higher frequency result.[10] This also happens in esters when electron attracting groups are put on the single bonded oxygen atom.

Conjugation of carbonyls with double bonds or aromatic rings usually results in a band shift to lower wavenumbers of about 20–30 cm^{-1}, due again to a redistribution of electrons which weakens the C=O bond. Steric effects may remove the coplanarity of the conjugated system and thus reduce the effect of conjugation.

Hydrogen bonding affects carbonyl frequencies, but the largest effects occur when hydrogen bonding is combined with mesomeric effects. When a carbonyl is hydrogen bonded and resonance can occur which puts a partial negative charge on the oxygen atom accepting the hydrogen bond and a positive charge

[7] J. Overend and J. R. Scherer, *Spectrochim. Acta* **16**, 773 (1960).

[8] R. N. Jones, D. A. Ramsay, F. Herling, and K. Dobriner, *J. Am. Chem. Soc.* **74**, 2828 (1952).

[9] L. J. Bellamy and R. L. Williams, *J. Chem. Soc.* **1957**, 4294.

[10] L. J. Bellamy, *Spectrochim. Acta* **13**, 60 (1958).

on the atom donating the hydrogen, the partial "transfer of allegiance" of the proton enhances resonance

$$(C{=}O \cdot\cdot H{-}X{-} \longleftrightarrow C{-}\bar{O} \cdot\cdot H{-}\overset{+}{X}{=})$$

and lowers the $C{=}O$ frequency. This effect can be seen in o-hydroxy aceto-phenones, the enol form of acetyl acetone types, carboxylic acid dimers, etc.

9.6 Ketones

Ketones are best characterized by the strong $C{=}O$ stretching frequency absorption near 1715 cm^{-1}. Ketone carbonyls between saturated hydrocarbon groups absorb strongly at 1725–1705 cm^{-1},[11] in most cases. A CH_3 group next to the carbonyl has a strong band due to symmetric CH_3 deformation at 1370–1350 cm^{-1},[12] which is lower and more intense than the alkane CH_3 group absorption. A CH_2 group next to the carbonyl has a strong band due to CH_2 deformation at 1440–1405 cm^{-1}.[12] In CH_2-CO-CH_2 compounds, the asymmetric $C{-}C{-}C$ stretching vibration gives rise to a medium intensity band at 1230–1100 cm^{-1}. Methyl alkyl ketones have this band at 1170 cm^{-1} and a carbonyl deformation band at 595 cm^{-1}.[13]

9.7 α-Chloro Ketones

Ketones with a chlorine on the α-carbon will absorb at higher frequencies when the chlorine is rotated near the oxygen than when the chlorine is not near the oxygen due to a field effect.[8,9]

Examples of this may be seen in the difference between the rotational isomers of α-chloro acetone at 1745 and 1725 cm^{-1} or in equatorial (ca. 1745 cm^{-1}) and axial (ca. 1725 cm^{-1}) α-halogenated cyclic ketones.[8,9]

9.8 Conjugated Ketones

Conjugation without hydrogen bonding results in a lowering of the carbonyl stretching frequency to 1700–1640 cm^{-1}. Singly conjugated ketones such as alkyl phenones and carbonyl conjugated olefins usually absorb near 1700–

[11] C. N. R. Rao, G. K. Goldman, and C. Lurie, *J. Phys. Chem.* **63**, 1311 (1959).
[12] N. B. Colthup, *J. Opt. Soc. Am.* **40**, 397 (1950).
[13] H. W. Thompson and P. Torkington, *J. Chem. Soc.* **1945**, 640.

1670 cm^{-1} though the frequency may be lower in certain cases.[14,15] The intensities of aryl ketone carbonyls are considerably lower than the intensities of amide carbonyls which absorb in the same region.[16] Doubly conjugated ketones, quinones, and benzophenones usually absorb near 1680–1640 cm^{-1}. The aromatic ketones have a medium band at 1300–1230 cm^{-1} [12] due to the phenyl-carbonyl C—C stretch. The 1600 cm^{-1} aromatic band is usually a doublet, but the 1500 cm^{-1} aromatic band may be very weak.

The carbonyl frequencies in *para* and *meta* substituted acetophenones have been correlated with Hammett σ constants.[14] Amino substitution lowers and nitro substitution raises the carbonyl frequency.

In α, β-unsaturated ketones, a difference has been noted between compounds where the C=O and C=C have *trans* or *cis* orientation.[17] In *s-cis* ketones the C=O and C=C bands are further apart than in *s-trans*. The infrared intensities of the *s-cis* C=C are much higher and the C=O somewhat lower than those of *s-trans* ketones.

$$s\text{-}trans \quad C{=}O \quad 1690\text{–}1675 \text{ cm}^{-1} \quad C{=}C \quad 1644\text{–}1618 \text{ cm}^{-1}$$
$$s\text{-}cis \quad\;\; C{=}O \quad 1700\text{–}1687 \text{ cm}^{-1} \quad C{=}C \quad 1624\text{–}1617 \text{ cm}^{-1}$$

Carbonyls conjugated with other carbonyls in α-diketones such as diacetyl and benzil are hardly different in frequency from comparable ketones without the carbonyl-carbonyl conjugation, (1726 cm^{-1} in 11:12 diketone steroids).[18,19]

9.9 Conjugated Hydrogen Bonded Ketones

When ketones are conjugated and hydrogen bonded in such a way that resonance puts a negative charge on the carbonyl oxygen and a positive charge on the atom which carries the bonding proton, a further change occurs. Because of hydrogen bonding, resonance is increased, resulting in weakening of the C=O and C=C bonds. An example of this is seen in *ortho* hydroxy aryl carbonyl compounds which absorb at 1670–1630 cm^{-1}.[20] Another example is

[14] R. N. Jones, W. F. Forbes, and W. A. Mueller, *Can. J. Chem.* **35**, 504 (1957).
[15] R. N. Jones and E. Spinner, *Can. J. Chem.* **36**, 1020 (1958).
[16] H. W. Thompson and D. A. Jameson, *Spectrochim. Acta* **13**, 236 (1958).
[17] R. Mecke and K. Noack, *Spectrochim. Acta* **12**, 391 (1958).
[18] R. S. Rasmussen, R. D. Tunnicliff, and R. R. Brattain, *J. Am. Chem. Soc.* **71**, 1068 (1949).
[19] R. N. Jones, P. Humphries, and K. Dobriner, *J. Am. Chem. Soc.* **72**, 956 (1950).
[20] I. M. Hunsberger, *J. Am. Chem. Soc.* **72**, 5626 (1950).

the enol form of compounds where two carbonyls are separated by one CH_2 group (β-diketones).

$$\underset{\text{keto (1710 cm}^{-1}\text{)}}{\overset{\displaystyle O \qquad\quad O}{\underset{\displaystyle \parallel \qquad\quad \parallel}{-C-CH_2-C-}}} \qquad \underset{\text{enol (1600 cm}^{-1}\text{)}}{\overset{\displaystyle O\ \cdots\ H-O}{\underset{\displaystyle \parallel \qquad\ \ \ |}{-C-CH=C-}} \longleftrightarrow \overset{\displaystyle -O\ \cdots\ H-O+}{\underset{\displaystyle | \qquad\quad\ \parallel}{-C=CH-C-}}}$$

A vibration best described as asymmetric OCC stretching in the enol tautomer absorbs broadly and strongly at 1640–1580 cm^{-1},[18],[21–23] the low frequency implying a large amount of resonance. As there are four nearly equivalent bonds in the enol nucleus (two CO and two CC bonds), four stretching frequencies are expected involving all the bonds. These usually occur near 1600, 1500, 1450, and 1260 cm^{-1}.[21] The bonded OH group in these compounds absorbs weakly and broadly around 3000–2700 cm^{-1}. Certain 1,3 diketones with bulky substituents (t-Bu-CO-CH$_2$-CO-t-Bu)[23] have no 1700 cm^{-1} absorption at all indicating the absence of the keto form. This is due to steric effects which hinder the formation of rotational isomers other than that form required for the chelated enol ring.[23] Unsubstituted and 2-monosubstituted 1,3 cyclohexanedione derivatives enolize strongly in CCl$_4$ solution.[24] The enol form of the monosubstituted ones exists as a hydrogen bonded dimer

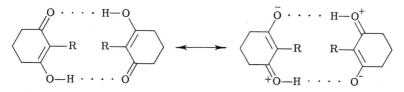

which absorbs at 1630–1607 cm^{-1}, and as a monomer, absorbing at 1649–1646 cm^{-1} more like an ordinary conjugated ketone. The 2-disubstituted derivatives have no enol form of course. The keto form of the 1,3 cyclohexanediones has two bands, asymmetric C=O stretch 1707–1694 cm^{-1} (strong) and symmetric C=O stretch 1739–1725 cm^{-1}, less than half as intense as the 1700 cm^{-1} band.[24] Metal chelates or salts[25–28] of the 1,3 diketones absorb near 1580 cm^{-1} since here the two C$\cdots$O and C$\cdots$C bonds are nearly equivalent (all

[21] R. Mecke and E. Funk, *Z. Elektrochem.* **60**, 1124 (1956).

[22] D. Hadzi and N. Sheppard, *Trans. Faraday Soc.* **50**, 911 (1954).

[23] G. S. Hammond, W. G. Bordium and G. A. Guter, *J. Am. Chem. Soc.* **81**, 4682 (1959).

[24] S. N. Anachenko, I. V. Berezin, and I. V. Torgov, *Izvest. Akad. Nauk SSSR* **9**, 1644 (1960).

[25] L. Bellamy, G. S. Spicer, and J. D. H. Strickland, *J. Chem. Soc.* **1952**, 4653.

[26] H. F. Holtzclaw, Jr. and J. P. Collman, *J. Am. Chem. Soc.* **79**, 3318 (1957).

[27] J. Charette and P. Teyssié, *Spectrochim. Acta* **16**, 689 (1960).

[28] K. Nakamoto, P. J. McCarthy, and A. E. Martell, *J. Am. Chem. Soc.* **83**, 1272 (1961).

approximately a "bond and a half"). The regions for the vibrations of the metal chelates, each involving all four "bond and a half" bonds are 1600–1560, 1530–1500, ca. 1450, and ca. 1250 cm^{-1}. There is some relation between the 1580 cm^{-1} band frequency and the stability of the complex.[26-27] Detailed assignments have been made for acetyl acetonates. Calculations indicate that the highest frequency band in the 1600 cm^{-1} region involves more C⋯C stretching than C⋯O.[28]

Another example of conjugated hydrogen bonded systems is found in 6 hydroxy fulvenes with a carbonyl in the 1 position.

The OH stretch is very weak like acetyl acetone, and bands involving C⋯O and C⋯C stretching occur at 1635 and 1545 cm^{-1}.

Tropolones, in solution, absorb near 3200-3100 (OH), near 1620 (C=O), and 1550 cm^{-1} (C=C).[29]

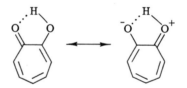

9.10   Bond Angle Effects in Ketones

Ketones in strained rings have frequencies which are higher than normal as the C—C—C bond angle decreases,[3] due predominantly to increased interaction with the C—C stretching vibration.[1,2] Ketone carbonyls in six membered rings are about the same as noncyclic ketone carbonyls. The C=O frequency steadily increases as the ring gets smaller.

acetone	1715 cm^{-1}	
cyclohexanone	1717	
cyclopentanone	1750–1730[30]	(Fermi resonance doublet)
cyclobutanone	1782[2]	

[29] W. E. Doering and L. H. Knox, *J. Am. Chem. Soc.* **75**, 297 (1953).

[30] C. L. Angell, P. J. Krueger, R. Lauzon, L. C. Leitch, K. Noack, R. D. Smith, and R. N. Jones, *Spectrochim. Acta* **15**, 926 (1959).

Unconjugated ketones in five membered rings absorb at 1750-1740 cm^{-1} in sterols, conjugation lowering the band to near 1716 cm^{-1}.[19]

The compound di-*t*-butyl ketone absorbs at 1686 cm^{-1}, lower than normal ketone C=O bands, primarily due to a steric increase in the C—C—C angle.[3]

9.11 Aldehyde CH Vibrations

In most aldehydes with alkyl groups or an aromatic ring next to the carbonyl, the aldehyde CH gives rise to two bands at 2900–2800 cm^{-1} and 2775–2695 cm^{-1} and to a band at 1410–1380 cm^{-1}.[31-33] The 1390 cm^{-1} band is assigned to the in plane hydrogen rock vibration.[23]

Aliphatic aldehydes have bands at 2830-2810 cm^{-1} and 2720–2695 cm^{-1}.[31] Some *ortho* substituted benzaldehydes with substituents such as halogen, nitro, or methoxy absorb at 2900–2860 cm^{-1} and 2765–2747 cm^{-1}, these regions differing somewhat from all other benzaldehydes which absorb at 2832–2812 cm^{-1} and 2745–2720 cm^{-1},[32] due possibly to a steric effect.[34]

The two bands in the CH stretch region where only one fundamental is expected is most satisfactorily explained as an interaction of the CH stretch fundamental with the overtone of the CH bending vibration near 1390 cm^{-1}.[33] Since aldehydes with a large variety of side groups give rise to this same doublet, it is unconvincing to assign this to any interactions with overtones or combinations of the side groups. Since the intensities of both bands in the stretching region are comparable in intensity to the 1390 cm^{-1} band, both are too intense for either to be a simple overtone. This must involve Fermi resonance of the overtone with the fundamental, which means that both bands near 2830 and 2740 cm^{-1} involve aldehyde CH stretch, and both bands involve the overtone of the 1390 cm^{-1} CH rock.

A few aldehydes do not have the doublet, having only one band near 2870–2830 cm^{-1}. The CH rock is usually shifted in these cases so that there is no longer close coincidence between the frequency of the overtone and fundamental. Chloral is an example with bands at 2870 and 1360 cm^{-1}.

The CH out of plane wag (about 900–700 cm^{-1} in some simple aldehydes from the literature) is disappointingly weak and is therefore useless for correlation purposes.

[31] S. Pinchas, *Anal. Chem.* **27**, 2 (1955).
[32] S. Pinchas, *Anal. Chem.* **29**, 334 (1957).
[33] D. F. Eggers, Jr. and W. E. Lingren, *Anal. Chem.* **28**, 1328 (1956).
[34] R. West and L. S. Whatley, *Chem. Ind. (London)* **1959**, 333.

9.12 Aldehyde Carbonyl Vibrations

The most intense band in the aldehyde spectrum is usually due to the carbonyl stretching vibration. Most aliphatic aldehydes absorb strongly at 1740–1720 cm^{-1}. Most aromatic aldehydes absorb at 1710–1685 cm^{-1}.[32] Salicylaldehyde absorbs at 1666 cm^{-1} due to conjugated internal hydrogen bonding as in the *ortho* hydroxy phenones. As with other carbonyl compounds, conjugation lowers the frequency while electronegative groups next to the carbonyl raise the frequency. The chloro acetaldehydes in CCl$_4$ absorb as follows: trichloro, 1768 cm^{-1}; dichloro, 1748 cm^{-1}; monochloro, 1730 cm^{-1}; and acetaldehyde, 1730 cm^{-1}. No doubling is observed as in the chloro ketones.[35]

9.13 Aldehyde C—C

Aromatic aldehydes have a band[12,33] usually at 1210–1160 cm^{-1} which probably involves stretching of the phenyl-C bond. An aromatic ring band usually absorbs at 1310–1260 cm^{-1}.

9.14 Ester C=O

Esters are characterized by the strong absorption due to the C=O stretching frequency[36] near 1740 cm^{-1} and by the strong absorption involving the stretching of the C—O near 1200 cm^{-1}.[37]

The C=O stretching frequency for normal formate esters is at 1725–1720 cm^{-1}.[13] For most other alkyl substituted, saturated esters, the C=O frequency is at 1750–1735 cm^{-1}.[13] Ester C=O groups conjugated with C=C groups or aromatic rings absorb at 1740–1715 cm^{-1}.[38–40] When an electron

[35] L. J. Bellamy and R. L. Williams, *J. Chem. Soc.* **1958**, 3465.
[36] E. J. Hartwell, R. E. Richards, and H. W. Thompson, *J. Chem. Soc.* **1948**, 1436.
[37] R. G. Fowler and R. M. Smith, *J. Opt. Soc. Am.* **43**, 1054 (1953).
[38] W. L. Walton and R. B. Hughes, *Anal. Chem.* **28**, 1388 (1956).
[39] W. L. Walton and R. B. Hughes, *J. Am. Chem. Soc.* **79**, 3985 (1957).
[40] J. L. Mateos, R. Cetina, E. Olivera, and S. Mesa, *J. Org. Chem.* **26**, 2494 (1961).

withdrawing group such as a vinyl or phenyl group is placed on the single bonded oxygen, the carbonyl frequency will be raised. Vinyl acetate, for example, absorbs at 1770 cm^{-1} whereas ethyl acetate absorbs at 1740 cm^{-1}. The tendency for the carbonyl oxygen to draw electrons from the other oxygen and thus weaken the C=O bond is reduced by the action of the group.[10]

$$\text{(1)} \quad CH_3-\overset{O-}{\underset{|}{C}}=\overset{+}{O}-CH=CH_2 \longleftrightarrow \text{(2)} \quad CH_3-\overset{O}{\overset{\|}{C}}-\overset{-}{O}=CH-\overset{-}{C}H_2$$

This same group which stiffens the C=O bond will also weaken the C—O bond at the same time, resulting in a higher C=O frequency but a lower C—O frequency.

9.15 Ester C—O

The C—O stretching frequency, so-called for convenience, actually involves some interaction with all the C—C bonds in the molecule. The most intense and therefore the most useful of these single bond vibrations is the highest asymmetric stretching frequency near 1200 cm^{-1}. Actually the C—O next to the carbonyl is stiffer than the other single bonds due to resonance which tends to localize the high vibration in the C—O bond. All the normal saturated esters except acetates absorb strongly at 1210–1160 cm^{-1}.[13] Normal acetates absorb at 1260–1230 cm^{-1}.[13] Acetates which were made from primary alcohols, where there is a CH$_2$ or CH$_3$ group on the single bonded oxygen, have a second correlatable single bond vibration at 1060–1035 cm^{-1}.[13] When the acetate is made from other than primary alcohols, a band appears at higher frequencies (1100 cm^{-1} for sec-alcohol). We can ascribe the band near 1250 cm^{-1} to asymmetric C—$\overset{\|}{C}$—O stretching and the band near 1050 cm^{-1} to O—CH$_2$—C asymmetric stretching. This is a convenient nomenclature since the lower band is more sensitive to branching changes in the alcohol part of the ester. There is a tendency for this lower band near 1050 cm^{-1} to appear in other saturated esters made from primary alcohols, but it is usually not as clear as in the acetates.

Esters conjugated with double bonds such as acrylates, methacrylates, fumarates, etc. usually have multiple bands at 1300–1160 cm^{-1}.[38–39] Esters conjugated with an aromatic ring such as phthalates and benzoates usually have a strong band near 1280 cm^{-1} and a second band for esters of primary alcohols near 1120 cm^{-1}.

Tables 9.2–9.4 summarize the absorption regions for various esters.

TABLE 9.2
Bands for O-Alkyl Saturated Esters[13] (CM^{-1})

Formates	Acetates	Propionates	n-Butyrates	Isobutyrates
1724–1722 (C=O)	1740 (C=O)	1740–1735 (C=O)	1735 (C=O)	1735 (C=O)
1214–1185 strong (C–O)	1370 (CH_3)	1275	1300	1260
1160	1245 strong (C–O)	1200–1190 strong (C–O)	1255	1200 strong (C–O)
	1040 (OCH_2)	1080 (OCH_2)	1190 strong (C–O)	1160
	640	1020 (OCH_2)	1100	1080
	612	810	750	755
		610	590	
		590		

TABLE 9.3
Bands for O-Alkyl α,β-Unsaturated Esters[38],[39] (CM^{-1})

Acrylates	Methacrylates	Crotonates (trans)	Maleates	Fumarates
1725 (C=O)	1725 (C=O)	1720 (C=O)	1725 (C=O)	1725 (C=O)
1640 (C=C)	1640 (C=C)	1660 (C=C)	1645 (C=C)	1650 (C=C)
1625 (2 × 811)	1410 (=CH_2 deformation)		1410 (cis CH rk)	
1410 (=CH_2 deformation)	1325	1280	1290	1300
1280 (=CH rk)	1300	1190	1250	1265
1200 (C–O)	1180		1220 strong	1225 weak
1065 ± 5 (=CH_2 rock)	939 ± 4 (=CH_2 wag)	975 ± 5 (trans CH wag)	1162	1175
985 ± 5 (trans CH wag)	815 ± 2 (=CH_2 twist)	838 ± 4		1165
965 ± 5 (=CH_2 wag)	652 ± 6 (C=O wag)	685 ± 10 (C=O wag)	850 ± 50 (cis CH wag)	979 ± 3 (trans CH wag)
811 ± 3 (=CH_2 twist)				775 ± 3
657 ± 12 (C=O wag)				667 ± 3

TABLE 9.4

BANDS FOR O-ALKYL AROMATIC ESTERS (CM^{-1})

Benzoates	Phthalates	Terephthalates	Isophthalates
1725 (C=O)	1725 (C=O)	1725 (C=O)	1725 (C=O)
1605 (ring)	1605 (ring)	(no 1600 aromatic bands)	1613 (ring)
1585 (ring)	1585 (ring)		1587 (ring)
1280 strong (C−O)	1280 strong (C−O)	1280 strong (C−O)	1250 (C−O)
1110 (OCH$_2$)	1120 (OCH$_2$)	1110 (OCH$_2$)	1110 (OCH$_2$)
1070 (ring)	1080		
1030 (ring)	1040 (ring)		
710 (ring)	745 (ring)	730 (ring)	730 (ring)

9.16   Out-of-Plane Hydrogen Vibrations in Unsaturated Esters

Polarized Raman spectra of α,β-unsaturated esters with a plane of symmetry help in distinguishing out-of-plane vibrations (weak depolarized Raman lines) from in-plane vibrations (medium-strong polarized Raman lines). (See Table 9.5.)

TABLE 9.5

POLARIZED RAMAN SPECTRA[a]

	CH$_2$ Wag	C−C−O, symmetric stretch	CH$_2$ Twist	C=O Wag, out-of-plane
Methyl acrylate	975 DP weak	855 P medium	812 DP weak	665 DP weak
Methyl methacrylate	937 DP weak	836 P medium	817 DP weak	660 DP weak
Methyl crotonate (trans)		840 P medium		690 DP weak

[a] P = polarized; DP = depolarized.

Thus the Raman spectrum helps to identify the polarized 840 cm^{-1} band in methyl crotonate, which is the only band between 900 and 725 cm^{-1}, as an in plane vibration (probably symmetrical C−C−O−C stretch) and confirms the 815 cm^{-1} assignment in acrylates, methacrylates, acrylic acid, and acrylamide as CH$_2$ twist with the carbonyl wag out-of-plane band at 700–640 cm^{-1} in these compounds. All of the above depolarized bands have "C" type contours in the infrared spectra of the gas phase, verifying their out-of-plane character.

The lowest hydrogen wag of the vinyl group in hydrocarbons[41]

$$\left({}^{+H}C = C^{H^+}_{H^-} \text{ ca. } 630 \text{ cm}^{-1} \right)$$

involving *cis* wag and CH_2 twist, seems to be the parent of the vinylidene twist

$$\left(C = C^{H^+}_{H^-} \text{ ca. } 700 \text{ cm}^{-1} \right)$$

and the in phase *cis* wag

$$\left({}^{+H}C = C^{H^+} \text{ ca. } 700 \text{ cm}^{-1} \right),$$

all three at about the same frequency ($+$ and $-$ here are motions out-of-plane). This suggests comparable assignments for acrylates (811 cm^{-1}), methacrylates (815 cm^{-1}), and maleates (850 cm^{-1}). These particular hydrogen bending modes all require a small out-of-plane counter motion of the attached group so it is likely that some interaction with the C=O wag occurs. In acrylates and methacrylates this may account in part for the unusually high CH_2 twist frequencies as well as the C=O wagging frequencies which are somewhat lower than they are in crotonates. The CH_2 wagging frequencies are insensitive to interaction.[41]

9.17   Groups Next to the Carbonyl in Esters

There are alterations of the group next to the carbonyl in esters which are useful for identification.[42] In acetates, the methyl next to the C=O absorbs strongly near 1374 cm^{-1} due to the symmetric CH_3 deformation; the asymmetric CH_3 deformation absorbs weakly near 1430 cm^{-1}; and the CH_3 stretching absorbs weakly near 2990 cm^{-1}. The CH_2 next to the carbonyl in other saturated esters has a deformation frequency near 1420 cm^{-1}.

Acrylates have a temperature insensitive doublet in the double bond region at 1640 and 1625 cm^{-1} (intensity ratio ca. 10:8, infrared, ca. 10:1 Raman) due to interaction with the overtone of a band at 814–808 cm^{-1} which is due to the lowest vinyl hydrogen wag vibration described as "*cis* wag-CH_2 twist." Normal benzoates with an unsubstituted ring have ring vibrations near 1070 cm^{-1} and 1030 cm^{-1} and a strong band near 710 cm^{-1}. The aromatic esters are exceptions to the normal *ortho*, *meta*, *para* distribution of bands in the 850–700 cm^{-1} region, the complications possibly due to interaction with the out-of-plane carbonyl wag. Normal phthalates have aromatic bands at 1040 cm^{-1} and 745 cm^{-1}. Terephthalates and isophthalates have an aromatic band near 730 cm^{-1}. Terephthalates have no 1600 cm^{-1} aromatic bands because of the center of symmetry.

[41] J. K. Brown and N. Sheppard, *Trans. Faraday Soc.* **51**, 1611 (1955).
[42] A. R. Katritzky, J. M. Lagowski, and J. A. T. Beard, *Spectrochim. Acta* **16**, 964 (1960).

9.18 Groups on the Oxygen Atom in Esters

The alcohol from which the ester is made may be characterized in some cases.[43] A methyl ester has an asymmetric stretch near 2960 cm^{-1} and a deformation near 1440 cm^{-1}. An ethyl ester has an asymmetric CH$_3$ stretch near 2980 cm^{-1} with weaker bands near 2950 and 2900 cm^{-1}. The deformation of the O—CH$_2$ group absorbs near 1475 cm^{-1}, the asymmetric CH$_3$ deformation near 1455 cm^{-1}, the O—CH$_2$ wag near 1400 cm^{-1}, and the symmetric CH$_3$ deformation near 1375 cm^{-1}. When the CH$_2$ of the O—CH$_2$—CH$_3$ group is substituted as in O-sec-butyl, O—CH(C$_2$H$_5$)—CH$_3$, the 1400 cm^{-1} band disappears and the CH$_3$ absorbs near 1382 cm^{-1}. In the O-ethyl case there is probably interaction between the CH$_3$ symmetric deformation and the CH$_2$ wag so that both bands involve both vibrations. The O—CH$_2$ wag is still visible in n-propyl esters near 1390 cm^{-1} (CH$_3$ deformation near 1383 cm^{-1}). As with any other correlations, the usefulness of these bands depends on how much interference there is from the rest of the molecule.

9.19 Lactones

Lactones with unstrained six membered rings are similar to noncyclic esters. As the ring becomes smaller the C—C—O angle decreases and the frequency of the carbonyl stretching vibration increases. Saturated δ lactones (six membered ring) have a carbonyl band at 1750-1735 cm^{-1}.[44] Saturated γ-lactones (five membered ring) have carbonyl bands at 1795–1760 cm^{-1}.[45]

Unsaturated lactones of certain types in solution exhibit two bands in the carbonyl region due probably to a Fermi resonance effect.[45]

(I)   (II)

Lactones of type I have bands at 1790–1777 cm^{-1} and 1765–1740 cm^{-1}. Lactones of type II have bands at 1775–1740 cm^{-1} and 1740–1715 cm^{-1}.[45]

[43] A. R. Katritzky, J. M. Lagowski, and J. A. T. Beard, *Spectrochim. Acta* 16, 954 (1960).
[44] R. N. Jones and B. S. Gallagher, *J. Am. Chem. Soc.* 81, 5242 (1959).
[45] R. N. Jones, C. L. Angell, T. Ito, and R. J. D. Smith, *Can J. Chem.* 37, 2007 (1959).

9.20   Thiol Esters and Related Compounds

Compounds which contain the group $-S-C=O$ are characterized by carbonyl bands lower than normal esters[46] due to increased resonance $(-\overset{+}{S}=C-\overset{-}{O})$. As with normal esters, S-aryl substitution raises the $C=O$ frequency relative to S-aliphatic substitution. Bands can also be assigned to vibrations involving the $C-S$ and $C-C$ stretch. See Table 9.6.[46]

TABLE 9.6

THIOL CARBONYL COMPOUNDS

	C=O	C−C	C−S
Aliph−CO−S−aliph	1700–1680 cm⁻¹	1140–1070	1030–930
Aliph−CO−S−aryl	1710–1690	1110–1060	1020–920
Aryl−CO−S−aliph	1680–1640	1210–1190	940–905
Aryl−CO−S−aryl	1700–1650	1205–1190	920–895
Aliph−S−CO−CO−S−aliph	1680	—	790
Aryl−S−CO−CO−S−aryl	1698	—	770
H−CO−S−aliph	1675	—	755
H−CO−S−aryl	1693	—	730
CH₃−CO−SH	1712	1122	988
Aryl−CO−SH	1700–1690	1210–1205	950–945

The thiol formates have CH vibrations which absorb at 2835–2825 (CH stretch), 1345–1340 (CH deformation), and 2680–2660 cm⁻¹ (deformation overtone). The thiol acids in solution absorb at 2585–2565 cm⁻¹ (SH stretch) and at 837–828 cm⁻¹ (SH in plane deformation)[46].

9.21   Organic Carbonate Derivatives and Related Compounds

Table 9.7 lists frequencies for a number of compounds related to organic carbonates run in CCl_4 above 1333 cm⁻¹ and CS_2 below.[47] The list clearly demonstrates that both substituents affect the carbonyl frequency. An alkoxy group next to the $C=O$ raises its frequency and a chlorine raises it even more. A sulfur or nitrogen next to the carbonyl lowers its frequency. Changing the aliphatic group on the sulfur or oxygen to an aromatic group raises the frequency. Carbonyls in five membered rings are somewhat higher in frequency than in

[46] R. A. Nyquist and W. J. Potts, *Spectrochim. Acta* **15**, 514 (1959).
[47] R. A. Nyquist and W. J. Potts, *Spectrochim. Acta* **17**, 679 (1961).

noncyclic compounds. Note ethylene carbonate at 1831 cm^{-1}, ethylene mono-thiol carbonate, 1757 cm^{-1}, and ethylene dithiol carbonate, 1678 cm^{-1}.[47] In carbonic ester derivatives most of the noncyclic carbonates absorb at 1780–1740 cm^{-1} while the five-membered ring cyclic carbonates absorb at 1850–1790 cm^{-1}.[48,49]

TABLE 9.7
ORGANIC CARBONATE DERIVATIVES AND RELATED COMPOUNDS[47]

	C=O Stretching region	Other bands
R−O−CO−O−R	1741-1739 cm^{-1}	1280–1240 (O−C−O asymmetric)
R−O−CO−O−Ø^a	1787–1754	1248–1211
Ø−O−CO−O−Ø	1819–1775	1221–1205
R−S−CO−S−R	1655–1640	880–870 (S−C−S asymmetric)
R−S−CO−S−Ø	1649	839
Ø−S−CO−S−Ø	1718–1714	833–827
R−O−CO−S−R	1710–1702	1162–1142 (C−O)
R−O−CO−S−Ø	1731–1719	1141–1125
Ø−O−CO−S−R	1739–1730	1102–1056
Cl−CO−O−R	1780–1775	1169–1139
Cl−CO−O−Ø	1784	1113
Cl−CO−S−R	1772–1766	—
Cl−CO−S−Ø	1775–1769	—
Cl−CO−N R$_2$	1739	—
Cl−CO−N Ø$_2$	1742	—
R−O−CO−NH−R	1738–1732	1250–1210 (C−N)
R−S−CO−NH$_2$	1699	—
R−S−CO−NH−R	1695–1690	1230–1170
R−S−CO−NH−Ø	1662–1649	1165–1152
Ø−S−CO−NH−Ø	1659–1652	1160–1152
R−S−CO−NR$_2$	1666	1248
R−S−CO−N Ø$_2$	1670	1275

^{a} Ø = Phenyl.

9.22 Anhydrides

Anhydrides are characterized by two bands in the carbonyl region due to the asymmetric and symmetric carbonyl stretching vibrations.[50,51] Noncyclic satur-ated anhydrides absorb near 1820 cm^{-1} and 1750 cm^{-1}, while noncyclic con-jugated anhydrides absorb near 1775 cm^{-1} and 1720 cm^{-1}. The band at higher wavenumbers is the more intense in both cases.

[48] L. Hough, J. E. Priddle, R. S. Theobald, G. R. Barker, T. Douglas, and J. W. Spoors, *Chem. Ind. (London)* **1960**, 148.

[49] J. L. Hales, J. I. Jones, and W. Kynaston, *J. Chem. Soc.* **1957**, 618.

[50] W. G. Dauben and W. W. Epstein, *J. Org. Chem.* 24, 1595 (1959).

[51] L. J. Bellamy, B. R. Connelly, A. R. Philpotts, and R. L. Williams, *Z. Elektrochem.* 64, 563 (1960).

Saturated anhydrides in a five membered ring absorb near 1860 cm^{-1} and 1780 cm^{-1}, while conjugated anhydrides in a five membered ring absorb near 1850 cm^{-1} and 1760 cm^{-1}. The band at lower wavenumbers is the more intense in both cases. The relative intensities of the two bands is a good indication of whether the anhydride is cyclic or not. See Table 9.8.

TABLE 9.8

ANHYDRIDE C=O REGIONS

Noncyclic, unconjugated	1825–1815 stronger	1755–1745 weaker
Noncyclic, conjugated	1780–1770 stronger	1725–1715 weaker
Cyclic, unconjugated (five membered ring)	1870–1845 weaker	1800–1775 stronger
Cyclic, conjugated (five membered ring)	1860–1850 weaker	1780–1760 stronger

Absorbance ratios of the high frequency band to the low, $A_H/A_L = 0.81$–0.93 for saturated noncyclic anhydrides and 6.3–11.1 for five membered ring cyclic anhydrides. Glutaric anhydride (six membered ring) is intermediate where $A_H/A_L = 2.7$.[50] This is explained in terms of the relative orientation of the two carbonyl groups, which in five membered rings are nearly linearly and oppositely oriented. As a result, in the symmetric stretching vibration, the dipoles almost cancel each other and the intensity is weak in five membered rings. The high frequency band is assigned to the symmetric stretching vibration.[50-51] In the six membered ring, the orientation is about 120° which gives rise to a smaller A_H/A_L ratio. Noncyclics have several possible orientations and may orient with the two carbonyls pointing in the same direction, where the symmetric stretch would give rise to a stronger band than the asymmetric stretching vibration.[50-51]

Unconjugated straight chain anhydrides (except acetic-1125 cm^{-1}) absorb strongly at 1050–1040 cm^{-1}. The cyclic anhydrides absorb strongly at 955–895 cm^{-1} and 1300–1180 cm^{-1}. The nonconjugated cyclic anhydrides also absorb strongly at 1130–1000 cm^{-1}. These bands involve stretching of the C−C−O−C−C bands.

9.23 Peroxides

The peroxide group O=C−O−O−C=O gives rise to two bands due to the carbonyl vibrations found at 1816–1787 cm^{-1} and 1790–1765 cm^{-1}.[51]

9.24 Acid Chlorides

Most acid chlorides with aliphatic groups attached to the carbonyl absorb strongly near 1810–1795 cm^{-1}. The presence of the electronegative chlorine atom next to the carbonyl greatly reduces the tendency for oxygen to draw electrons. Thus the contribution from the

$$
[1] \quad R-\overset{\overset{\displaystyle O}{\|}}{C}-Cl \quad \longleftrightarrow \quad [2] \quad R-\overset{\overset{\displaystyle O^-}{|}}{\underset{}{C}}\overset{+}{-}Cl
$$

carbonyl bond weakening resonance form no. [2] is greatly reduced relative to ketones, resulting in absorption at higher wavenumbers. Another band is found at 965-920 cm^{-1} (probably involving C—C=stretch).

In the gas phase, acetyl bromide has a carbonyl absorption at 1821 cm^{-1}, acetyl chloride, 1822 cm^{-1}, and acetyl fluoride, 1869 cm^{-1}.[7]

Aromatic acid chlorides absorb strongly at 1785–1765 cm^{-1}. A second weaker band at 1750–1735 cm^{-1} involves an overtone of a strong band near 875 cm^{-1} intensified by Fermi resonance with the carbonyl.[45] The aryl acid chlorides have absorption near 1200 cm^{-1} and at 890–850 cm^{-1}. (C—C stretch.) Benzoyl fluoride has comparable bands at 1812 cm^{-1} 1253-1237 cm^{-1}, and 1008 cm^{-1}.[52]

9.25 Chloroformates

Chloroformates (also called chlorocarbonates) absorb at 1800–1760 cm^{-1} (C=O), 1172–1134 cm^{-1} (C—O), 694–689 cm^{-1} (C—Cl) and 487–471 cm^{-1} (deformation).[47,49,53]

9.26 Carboxylic Acid OH Stretch

Carboxylic acids are usually characterized in the condensed state by a strongly bonded, very broad OH stretching band centering near 3000 cm^{-1}. While this is superimposed on the CH stretching bands (3100–2800 cm^{-1}) the broad wings of the OH stretch can be seen on either side of the narrow CH bands. Distinctive shoulders between 2700 and 2500 cm^{-1} appear regularly in carboxyl dimers and are due to overtones and combinations of the 1300 and 1420 cm^{-1} bands, due to interacting C—O stretch and OH deformation vibrations.[54] Monomeric acids absorb weakly and sharply at 3580—3500 cm^{-1}.[55]

[52] F. Seel and J. Langer, *Chem. Ber.* **91**, 2553 (1958).
[53] H. A. Ory, *Spectrochim. Acta* **16**, 1488 (1960).
[54] S. Bratoz, D. Hadzi, and N. Sheppard, *Spectrochim. Acta* **8**, 249 (1956).
[55] J. D. S. Goulden, *Spectrochim. Acta* **6**, 129 (1954).

9.27 Carboxyl-Carbonyl Stretch

Carboxylic acids with no other polar groups in the molecule usually exist predominantly as the hydrogen-bonded dimer, even in CCl_4 solution, although some acids exist at least partially in the hydrogen-bonded polymeric form.

When the dimer is considered as a whole, there will be two carbonyl stretching frequencies, symmetric and asymmetric. The dimer molecule has a center of symmetry, so the symmetric carbonyl stretch will be Raman active only, and the asymmetric stretch will be infrared active only. Most carboxyl dimers have a band in the infrared at 1720-1680 cm^{-1} (asymmetric C=O stretch). In the Raman spectrum, a band appears at 1680–1640 cm^{-1} (symmetric C=O stretch).[56]

Solid trichloro acetic acid is dimeric and has a Raman band[57] at 1687 cm^{-1} and an infrared band at 1742 cm^{-1}.[54] This is an example of the effect of strong electron withdrawing groups on the carbon of the acid, but studies of this kind are complicated due to hydrogen bonding permutations.

Resonance causes a positive charge to appear on the proton donor atom and a negative charge to appear on the receiver atom which tends to encourage the hydrogen bond. The increased association of the proton with the acceptor atom and the decreased association with the donor atom tends to encourage the resonance. Thus, hydrogen bonding and resonance are mutually enhancing. Resonance weakens the carbonyl bond and lowers the frequency.

When a hydroxyl or an ether group is in the same molecule with the carboxyl group, or when an acid is dissolved in a solvent containing hydroxyl or ether groups, there exists the opportunity for other types of hydrogen bonding to occur involving hydroxyl-carboxyl bonds, or carboxyl-ether bonds as an alternate to carboxyl dimer bonding. When this happens, symmetry is destroyed and the carbonyl vibrations appear in both the infrared and Raman. When the carbonyl is not hydrogen bonded as in carboxyl-ether bonding, a band appears at 1760–1735 cm^{-1} in both infrared and Raman. When the carbonyl is hydrogen bonded but not dimerized, as in alcohol-carbonyl bonds, a band appears at 1730–1705 cm^{-1} in both infrared and Raman. When the carbonyl group is dimerized, as we have seen above, a band appears at 1680–1640 cm^{-1} in the

---

[56] K. W. F. Kohlrausch, "Ramanspektren." Akademische Verlagsges., Leipzig, 1943.
[57] I. D. Poliakova and S. S. Raskin, *Opt Spectry.* (*USSR*) (*English Transl.*) 6, 220 (1959).

Raman effect and at 1720–1690 cm^{-1} in the infrared. From this it can be seen that the most unambiguous band in this region for the carboxyl dimer is the Raman band at 1680–1640 cm^{-1}.[56]

Lactic acid, for example, has no Raman bands between 1700 and 1600 cm^{-1}. Its carbonyl in the Raman effect resembles the infrared carbonyl at 1723 cm^{-1}. Therefore, no dimer with a center of symmetry is present. Methoxy acetic acid has a very weak Raman band at 1666 cm^{-1} and a relatively strong Raman band at 1741 cm^{-1} like the infrared band.[56] This indicates only a small amount of dimer is present.

9.28 Carboxyl OH Bending and C—O Stretching

The best infrared band for the carboxyl dimer is a broad, medium intensity band at 960–875 cm^{-1} due to out of plane OH $\cdots$ O hydrogen deformation.[58] This band is present here only for the dimer and is usually noticeably broader than other bands in this region. The absence of a band here would be fairly good evidence for the lack of the dimer form.

Carboxylic acids have a strong band in the region 1315–1200 cm^{-1}. Dimers usually absorb in the narrower region 1315–1280 cm^{-1}.[58] Another somewhat weaker band is found at 1440–1395 cm^{-1}.[58] These bands involve stretching of the C—O bond and in-plane deformation of the C—O—H angle which interact somewhat[58] so that both bands to some extent involve both OH deformation and C—O stretch, in and out of phase. Due to the similarity of the 1315–1200 cm^{-1} band to the ester C—O stretching bands, it is a nomenclature convenience to call this band in acids predominantly C—O stretching. In the same region as the "OH deformation" band at 1440–1395 cm^{-1} is found the deformation of the CH$_2$ group next to the carbonyl when it is present. The carboxyl dimer infrared bands are summarized in Table 9.9.[54,58,59]

TABLE 9.9

CARBOXYL DIMER SPECTRAL REGIONS

OH stretch	ca. 3000 cm^{-1} very broad
Overtones and combinations	2700–2500
C=O stretch	1740–1680
OH deformation in plane	1440–1395
C—O stretch	1315–1280
OH deformation out of plane	960–875

[58] D. Hadzi and N. Sheppard, *Proc. Roy. Soc.* **A216**, 247 (1953).
[59] F. Gonzalez-Sanchez, *Spectrochim. Acta* **12**, 17 (1958).

9.29 Monomeric Acids

When carboxylic acids are run in the vapor state at about 150°C, carboxylic acids are monomeric in form.[60] Some monomer is present in the vapor state at room temperature or in solutions.[54] Bands at 1380–1280 cm^{-1} (medium) and 1190–1075 cm^{-1} (strong) involve interacting OH deformation in-plane and C—O stretching.[60]

The OH stretching vibration absorbs sharply and weakly at 3550–3500 cm^{-1} in CCl$_4$ solution[55] and somewhat higher in the vapor phase.[54] The C=O stretching vibration absorbs at 1800–1740 cm^{-1}.[54] Table 9.10 lists carboxyl monomer bands.

TABLE 9.10

CARBOXYL MONOMER SPECTRAL REGIONS

OH stretch	3580–3500 cm^{-1}
C=O stretch	1800–1740
OH deformation	1380–1280
C—O stretch	1190–1075

9.30 Aliphatic Peroxy Acids

Peroxy acids in the vapor state have the bands listed in Table 9.11.[61,62] The peroxy acid band at 3280 cm^{-1} is distinctly different from bands of either the monomer or dimer of the normal acid vapor.

TABLE 9.11

SPECTRAL BANDS FOR ALIPHATIC PEROXY ACIDS IN THE VAPOR STATE

OH stretch	ca. 3280 cm^{-1}
C=O stretch	1760
OH bend	1450
C—O stretch	1175
O—O stretch	865

[60] D. Hadzi and M. Pintar, *Spectrochim. Acta* 12, 162 (1958).
[61] E. R. Stephens, P. L. Hanst, and R. C. Doerr, *Anal. Chem.* 29, 776 (1957).
[62] P. A. Giguère and A. W. Olmos, *Can. J. Chem.* 30, 821 (1952).

9.31 Aromatic Acids

Derivatives of benzoic and toluic acids[63] have C=O bands due to dimers at 1715–1680 cm^{-1} and to monomers in dilute solution about 40–45 cm^{-1} higher at 1760–1730 cm^{-1}. A hydroxyl group in the *ortho* position causes about a 55 cm^{-1} lowering of the band and an *ortho* amino group about a 30 cm^{-1} lowering due to internal hydrogen bonding. The band position has been related to the pK of the acid.[63]

The methyl esters absorb about 13 cm^{-1} lower than the comparable acid monomers.[63] The aromatic bands at 900–700 cm^{-1} in acids and derivatives with a carbonyl group on the ring do not resemble those of unconjugated aromatics and should be considered separately.

9.32 Aliphatic Bands in Long Chain n-Aliphatic Carboxylic Acids, Esters, and Soaps

In the solid state spectra of fatty acids, esters, and soaps a regularly spaced progression of fine bands appears between 1345 and 1180 cm^{-1},[64–66] due to the various CH$_2$ waggings.[67]

A correlation has been made for the number of bands in the "band progression" with the number of carbon atoms.[65]

For acids with even numbers of carbons, the number of bands in the progression series equals the number of carbons in the acid divided by two. For the acids with odd numbers of carbons, the number of bands equals the number of carbons in the acid plus one, divided by two.[65]

This works for either acids or soaps and is more definite in the latter, particularly above C$_{26}$, due to lack of interference from the C—O in the acid.

[63] D. Peltier, A. Pichevin, P. Dizabo, and M. L. Josien, *Compt. rend.* **248**, 1148 (1959).

[64] R. N. Jones, A. F. McKay, R. G. Sinclair, *J. Am. Chem. Soc.* **74**, 2575 (1952).

[65] R. A. Meiklejohn, R. J. Meyer, S. M. Aronovic, H. A. Schuette, and V. W. Meloche, *Anal. Chem.* **29**, 329 (1957).

[66] P. J. Corish and D. Chapman, *J. Chem. Soc.* **1957**, 1746.

[67] J. K. Brown, N. Sheppard, and D. M. Simpson, *Trans. Roy. Soc. (London)* **A247**, 35 (1954).

9.33 Carboxyl Salts

When a salt is made from a carboxylic acid, the $C=O$ and $C-O$ are replaced by two equivalent carbon-oxygen bonds which are intermediate in force constant between the $C=O$ and $C-O$.

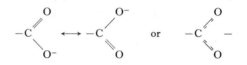

These two "bond-and-a-half" oscillators are strongly coupled resulting in a strong asymmetric CO_2 stretching vibration at 1650–1550 cm^{-1} and a somewhat weaker symmetric CO_2 stretching vibration at 1440–1360 cm^{-1}.[12]

Acetate salts absorb strongly at 1600–1550 and 1450–1400 cm^{-1} and weakly near 1050, 1020, and 925 cm^{-1}.[68] Formate salts absorb near 1600, 1360, and 775 cm^{-1}.

9.34 Amino Acids

Amino acids usually exist as the Zwitter-ion.

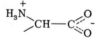

They have, therefore, the absorption of an ionized carboxyl group and an amine salt.

The NH_3^+ stretching frequencies are found between 3100–2600 cm^{-1} in the form of a broad strong band with multiple peaks on the low frequency wing which continue until about 2200 cm^{-1}. Between 2200 and 2000 cm^{-1} is found a relatively prominent combination band which resembles the similar band in primary amine hydrochlorides. This is assigned as a combination band of NH_3^+ asymmetric deformation and NH_3^+ hindered rotation (see amine salts).

The spectra of d-and $l\alpha$-amino acids are identical[69] but may differ from that of the dl form. They have the following characteristic bands[69–71]: 1665–1585 cm^{-1}

[68] F. Vratny, C. N. R. Rao and M. Dilling, *Anal. Chem.* **33**, 1455 (1961).

[69] R. J. Koegel, J. P. Greenstein, M. Winitz, S. M. Birnbaum, and R. A. McCallum, *J. Am. Chem. Soc.* **77**, 5708 (1955).

[70] K. Fukushima, T. Onishi, T. Shimanouchi, and S. Mizushima, *Spectrochim. Acta* **15**, 236 (1959).

[71] H. M. Randall, R. G. Fowler, N. Fuson, and R. Dangl, "Infrared Determination of Organic Structures." Van Nostrand, New York, 1949.

(asymmetric NH_3 deformation), not resolved in most normal chain amino acids; 1605–1555 cm^{-1} (asymmetric CO_2 stretch); 1530–1490 cm^{-1} (symmetric NH_3 deformation); 1425–1393 cm^{-1} (symmetric CO_2 stretch); and 1340–1315 cm^{-1} (CH deformation). More variable bands are found at 3100–2850, 2650–2500, and 2120–2010 cm^{-1}.

9.35 Amido Acids

Bands for α amido acids are found in the solid state at 3390–3260 (NH), 1724–1695 (acid C=O), 1621–1600 cm^{-1} (amide C=O), and 1565–1508 cm^{-1} (CNH).[71-73] The amide C=O at or below 1620 cm^{-1} is characteristic for the α amido acids, other amido acids absorbing on the high frequency side of 1620 cm^{-1},[71] in the solid state.

9.36 Unsubstituted Amides

Normal amides are characterized by a strong absorption at 1695–1630 cm^{-1} due to C=O stretching. Unsubstituted amides in the solid state are characterized by asymmetric and symmetric NH_2 stretching frequencies near 3350 cm^{-1} and 3180 cm^{-1}, and a strong band at 1670–1620 cm^{-1}, which is usually a doublet near 1655 and 1630 cm^{-1} involving C=O stretch and NH_2 deformation.[74] In solution these bands are replaced by bands near 3520, 3400, 1690–1670 (C=O) and 1620–1614 cm^{-1} (NH_2 deformation-weak). These differences result from hydrogen bonding.[74,75] The amide group has a large contribution from resonance structure no. [2] which weakens the C=O bond and stiffens the C—N bond.

$$[1] \quad -\overset{\overset{\displaystyle O}{\|}}{C}-NH_2 \quad \longleftrightarrow \quad [2] \quad -\overset{\overset{\displaystyle O^-}{|}}{C}=\overset{+}{N}H_2$$

An electron withdrawing group on the nitrogen will reduce the contribution form 2, and a higher frequency carbonyl band will result.[10]

[72] N. Fuson, M. L. Josien, and R. L. Powell, *J. Am. Chem. Soc.* **74**, 1 (1952).

[73] H. H. Freedman, *J. Am. Chem. Soc.* **77**, 6003 (1955).

[74] R. E. Richards and H. W. Thompson, *J. Chem. Soc.* **1947**, 1248.

[75] T. L. Brown, J. F. Regan, R. D. Schuetz, and J. Sternberg, *J. Phys. Chem.* **63**, 1324 (1959).

In unsubstituted amides, a vibration involving the C—N stretch absorbs somewhere near 1400 cm^{-1}. A weaker band somewhere near 1150 cm^{-1} can sometimes be seen which involves the NH$_2$ rock (in plane). A broad band at 750–600 cm^{-1} is due to NH$_2$ wag (out-of-plane).

9.37   N-Substituted Amides (trans)

N-Monosubstituted amides exist mainly with the NH and C=O in the *trans* configuration. In the solid state, the NH stretch gives rise to a strong band near 3300 cm^{-1}. A weaker band appears near 3100 cm^{-1} due to an overtone of the 1550 cm^{-1} band.[76] The carbonyl vibration absorbs strongly at 1680–1630 cm^{-1}.[74] The in-plane NH bending frequency and the resonance stiffened C—N bond stretching frequency fall close together and therefore interact. The CNH vibration where the nitrogen and hydrogen move in opposite directions relative to the carbon involves both NH bending and C—N stretching and absorbs strongly near 1550 cm^{-1}.[77–81] This band is very characteristic for monosubstituted amides. The CNH vibration where the N and H atoms move in the same direction relative to the carbon gives rise to a weaker band near 1250 cm^{-1}. The out-of-plane NH wag absorbs broadly near 700 cm^{-1}.[77–81]

In solution comparable bands appear near 3440–3400, 1700–1670, and 1540–1510 cm^{-1}.[74] Electron withdrawing groups on the nitrogen raise the carbonyl frequency.

9.38   N-Substituted Amides (cis) (Lactams)

Monosubstituted amides which are forced into the *cis* configuration in cyclic structures such as lactams have a strong NH stretching absorption in the solid state near 3200 cm^{-1} and a weaker band near 3100 cm^{-1} due to a combination band of the C=O stretching and NH bending bands.[76,82] The carbonyl vibration

[76] T. Miyazawa, *J. Mol. Spectry.* **4**, 168 (1960).
[77] T. Miyazawa, T. Shimanouchi, and S. Mizushima, *J. Chem. Phys.* **24**, 408 (1956).
[78] T. Miyazawa, T. Shimanouchi, and S. Mizushima, *J. Chem. Phys.* **29**, 611 (1958).
[79] R. D. B. Fraser and W. C. Price, *Nature* **170**, 490 (1952).
[80] M. Beer, H. B. Kessler, and G. B. B. M. Sutherland, *J. Chem. Phys.* **29**, 1097 (1958).
[81] C. G. Cannon, *Spectrochim. Acta* **16**, 302 (1960).
[82] T. Miyazawa, *J. Mol. Spectry.* **4**, 155 (1960).

absorbs near 1650 cm^{-1} in six or seven membered rings as in the noncyclic *trans* case. Lactams in five membered rings absorb at 1750–1700 cm^{-1}. Unfused lactams in four membered rings absorb at 1760–1730 cm^{-1}, while β-lactams fused to unoxidized thiazolidine rings absorb at 1780–1770 cm^{-1}.[83] There is, in the cyclic monosubstituted amide, no band in the 1600–1500 cm^{-1} region comparable to the 1550 cm^{-1} CNH band in the *trans* case. The *cis* NH bending vibration absorbs at 1490–1440 cm^{-1} and the C—N stretching vibration at 1350–1310 cm^{-1}.[82,84] There is much less interaction between these modes than in the *trans* case.[82] The NH wag absorbs broadly near 800 cm^{-1}.

Trans and *cis* monosubstituted amides are best distinguished by the NH vibrations.[85] Hydrogen bonded *trans* monosubstituted amides (polymers) absorb near 3300, 3080, and 1550 cm^{-1}, and hydrogen bonded *cis* monosubstituted amides (dimers) absorb at 3200 and 3080 cm^{-1}. In dilute solution, the *trans* form absorbs at 3440–3400 cm^{-1} while the *cis* form absorbs 20–40 cm^{-1} lower. In solution, the association NH band of the *trans* form shifts to higher frequencies 3370–3300 cm^{-1} with dilution (shorter polymers) while the associated *cis* NH band does not shift (dimers). The *cis* form remains associated at lower concentration than the *trans* form. At a concentration of 0.003 moles/liter in CCl$_4$, the *trans* form is mostly unassociated while the cis is still mostly associated.[85]

9.39   Disubstituted Amides

N-Disubstituted amides are characterized by the strong C=O stretching at 1680–1630 cm^{-1}.[74] Strong electron withdrawing groups substituted on the nitrogen atom will reduce the tendency for the carbonyl oxygen to draw electrons ($\overset{+}{N}$=C—$\overset{-}{O}$) and thus raise the carbonyl frequency.[10]

9.40   Ureas

Ureas are not too different from amides. A single substituent on the nitrogen will give the same CNH band as monosubstituted amides. As with amides, a strong electron withdrawing group on the nitrogen atom will raise the C=O stretching frequency.

[83] H. T. Clarke, ed., "The Chemistry of Penicillin," p. 390. Princeton Univ. Press, Princeton, New Jersey, 1949.

[84] H. Brockmann and H. Musso, *Chem. Ber.* **89**, 241 (1956).

[85] I. Suzuki, M. Tsuboi, T. Shimanouchi, and S. Mizushima, *Spectrochim. Acta* **16**, 471 (1960).

9.41 Carbamates

The carbonyl frequencies in carbamates are somewhat higher than in amides and lower than in esters, being found in the region 1740–1683 cm^{-1}.[86-88] In CHCl$_3$ solution, most primary carbamates absorb at 1728–1722 cm^{-1}, secondary carbamates at 1722–1705 cm^{-1}, and tertiary, at 1691–1683 cm^{-1}.[87] In the solid state they are much the same,[87] except that some primary carbamates give very broad bands which may absorb as low as 1690 cm^{-1}. The C=O frequency for linear carbamates with a cyclic N atom depends upon the electronic effects in the ring.[87]

In N-monosubstituted carbamates, the NH group absorbs at 3340-3250 cm^{-1}, and the CNH group absorbs near 1540–1530 cm^{-1} in the condensed state as in amides. In solution these bands appear at 3480–3390 and 1530–1510 cm^{-1}. The NH$_2$ group when present also resembles the NH$_2$ in amides absorbing at 3450–3200 cm^{-1} and near 1620 cm^{-1}.

The 2-oxazolidones absorb at 1810–1746 cm^{-1} and also at 1059–1029 cm^{-1}.[87]

9.42 Hydroxamic Acids

Hydroxamic acids (R—CO—NH—OH) are characterized in the solid state by three bands between 3300 and 2800 cm^{-1}, a band near 1640 cm^{-1} (C=O), and a band near 1550 cm^{-1} (CNH), a variable intensity band at 1440–1360 cm^{-1}, and a strong band near 900 cm^{-1}.[89]

9.43 Imides

In the solid state imides (R—CO—NH—CO—R) have a strong band at 1740–1670 cm^{-1} and a bonded NH band near 3250 cm^{-1}.[71,90-92] In noncyclic

[86] D. A. Barr and R. N. Haszeldine, *J. Chem. Soc.* **1956**, 3428.
[87] S. Pinchas and D. Ben Ishai, *J. Am. Chem. Soc.* **79**, 4099 (1957).
[88] A. R. Katritzky and R. A. Jones, *J. Chem. Soc.* **1960**, 676.
[89] D. Hadzi and D. Prevorsek, *Spectrochim. Acta* **10**, 38 (1957).
[90] J. Uno and K. Machida, *Bull. Chem. Soc. Japan* **34**, 545 and 551 (1961).
[91] R. A. Abramovitch, *J. Chem. Soc.* **1957**, 1413.
[92] N. A. Borisevich and N. N. Khovratovich, *Opt and Spectry.* (*USSR*) (*English Transl.*) **10**, 309 (1961).

imides the CNH group gives rise to bands at 1507–1503 and 1236–1167 cm⁻¹ like the monosubstituted amides. Most of the dialkyl imides exist in the "B" form where the carbonyls are parallel and *trans-trans* relative to the NH.[90] These are characterized by bands at 3280, 3200, 1737–1733, 1505–1503, 1236–1167, and 739–732 cm⁻¹ (NH wag).[90] Sometimes a weak band is visible at 1695–1690 cm⁻¹. Diacetamide can be in either "A" or "B" forms but is usually found in the "A" form (*trans-cis*) which is distinguished from the "B" form by a NH band at 3245 with weaker companions at 3270 and 3190, C=O bands at 1700 with weaker companions at 1734 and 1650 cm⁻¹ and NH wag bands at 836–816 cm⁻¹.[90]

Imides which are part of five-membered rings such as phthalimides[92] have C=O bands at 1790–1735 and 1745–1680 cm⁻¹. The lower frequency band is the more intense. The cyclic imides do not have the 1505 cm⁻¹ CNH band.

9.44 Isocyanurates

Aliphatic isocyanurates (isocyanate trimers) have a strong C=O band at 1700–1680 cm⁻¹ with a weak shoulder near 1755 cm⁻¹. Aromatic isocyanurates[93] have a higher C=O frequency at 1715–1710 cm⁻¹ with a weak shoulder near 1780 cm⁻¹ because of the electron withdrawing group on the nitrogen.

Aromatic isocyanate dimers[93]

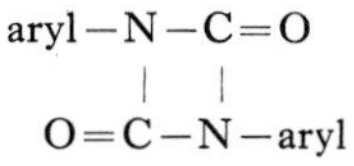

$$aryl-N-C=O$$
$$\quad\ \ |\quad\ |$$
$$O=C-N-aryl$$

have a carbonyl band at 1785–1775 cm⁻¹.

9.45 Acid Hydrazides

Monoacid hydrazides[94] (—CO—NH—NH₂) have NH or NH₂ bands at 3320–3180 cm⁻¹, a C=O band at 1700–1640 cm⁻¹, an NH₂ deformation band at 1633–1602 cm⁻¹, a CNH band at 1542–1522 cm⁻¹, and an NH₂ band at 1150–1050 cm⁻¹.

[93] B. Taub and C. E. McGinn, *Dyestuffs* **42**, 263 (1958).
[94] M. Mashima, *Bull. Chem. Soc. Japan* **35**, 1882, 2020 (1962).

Diacid hydrazides[95] ($-CO-NH-NH-CO-$) have bands in acetonitrile solution at 3330–3280 cm^{-1} (NH stretch), 1742–1700 cm^{-1} (C=O), and 1707–1683 cm^{-1} (C=O). In the solid state aliphatic diacid hydrazides absorb at 3210–3100 cm^{-1}, 3060–3020 cm^{-1}, 1623–1580 cm^{-1} (C=O), 1506–1480 cm^{-1} (CNH), and 1260–1200 cm^{-1} (CNH); and aromatic diacid hydrazides absorb at 3280–2980 cm^{-1}, 1730–1669 cm^{-1} (C=O), 1658–1635 cm^{-1} (C=O), 1535–1524 cm^{-1} (CNH), and 1285–1248 cm^{-1} (CNH).

Phthalhydrazides in the solid state have a very broad NH band centering near 3000 cm^{-1}, and a C=O band at 1670–1635 cm^{-1}.

[95] M. Mashima, *Bull. Chem. Soc. Japan* **35**, 332, 423 (1962).

CHAPTER 10

ETHERS, ALCOHOLS, AND PHENOLS

10.1 Aliphatic Ethers

When an oxygen atom is substituted for a carbon atom in a normal aliphatic chain, the positions of the skeletal stretching frequencies (ca. 1150–800 cm^{-1}) are altered somewhat. Far more spectacular, however, is the change in intensity of the highest skeletal stretching frequency. The group CH_2-O-CH_2 gives rise to a strong band at 1140–1085 cm^{-1}. Most of the simpler aliphatic ethers absorb near 1125 cm^{-1}. While we call this band the asymmetric $C-O-C$ stretching band, it is understood that during this vibration in a normal ether, other skeletal bonds are involved.

Branching of the carbon atoms next to the oxygen causes complications, but usually there remains a band near 1100 cm^{-1} involving the stretching of the $C-O$ bond and, in the case of a t-butoxy ether type, absorption near 1200 cm^{-1} involving the asymmetric motion of the branched carbon atom and methyl rocking.

The aliphatic groups next to the oxygen have bands listed in Table 10.1.[1]

TABLE 10.1

ALIPHATIC GROUPS IN ETHERS

$(R-O-)CH_3$	2992–2955 asymmetric stretch
	2897–2867 symmetric stretch
	1470–1440 asymmetric and symmetric deformation
$(R-O-)CH_2-$	2955–2922 asymmetric stretch
	2878–2835 symmetric stretch
	1475–1445 deformation

The intensity of the symmetric stretching band of the OCH_2 group is enhanced, so that it is more nearly comparable to the intensity of the asymmetric stretch in contrast to the hydrocarbon case where the symmetric stretch is always weaker.

[1] S. E. Wiberley, S. C. Bunce, and W. H. Bauer, *Anal. Chem.* **32**, 217 (1960).

The largest frequency shift is in the symmetric CH_3 deformation which shifts from 1375 cm^{-1} for $C—CH_3$ to about 1450 cm^{-1} for $O—CH_3$. This is due to the electronegativity of the oxygen (see CH_3 groups).

Table 10.2 gives the regions for the strong bands due to the asymmetric stretching of the $C—O—C$ bonds.

TABLE 10.2

ASYMMETRIC $C—O—C$ SPECTRAL REGIONS

Aliphatic ethers	1140–1085 cm^{-1}
Aromatic ethers	1310–1210 and 1050–1010($O—CH_2$)
Vinyl ethers	1225–1200
Oxirane ring (monosubstituted)	880– 805

10.2 Aromatic Ethers

An alkoxy on an aromatic ring usually gives rise to two correlatable bands, 1310–1210 cm^{-1} and 1050–1010 cm^{-1}.[2-4] The band near 1250 cm^{-1} may be looked upon as an aromatic carbon-oxygen stretching frequency (like phenols), and the band near 1040 cm^{-1}, as the highest aliphatic carbon-oxygen stretching frequency (like primary alcohols). Diphenyl ether does not have a 1040 cm^{-1} "OCH_2" band, only the 1240 cm^{-1} "aryl-O" band (asymmetric $C—O—C$ stretch). Since there is undoubtedly interaction, the convenient nomenclature of aryl-O and OCH_2 stretch could be described as asymmetric and symmetric $C—O—C$ stretching in anisole. In phenetoles we have three skeletal single bonds and three stretching frequencies absorbing near 1240, 1040, and 920 cm^{-1} (weaker), the first two of which are correlatable with other alkoxy aromatics. Methylene 1,2 dioxy benzenes ($O—CH_2—O$) have aromatic ether bands at 1266–1227 and 1047–1025 cm^{-1}. Other bands for this group appear at 1376–1350 (variable intensity) and 938–919 cm^{-1} (strong).[3]

The aromatic carbon-oxygen bond has a higher force constant than the aliphatic carbon-oxygen bond due to resonance, which is one of the reasons for the higher vibrational frequency.

[2] A. R. Katritzky and N. A. Coats, *J. Chem. Soc.* **1959**, 2062.

[3] L. H. Briggs, L. D. Colebrook, H. M. Fales, and W. C. Wildman, *Anal. Chem.* **29**, 904 (1957).

[4] K. J. Sax, W. S. Saari, C. L. Mahoney, and J. M. Gordon, *J. Org. Chem.* **25**, 1590 (1960).

The contributions of the $=\overset{+}{O}-$ forms stiffen that bond and concentrate negative charges in the *ortho* and *para* position. When electron-repelling groups such as methyls are put on the ring in the *ortho* or *para* positions, the resonance is reduced relative to *meta* substitution. The aryl C—O band is found at higher frequencies in *meta* than in *ortho* or *para* as a result. Conversely, electron attracting groups such as chlorine, enhance the resonance in *ortho* and *para* substitution relative to *meta*, and here the aryl C—O band is lower in *meta*.

In 1, 2, 3 trimethoxy benzene the strongest band in the C—O region is at 1115 cm⁻¹. Some other highly substituted methoxy benzenes are similar. This reflects the fact that the aryl C—O vibration interacts with ring frequencies and is therefore not completely mechanically independent of other single bonds attached to the ring.

10.3 Vinyl Ethers

The asymmetric C—O—C stretch of alkyl vinyl ethers gives rise to a strong band at 1225–1200 cm⁻¹,[5] very near 1203 cm⁻¹ in most cases. The vinyl carbon-oxygen bond is stiffened by resonance as was the aromatic carbon-oxygen bond.

$$CH_2=CH \quad \longleftrightarrow \quad \bar{C}H_2-CH$$
$$\underset{O-C}{|} \qquad\qquad \underset{\underset{+}{O-C}}{\|}$$

Frequencies of the vinyl group are altered by the oxygen, the most notable of which is a doubling and intensifying of the strong C=C stretching frequency. One band is found near 1640 cm⁻¹ and a slightly stronger one near 1620 cm⁻¹. These bands are temperature dependent, with the 1640⁻¹ band increasing in intensity with increasing temperature. In 2-ethyl hexyl vinyl ether the ratio of absorbancies is A 1615 cm⁻¹ $\div$ A 1640 cm⁻¹ = 1.91 at 25°C and 1.21 at 125°C. This shows that the doubling is caused by rotational isomers, resulting from rotation of the vinyl carbon-oxygen bond. The 1620 cm⁻¹ band is due to the more stable form, which is the resonance stabilized planar *trans* configuration shown above, with a weakened C=C bond. The 1640 cm⁻¹ is due to a non-planar *gauche* form with a normal C=C. The planar *cis* form is sterically blocked, so resonance (which requires coplanarity) is reduced, resulting in less weakening of the C=C bond.

Resonance can be reduced in the planar *trans* form by substitution with an electron withdrawing group. Phenyl vinyl ether for example absorbs at 1653 and 1635 cm⁻¹.[5]

[5] Y. Mikawa, *Bull. Chem. Soc. Japan* **29**, 110 (1956).

The bands for alkyl vinyl ethers are summarized in Table 10.3.[5]

TABLE 10.3

SPECTRAL REGIONS FOR ALKYL VINYL ETHERS

Vinyl CH stretch	3125–3098, 3078–3060, 3050–3000 cm⁻¹
C=C *gauche*	1660–1635
C=C *trans*	1620–1610
=CH rock	1323–1320
C−O−C asymmetric stretch	1225–1200
trans =CH wag	970– 960
=CH₂ wag	820– 810

10.4 Cyclic Ether Linkages

The CH_2-O-CH_2 linkage in six-membered rings absorbs in about the same region that the noncyclic ethers do, due to an asymmetric $C-O-C$ stretching vibration. As the ring becomes smaller, the frequency of a band involving the asymmetric stretch of the $C-O-C$ bonds decreases, and the symmetric $C-O-C$ (ring breathing) frequency increases. This is due mainly to the geometry change rather than to force constant changes. The asymmetric $C-O-C$ stretch is usually a strong infrared band and a weaker depolarized Raman band. The symmetric $C-O-C$ is usually a strong polarized Raman band[6] and a weaker infrared band. See Table 10.4.

TABLE 10.4

CYCLIC ETHER COMPOUNDS

Ring size	Compound	Asymmetric $C-O-C$	Symmetric $C-O-C$
Six-membered	Pentamethylene oxide	1098 cm⁻¹	813 cm⁻¹
Five-membered	Tetramethylene oxide	1071	913
Four-membered	Trimethylene oxide	983	1028
Three-membered	Ethylene oxide[7]	839	1270
(Two-membered)	(Formaldehyde)	—	(1740)

[6] K. W. F. Kohlrausch, "Ramanspektren," Akademische Verlagsges. Leipzig, 1943.
[7] F. Halverson, private communication (1962).

10.5   Oxirane Ring Compounds

Epoxy ring compounds[8-12] absorb at 1280–1230 cm^{-1} due to the ring breathing vibration (C—C, C—O, and C—O bonds all stretching in phase). There are two other ring vibrations approximately described as follows; (1) the C—C bond contracts while both C—O bonds stretch and (2) the C—C bond does not change in length while one C—O bond stretches and the other contracts. These two probably give rise to the observed bands at 950–815 cm^{-1} and 880–750 cm^{-1}. This lowest band has been used to distinguish monosubstituted oxirane rings at 880–805 cm^{-1}, disubstituted rings (1,1 and 1,2) at 850–775 cm^{-1} and trisubstituted rings at 770–750 cm^{-1}.[8]

The CH and CH$_2$ groups in the rings absorb either at 3050–3029 cm^{-1} or 3004–2990 cm^{-1} or in a few cases, in both regions.[12]

10.6   OH Stretch in Alcohols and Phenols

Alcohols are characterized by several bands all of which are sensitive to the environment. In the pure liquid or solid state, alcohols and phenols usually exist as hydrogen bonded polymers. In dilute solution in non polar solvents, the alcohols are essentially free. In concentrated solutions or mixtures, both free and bonded forms may be present.

Alcohols in the liquid or solid state have very broad strong absorption near 3300 cm^{-1} due to the stretching of the O—H··O bonds.[13] In CCl$_4$ solution they absorb near 3640 cm^{-1} as a sharp weak band due to free OH stretch.[13] In the triterpenoids and similar compounds, in CCl$_4$ solution, primary alcohols absorb at 3641–3640 cm^{-1}, axial secondary at 3638–3635 cm^{-1}, equatorial secondary at 3630–3628 cm^{-1}, and tertiary at 3618–3613 cm^{-1} (axial 3617 cm^{-1}— equatorial 3613 cm^{-1}).[14,14a]

[8] J. Bomstein, *Anal. Chem.* **30**, 544 (1958).

[9] W. A. Patterson, *Anal. Chem.* **26**, 823 (1954).

[10] O. D. Shreve, M. R. Heether, H. B. Knight, and D. Swern, *Anal. Chem.* **23**, 277 (1951).

[11] J. E. Field, J. O. Cole, and D. E. Woodford, *J. Chem. Phys.* **18**, 1298 (1950).

[12] H. B. Henbest, G. D. Meakins, B. Nicholls, and K. J. Taylor, *J. Chem. Soc.* **1957**, 1459.

[13] A. V. Stuart and G. B. B. M. Sutherland, *J. Chem. Phys.* **24**, 559 (1956).

[14] A. R. H. Cole, G. T. A. Muller, D. W. Thornton, and R. L. S. Willix, *J. Chem. Soc.* **1959**, 1218 and 1222.

[14a] A. R. H. Cole, P. R. Jeffries, and G. T. A. Muller, *J. Chem. Soc.* **1959**, 1222.

Phenols absorb at 3250–3200 cm^{-1} in the bonded state and at 3617–3593 cm^{-1} in solutions.[15,16] The vibrational frequency diminishes as the electron attracting power of the substituent on the ring increases.[16]

In some cases such as 2,6 di-tertiary butyl phenol, steric hindrance prevents bonding even in the pure state. In some cases internal bonding takes place, as in salicylaldehyde where bonding remains even in the dilute state.

10.7   C—O Stretch

The vibrations involving the stretching of the C—O bond give rise to strong infrared bands.[17] See Table 10.5.

TABLE 10.5

C—O SPECTRAL REGIONS

Primary alcohols CH_2—OH	1075–1000 cm^{-1}
Aliphatic secondary alcohols (alkyl—CHOH—alkyl)	1125–1090
Aromatic secondary alcohols (phenyl—CHOH—)	1075–1000
Cyclic equatorial secondary alcohols	1065–1037
Cyclic axial secondary alcohols	1036– 970
Tertiary alcohols	1210–1100
Phenols	1260–1180

In primary alcohols, this band involves asymmetric C—C—O stretching. In secondary and tertiary alcohols, the asymmetric motion of the branched carbon atom against its neighbors gives rise to bands which might be described as asymmetric C—C—O when the branched carbon moves along the C—O bond and asymmetric C—C—C when it moves at right angles to the C—O bond. Both of these can interact with methyl rocking vibrations of the same symmetry type. The vibration involving C—O usually shifts a little when hydrogen bonding is eliminated by dilution. As seen in Table 10.5 an aromatic ring next to the secondary alcohol group lowers its frequency.[17] Equatorial cyclic secondary alcohols absorb near 1050 cm^{-1} and axial cyclic secondary alcohols absorb near 1000 cm^{-1}.[18-20]

[15] R. E. Richards and H. W. Thompson, *J. Chem. Soc.* **1947**, 1260.
[16] P. J. Stone and H. W. Thompson, *Spectrochim. Acta* **10**, 17 (1957).
[17] H. Zeiss and M. Tsutsui, *J. Am. Chem. Soc.* **75**, 897 (1953).
[18] R. N. Jones and F. Herling, *J. Am. Chem. Soc.* **78**, 1152 (1956).
[19] I. N. Nazarov, A. F. Vasil'ev and I. A. Gurvich, *J. Gen. Chem. USSR (English Transl.)* **29**, 749 (1959).
[20] W. Hückel and Y. Riad, *Ann.* **637**, 33 (1960).

10.8   OH Deformation

The out-of-plane C—OH deformation in the bonded state absorbs very broadly and diffusely near 650 cm⁻¹.[13] The in-plane C—OH deformation is complicated by interaction with hydrogen wagging vibrations in primary and secondary alcohols.[13,21,22] The hydrogens on the oxygen and on the carbon move more or less parallel to the C—O bond in the same direction in one case and the opposite direction in the other case, giving rise to more than one band that involves OH deformation.

Primary alcohols in the bonded state have diffuse association bands near 1420 and 1330 cm⁻¹ (OH deformation and CH_2 wag), which disappear upon dilution, the lower band shifting to 1300–1200 cm⁻¹.[13]

Secondary alcohols in the bonded state have bands near 1420 and 1330 cm⁻¹ (OH deformation + CH wag) which disappear in solution, the lower band shifting upon dilution to about 1225 cm⁻¹.[13,21] In both the primary and secondary alcohols, the 1420 cm⁻¹ band shifts to about 1385 cm⁻¹ where it is overlapped by CH_3 absorption.

Tertiary alcohols absorb near 1410 cm⁻¹ (OH deformation) in the bonded state and near 1320 cm⁻¹ in solution. There is no second band at 1330–1325 cm⁻¹ as in the alcohols with α hydrogens.[13]

10.9   Phenols

Phenols[15] in the solid state absorb at 1390–1330 cm⁻¹ (medium) and 1260–1180 cm⁻¹ (strong) which represent OH deformation and C—O stretch which interact somewhat.[23] In solution these bands are shifted to lower frequencies. Detailed correlations have been made for the alkyl phenols in solution[24] from 1400 to 650 cm⁻¹ only some of which will be given here. Phenols substituted with alkane groups in the 2 position absorb strongly at 1321–1319, 1256–1242 and 1171–1160 cm⁻¹, 3 alkyl phenols absorb strongly at 1285–1269, 1188–1180, and 1160–1149 cm⁻¹, and 4 alkyl phenols absorb strongly at 1260–1248 and 1174–1166 cm⁻¹.[24] Some of these bands are aromatic ring bands.

[21] S. Krimm, C. Y. Liang, and G. B. B. M. Sutherland, *J. Chem. Phys.* 25, 778 (1956).

[22] D. M. W. Anderson, L. J. Bellamy, and R. L. Williams, *Spectrochim. Acta* 12, 233 (1958).

[23] R. Mecke and G. Rossmy, *Z. Elektrochem.* 59, 866 (1955).

[24] D. D. Shrewsbury, *Spectrochim. Acta* 16, 1294 (1960).

10.10   Noncyclic Acetals and Related Compounds

Acetals and *ortho*-formates and compounds such as dialkoxy acetonitriles have strong multiple bands in the region 1160–1040 cm^{-1} involving stretching of the C—O bonds. The O—CH—O group gives rise to a band at 1350–1325 cm^{-1} (CH deformation) which disappears when the hydrogen is missing as in *ortho*-acetates. When the carbon between the oxygens is tetra substituted, additional absorption usually occurs at 1235–1175 cm^{-1} probably involving the asymmetric motion of the branched carbon atom.

10.11   Cyclic Acetals

In substituted dioxolane rings, ring vibrations occur at 1181–1153 cm^{-1} and 1093–1070 cm^{-1}.[25,26] Bands are also found at 1126–1104 and 1055–1029 cm^{-1}.[26]

10.12   Carbohydrates

Carbohydrates[27,28] have many bands in the region 1125–1000 cm^{-1} involving stretching of the C—O bond, and broad absorption near 3300 cm^{-1} due to bonded OH stretch.

10.13   Peroxides

In primary and secondary alkyl hydroperoxides the bonded OH stretching band is usually at a little higher frequency (30 cm^{-1}) than the corresponding alcohols[29] but this is not necessarily true for all types of peroxides.[30]

[25] S. A. Barker, E. J. Bourne, R. M. Pinkard, and D. H. Whiffen, *J. Chem. Soc.* **1959**, 807.
[26] R. S. Tipson, H. S. Isbell, and J. E. Stewart, *J. Research Natl. Bur. Standards* **62**, 257 (1959).
[27] L. P. Kuhn, *Anal. Chem.* **22**, 276 (1950).
[28] R. L. Whistler and L. R. House, *Anal. Chem.* **25**, 1463 (1953).
[29] H. R. Williams and H. S. Mosher, *Anal. Chem.* **27**, 517 (1955).
[30] N. A. Milas and O. L. Mageli, *J. Am. Chem. Soc.* **75**, 5970 (1953).

Primary hydroperoxides (CH_2—O—OH) show distinct satellite bands at 1488 and 1435 cm^{-1} on either side of the 1465 cm^{-1} band while most corresponding alcohols have only the 1465 cm^{-1} band.[29] Secondary hydroperoxides (CH—O—OH) have a band at 1352–1334 cm^{-1} [29] (CH wag). The comparable band in secondary alcohols is shifted from this position due to interaction with the deformation of the adjacent OH group.

The bands between 1150 and 1030 cm^{-1} (C—O) follow the pattern of the alcohols.[29] The primary alcohol band near 1050 cm^{-1} shifts only about 10 cm^{-1} to lower frequencies in the corresponding hydroperoxides.

A weak band at 880–845 cm^{-1} has been proposed characteristic for the O—O linkage[31] but its lack of intensity in this well populated spectral region[29,32] limits its usefulness. In the normal alkyl hydroperoxides a second characteristic region is found at 835–800 cm^{-1}. When there are an even number of carbon atoms two bands are found at 827 and 807 cm^{-1}. When the carbon atoms are odd in number, one band appears at 814 cm^{-1}.[29]

[31] O. D. Shreve, M. R. Heether, H. B. Knight, and D. Swern, *Anal. Chem.* 23, 282 (1951).
[32] A. R. Philpotts and W. Thain, *Anal. Chem.* 24, 638 (1952).

CHAPTER 11

AMINES, C=N, AND N=O COMPOUNDS

11.1 NH₂ Stretch in Amines

The NH_2 group gives rise to absorption at 3550–3330 cm^{-1} (asymmetric stretch) and at 3450–3250 cm^{-1} (symmetric stretch). A relationship has been developed relating the two bands,[1] namely, $\nu_{sym.} = 345.5 + 0.876 \, \nu_{asym.}$, this relationship holding for NH_2 groups in which the two NH bonds are equivalent. Cases of asymmetric bonding are revealed by a breakdown of the relationship. Using equations related to those for the triatomic case,* this relationship has been reduced[2] to $\nu_{sym.} = 0.98 \, \nu_{asym.}$. The relationship holds since the NH_2 angle is not a variable, while variations in the force constant for the two equal NH bonds changes both frequencies proportionately.

In liquid amines there is usually a shoulder near 3200 cm^{-1} which is probably an overtone of the 1610 cm^{-1} NH_2 deformation intensified by Fermi resonance due to its proximity to the stretching fundamentals.

Most liquid aliphatic primary amines absorb at 3400–3330 and 3330–3250 cm^{-1} with a shoulder near 3200 cm^{-1}. Most liquid aromatic amines absorb at 3500–3390 and 3420–3300 cm^{-1} with a weaker band at 3250–3170 cm^{-1}. Aromatic primary amines in solution absorb at 3520–3420 cm^{-1} and 3420–3325 cm^{-1}.

11.2 NH₂ Deformation in Amines

Most primary amines have an NH_2 deformation band at 1650–1590 cm^{-1}.[2,3] In liquid aliphatic amines the NH_2 wagging and twisting vibrations give rise to broad, strong, usually multiple absorption bands at 850–750 cm^{-1}.[2]

[1] L. J. Bellamy and R. L. Williams, *Spectrochim. Acta* 9, 341 (1957).
[2] J. E. Stewart, *J. Chem. Phys.* 30, 1259 (1959).
[3] A. R. Katritzky and R. A. Jones, *J. Chem. Soc.* 1959, 3674.
[4] J. J. Elliott and S. F. Mason, *J. Chem. Soc.* 1959, 1275.
[5] P. J. Krueger and H. W. Thompson, *Proc. Roy. Soc. (London)* A243, 143 (1957).
* See Section 4.10.

11.3 NH

The NH stretching vibration gives rise to a weak band at 3500–3300 cm⁻¹. A stronger band at 750–700 cm⁻¹ in secondary aliphatic amines is due to NH wagging.[2] In solution N-methyl anilines absorb at 3460–3420 cm⁻¹.[3,5]

Secondary aromatic amines have a CNH bending absorption near 1510 cm⁻¹ near the 1500 cm⁻¹ aromatic band.[6] Most aliphatic secondary amines have no visible NH bending band above the 1470 cm⁻¹ aliphatic bands.

11.4 C—N in Aliphatic Amines

In amines, as in alcohols, single-bond frequencies are affected by branching at the α carbon atom. In the case of amines, they are also affected by amine substitution, primary and secondary amines being comparable to alcohols and ethers respectively.

Aliphatic primary amines with a primary α carbon (CH_2–NH_2) have a medium intensity band at 1090–1068 cm⁻¹.[2] Aliphatic secondary amines with primary α carbons (CH_2—NH—CH_2) have a medium strong band at 1146–1132 cm⁻¹.[2] These bands involve asymmetric C—C—N and C—N—C stretching, respectively.

Secondary branching at the α carbon in noncyclic secondary amines (CH—NH—C) gives rise to a band at 1191–1171 cm⁻¹.[2]

As in the alcohols, several vibrations result from the asymmetric motion of the branched carbon atom against its neighbors. Motion along the C—N bond can be described as asymmetric C—C—N, whereas motion at right angles to the C—N bond can be described as asymmetric C—C—C.

Primary amines with secondary α carbon atoms (CH—NH_2) absorb weakly[2] at 1043–1037 cm⁻¹ and more strongly at 1140–1080 cm⁻¹.

Primary amines with tertiary α carbon atoms (C—NH_2) absorb weakly[2] at 1038–1022 cm⁻¹ and more strongly at 1240–1170 cm⁻¹.

Tertiary aliphatic amines are difficult to characterize in the 1300–1000 cm⁻¹ region. If there is no absorption in the NH stretch region and a tertiary amine is suspected, a spot check may be made by mixing 2 drops of the suspected amine and one drop of a 50% alcohol–50% concentrated HCl mixture directly

[6] D. Hadzi and M. Skrbljak, J. Chem. Soc. 1957, 843.

between CaF_2 plates. Absorption near 2600 cm^{-1} indicates the presence of a tertiary amine hydrochloride. Tertiary amines may also be detected by changes in the aliphatic groups next to the nitrogen.

11.5 C—N in Aromatic Amines

Primary aromatic amines with the nitrogen directly on the ring absorb strongly at 1330–1260 cm^{-1},[3] due to stretching of the phenyl carbon-nitrogen bond.

Secondary aromatic amines absorb strongly at 1342–1320 cm^{-1} and 1315–1250 cm^{-1}.[3,6]

Dimethyl anilines absorb strongly at 1380–1332 cm^{-1}.[3] For all tertiary anilines, the region is 1380–1265 cm^{-1}.

The C—N in anilines is higher in frequency than aliphatic amines due to resonance which stiffens the C—N bond.

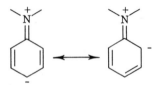

Thus electron withdrawing and donating groups on the *ortho* and *para* position can affect this resonance contribution relative to meta substitution and shift the frequency.

The intensity of this band is remarkably reduced in aniline salts where this type of resonance is suppressed.

11.6 Aliphatic Bands in Amines

The CH_2 or CH_3 groups next to the nitrogen atom in amines are shifted somewhat. The symmetric stretch at 2830–2770 cm^{-1} is lowered in frequency and intensified and so stands out among other aliphatic bands. This only applies for amines and not for amides or amine salts[7,8] (see Table 11.1).

[7] R. D. Hill and G. D. Meakins, *J. Chem. Soc.* **1958**, 760.

[8] W. B. Wright, Jr., *J. Org. Chem.* **24**, 1362 (1959).

TABLE 11.1

ALIPHATIC GROUPS IN AMINES

Aliphatic $-N-CH_3$	2805–2780 cm^{-1}	
Aromatic $-N-CH_3$	2820–2810	
Aliphatic $-N-(CH_3)_2$	2825–2810	2775–2765
Aromatic $-N-(CH_3)_2$	2810–2790	
$N-CH_2$ (aliphatic secondary and tertiary amines)	2820–2760	

11.7 The Ammonium Ion

The ammonium ion[9,10] has bands at 3332–3100 cm^{-1} (NH_4 stretch) and 1484–1390 cm^{-1} (NH_4 deformation). There is also a variable combination band assigned as NH_4 deformation plus NH_4 torsional oscillation[9] appearing at 1712 cm^{-1} in NH_4Br, 1762 cm^{-1} in NH_4Cl, 2007 cm^{-1} in NH_4F, and 1990 cm^{-1} in $NH_4(CH_3CO_2)$, these changes being due mainly to changes in the strength of the hydrogen bond.

11.8 Amine Salts

Primary amine salts are characterized by strong absorption between 3200 cm^{-1} and 2800 cm^{-1} due to the asymmetric and symmetric NH_3^+ stretch.[11,12] Aromatic amine salts absorb at somewhat lower frequencies than aliphatic amine salts. In addition, between 2800 cm^{-1} and 2000 cm^{-1} there are a number of weaker bands, the most interesting of which is an isolated band usually near 2000 cm^{-1}, the intensity of which increases when the symmetry is reduced.[11] It is strong in aromatic primary amine salts. This band is sensitive to changes in hydrogen bonding, having a tendency to increase in frequency in salts made from weaker acids where stronger hydrogen bonding can occur. Tertiary butyl amine salts absorb as follows; bromide 2030 cm^{-1}, acid sulfate 2065 cm^{-1}, chloride 2080 cm^{-1}, nitrate 2080 cm^{-1}, sulfate 2085 cm^{-1}, and acetate 2220 cm^{-1}. This band is assigned to a combination band of the NH_3^+ torsional oscillation (about 480 cm^{-1})

[9] T. C. Waddington, *J. Chem. Soc.* **1958**, 4340.
[10] E. L. Wagner and D. F. Hornig, *J. Chem. Phys.* **18**, 296 (1950).
[11] C. Brissette and C. Sandorfy, *Can. J. Chem.* **38**, 34 (1960).
[12] B. Chenon and C. Sandorfy, *Can. J. Chem.* **36**, 1181 (1958).

and the asymmetric NH_3^+ deformation (about 1580 cm^{-1}).[11] Sharp bands at 2800–2400 cm^{-1} are due to combination bands of NH_3^+ bending vibrations.[11] Aromatic primary amine salts have two main bands, about 2800 cm^{-1} (NH stretching vibrations) and 2600 cm^{-1} (deformation combination bands).[11] The complicated fine structure associated with the NH stretching bands is a characteristic of amine salts.

The asymmetric NH_3^+ deformation absorbs at 1625–1560 cm^{-1}, and the symmetric NH_3^+ deformation absorbs at 1550–1505 cm^{-1}.[12]

As with other hydrogen bonded compounds, stronger hydrogen bonding in amine salts (I$^-$ < Br$^-$ < Cl$^-$) lowers hydrogen stretching frequencies but raises deformation frequencies (and their overtones).

Secondary amine hydrochlorides have strong multiple absorption bands between 3000 and 2700 cm^{-1} [11–15] involving the asymmetric and symmetric NH_2^+ stretch, weaker combination bands at 2700–2300 cm^{-1}, and a medium absorption band[12–15] at 1620–1560 cm^{-1} due to NH_2^+ deformation.

Tertiary amine hydrochlorides have multiple absorption bands[11–13,15,16] between 2700 and 2330 cm^{-1} involving the NH$^+$ stretching vibration. This absorption in a given tertiary amine moves toward higher frequencies in the order Cl < Br < I.

11.9 C=N Groups

Aliphatic Schiff (R—C=N—R) bases absorb near 1670 cm^{-1}. Aromatic Schiff bases absorb near 1630 cm^{-1}.[17] The C=N intensities are intermediate between C=O and C=C bands on the whole.

Oximes (C=N—OH) including aliphatic,[18–20] aromatic, and amide oximes absorb broadly at 3300–3150 cm^{-1} due to bonded OH stretch, at 1690–1620 cm^{-1} due to C=N stretch,[17] and near 930 cm^{-1} due to N—O stretching.

Imino carbonates [(RO)$_2$C=NH] and imidates[17,21] absorb near 3300 cm^{-1} due to bonded NH stretch, and at 1690–1645 cm^{-1} due to C=N stretch. Bands

[13] E. A. V. Ebsworth and N. Sheppard, *Spectrochim. Acta* 13, 261 (1959).
[14] R. A. Heacock and L. Marion, *Can. J. Chem.* 34, 1782 (1956).
[15] P. J. Stone, J. C. Craig, and H. W. Thompson, *J. Chem. Soc.* 1958, 52.
[16] R. C. Lord and R. E. Merrifield, *J. Chem. Phys.* 21, 166 (1953).
[17] J. Fabian, M. Legrand, and P. Poirier, *Bull. Soc. Chim. France* 23, 1499 (1956).
[18] J. F. Brown, Jr., *J. Am. Chem. Soc.* 77, 6341 (1955).
[19] A. Palm and H. Werbin, *Can. J. Chem.* 32, 858 (1954).
[20] D. Hadzi, *J. Chem. Soc.* 1956, 2725.
[21] D. Hadzi and D. Prevorsek, *Spectrochim. Acta* 10, 38 (1957).

appear near 1325 and 1100 cm^{-1} which involve C—O stretching like the esters. Imidate hydrochlorides absorb strongly and broadly near 3000 cm^{-1} due to NH_2^+ stretch, 1685–1635 cm^{-1} due to C=N stretch, and 1590–1540 cm^{-1} due to NH_2^+ deformation.

Guanidines and their salts ($N_2C=N$) usually have absorption[17,22] at 1670–1500 cm^{-1} due to NH deformation and CN stretching vibrations. Biguanides are quite similar. The C=N is weakened by resonance, so its vibrations more appropriately should be described as asymmetric NCN stretch, particularly in the salts where the three CN bonds should be identical as the CO bonds are in ionized carboxyls. The NH_2 groups absorb at 3400–3200 cm^{-1} and at 1670–1620 cm^{-1}. If there are no NH_2 groups, there is usually no absorption above 1635 cm^{-1}. On the whole, there is considerably less change in the NH_2 frequencies when going from the free base to the hydrochloride than there is in amines due to the fact that the charge is distributed over several nitrogen atoms. Other compounds involving the N_2—C=N group are in general similar to the guanidines.

Trialkyl isoureas

$$\begin{array}{c} O-R' \\ | \\ R-NH-C=N-R'' \end{array}$$

absorb near 1672–1655 cm^{-1} (C=N).[17] Conjugation lowers the C=N frequency (N-cyano- 1582 cm^{-1}).

Substituted amidines[23–26] (N—C=N) are characterized by strong CN absorption, 1685–1580 cm^{-1}. Amidines of the type

$$\begin{array}{c} N-\!\!\!- \\ | \quad || \\ -C-C-NH-R' \\ | \end{array}$$

show a band near 1540 cm^{-1} which shifts to about 1515 cm^{-1} in solution. This is assigned to the CNH group as in monosubstituted amides (NH bend and C—N stretch interacting). This band is absent in N-dialkyl amidines. The free NH groups absorb at 3470–3380 cm^{-1} in solution and 3300–3100 cm^{-1} in the condensed state.

Unsubstituted amidine hydrochlorides or bromides $R-C(NH_2)_2^+$ absorb strongly at 1710–1675 cm^{-1} and weakly at 1530–1500 cm^{-1} with a third weak band appearing at 1575–1540 cm^{-1} in about a third of the samples. Substituted

[22] E. Lieber, D. R. Levering, and L. J. Patterson, *Anal. Chem.* **23**, 1594 (1951).
[23] J. Fabian, V. Delaroff, and M. Legrand, *Bull. Soc. Chim. France* **23**, 287 (1956).
[24] D. Prevorsek, *Compt. rend.* **244**, 2599 (1957).
[25] D. Prevorsek, *Bull. Soc. Chim. France* **25**, 788 (1958).
[26] J. C. Grivas and A. Taurins, *Can. J. Chem.* **37**, 795 (1959).

amidine salts absorb strongly at 1700–1600 cm^{-1}.[26,27] In N-disubstituted amidine hydrochlorides the NH_2^+ deformation absorbs at 1590–1530 cm^{-1}.[26,27]

In all compounds with the group $C=NH_2^+$, there is undoubtedly much interaction between the $C=N$ stretching vibration and the NH_2 deformation.

The cyclic $C=N$ group in pyrrolines and related compounds absorbs at 1655–1560 cm^{-1} depending on the substituents.[28]

The spectral regions for the $C=N$ group are summarized in Table 11.2.[17]

TABLE 11.2

SPECTRAL REGIONS FOR C=N GROUPS

$R-CH=N-R$	1674–1665 cm^{-1}
$C_6H_5-CH=N-R$	1656–1629
$C_6H_5-CH=N-C_6H_5$	1637–1626
$R_2C=N-R$	1662–1649
$\begin{matrix} C_6H_5 \\ \diagdown \\ C=N-R \\ \diagup \\ R \end{matrix}$	1650–1640
$\begin{matrix} C_6H_5 \\ \diagdown \\ C=N-C_6H_5 \\ \diagup \\ CH_3 \end{matrix}$	1640–1630
$R_2C=NH$	1646–1640
$\begin{matrix} C_6H_5 \\ \diagdown \\ C=NH \\ \diagup \\ R \end{matrix}$	1633–1620
$R-CH=NOH$	1673–1652
$C_6H_5-CH=NOH$	1645–1614
$R_2C=NOH$	1684–1652
$\begin{matrix} C_6H_5 \\ \diagdown \\ C=NOH \\ \diagup \\ R \end{matrix}$	1640–1620
$-S-C=N-$	1640–1607
$-O-C=N-$	1690–1645
$-N-C=N-$	1685–1582

[27] J. C. Grivas and A. Taurins, Can. J. Chem. 37, 1260 (1959).
[28] A. I. Meyers, J. Org. Chem. 24, 1233 (1959).

11.10 Nitro Group

The nitro group has two identical NO bonds

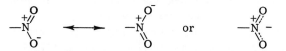

which vibrate asymmetrically causing strong absorption at 1556–1545 cm^{-1} in aliphatic nitro compounds and symmetrically causing somewhat weaker absorption at 1390–1355 cm^{-1}.[18,29–31] Electronegative substituents such as halogens on the α carbon cause the nitro stretching frequencies to diverge. When a CH_3 group is on the α carbon, interaction occurs between the symmetric NO_2 stretch and the symmetric CH_3 deformation. The group CH_3-C-NO_2 gives rise to two bands near 1390 and 1360 cm^{-1}.[18]

Nitro alkenes usually absorb at 1550–1500 and 1360–1290 cm^{-1},[18] conjugation lowering both frequencies.

Aromatic nitro groups absorb strongly at 1530–1500 cm^{-1} and somewhat more weakly at 1370–1330 cm^{-1}.[18,32,33] In addition, aromatic nitro compounds usually have strong aromatic ring absorption at 760–705 cm^{-1}. The usual o-m-p bands at 900–700 cm^{-1} are upset in the nitro aromatics and not very reliable, probably due to interaction with the out of plane NO_2 bending frequency. Steric effects which destroy the nitro-ring coplanarity and thus reduce conjugation make aromatic nitro groups resemble aliphatic nitro groups.[34,35] The frequency of the asymmetric NO_2 stretch in p-substituted nitrobenzenes has been correlated with the electron donating or withdrawing characteristics of the substituent.[33] The symmetric stretch does not correlate due to interaction with the C−N bond.[18,33] In the nitro anilines for example, the electron withdrawing properties of the nitro group and the electron donating properties of the amino group cause a large amount of resonance to occur in the *ortho* and *para* isomers which weaken the N−O

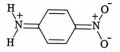

[29] R. N. Hazeldine, *J. Chem. Soc.* **1953**, 2525.
[30] W. H. Lunn, *Spectrochim. Acta* **16**, 1088 (1961).
[31] Z. Eckstein, P. Gluzinsky, W. Sobotka, and T. Urbanski, *J. Chem.Soc.* **1961**, 1370.
[32] R. R. Randle and D. H. Whiffen, *J. Chem. Soc.* **1952**, 4153.
[33] R. D. Kross and V. A. Fassel, *J. Am. Chem. Soc.* **78**, 4225 (1956).
[34] C. P. Conduit, *J. Chem. Soc.* **1959**, 3273.
[35] R. J. Francel, *J. Am. Chem. Soc.* **74**, 1265 (1952).

bonds relative to the *meta* isomers where this mesomeric effect does not occur. The strongest band in the spectra of nitro anilines probably involves the NO_2 symmetric stretch, since it shifts as expected from mesomeric effects, and the $C-N(H_2)$ band which is an alternate assignment would be expected to shift the other way. It occurs in the pure materials at 1350 cm^{-1} in *meta*, 1305 cm^{-1} in *para*, and 1245 cm^{-1} in *ortho*. The usual strong nitro aromatic band near 740 cm^{-1} is also altered in the *ortho* and *para* isomers.

A number of 3 and 5 nitro-2 amino pyridines with various other substituents have been studied and show a very strong band at 1310–1270 cm^{-1} for the 5 nitro-2 amino and at 1250–1210 cm^{-1} for the 3 nitro-2 amino pyridines. As in the nitro anilines, when the nitro and amino groups are ortho to each other, there is an extra shift due to the proximity of the two groups.

The NO_2 stretching frequencies are summarized in Table 11.3.

TABLE 11.3

NO$_2$ STRETCHING FREQUENCIES

	Asymmetric stretch	Symmetric stretch
$C-CH_2-NO_2$	1556–1545 cm^{-1}	1388–1368 cm^{-1}
$C-CH(CH_3)-NO_2$	1549–1545	1364–1357
$C(CH_3)_2-NO_2$	1553–1530	1359–1342
CHX–NO$_2$(X=Cl, Br)	1580–1556	1368–1340
CX_2-NO_2	1597–1569	1339–1323
CCl_3-NO_2	1610	1307
$C(NO_2)_2$	1590–1570	1340–1325
$N-NO_2$	1630–1530	1315–1260
$O-NO_2$	1660–1625	1285–1270
Nitro alkene	1550–1500	1360–1290
Aromatic nitro	1530–1500	1370–1330
p-Amino nitro aromatic	(Hydrogen bonded)	1330–1270
o-Amino nitro aromatic	(Hydrogen bonded)	1260–1210

11.11   Organic Nitrates

Organic nitrates $R-O-NO_2$ are characterized by strong bands near 1660–1625 cm^{-1} (NO_2 asymmetric stretch), 1285–1270 cm^{-1} (NO_2 symmetric stretch), and 870–840 cm^{-1} ($N-O$ stretch), 760–745 cm^{-1} (out of plane deformation), and 710–690 cm^{-1} (NO_2 deformation).[18,36–38]

[36] F. Pristera, *Anal. Chem.* **25**, 844 (1953).
[37] R. A. G. Carrington, *Spectrochim. Acta* **16**, 1279 (1960).
[38] R. D. Guthrie and H. Spedding, *J. Chem. Soc.* **1960**, 953.

11.12   Nitramines

Nitramines $(N-NO_2)$, nitroguanidines, and related compounds have an asymmetric NO_2 stretch at 1630–1530 cm^{-1} and a symmetric stretch at 1315–1260 cm^{-1}.[22,39,40]

11.13   Organic Nitrites

Organic nitrites $R-O-N=O$ are characterized by two bands in the $N=O$ region due to rotational isomers.[41] A strong band occurs at 1681–1648 cm^{-1} (*trans*) and a somewhat weaker band at 1625–1605 cm^{-1} (cis).[41,42] A strong $N-O$ absorption occurs at 814–751 cm^{-1}.[41]

Alkyl thionitrites $R-S-N=O$ absorb near 1534 cm^{-1} due to $N=O$ stretch.[43]

11.14   Inorganic Nitrates and Nitrites

Nitrate salts absorb strongly at 1380–1350 cm^{-1} (asymmetric NO_3 stretch), 835–815 cm^{-1} (medium-sharp), and 740–725 cm^{-1} (weak).[44]

Nitrite salts absorb strongly at 1275–1235 cm^{-1} (asymmetric NO_2 stretch) and have a medium sharp band at 835–820 cm^{-1}.[44]

11.15   N=N Azo

The $N=N$ stretching vibration of the *trans* symmetrically substituted azo group is forbidden in the infrared spectrum as this is a symmetrical vibration in a molecule having a center of symmetry. It is active in the Raman effect, however.

The Raman spectrum of azomethane has an $N=N$ stretching band at

[39] W. D. Kumler, *J. Am. Chem. Soc.* **76**, 814 (1954).
[40] L. J. Bellamy, "The Infrared Spectra of Complex Molecules." Wiley, New York, 1954
[41] P. Tarte, *J. Chem. Phys.* **20**, 1570 (1952).
[42] R. N. Hazeldine and B. J. H. Mattinson, *J. Chem. Soc.* **1955**, 4172.
[43] R. J. Philippe and H. Moore, *Spectrochim. Acta* **17**, 1004 (1961).
[44] F. A. Miller and C. H. Wilkins, *Anal. Chem.* **24**, 1253 (1952).

1576 cm⁻¹.⁴⁵ The Raman spectrum of azo bis (isobutyronitrile) has an N=N band at 1580 cm⁻¹. These frequencies are probably representative of the N=N stretching frequency in unconjugated cases of the type C−N=N−C. The Raman spectrum of *trans* azobenzene has a N=N stretching band at 1419 cm⁻¹.⁴⁶ In unsymmetric aromatic azo compounds of the type

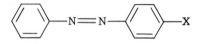

where X = OH, NH₂ and N(CH₃)₂ the N=N stretching frequency occurs at 1416, 1418, and 1410 cm⁻¹, respectively, in the infrared spectrum.⁴⁷ The assignment was proved by the shifts due to N¹⁵ substitution. In the same manner, the N=N stretching frequency in *cis* azobenzene was located at 1511 cm⁻¹ in the infrared.⁴⁷ Here, steric effects prevent coplanarity so conjugation is reduced relative to the *trans* isomer. Infrared correlations indicate the region 1450–1400 cm⁻¹ for the N=N stretching frequency in azoaryls and other compounds studied⁴⁸⁻⁵¹ when it is expected to be infrared active. Since this region is well populated with both aryl and aliphatic bands, this correlation should be used with discretion.

The infrared spectrum of ethyl and *n*-propyl azodiformates have high frequency carbonyls near 1780 cm⁻¹ due to the election withdrawing character of the N=N bond.⁵¹ Strong bands involving the C−O bonds appear near 1260–1220 and 1060–1020 cm⁻¹.

In diazoaminobenzene (Ø−N=N−NH−Ø)N¹⁵ substitution studies indicated the following assignments, NH deformation 1522, N=N stretch 1416, phenyl-N 1248, N−N stretch 1202, phenyl-N 1178, and N=N−N bend 637 cm⁻¹.⁴⁷

11.16   Azoxy and Azothio Groups

When azoxy compounds are compared with the analogous azo compounds, the N=N bond is now unsymmetrically substituted. The azoxy group has two

⁴⁵ K. W. F. Kohlrausch, "Ramanspektren." Akademische Verlagsges., Leipzig, 1943.
⁴⁶ F. X. Powell, E. L. Lippincott, and D. Steele, *Spectrochim. Acta* 17, 880 (1961).
⁴⁷ R. Kubler, W. Lüttke, and S. Weckherlin, *Z. Elektrochem.* 64, 650 (1960).
⁴⁸ R. J. W. Le Fèvre, M. F. O'Dwyer, and R. L. Werner, *Chem. Ind.(London)* 1953, 378.
⁴⁹ R. J. W. Le Fèvre, M. F. O'Dwyer, and R. L. Werner, *Australian J. Chem.* 6, 341 (1953).
⁵⁰ R. J. W. Le Fèvre and R. L. Werner, *Australian J. Chem.* 10, 26 (1957).
⁵¹ R. J. W. Le Fèvre, W. T. Oh, I. H. Reece, R. Roper, and R. L. Werner, *Australian J. Chem.* 11, 92 (1958).

bands associated with the $N=N \rightarrow O$ group, a band at 1480–1450 cm^{-1} (near the 1500 cm^{-1} aromatic band) described as asymmetric NNO (or mainly $N=N$) stretch and at 1335–1315 cm^{-1} due to symmetric NNO (or mainly $N \rightarrow O$ stretch).[52-54] Aliphatic azoxy compounds absorb at 1530–1495 cm^{-1}.[55] The azothio group has two bands due to the $N=N \rightarrow S$ group at 1465–1445 cm^{-1} (mainly $N=N$ stretch) and at 1071–1058 cm^{-1} (mainly $N \rightarrow S$ stretch).[56]

11.17 C-Nitroso Compounds

Aliphatic and aromatic C-nitroso compounds usually exist in the solid state as the dimer in a *cis* or *trans* configuration,[57]

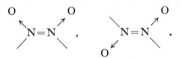

These compounds have strong infrared absorption in the following regions;[18,57-61]

Aliphatic *trans* dimer   1290–1176 cm^{-1}
Aliphatic *cis* dimer   1420–1330 and 1344–1323 cm^{-1}
Aromatic *trans* dimer   1299–1253 cm^{-1}
Aromatic *cis* dimer   ca. 1409 and 1397–1389 cm^{-1}

Monomeric C-nitroso compounds give rise to absorption in the following regions due to the $N=O$ stretching frequency;[57,60,62-64]

Aliphatic nitroso monomer   1621–1539 cm^{-1}
Aromatic nitroso monomer   1513–1488 cm^{-1}

[52] W. Maier and G. Englert, Z. Elektrochem. **62**, 1020 (1958).
[53] B. Witkop and H. M. Kissman, J. Am. Chem. Soc. **75**, 1975 (1953).
[54] J. Jander and R. N. Hazeldine, J. Chem. Soc. **1954**, 919.
[55] B. W. Langley, B. Lythgoe, and N. V. Riggs, J. Chem. Soc. **1951**, 2309.
[56] A. Foffani, G. Leandri, I. Zanon, and C. Carpanelli, Tetrahedron Letters, No. 11, 21 (1959).
[57] B. G. Gowenlock and W. Lüttke, Quart. Rev. **12**, 321 (1958).
[58] W. Lüttke, Angew. Chem. **68**, 417 (1956); **69**, 99 (1957).
[59] W. Lüttke, Z. Elektrochem. **61**, 976 (1957).
[60] P. Tarte, Bull. Soc. Chim. Belges **63**, 525 (1954).
[61] B. G. Gowenlock, H. Spedding, L. Trotman, and D. H. Whiffen, J. Chem. Soc. **1957**, 3927.
[62] W. Lüttke, J. Phys. Radium **15**, 633 (1954).
[63] W. Lüttke, Z. Elektrochem. **61**, 302 (1957).
[64] J. Mason and J. Dunderdale, J. Chem. Soc. **1956**, 754.

The C–N frequency couples with vibrations of the rest of the molecule, generally resulting in a band[57] about 1100 cm^{-1} and at 860–750 cm^{-1}.[57]

Nitroso phenols are in tautomeric equilibrium with the quinone oximes. Nitroso anilines are resonance hybrids.

11.18   Nitrosoamines

In the vapor state, aliphatic nitrosoamines ($R_2N-N=O$) absorb near 1490 cm^{-1}. In the liquid state, they absorb near 1448 cm^{-1}. This band is due to unassociated $N=O$ stretching.[42,65] A band at 1065–1015 cm^{-1} is assigned to $N-N$ stretch.

[65] P. Tarte, *J. Chem. Phys.* **23**, 979 (1955).

CHAPTER 12

COMPOUNDS CONTAINING BORON, SILICON, PHOSPHORUS, SULFUR, OR HALOGEN

12.1 Boron Compounds

The spectral regions for boron compounds are listed in Table 12.1.

TABLE 12.1

BORON CORRELATIONS

BH	2640–2350 cm^{-1}
BH (boron octet complete)	2400–2200
B··H··B bridge	2220–1540
B$-$O	1380–1310
B$-$N	1465–1330
B$-$O$-$H	3300–3200

12.2 B—O

Compounds containing the B$-$O linkage such as borates, boronates, boronites, boronic anhydrides, borinic acids, and boronic acids are characterized by intense absorption at 1380–1310 cm^{-1},[1–9] involving the stretching of the B$-$O bond.

[1] L. J. Bellamy, W. Gerrard, M. F. Lappert, and R. L. Williams, *J. Chem. Soc.* 1958, 2412.

[2] R. L. Werner and K. G. O'Brien, *Australian J. Chem.* 8, 355 (1955).

[3] R. L. Werner and K. G. O'Brien, *Australian J. Chem.* 9, 137 (1956).

[4] S. H. Dandegaonker, W. Gerrard and M. F. Lappert, *J. Chem. Soc.* 1957, 2872.

[5] E. W. Abel, W. Gerrard and M. F. Lappert, *J. Chem. Soc.* 1957, 3833.

[6] W. J. Lehmann, T. O. Onak, and J. Shapiro, *J. Chem. Phys.* 30, 1215 (1959).

[7] W. J. Lehmann, T. O. Onak, and J. Shapiro, *J. Chem. Phys.* 30, 1219 (1959).

[8] W. J. Lehmann, H. G. Weiss, and J. Shapiro, *J. Chem. Phys.* 30, 1222 (1959).

[9] W. J. Lehmann, H. G. Weiss, and J. Shapiro, *J. Chem. Phys.* 30, 1226 (1959).

The high frequency and intensity is due to the fact that the B—O has some polar double bond character ($\bar{B}=\overset{+}{O}$—). However, in B—O compounds where a nitrogen atom is coordinated to the boron atom, no strong band is usually found near this region. It is difficult in this case to find any B—O band, the intensity of which is markedly reduced when the boron octet is complete[1] due to a reduction of bond polarity. In alkoxy boranes with CH_2 or CH groups next to the oxygen, there is possibly interaction[8,9] between the B—O stretch near 1340 cm^{-1} and the OCH_2 wag, which in carboxyl and phosphorus esters absorbs near 1400 cm^{-1}.

12.3   B—OH

The OH groups in boronic acids (and boric acid) in the solid state absorb broadly near 3300–3200 cm^{-1} due to bonded OH stretch. In the aromatic boronic acids, there are usually broad, medium intensity bands near 1000 cm^{-1} and in the 800–700 cm^{-1} region, not present in the comparable anhydrides.

12.4   B—N

Compounds having a B—N linkage such as borazines and amino boranes[10,11] have strong absorption at 1465–1330 cm^{-1} involving the stretching of the B—N bond. This bond has some polar double bond character ($\bar{B}=\overset{+}{N}$) like the B—O bond. Aliphatic groups adjacent to the nitrogen atom in B—N compounds have intensified deformation frequencies. In amino boranes, the dimethyl amino group has strong absorption near 1515 cm^{-1}. The CH_2 deformation in diethyl amino boranes absorbs strongly near 1490 cm^{-1}.

The boron-nitrogen dative bond in amine-borane complexes (B←N) gives rise to a band in the region near 800–650 cm^{-1}.[12] This band may be shifted by interaction and is not necessarily a strong infrared band. Its analytical value is limited.

[10] K. Neidenzu and J. W. Dawson, *J. Am. Chem. Soc.* **81**, 5553 (1959).

[11] H. Watanabe, M. Narisada, T. Nakagawa, and M. Kubo, *Spectrochim. Acta* **16**, 78 (1960).

[12] R. C. Taylor and C. L. Cluff, *Nature* **182**, 390 (1958).

12.5 B—H

Normal BH and BH_2 groups absorb at 2640–2350 cm^{-1} due to BH stretch.[1] The BH_2 absorption is usually a doublet due to symmetric and asymmetric vibrations. The BH_2 deformation vibration absorbs at 1205–1140 cm^{-1}, and the BH_2 wagging vibration absorbs at 975–920 cm^{-1}.[1] The B··H··B bridge bonds cause a series of absorptions at 2220–1540 cm^{-1} with usually at least one band at 1900–1800 cm^{-1}.[1]

In alkyl diboranes[13] the terminal BH_2 absorbs at 2532–2488 cm^{-1}, strong (asymmetric stretch), 2640–2571 cm^{-1}, strong (symmetric stretch), 1170–1140 cm^{-1} medium-strong (deformation) and 940–920 cm^{-1}, medium (wag). The single terminal BH absorbs at 2565–2481 cm^{-1}, strong, (stretch), 1180–1110 cm^{-1}, strong (in plane bend), and 920–900 cm^{-1}, medium weak, (out-of-plane bend). The diborane

bridge absorbs very strongly at 1610–1540 cm^{-1} due to asymmetric, in-phase hydrogen motions ($\rightarrow \atop \rightarrow$). The symmetric, out-of-phase hydrogen motions (↑↑) give rise to weak bands at 1990–1850 cm^{-1}. The other two motions give rise to weak to medium intensity bands depending on the molecular symmetry, 1800–1710 cm^{-1}, asymmetric, out of phase ($\rightarrow \atop \leftarrow$), and 2140–2080 cm^{-1}, symmetric, in phase (↑↓).

The BH stretch in borazines absorbs at 2580–2450 cm^{-1}. Compounds where the boron octet is complete such as in borohydride salts or amine-borane coordination complexes absorb at 2400–2200 cm^{-1} due to BH stretch.

12.6 B—Cl

The B-Cl stretching vibration is variable in position (1037–579 cm^{-1})[7] and not too characteristic. However, in alkyl phenyl chloro boronites the range is 909–893 cm^{-1}.[1]

[13] W. H. Lehmann and I. Shapiro, *Spectrochim. Acta* **17**, 396 (1961).

12.7 $B-CH_3$

The $B-CH_3$ group has asymmetric and symmetric CH_3 deformation frequencies which absorb at 1460-1405 cm^{-1} and 1330–1280 cm^{-1}. [1,13]

12.8 B-Phenyl

Compounds which have the B-phenyl group have a strong sharp band at 1440–1430 cm^{-1} due to the ring vibration[1] normally found in this region.

The diphenyl boron group has strong absorption[1] at 1280–1250 cm^{-1} which is probably due to $C-B-C$ asymmetric stretch. Alkyl phenyl chloro boronites absorb strongly at 1220–1198 cm^{-1}. When there is more than one phenyl on a boron atom, the 760 cm^{-1} phenyl CH wag frequency becomes a doublet with about a 20 cm^{-1} separation.[4]

12.9 Silicon Compounds

The more common silicon correlations are summarized in Table 12.2.[14]

TABLE 12.2

SILICON CORRELATIONS

SiH	2250–2100 and 950–800 cm^{-1}
SiCH$_3$	1280–1255 and 860–760
SiC$_2$H$_5$	1250–1220, 1020–1000, and 970–945
SiC$_6$H$_5$	1430, 1125–1100, 730, and 700–690
Si$-$O$-$CH$_3$	2860 and 1190
Si$-$O$-$CH$_2$$-$R	1190–1140, 1100–1075, and 990–945
Si$-$O$-$aryl	970–920
Si$-$Cl	625–420
Si$-$OH	3700–3200, and 955–835
Si$-$O$-$Si	1125–1010
Si$-$CH$=$CH$_2$	1615–1590, 1020–1000, and 980–950

[14] A. L. Smith, *Spectrochim. Acta* 16, 87 (1960).

12.10   Si—H

The Si—H gives rise to absorption at 2250–2100 cm^{-1}.[15,16] Si—H bending frequencies absorb in the region 950–800 cm^{-1}.[14,16] A summary of the approximate positions of Si—H absorption bands for alkyl and aryl substituted Si—H compounds is presented in Table 12.3 [16]

TABLE 12.3
ALKYL AND ARYL Si—H SPECTRAL REGIONS

Compound	SiH Stretch	Deformation		Wag
Aryl SiH$_3$	2157–2152 cm^{-1}	945–930	930–910 cm^{-1}	
Alkyl SiH$_3$	2153–2142	945–930	930–910	
Diaryl SiH$_2$	2147–2130	940–928		870–843
Aryl-alkyl SiH$_2$	2142–2128	938–923		870–843
Dialkyl SiH$_2$	2138–2117	942–933		895–885
Trialkyl SiH	2132–2112	—		842–800
Diaryl-alkyl SiH	2125–2115	—		842–800
Aryl-dialkyl SiH	2115–2103	—		842–800
Trialkyl SiH	2100–2094	—		842–800

SiH$_3$ groups have two bands in the 950–900 cm^{-1} region due to asymmetric and symmetric deformation, where the SiH$_2$ group has one band due to SiH$_2$ deformation.[16] The SiH$_2$ wag vibration absorbs at 900–845 cm^{-1}, and the SiH wag vibration absorbs at 845–800 cm^{-1}.[16] The SiH group is best distinguished by the lack of strong absorption at 945–910 cm^{-1}.[16] The SiH stretching frequencies are relatively insensitive to mesomeric or mass effects. They are sensitive to inductive effects, however,[15] the SiH stretching frequencies being increased by the substitution of increasingly electronegative groups. The contributions of various substituents to the SiH stretching frequency in CCl$_4$ solution have been evaluated indicating that each group except for oxygen substitution has a strictly additive effect on the SiH frequency which can be predicted closely.[15]

12.11   Si—CH$_3$

The Si—CH$_3$ group is characterized by a very strong sharp band[14,17] at 1280–1255 cm^{-1} due to CH$_3$ symmetric deformation and an absorption at

[15] A. L. Smith and N. C. Angelotti, *Spectrochim. Acta* 15, 412 (1959).
[16] R. N. Kniseley, V. A. Fassel and E. E. Conrad, *Spectrochim. Acta* 15, 651 (1959).
[17] N. Wright and M. J. Hunter, *J. Am. Chem. Soc.* 69, 803 (1947).

860–760 cm^{-1} due to methyl rocking and Si—C stretching.[14] One methyl on a silicon usually absorbs near 765 cm^{-1}, two methyls near 855 cm^{-1} and 800 cm^{-1}, and three methyls near 840 cm^{-1} and 765 cm^{-1}.[17,18] The asymmetric CH$_3$ deformation absorbs weakly near 1410 cm^{-1}.

12.12   Si—CH₂—R

A medium intensity band due to the Si—CH$_2$—R group absorbs[14] at 1250–1200 cm^{-1} with longer aliphatic chains absorbing at the low frequency end of the region. In straight chain compounds, absorption at 760–670 cm^{-1} is due to CH$_2$ rock.[14] In line with CH$_2$ assignments on halogens, phosphorus, and sulfur, a band near 1410 cm^{-1} is probably due to CH$_2$ deformation and the band at 1250–1200 cm^{-1}, to CH$_2$ wag.

The Si—C$_2$H$_5$ group absorbs at 1250–1220 cm^{-1}, 1020–1000 cm^{-1}, and 970–945 cm^{-1}.[14]

12.13   Si—C₆H₅

The Si—C$_6$H$_5$ group gives rise to a band[16] at 1125–1100 cm^{-1} which is due to a planar ring vibration[19] having some Si—C stretching character. Phenyl bands are found near 1430, 730, and 695 cm^{-1}.[14]

12.14   Si—CH=CH₂

The Si—CH=CH$_2$ group is characterized by vinyl vibrations at 1615–1590 cm^{-1} (C=C stretch), 1410–1390 cm^{-1} (CH$_2$ deformation), 1020–1000 cm^{-1} (*trans* CH wag), and 980–950 cm^{-1} (CH$_2$ wag).[14]

12.15   Si—O—R

The Si—O—R group (R=saturated aliphatic group) has at least one strong band [14] at 1110–1000 cm^{-1} due to an asymmetric Si—O—C stretching vibration. This absorbs at the same place as the Si—O—Si group.

[18] R. E. Richards and H. W. Thompson, *J. Chem. Soc.* **1949**, 124.
[19] D. H. Whiffen, *J. Chem. Soc.* **1956**, 1350.

The Si—O—CH$_3$ group absorbs near 2820 cm^{-1} (CH$_3$ symmetric stretch) and 1190 cm^{-1} (CH$_3$ rock). The asymmetric and symmetric stretchings of the Si—O—C bonds give rise to bands near 1100 cm^{-1} and 850–800 cm^{-1}. The Si—O—C$_2$H$_5$ group absorbs at 1175–1165 cm^{-1}, 1100–1075 cm^{-1} (double band), and 965–940 cm^{-1}.[14]

12.16   Si—O—C$_6$H$_5$

The Si—O—C$_6$H$_5$ group absorbs[14,20] at 970–920 cm^{-1} due to stretching of the Si—O bond.

12.17   Si—O—Si

Siloxanes are characterized by at least one strong band[14,17,18] at 1100–1000 cm^{-1} due to asymmetric Si—O—Si stretching. In infinite siloxane chains, absorption maxima occur near 1085 cm^{-1} and 1020 cm^{-1}.[17,18]

Cyclotrisiloxane rings absorb near 1020 cm^{-1}.[17,21] Cyclic tetramers and pentamers have absorption near 1090 cm^{-1}.[21]

12.18   Si—OH

The Si—OH group absorbs, like the alcohols, at 3700–3200 cm^{-1} due to monomers (in solution) and hydrogen bonded polymers. A strong band due to Si—O stretching vibration occurs at 910–830 cm^{-1}.[14] In the condensed state a broad medium-weak intensity band occurs near 1030 cm^{-1} which shifts appropriately on deuteration[22] and may be described as Si–OH deformation.

12.19   Si—Halogen

The SiF group absorbs at 1000–800 cm^{-1}. The SiF$_3$ group absorbs at 980–945 cm^{-1} (strong) and 910–860 cm^{-1} (medium). The SiF$_2$ group absorbs at

[20] G. R. Wilson, A. G. Smith, and F. C. Ferris, *J. Org. Chem.* **24**, 1717 (1959).

[21] C. W. Young, P. C. Servais, C. C. Currie, and M. J. Hunter, *J. Am. Chem. Soc.* **70**, 3758 (1948).

[22] Y. I. Ryskin, M. G. Voronkov, and Z. I. Shabarova, *Izv. Akad. Nauk SSSR* **1959**, 1019.

945–915 cm^{-1} (strong) and 910–870 cm^{-1} (medium), and the SiF vibration absorbs at 920–820 cm^{-1}.[14] The two bands in SiF_2 and SiF_3 probably represent asymmetric and symmetric stretching vibrations.[14]

The SiCl group absorbs at 625–420 cm^{-1}.[14] The $SiCl_3$ group absorbs at 620–570 cm^{-1} (strong) and 535–450 cm^{-1} (medium). The $SiCl_2$ group absorbs at 600–535 cm^{-1} (strong) and 540–460 cm^{-1} (medium), and the SiCl vibration absorbs at 550–470 cm^{-1}.[14,23]

Halosilanes react so readily with moisture to form siloxanes that precautions should be observed.[24]

12.20   Si—N

The Si—NH_2 group has two bands between 3570 and 3390 cm^{-1} in solution. The NH_2 deformation band occurs near 1540 cm^{-1}.[14]

The Si–NH–Si group absorbs near 3400 cm^{-1}, 1175 cm^{-1}, and 935 cm^{-1}.[25]

12.21   Phosphorus Compounds

Correlations for phosphorus groups are listed in Table 12.4

TABLE 12.4

PHOSPHORUS CORRELATIONS

PH	2440–2275 cm^{-1}
P=O	1300–1140
P—OH	2700–2550, 2300–2100, 1040–910
Phosphinic acids	ca. 1660 broad
P—O—P	1000–870
PO_3^{2-}	1030–970
PO_4^{3-}	1100–1000
P—O—C (aliphatic)	1050–970
P—O—CH_3	ca. 2960, 1460, 1190–1170
P—O—C_2H_5	ca. 2990, 1485, 1450, 1395, 1375, 1165–1155
P—O—C_6H_5	1240–1160, 994–855
P—CH_2	1440–1405
P—CH_3	1310–1280, 960-860
P—C_6H_5	1450–1425, 1130–1090, 1010–990
P=S	750–580
P—N	1110–930
P=N (cyclic)	1320–1100
P—Cl	580–440

[23] A. L. Smith, *J. Chem. Phys.* **21**, 1997 (1953).
[24] A. L. Smith and J. A. McHard, *Anal. Chem.* **31**, 1174 (1959).
[25] R. Fessenden, *J. Org. Chem.* **25**, 2191 (1960).

12.22 P—H

The PH stretching vibrations give rise to absorption at 2440–2275 cm^{-1}.[26-29] This band is usually sharp and of medium intensity. In aliphatic and aromatic phosphines, absorption occurs at the low frequency end of the region at 2320–2275 cm^{-1}. With rocksalt optics, the PH$_2$ in mono alkyl phosphines is not resolved but gives rise to a single band in the PH stretch region. The PH$_2$ deformation gives rise to a medium intensity band near 1090–1080 cm^{-1} in aliphatic and aromatic phosphines. The PH$_2$ wagging vibration gives rise to a band at 940–910 cm^{-1}.

The PH wagging vibration is probably involved in medium to strong bands in R$_2$—P($=$O)—H at 990–965 cm^{-1} and R$_2$—P($=$S)—H at 950–910 cm^{-1} where R $=$ alkyl or phenyl groups. Phosphorus acid esters (RO)$_2$—P($=$O)—H, have a very strong band at 980–960 cm^{-1} which is somewhat lower than the normal position for the P—O—C asymmetric stretch band when the hydrogen is not present probably due to P—O—C interaction with the PH wagging vibration.

12.23 P=O

The stretching of the P$=$O bond gives rise to a strong band at 1300–1140 cm^{-1}.[26-30] The exact position of the band varies with the sum of the electronegativities of the attached groups.[31] Aliphatic phosphine oxides usually absorb near 1150 cm^{-1} and aromatic phosphine oxides near 1190 cm^{-1}. Most phosphorus esters with two or three alkoxy groups on the P$=$O absorb at 1300–1250 cm^{-1}. Attached electronegative groups tend to pull electrons from the phosphorus thus competing with the bond weakening tendency for the double bonded oxygen to attract electrons ($\overset{+}{P} - \overset{-}{O}$), resulting in a stiffer P$=$O bond and a higher frequency. Hydrogen bonding will lower the P$=$O frequency as seen in the hydrogen bonded phosphorus acids, where the P$=$O absorption is broadened and shifted to lower frequencies and may be hard to identify.

[26] L. W. Daasch and D. C. Smith, *Anal. Chem.* **23**, 853 (1951).
[27] L. J. Bellamy and L. Beecher, *J. Chem. Soc.* **1952**, 475; *ibid.* 1701.
[28] L. J. Bellamy and L. Beecher, *J. Chem. Soc.* **1953**, 728.
[29] D. E. C. Corbridge, *J. Appl. Chem.* (*London*) **6**, 456 (1956).
[30] R. C. Gore, *Discussions Faraday Soc.* **1950**, No. 9, 138.
[31] J. V. Bell, J. Heisler, H. Tannenbaum, and J. Goldenson, *J. Am. Chem. Soc.* **76**, 5185 (1954).

12.24 P—OH

Most organic phosphorus acids which have a P—OH group have a strong band at 1040–910 cm^{-1} probably involving the stretching of the P—O(H) bond.[32,33] This includes phosphinic acids, phosphonic acids, phosphonous acids, half esters of phosphonic acids, and acid salts of phosphonic acids.

The OH stretching vibration gives rise to broad medium intensity bands at 2700–2550 cm^{-1} and 2300–2100 cm^{-1}. When there is one P—OH with one P=O as in phosphinic acids, phosphonous acids, dialkyl phosphoric acids[34] and half esters of phosphonic acids, a broad band appears centering near 1660 cm^{-1}.[26] This is thought to be due to in plane OH deformation[35] of a dimer related to the carboxyl dimer. Phosphonic acids (with two OH groups) do not generally have this band.[26] Acid salts containing the POH group show broad bands at 2700–2560 cm^{-1} and 2500–1600 cm^{-1}.[36]

12.25 P—O—P

The P—O—P group gives rise to a strong band at 1000–870 cm^{-1} due to the asymmetric stretching of the P—O—P bonds.[29,33,37] A much weaker band near 700 cm^{-1} has also been associated with the P—O—P group.[29]

12.26 PO_2^-, POS^-, PO_3^{2-}, PO_4^{3-}

Salts of alkyl and aryl phosphinic $R_2PO_2^-$ and phosphonous acids $R(H)PO_2^-$ have two strong bands probably due to asymmetric and symmetric PO_2 stretching[33] at 1190–1100 and 1075–1000 cm^{-1}. When the substituent electro-

[32] R. A. McIvor and C. E. Hubley, *Can. J. Chem.* **37**, 869 (1959).
[33] L. C. Thomas and R. A. Chittenden, *Chem. Ind. London* **1961**, 1913.
[34] D. F. Peppard, J. R. Ferraro, and G. W. Mason, *J. Inorg. and Nucl. Chem.* **7**, 231 (1958).
[35] J. W. Maarsen, M. C. Smit, and J. Matze, *Rec. Trav. Chim.* **76**, 713 (1957).
[36] J. V. Pustinger, Jr., W. T. Cave, and M. L. Neilsen, *Spectrochim. Acta* **15**, 909 (1959).
[37] R. A. McIvor, G. A. Grant, and C. E. Hubley, *Can. J. Chem.* **34**, 1611 (1956).

negativity is higher the bands are higher. The salt $(RO)_2PO_2^-$ absorbs at 1282–1210 and ca. 1100 cm^{-1}.[38]

Inorganic salts containing the PO_2^- group absorb at 1300–1150 cm^{-1}.[29,36]

Salts containing the POS^- group absorb at 1163–1064 cm^{-1} (strong) and 652–560 cm^{-1} (medium strong).[33]

Salts containing the PO_3^{2-} group absorb at 1090–970 cm^{-1} (asymmetric stretch) and 990–920 cm^{-1} (symmetric stretch).[29,33]

The PO_4^{3-} ion absorbs strongly at 1100–1000 cm^{-1}.[29]

12.27 P—O—C (Aliphatic)

A very strong band[26,30,37] occurs at 1050–970 cm^{-1} in all compounds having the P—O—C (aliphatic) link. This band is probably due to an asymmetric P—O—C stretching vibration. In most ethoxy phosphorus compounds this band is a doublet. In methoxy and ethoxy phosphorus compounds a second strong band appears at 830–740 cm^{-1} probably due to symmetric P—O—C stretching. This band is usually absent in other alkoxy phosphorus compounds.

In the hydrogen stretching and deformation regions, methyl and ethyl phosphorus esters resemble carbonyl esters. A methoxy group on a phosphorus atom absorbs near 2960, 1460, and at 1190–1170 cm^{-1} (CH_3 rock), and an ethoxy group on a phosphorus atom absorbs near 2990 (CH_3 asymmetric stretch), 1485 (O—CH_2 deformation), 1450 (CH_3 asymmetric deformation), 1395 (O–CH_2 wag), 1375 (CH_3 symmetric deformation), and 1165–1155 cm^{-1} (CH_3 rock).[37] The bands at 1190–1170 cm^{-1} for the methoxy group and 1165–1155 cm^{-1} for the ethoxy group on a phosphorus atom are probably the best distinguishing bands.[29] An isopropoxy group has the usual doublet near 1385 and 1370 cm^{-1} (symmetric CH_3 deformation), 1350 cm^{-1} (CH deformation), and a triplet of bands between 1200 and 1100 cm^{-1},[37] some of which involve the asymmetric motion of the branched carbon (asymmetric C—C—C, asymmetric C—C—O). A medium band at 900–870 cm^{-1} [32] is probably due to CH_3 rock.

12.28 P—O—C (Phenyl)

The P—O-phenyl linkage gives rise to two bands. Strong absorption[29] at 1260–1160 cm^{-1} is mainly due to the stretching of the C—O bond of the

[38] J. R. Ferraro, *Pittsburg Conf. on Appl. Spectry.* 1962, Paper 162.

phenoxy group, and a strong absorption at 994–914 cm^{-1} in pentavalent phosphorus compounds and 875–855 cm^{-1} in trivalent phosphorus compounds[33,39] is mainly due to stretching of the P—O bond.

12.29   P—CH$_2$

In alkyl phosphines, the CH$_2$ deformation of the CH$_2$ next to the phosphorus absorbs at 1440–1405 cm^{-1}, where it can be seen in the presence of the remaining normal hydrocarbon groups. In a trialkyl phosphine, this is the only indication of the presence of phosphorus.

12.30   P—CH$_3$

The symmetric deformation of the CH$_3$ group attached to a phosphorus gives rise to medium intensity absorption at 1310–1280 cm^{-1}.[29] The CH$_3$ rocking usually gives rise to a strong band near 940 cm^{-1} for P(CH$_3$)$_2$ compounds, at 920–860 cm^{-1} for P—CH$_3$ compounds, and 880–875 cm^{-1} for monomethyl tertiary phosphines.[39a]

12.31   P—Phenyl

When a phenyl group is attached to a phosphorus, the bands due to the phenyl ring near 3050 (weak), 1600 (weak), 1500 (weak), 1450–1425 (strong), 750 (strong), and 700 cm^{-1} (strong) all can be seen. Another strong band usually occurs at 1130–1090 cm^{-1} due probably to an aromatic vibration involving some P—C stretching. A medium, sharp phenyl band occurs at 1010–990 cm^{-1}.[29]

12.32   P=S

The P=S group appears[30,40] at 750–580 cm^{-1} but unfortunately, unlike the P=O vibration which always gives rise to a strong infrared band, the P=S

[39] A. C. Chapman and R. Harper, *Chem. Ind. (London)* **1962**, 985.
[39a] K. B. Mallion, F. G. Mann, B. P. Tong, and V. P. Wystrach, *J. Chem. Soc.* **1963**, 148.
[40] E. M. Popov, T. A. Mastryukova, N. P. Rodionova, and M. I. Kabachnik, *Zh. Obshch. Khim.* **29**, 1998 (1959).

band varies in intensity making its identification difficult in the infrared. The P=S stretching vibration is expected to interact mechanically with the attached P—O and P—C stretching vibrations at 850–650 cm^{-1} to a greater extent than the P=O stretching vibration does. This probably is the reason why two regions 835–713 (medium) and 675–568 cm^{-1} (variable) have been given as being characteristic for the P=S group.[33] The Raman spectrum is very valuable here, as its identification of the P=S vibration is more definite in some cases than the infrared. The band position varies when different groups are attached to the phosphorus, so it is necessary to be specific about atoms next to the phosphorus. The approximate positions of some examples are given in Table 12.5.[40]

TABLE 12.5

APPROXIMATE P=S SPECTRAL REGIONS IDENTIFIED BY BOTH INFRARED
AND RAMAN STUDIES

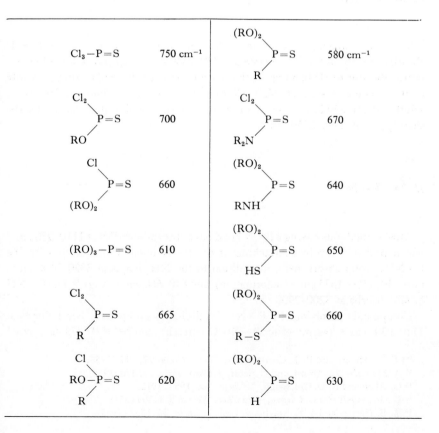

Cl$_3$—P=S	750 cm^{-1}	(RO)$_2$\P=S/R	580 cm^{-1}
Cl$_2$\P=S/RO	700	Cl$_2$\P=S/R$_2$N	670
Cl\P=S/(RO)$_2$	660	(RO)$_2$\P=S/RNH	640
(RO)$_3$—P=S	610	(RO)$_2$\P=S/HS	650
Cl$_2$\P=S/R	665	(RO)$_2$\P=S/R—S	660
Cl\RO—P=S/R	620	(RO)$_2$\P=S/H	630

The force constant of the P=S group is not affected as much as that of the P=O group by changes in the electronegativities of the substituents.[40a] Therefore, the frequency shifts are largely due to mechanical effects. The isolated P=S frequency has been calculated to be 675 cm^{-1}. If the attached P—X single bonds have frequencies below this (P—Cl, P—S) out-of-phase interaction will raise the P=S frequency. If the P—X frequencies are higher than this (P—OR, P—CH$_2$) in-phase interaction will lower the P=S frequency. The closer the P—X and P=S frequencies are the greater will be the magnitude of the shift.[40a] The approximate P=S frequency can be predicted fairly well by modifying the 675 cm^{-1} P=S frequency with the following empirical corrections for each substituent: Cl, +23 cm^{-1}; S, +23 cm^{-1}; H, 0 cm^{-1}; OR, −23 cm^{-1}; and CH$_2$, −50 cm^{-1}.

12.33   P—SH

The SH stretching vibration in dialkyl dithoiphosphoric acids [(RO)$_2$PSSH] absorbs broadly in the liquid state at 2480–2440 cm^{-1}. A band at 865–835 cm^{-1} is probably due to SH bending. Dithiophosphinic acids (R$_2$PSSH) absorb broadly in the condensed state at 2420–2300 cm^{-1} due to SH··S bonding. In dilute solution the free SH in the above dithiophosphoric and phosphinic acids absorbs sharply[41,42] at 2590–2550 cm^{-1}.

12.34   P—N

Most compounds having a P—N bond have absorption[32,43,44] at 1110–930 cm^{-1} which probably involves stretching of the P—N bond. Compounds with the P—NH$_2$ group absorb here, in addition to the NH$_2$ bands at 3330–3100 cm^{-1} (stretch), 1600–1535 cm^{-1} (deformation), and 840–660 cm^{-1} (wag).[36] The P—NH group absorbs at 3200–2900 cm^{-1}.[36]

Compounds involving the P—N—C (aliphatic) group have bands[32,43,44] at 1110–930 cm^{-1} (asymmetric P—N—C stretch) and[29,32,43,44] 770–680 cm^{-1}

[40a] F. N. Hooge and P. J. Christen, *Rec. Trav. Chim.* **77**, 911 (1958).
[41] A. Memefee, D. Alford, and C. Scott, *J. Chem. Phys.* **25**, 370 (1956).
[42] G. Allen and R. O. Colclough, *J. Chem. Soc.* **1957**, 3912.
[43] B. Holmstedt and L. Larson, *Acta Chem. Scand.* **5**, 1179 (1951).
[44] R. B. Harvey and J. E. Mayhood, *Can. J. Chem.* **33**, 1552 (1955).

(symmetric P—N—C stretch). In addition to these bands, absorption occurs for P—N(CH$_3$)$_2$ at 1316–1270 cm^{-1}, near 1190 cm^{-1}, and near 1064 cm^{-1},[32,44] for P—N(C$_2$H$_5$)$_2$ near 1210 cm^{-1} and near 1175 cm^{-1},[32] and for P—N(i-Pr)$_2$ near 1200, 1183, 1160, 1139 (shoulder), and 1129 cm^{-1}.[32]

The P—N-(phenyl) group absorbs near 1290 cm^{-1} (phenyl-N) and near 932 cm^{-1} (P—N).

The above suggested assignments indicate the basic similarity of P—N frequencies to comparable P—O frequencies as might be expected. The intensities are somewhat weaker.

12.35   P=N

Cyclic P=N compounds such as phosphonitrilic chlorides, phosphonitrilic esters and salts of phosphonitrilic acids absorb strongly[26,29,45,46] at 1320–1100 cm^{-1} due to the stretching of the P=N bond. Compounds of the type (RO)$_3$P=N—C$_6$H$_5$ and (RO)$_2$(R)P=N—C$_6$H$_5$ give rise to a strong band at 1385–1325 cm^{-1}.[47]

12.36   P—F, P—Cl, P—C

The P—F group gives rise to absorption at 835–720 cm^{-1} for phosphorfluoridate salts.[29] Organic phosphorus-fluorine compounds absorb at 890–805 cm^{-1} for pentavalent phosphorus.[26,27,33]

The P-Cl group gives rise to bands at 587–435 cm^{-1}.[29,33]

The P—C linkage gives rise to bands at 770–650 cm^{-1}, but these are weak and not of too much value.[29]

12.37   S—H

The SH stretch in mercaptans and thiophenols absorbs at 2590–2540 cm^{-1}.[48] The band is weak in the infrared but strong in the Raman spectrum. Thiol

[45] L. W. Daasch, *J. Am. Chem. Soc.* **76**, 3403 (1954).

[46] D. E. C. Corbridge and E. J. Lowe, *J. Chem. Soc.* **1954**, 4555.

[47] M. I. Kabachnik, V. A. Gilyarov, and E. N. Tsvetkov, *Izvest. Akad. Nauk. SSSR* **1959**, 2135.

[48] N. Sheppard, *Trans. Faraday Soc.* **46**, 429 (1950).

acids C(=O)SH absorb in the same region and show only small hydrogen bonding shifts. The PSSH group absorbs broadly at 2480–2300 cm^{-1} in the bonded condensed state and sharply at 2590–2550 cm^{-1} in dilute solution.[41,42]

12.38 Sulfides and Disulfides

The C—S stretch (705–570 cm^{-1}, medium weak)[48,49] does not give rise to strong bands in the infrared nor does the S—S stretch (500 cm^{-1}) in disulfides which makes these linkages difficult to detect in some cases. They are both better bands in the Raman effect. The most characteristic bands are those of the CH$_2$ or CH$_3$ groups attached to the sulfur.

12.39 CH$_2$—S

The CH$_2$ next to an unoxidized sulfur atom gives rise to the bands in Table 12.6.[49,50]

TABLE 12.6

CH$_2$—S SPECTRAL REGIONS

Asymmetric stretch	2948–2922 cm^{-1}
Symmetric stretch	2878–2846
Deformation	1435–1410
Wag	1270–1220 (strong)

12.40 CH$_3$—S

The CH$_3$ next to an unoxidized sulfur atom gives rise to the bands in Table 12.7.[48–50]

[49] I. F. Trotter and H. W. Thompson, *J. Chem. Soc.* **1946**, 481.
[50] S. E. Wiberley, S. C. Bunce, and W. H. Bauer, *Anal. Chem.* **32**, 217 (1960).

TABLE 12.7

CH_3-S SPECTRAL REGIONS

Asymmetric stretch	2992–2955 cm⁻¹
Symmetric stretch	2897–2867
Asymmetric deformation	1440–1415
Symmetric deformation	1330–1290
Rock	1030– 960

The group SO_2CH_3 absorbs at 1325–1310 cm⁻¹ (symmetric deformation) and at 976–964 cm⁻¹,[51] (probably CH_3 rock).

12.41 S—CH=CH₂

The $R-S-CH=CH_2$ group gives rise to vinyl bands near 1590 cm⁻¹, 965 cm⁻¹, and 860 cm⁻¹.

12.42 S-Aryl

A band near 1090 cm⁻¹ is usually characteristic for the aryl-S linkage. It is thought to be an aromatic ring vibration having some $C-S$ stretching character.[52]

12.43 S—F

The $S-F$ stretching frequency appears as a strong infrared band at 815–755 cm⁻¹.[52]

12.44 SO

The $S=O$ stretching vibration in alkyl and aryl sulfoxides gives rise to strong absorption at 1065–1030 cm⁻¹.[53] The $S=O$ stretching vibration in dialkyl sulfites gives rise to strong absorption at 1220–1195 cm⁻¹.[54,55] Alkyl chlorosulfites

[51] E. Merian, *Helv. Chim. Acta* **43**, 1122 (1960).
[52] N. S. Ham, A. N. Hambly, and R. H. Laby, *Australian J. Chem.* **13**, 443 (1960).
[53] D. Barnard, J. M. Fabian, and H. P. Koch, *J. Chem. Soc.* **1949**, 2442.
[54] S. Detoni and D. Hadzi, *Spectrochim. Acta* **11**, 601 (1957).
[55] H. H. Szmant and W. Emerson, *J. Am. Chem. Soc.* **78**, 454 (1956).

absorb at 1216–1210 cm^{-1}.[55] The S=O frequency has been correlated with the sum of the electronegativities of the attached groups.[56] Electronegative substituents reduce the resonance contribution from the polar form $\overset{+}{S}-\overset{-}{O}$, resulting in a stiffer S=O bond and a higher frequency.

Dialkyl sulfites have bands due to the S—O—CH$_2$ group at 1050–850 cm^{-1} and two bands between 750 and 690 cm^{-1}.[54]

12.45 SO$_2$

The SO$_2$ group results in two strong bands due to symmetric (1200–1100 cm^{-1}) and asymmetric (1400–1300 cm^{-1}) stretch of the SO$_2$ group. (See Table 12.8). The frequencies of both bands have been correlated with the sum of the electronegativities of the substituents.[56] Substituents with higher electronegativities reduce resonance contributions from polar forms which result in stiffer SO bonds and higher frequencies. The SO$_2$ bonds are sensitive to inductive effects but not to mesomeric effects.[62]

The approximate ratio of the wavenumbers of the two bands[62] is asymmetric stretch $\div$ symmetric stretch = 1.16.

12.46   Sulfones

Sulfones absorb[53,57,58] strongly at 1340–1290 and 1165–1120 cm^{-1} due to the stretching of the SO$_2$ group. The higher frequency band as measured in CCl$_4$ solution very frequently consists of a triplet with the regions 1333–1318, 1316–1306, and 1302–1287 cm^{-1} with the highest frequency band being most intense in solution.[57] These bands are shifted down 3–20 cm^{-1} in nujol mulls.

Most sulfones have the lower frequency band in the range 1165–1120 cm^{-1}. Some sulfones give an additional band at 1130–1100 cm^{-1}, and a few have a band at 1185–1175 cm^{-1}.[57]

12.47   Sulfonamides

Sulfonamides absorb strongly at 1180–1140 and 1380–1310 cm^{-1} due to the stretching of the SO$_2$ group.[51,58,59]

[56] L. W. Daasch, *Spectrochim. Acta* **13**, 257 (1958).

TABLE 12.8

SO$_2$ SPECTRAL REGIONS

Compound	Functional Group	Symmetric stretch cm^{-1}	Asymmetric stretch cm^{-1}	References
Sulfones	C—SO$_2$—C	1165–1120	1340–1290	53, 57, 58
Sulfonamides	C—SO$_2$—N	1180–1140	1380–1310	51, 58, 59
Anhydrous sulfonic acids	C—SO$_2$—OH	1165–1150	1352–1342	54, 58
Sulfonates	C—SO$_2$—O—C	1195–1165	1375–1335	58, 60
Sulfonyl chlorides	C—SO$_2$Cl	1185–1168	1390–1361	52, 58, 61
Dialkyl sulfates	C—O—SO$_2$—O—C	1200–1187	1415–1390	54. 58
Sulfonyl fluorides	C—SO$_2$F	1213–1203	1412–1398	52, 58

[57] P. M. G. Bavin, G. W. Gray, and A. Stephenson, *Spectrochim. Acta* **16**, 1312 (1960).
[58] E. A. Robinson, *Can. J. Chem.* **39**, 247 (1961).
[59] J. N. Baxter, J. Cymerman-Craig, and J. B. Willis, *J. Chem. Soc.* **1955**, 669.
[60] R. D. Guthrie and H. Spedding, *J. Chem. Soc.* **1960**, 953.
[61] G. Geiseler and K. O. Bindernagel, *Z. Elektrochem.* **64**, 421 (1960).
[62] L. J. Bellamy and R. L. Williams, *J. Chem. Soc.* **1957**, 863.

Primary sulfonamides have bands near 3330 and 3250 cm^{-1} due to asymmetric and symmetric stretching of the NH_2 group. The deformation absorbs near 1570 cm^{-1}. A band is found at 910–900 cm^{-1} which may be due to the S—N(H$_2$) stretching vibration.

Secondary sulfonamides absorb at 3300–3270 cm^{-1} (NH stretch).[51]

12.48   Sulfonic Acids

Anhydrous sulfonic acids absorb at 1352–1342 cm^{-1} (asymmetric SO$_2$ stretch), 1165–1150 cm^{-1} (symmetric SO$_2$ stretch), and 910–895 cm^{-1} (S—O stretch). The OH gives rise to a strong broad band near 2900 cm^{-1} with a smaller band near 2400 cm^{-1}.[54]

Sulfonic acids hydrate very easily. Hydrated sulfonic acids are thought to exist as hydronium sulfonates (R—SO$_3^-$ H$_3$O$^+$) and therefore resemble sulfonate salts with strong absorption in the 1230–1120 cm^{-1} region. A very broad band at 2800–1650 cm^{-1} with diffuse minima near 2600, 2250, and 1680 cm^{-1} is thought to be due to the hydronium ion.[54]

12.49   Sulfonic Acid Salts

Sulfonic acid salts absorb strongly at 1230–1120 cm^{-1} and weakly at 1080–1025 cm^{-1} due to the asymmetric and symmetric stretching of the SO$_3$ group. In the aromatic sulfonic acid salts there are frequently four bands here near 1230, 1190, 1130, and 1040 cm^{-1} (three SO and one S-phenyl vibrations interacting).

12.50   Sulfinic Acids

Sulfinic acids in the solid state (R—SOOH) have bands at 2790–2340 cm^{-1}, (OH stretch), 1090–990 cm^{-1} (S=O stretch), and 870–810 cm^{-1} (S—O stretch).[54]

12.51   HSO$_4^-$

The HO—SO$_3^-$ ion resembles the sulfonic acid salts in that it has bands at 1190–1160 cm^{-1} (asymmetric SO$_3^-$ stretch) and 1080–1015 cm^{-1} (symmetric SO$_3^-$ stretch). It has a band the sulfonates do not have[63] at 870–850 cm^{-1} which might be loosely described as involving S—O(H) stretch.

[63] F. A. Miller and C. H. Wilkins, *Anal. Chem.* **24**, 1253 (1952).

12.52 SO_4^{2-}

The inorganic sulfate ion absorbs strongly at 1125–1080 cm^{-1} due to asymmetric SO_4 stretching. The symmetric SO_4 stretch is normally forbidden by symmetry but may occasionally be seen as a very weak sharp band near 1000 cm^{-1}.[63]

12.53 SO_3^{2-}

The sulfite ion absorbs strongly at 980–920 cm^{-1}.[63]

12.54 $S-O-CH_2$

The asymmetric stretching of the $S-O-CH_2$ bonds gives rise to strong absorption at 1020–850 cm^{-1}. Absorption also occurs near 830–690 cm^{-1} (symmetric $S-O-C$ stretch).

12.55 Thionylamine

The thionylamine group ($-N=S=O$) absorbs at 1300–1230 cm^{-1} (asymmetric NSO stretch) and 1180–1110 cm^{-1} (symmetric NSO stretch).[64,65]

12.56 C=S

The C=S group does not give rise to as characteristic a band as the C=O group does due to the complication of interaction.[66-80] Due to the greater mass

[64] W. K. Glass and A. D. E. Pullin, *Trans. Faraday Soc.* **57**, 546 (1961).

[65] G. Kresze and A. Maschke, *Chem. Ber.* **94**, 450 (1961).

[66] E. Spinner, *J. Org. Chem.* **23**, 2037 (1958).

[67] R. Mecke, R. Mecke, Jr., and A. Luttringhaus, *Chem. Ber.* **90**, 975 (1957).

[68] A. Yamaguchi, R. B. Penland, S. Mizushima, T. J. Lane, Columba Curran and J. V. Quagliano, *J. Am. Chem. Soc.* **80**, 527 (1958).

[69] M. Davies and W. J. Jones, *J. Chem. Soc.* **1958**, 955.

[70] J. I. Jones, W. Kynaston, and J. L. Hales, *J. Chem. Soc.* **1957**, 614.

[71] T. A. Scott and E. L. Wagner, *J. Chem. Phys.* **30**, 465 (1959).

[72] R. Mecke, R. Mecke, Jr., and A. Luttringhaus, *Z. Naturforsch.* **10B**, 367 (1955).

[73] L. J. Bellamy and P. E. Rogasch, *J. Chem. Soc.* **1960**, 2218.

[74] R. Mecke and R. Mecke, Jr., *Chem. Ber.* **89**, 343 (1956).

[75] H. M. Randall, R. G. Fowler, N. Fuson, and R. Dangl, "Infrared Determination of Organic Structures." Van Nostrand, New York, 1949.

[76] B. Bak, L. Hansen-Nygaard, and C. Pedersen, *Acta Chem. Scand.* **12**, 1451 (1958).

[77] C. S. Marvel, P. Radzitsky, and J. J. Brader, *J. Am. Chem. Soc.* **77**, 5997 (1955).

[78] N. Lozac'h and G. Guillouzo, *Bull. Soc. Chim. France* **1957**, 1221.

[79] C. N. R. Rao and R. Venkataraghavan, *Spectrochim. Acta* **18**, 541 (1962).

[80] I. Suzuki, *Bull. Chem. Soc. Japan* **35**, 1286, 1449, 1456 (1962).

of sulfur the C=S vibration is expected to occur at considerably lower frequencies than the C=O vibration, in the C—O or C—N region. This means that the C=S and the attached single bonds can interact with the result that more than one band involves C=S stretching. In thioamides the NH_2 rocking vibration can also interact.[68,80] Vibrational analysis reveals that thioformamide has a band at 843 cm^{-1} which is almost pure C=S stretching but that in other thioamides much mixing occurs.[80] Bands have been assigned as involving C=S stretching at 1420–700 cm^{-1}.[66-80] Thioacetamide has bands at 718, 975, and 1306 cm^{-1} involving C=S stretching.[73,80] Monosubstituted thioamides have bands near 1000 cm^{-1} which involve C=S.[80,81] The cyclic thioamides and ureas as well as so-called mercapto-N-heteroaromatic compounds usually have bands[74] probably involving C=S at 1210–1045 cm^{-1} not present in the oxygen analogs.

In noncyclic thioamides and ureas the NH frequencies are similar to those in amides and ureas. In the solid state the NH_2 group absorbs near 3380, 3180, and 1630 cm^{-1}. In the solid state the NH stretch absorbs near 3170 cm^{-1} and the CNH group absorbs near 1530 and 1350 cm^{-1}.[81] The cyclic CS—NH—R group gives rise to absorption[75] near 1550 cm^{-1} due to the CNH group, similar to noncyclic cases and unlike cyclic lactams which have no band near 1550 cm^{-1}.

The region 1250–1020 cm^{-1} has been assigned to vibrations involving C=S stretching in compounds where nitrogen is not attached to the C=S group.[79]

Dialkyl trithiocarbonates $(R—S)_3C=S$ have a C=S band near 1070 cm^{-1}.

Noncyclic dithio esters have strong absorption[73,76,77] at 1225–1170 cm^{-1} which is thought to involve the stretching of the C=S bond.

Compounds with the structure R—O—(C=S)—S—X such as O, S dialkyl xanthates, dixanthogens, and copper and zinc xanthates show bands involving the R—O—C=S group at 1250–1200 cm^{-1}, strong, 1140–1110 cm^{-1}, medium, and 1070–1020 cm^{-1}, strong.[82] The sodium and potassium xanthates are characterized by a number of strong bands between 1180 and 1030 cm^{-1} involving C—O and CS bonds.[82] These probably differ from the heavy metal xanthates because the two CS bonds are more nearly equivalent, $R—O—CS_2^-Na^+$.

Derivatives of thiobenzophenone have a medium-weak band[78] at 1224–1207 cm^{-1} not present in the comparable benzophenones.

Some frequencies which are thought to involve the C=S vibration in different types of molecules are listed in Table 12.9.[67] The noncyclic compounds are dimethyl derivatives and the cyclic compounds are dimethylene derivatives.

[81] D. Hadzi, *J. Chem. Soc.* **1957**, 847.
[82] L. H. Little, G. W. Poling and J. Leja, *Can. J. Chem.* **39**, 745 (1961).

TABLE 12.9

Some C=O and C=S Frequencies for Cyclic and Noncyclic "Compounds"

"Compound"	C=O Five-membered ring	C=O Noncyclic	C=S Five-membered ring	C=S Noncyclic
O−(C=X)−O	1798 cm⁻¹	1742	—	1127
CH₂−(C=X)−O	1773	1734	—	—
CH₂−(C=X)−CH₂	1742	1706	—	—
O−(C=X)−NH	1724	1703	1171	—
CH₂−(C=X)−NH	1692	1658	1109	1097
NH−(C=X)−NH	1638	1626	1201	1183
S−(C=X)−S	1638	1655	1058	1076
S−(C=X)−NH	—	—	1047	—
CH₂−(C=X)−N−CH₃	—	—	1136	1122

12.57 (FHF)⁻

The linear bifluoride ion (FHF)⁻ has one of the strongest hydrogen bonds known. The asymmetric FHF stretching vibration absorbs broadly at 1700–1400 cm⁻¹ and the FHF deformation absorbs at 1260–1200 cm⁻¹.[83,84]

12.58 FCH

A single hydrogen on a fluorine bearing carbon atom absorbs[85,87] near 3000 cm⁻¹ with some indication of shifts with the number of fluorine atoms on the carbon. CF_3H absorbs at 3062 cm⁻¹, $-CF_2H$ at 3008 cm⁻¹, and $>$ CFH at 2990 cm⁻¹.[85]

[83] J. A. A. Ketelaar, C. Haas, and J. van der Elsken, *J. Chem. Phys.* **24**, 624 (1956).

[84] J. A. A. Ketelaar and W. Vedder, *J. Chem. Phys.* **19**, 654 (1951).

[85] D. G. Weiblen, Infrared Spectra in Fluorocarbons. *In* "Fluorine Chemistry" J. H. Simons, ed. Vol. 2, Chapter 7. Academic Press, New York, 1954.

[86] D. C. Smith, J. R. Neilsen, L. H. Berryman, H. H. Claassen, and R. L. Hudson, Naval Res. Lab. Rept. 3567 (1949).

[87] D. C. Smith, M. Alpert, R. A. Saunders, G. M. Brown, and N. B. Moran, Naval Res. Lab. Rept. 3924 (1952).

12.59 FC=C

The C=C stretching frequency is unusually high when fluorine atoms are directly on the carbon atoms. The group C=CF$_2$ absorbs at 1755–1735 cm^{-1}, and the group —CF=CF$_2$ absorbs[85,86,88–90] at 1800–1780 cm^{-1}.

12.60 FC=O

Acid fluoride groups attached to fluorinated alkane groups (—CF$_2$—COF) absorb at 1900–1870 cm^{-1}.[85,91] In the gas phase acetyl fluoride absorbs at 1869 cm^{-1} and benzoyl fluoride absorbs at 1820 cm^{-1}.[92]

12.61 F-Aryl

Fluorine atoms directly attached to an aromatic ring give rise to bands in the region 1270–1100 cm^{-1}. Many of these compounds including the simpler ones with one fluorine only on the ring absorb near 1230 cm^{-1}. Fluorine substitution does not abnormally affect the ring frequencies at 850–700 cm^{-1}.

12.62 CF Stretch

The groups CF$_3$ and CF$_2$ on the whole are difficult to differentiate in the infrared.[85,86,93] The CF$_3$ group absorbs strongly at 1350–1120 cm^{-1},[86] and the CF$_2$ at 1280–1120 cm^{-1}.[86] Four or five membered cyclic CF$_2$ compounds absorb at

[88] P. Torkington and H. W. Thompson, *Trans. Faraday Soc.* 41, 236 (1945).

[89] T. J. Brice, J. D. La Zerte, L. J. Hals, and W. H. Pearlson, *J. Am. Chem. Soc.* 75, 2698 (1953).

[90] R. N. Haszeldine, *J. Chem. Soc.* 1952, 4423.

[91] R. N. Haszeldine, *Nature* 168, 1028 (1951).

[92] J. Overend and J. R. Scherer, *Spectrochim. Acta* 16, 773 (1960).

[93] H. W. Thompson and R. B. Temple, *J. Chem. Soc.* 1948, 1432.

1350–1140 cm^{-1}.[85] In the group $CF_3(CF_2)_nX$, a band is usually found at 1365–1325 cm^{-1} attributed to the CF_3 group.[94] When the CF_3 is absent in this type of compound, absorption here is usually not present. Another band involving the CF_3 group occurs at 780–680 cm^{-1}.[85] The narrower region of 745–730 cm^{-1} is characteristic for the group $CF-CF_3$.[95] The group $CF=CF_2$ absorbs strongly at 1340–1300 cm^{-1}.[85,86] The electronegative fluorinated alkane group causes some shifts in common functional groups when attached thereon. A summary of these positions is found in Table 12.10.[85]

TABLE 12.10

COMMON FUNCTIONAL GROUPS ATTACHED TO FLUORINATED ALKANE GROUPS

$-CF_2-C\equiv N$	2280–2270 cm^{-1}
$-CF_2-N=C=O$	2300
$-CF_2-CHO$	1785–1755
$-CF_2-CO-CH_2$	1770
$-CF_2-CO-CF_2$	1800
$-CF_2-COF$	1900–1870
$-CF_2-COCl$	1820–1795
$-CF_2-COOH$ (liquid)	1785–1750
$-CF_2-CO-O-CO-CF_2-$	1890 and 1820
$-CF_2-COO-CH_2$	1796–1784
$-CH_2-COO-CH_2-CF_2-$	1773–1761
$-CF_2-COO-CH_2-CF_2-$	1814–1802
$-CF_2-CO_2^-$ metal$^+$	1695–1615
$-CF_2-CO-NH_2$	1730–1700 and 1630–1610 (weaker)

12.63   C—Cl

The aliphatic C—Cl bond absorbs at 830–560 cm^{-1}.[96,97] The group C—CH_2—CH_2—Cl gives rise to two bands due to rotational isomers. The planar C—C—C—Cl *trans* zig-zag form absorbs near 726 cm^{-1}, and the *gauche* C—C—C—Cl form absorbs near 649 cm^{-1}.[97,98] Just as the *trans* form absorbs at higher wavenumbers than the *gauche*, the equatorial C—Cl absorbs higher than the axial C—Cl bond in cyclic rings. In steroids, the equatorial C-Cl

[94] M. Hauptschein, C. S. Stokes, and E. A. Nodiff, *J. Am. Chem. Soc.* **74**, 4005 (1952).
[95] L. J. Bellamy, "The Infrared Spectra of Complex Molecules." Wiley, New York, 1954.
[96] J. K. Brown and N. Sheppard, *Trans. Faraday Soc.* **50**, 1164 (1954).
[97] N. Sheppard, *Trans. Faraday Soc.* **46**, 527 (1950); *ibid.*, **46**, 533 (1950).
[98] J. K. Brown and N. Sheppard, *Proc. Roy. Soc. (London)* **A231**, 555 (1955).

absorbs at 755 cm^{-1} in the 2 position, at 782–750 cm^{-1} in the 3 position, and 749 cm^{-1} in the 7 position. Comparable axial C—Cl bands occur at 693, 730–617 cm^{-1}, and 588 cm^{-1}.[99] Monochloroalkanes, where the α carbon atoms are branched with methyl groups, have C—Cl bands at the lower wavenumber end of the region.[97] The complexity of the C—Cl region is indicative of C—Cl interaction with C—C and other oscillators. In chloroalkanes where there is one chlorine per carbon of an aliphatic compound, close correlations have been made, specifying the rotational isomers by specifying the atom X "*trans*" to the chlorine on the β carbon so that the atoms X—C—C—Cl zig-zag in one plane. In Table 12.11[100] P stands for primary (CH$_2$Cl), S for secondary (CHCl) and T for tertiary. The subscript C or H is the "*trans*" atom X. In this nomenclature the planar skeleton *trans* form of *n*-propyl chloride would be noted as P_C and the *gauche* skeleton form as P_H. Isopropyl chloride would be S_{HH} (two "*trans*" hydrogens).

TABLE 12.11

C—Cl BANDS IN CHLOROALKANES

P_C	730–723 cm^{-1}
P_H	657–648
P'_H	686–679 (β carbon branched)
S_{CC}	758
S_{CH}	674–655
S'_{HH}	637–627 (carbon chain bent)
S_{HH}	615–608
T_{CHH}	632–611
T_{HHH}	581–560

Putting more than one chlorine on a carbon raises the CCl frequency. The CCl$_3$ group has an asymmetric stretching vibration which causes a strong band at 830–700 cm^{-1}. The group CH$_2$—Cl has a strong CH$_2$ wag band at 1300–1240 cm^{-1}.[98]

12.64 C—Br

The aliphatic C-Br bond gives rise to bands in the region 680–515 cm^{-1}.[101] The group C—CH$_2$—CH$_2$—Br gives rise to two bands near 644 cm^{-1} (*trans*)

[99] D. H. R. Barton, J. E. Page, and C. W. Shoppee, *J. Chem. Soc.* **1956**, 331.
[100] J. J. Shipman, V. L. Folt and S. Krimn, *Spectrochim. Acta* **18**, 1603 (1962).
[101] F. S. Mortimer, R. B. Blodgett, and F. Daniels, *J. Am. Chem. Soc.* **69**, 822 (1947).

and 563 cm^{-1} (*gauche*)[96,98,101] in both infrared and Raman spectra due to two rotational isomers.[96,98] Branching of the α carbon with methyl groups lowers the band to 560–515 cm^{-1}.[97] Putting two or three bromines on the same carbon atom results in bands at the high frequency end of the region. The CH_2-Br group has strong CH_2 wag bands near 1230 cm^{-1}.[98]

12.65   C—I

The aliphatic C—I bond gives rise to bands about 610–485 cm^{-1}.[96–98] The group C—CH_2—CH_2—I gives rise to two bands near 594 and 503 cm^{-1}. The CH_2—I group has strong CH_2 wag bands near 1170 cm^{-1}.[98]

12.66   Aryl Halides

In aryl halides there are no bands obviously comparable to the aliphatic C—X stretching bands due to interaction with ring vibrations. One ring vibration which is mass sensitive and involves some C—X stretching[102] is found approximately at 1270–1100 cm^{-1} for aryl-F compounds. The same band for aryl-Cl[102] is found at 1096–1089 cm^{-1} for *para*, 1078–1074 cm^{-1} for *meta*, and 1057–1034 cm^{-1} for *ortho* substituted chloro benzenes.[103] Bands are found at 1073–1068 cm^{-1} for *para*, 1073–1065 cm^{-1} for *meta*, and 1042–1028 cm^{-1} for *ortho* substituted bromo benzenes. *Para* substituted iodo benzenes absorb at 1061–1057 cm^{-1}.[103]

12.67   Organometalic Compounds

The hydrogen stretching vibration in Ge-H compounds absorbs at 2160–2010 cm^{-1}.[104] The Sn—H group absorbs at about 1900–1800 cm^{-1}.[105,106] Complexes containing AlH_3 and AlH_4 absorb at 1810–1674 cm^{-1}.[107]

[102] A. Stojiljkovic and D. H. Whiffen, *Spectrochim. Acta* 12, 47 (1958).

[103] A. R. Katritzky and J. M. Lagowski, *J. Chem. Soc.* 1960, 2421.

[104] V. A. Ponomarenko, G. Y. Zueva, and N. S. Andreev, *Izvest. Akad. Nauk SSSR* 10, 1758 (1961).

[105] R. Mathis, M. Lesbre, and I. S. de Roch, *Compt. rend.* 243, 257 (1956).

[106] D. R. Lide, Jr., *J. Chem. Phys.* 19, 1605 (1951).

[107] R. Dautel and W. Zeil, *Z. Elektrochem.* 64, 1234 (1960).

The symmetric methyl deformation vibration absorbs strongly at 1240–1230 cm^{-1} in $Ge-CH_3$ compounds and 1200–1180 cm^{-1} in $Sn-CH_3$ compounds.[108] Methyl rocking vibrations absorb strongly at 900–700 cm^{-1}.

The CH_2-metal group absorbs at 1430–1415 cm^{-1} (CH_2 deformation) in compounds with such metals as mercury, zinc, cadmium, or tin.[109]

The $CH_2=CH$-(metal) group has bands at 1610–1565 cm^{-1} ($C=C$ stretch), 1410–1390 cm^{-1} (CH_2 deformation), 1265–1245 cm^{-1} (CH rock), 1010–985 cm^{-1} (CH wag), and 960–940 cm^{-1} (CH_2 wag).[109,110]

In C_6H_5-(metal) compounds a band in the region 1120–1050 cm^{-1} is sensitive to a change in the metal. This is a benzene ring vibration interacting with C-(metal) stretching vibration.[102] Examples of this are tetraphenylsilane 1100 cm^{-1}, tetraphenylgermane 1080 cm^{-1}, tetraphenyltin 1065 cm^{-1} and tetraphenyllead 1052 cm^{-1}.[110]

The Ge-O-Ge linkage has been tentatively assigned to the 900–700 cm^{-1} region where the $Ge-CH_3$ rocking vibrations also absorb.[108] The Sn-O-Sn linkage has been tentatively assigned to the 650-580 cm^{-1} region.[108] The Ti-O-Ti linkage usually absorbs[111,112] at 900–700 cm^{-1} and the Ti-O-Si linkage at about 950–900 cm^{-1}. [112]

Compounds with (metal) = O linkages where the oxygen is associated with only one metal generally absorb at 1100–900 cm^{-1} (example: $VOCl_3$, 1035 cm^{-1}).[111]

[108] M. P. Brown, R. Okawara, and E. G. Rochow, *Spectrochim. Acta* 16, 595 (1960).
[109] H. D. Kaesz and F. G. A. Stone, *Spectrochim. Acta* 15, 360 (1959).
[110] M. C. Henry and J. G. Noltes, *J. Am. Chem. Soc.* 82, 555 (1960).
[111] C. G. Barraclough, J. Lewis, and R. S. Nyholm, *J. Chem. Soc.* 1959, 3552.
[112] V. A. Zeitler and C. A. Brown, *J. Phys. Chem.* 61, 1174 (1957).

CHAPTER 13

MAJOR SPECTRA-STRUCTURE
CORRELATIONS BY SPECTRAL REGIONS

13.1 Introduction

In previous chapters, the spectra of various chemical groups were discussed under functional group categories. In this chapter, the infrared spectrum will be considered in terms of spectral regions. This discussion will be briefer than that given for functional groups with only the major bands being mentioned.

13.2 3700-3100 cm^{-1} (OH, NH, and $\equiv$CH)

Bands in the region from 3700 to 3100 cm^{-1} are usually due to various OH and NH stretching vibrations. The NH$_2$ group gives rise to a doublet with approximately 70 cm^{-1} separation. The OH compounds include water, alcohols, and phenols but not phosphorus acids or carboxylic acid dimers which have bands at lower wavenumbers. The bonded OH group usually give rise to a broader band than NH groups. All these bands shift to higher wave numbers and much become narrower and weaker in intensity when the hydrogen bond is broken by diluting the solute in a nonpolar solvent such as CCl$_4$. In concentrated solutions both bonded and unbonded forms may exist, giving rise to several bands.

The C$\equiv$C$-$H group has a CH stretching vibration which absorbs near 3300 cm^{-1}. This band is not nearly as broad as alcoholic bonded OH bands found in this region.

Overtones of lower bands occur here, notably overtones of carbonyls at twice the C$=$O frequency. These are weak bands in the 3500–3400 cm^{-1} region.

13.3 3100-3000 cm^{-1} (Aryl, Olefinic, and Three Membered Ring CH)

The C$-$H stretching vibrations of olefins, aromatic rings, and three membered rings absorb mainly in this region above 3000 cm^{-1}.

319

13.4 3000-2700 cm⁻¹ (Aliphatic CH)

In this region below 3000 cm^{-1} are found aliphatic C—H stretching vibrations. Aliphatic CH_2 and CH_3 groups each give rise to a doublet approximately 80 cm^{-1} separation at slightly different frequencies (aliphatic CH_3 2960, aliphatic CH_2 2930 cm^{-1} for the higher band) and so can be differentiated. In tertiary amines, the CH_2 and CH_3 groups next to the nitrogen absorb near 2800 cm^{-1}. Many aldehydes absorb near 2730 cm^{-1}.

13.5 3100-2400 cm⁻¹ (Acidic and Strongly Bonded Hydrogens)

In this region occur the broad bands of many acidic hydrogens. Carboxylic acid dimers absorb broadly near 3000 cm^{-1} with satellite bands near 2650 and 2550 cm^{-1}. Amine salts absorb in this region. Their bands have much fine structure. Phosphorus acids absorb broadly in this region. The strongly bonded hydrogen in the enol form of 1,3 diketones and related compounds absorbs broadly at 3100–2700 cm^{-1}.

13.6 2600-2100 cm⁻¹ (SH, BH, PH, and SiH)

Mercaptans and thiophenols absorb at 2590–2540 cm^{-1} due to the SH stretching vibration. Compounds with a BH group absorb at 2630–2350 cm^{-1}. Compounds with a PH group absorb at 2440–2275 cm^{-1}. Compounds with an SiH group absorb at 2250–2100 cm^{-1}.

13.7 2300-1900 cm⁻¹ (X≡Y and X=Y=Z)

In this region are found triple bonds (X≡Y) and cumulated double bonds (X=Y=Z). The bands of the latter tend to have considerably more intensity than the former. A combination band in primary amine salts occurs here. Metal carbonyl complexes (carbon monoxide complexes) absorb strongly in the lower part of the region.

13.8   2000-1700 cm^{-1} (Aryl and Olefinic Overtones)

Unusually intense overtones of aryl ring vibrations occur in this region. They form a pattern which can be used to differentiate substitution isomers. An unusually intense overtone of the CH$_2$ wag vibration in vinyl and vinylidine groups is an excellent check on the assignment of the fundamental near 900 cm^{-1}. These bands are somewhat weaker than fundamentals and are most clearly seen in spectra of moderately thick samples.

13.9   1900-1550 cm^{-1} (C=O)

Carbonyl compounds absorb strongly throughout this region. Those compounds absorbing above 1760 cm^{-1} are usually compounds with electronegative groups next to the carbonyl such as acid chlorides, compounds where the carbonyl is in a strained ring such as in cyclobutanone, or compounds with an anhydride group which gives rise to two strong bands. Very approximately, the carbonyl groups in saturated esters absorb near 1740 cm^{-1}, aldehydes near 1725 cm^{-1}, and ketones near 1715 cm^{-1}. Conjugation will lower these about 20 cm^{-1}. Carboxylic acid dimers absorb near 1700 cm^{-1} and amides near 1660 cm^{-1}. Increasing mesomerism increasingly lowers the carbonyl frequency. The extreme case is the carboxylic salt with two equivalent C=O bonds which absorbs near 1600 cm^{-1}. Also absorbing here is the enol form of 1,3 diketones where mesomerism is also extremely in evidence.

A convenient dividing line is 1600 cm^{-1}, where bands in the region 1800–1600 cm^{-1} are due to X=Y double bond stretching vibrations, and bands in the region 1600-1500 cm^{-1} are due to the asymmetric stretching of the X$\dot{\dot{-}}$Y$\dot{\dot{-}}$X "bond-and-a-half" bonds such as in carboxyl salts, nitro groups, and aromatic rings.

13.10   1700-1550 cm^{-1} (C=C and C=N)

Compounds containing the C=C group absorb in this region except for symmetric *trans* disubstituted olefins where the band is forbidden by symmetry. Most olefins absorb at 1680–1600 cm^{-1}. Compounds containing the C=N group absorb usually at 1690–1630 cm^{-1}, although some types such as guanidines absorb at lower wavenumbers.

13.11   1660-1450 cm⁻¹ (N=O)

Organic nitrates absorb at 1660–1625 cm⁻¹. Organic nitrites have two bands due to rotational isomers at 1681–1648 cm⁻¹ and 1625–1605 cm⁻¹. Aliphatic nitro compounds absorb at 1590–1535 cm⁻¹, and aromatic nitro compounds absorb at 1530–1500 cm⁻¹. Monomeric C-nitroso monomers absorb at 1620–1488 cm⁻¹, and monomeric N-nitroso compounds absorb at 1490–1445 cm⁻¹.

13.12   1660-1500 cm⁻¹ (NH₂, NH₃⁺, and CNH)

The NH_2 group has its scissors deformation frequency at 1660–1590 cm⁻¹. The NH_2^+ group absorbs near 1600 cm⁻¹ and the NH_3^+ group near 1600 and 1520 cm⁻¹. In a noncyclic monosubstituted amide or monosubstituted thioamide, the CHN group gives rise to a strong band near 1550 cm⁻¹. Liquid H_2O absorbs near 1640 cm⁻¹.

13.13   1620-1420 cm⁻¹ (Aromatic and Heteroaromatic Rings)

Aromatic rings are characterized by sharp bands near 1600, 1580, 1500, and 1460 cm⁻¹ which may vary in intensity with different substituents. Pyridines are closely related to the benzene compounds. Triazines have strong bands in the 1600–1500 cm⁻¹ region. Heterocyclic compounds with two double bonds in a five membered ring usually absorb at 1600–1530 and 1500–1430 cm⁻¹.

13.14   1500-1250 cm⁻¹ (CH₃ and CH₂)

In the region 1500–1400 are found the CH_2 scissors deformation and the CH_3 asymmetrical deformation which are near the same position when the substituents are the same. These bands are near 1460 cm⁻¹ in hydrocarbons and near 1420 cm⁻¹ when the group is on a sulfur, phosphorus, or silicon or is next to a carbonyl or nitrile. The symmetric CH_3 umbrella deformation varies in frequency with the electronegativity of the substituent, being found near 1450 cm⁻¹ for $O-CH_3$, 1375 cm⁻¹ for $C-CH_3$, and 1265 cm⁻¹ for $Si-CH_3$.

13.15 1470-1310 cm⁻¹ (B—O, B—N, NO₃⁻, CO₃²⁻, and NH₄⁺)

Compounds containing the B—O and B—N linkage usually absorb strongly in this region. The nitrate and carbonate ions absorb strongly and broadly near 1400 cm⁻¹, and the ammonium ion has a band near 1400 cm⁻¹.

13.16 1400-1000 cm⁻¹ (SO₂, SO₃⁻, SO, and SO₄²⁻)

The SO_2 group gives rise to two bands separated by about 180 cm⁻¹ in the region 1400–1300 and 1200–1100 cm⁻¹, the exact position of the two bands varying with the electronegativity of the substituents. Sulfonic acid salts absorb broadly near 1200 cm⁻¹. Dialkyl sulfites absorb near 1200 cm⁻¹, and sulfoxides absorb near 1050 cm⁻¹. The SO_4^{2-} group absorbs near 1120 cm⁻¹.

13.17 1300-1140 cm⁻¹ (P=O)

Compounds containing the P=O group absorb in the region 1300–1140 cm⁻¹, the exact position depending on the sum of the electronegativities of the substituents. Trialkyl phosphates for example absorb near 1290 cm⁻¹, and trialkyl phosphine oxides absorb near 1150 cm⁻¹. Cyclic P=N compounds also absorb in this region.

13.18 1350-1120 cm⁻¹ (CF₃ and CF₂)

The fluorinated alkane groups CF_3 and CF_2 absorb strongly in the region 1350–1120 cm⁻¹.

13.19 1350-1150 cm⁻¹ (CH₂ and CH wag)

In the region 1340–1190 cm⁻¹ occur the multiple weak bands due to CH_2 wagging vibrations in a normal hydrocarbon chain, the complexity of the band system increasing with chain length in the solid state spectra. The CH_2—Cl group absorbs strongly near 1275 cm^{-1}, CH_2—S near 1250 cm^{-1}, CH_2—Br near 1230 cm^{-1}, and CH_2—I near 1170 cm^{-1}. Comparable CH—Cl and CH—Br groups absorb near the CH_2 position but usually about 50 cm^{-1} lower.

13.20   1300-1000 cm^{-1} (C—O)

In this region occur strong bands involving the stretching of the C—O bonds. Bands in the region 1300–1150 cm^{-1} arise from those C—O bonds somewhat stiffened by resonance such as esters, phenols, phenyl ethers, and vinyl ethers. Saturated ethers absorb near 1125 cm^{-1}, and alcohols absorb in the region 1200–1000 cm^{-1}. Primary alcohols absorb at 1075–1000 cm^{-1}. Branching of the α carbon tends to raise the frequency.

13.21   1100-830 cm^{-1} (Si—O and P—O)

The Si—O—alkyl group gives rise to a strong band at 1100–1000 cm^{-1} where the Si—O—Si group also absorbs. The Si—OH group absorbs at 910–830 cm^{-1}.

The P—O—alkyl group absorbs at 1050–970 cm^{-1}, and the P—O—P and P—OH group absorb about 1000–900 cm^{-1}.

13.22   1000-600 cm^{-1} (Olefinic CH Wag)

Vinyl compounds absorb at 1000–940 cm^{-1} and at 960–810 cm^{-1}. (990 and 910 cm^{-1} for hydrocarbons). Vinylidene compounds absorb at 985–700 cm^{-1}. (890 cm^{-1} for hydrocarbons). *Trans* disubstituted ethylenes absorb at 980–890 cm^{-1} (965 cm^{-1} for hydrocarbons), and cis compounds absorb at 800–600 cm^{-1} (730–650 cm^{-1} for hydrocarbons). The position of the band within the regions can be predicted from the properties of the substituents.

13.23   900-700 cm⁻¹ (Aromatic CH Wag)

Bands near 770–730 cm^{-1} are due to the 5 adjacent hydrogens of mono-substituted benzene. The 4 adjacent hydrogens of *ortho* disubstitution absorb near 750 cm^{-1}. The 3 adjacent hydrogens of *meta* and vicinal tri absorb near 780 cm^{-1}, the two adjacent hydrogens of *para* and unsymmetrical tri, near 820 cm^{-1}, and the isolated hydrogens of *meta*, unsymmetrical tri and symmetrical tri, near 870 cm^{-1}. Mono, *meta*, and symmetrical trisubstitution have a ring bending vibration which absorbs near 700 cm^{-1}. This classification by adjacent hydrogens can be extended to substituted naphthalenes and pyridines.

13.24   830-500 cm⁻¹ (CCl, CBr, and CI)

The CCl group gives rise to bands at 830–570 cm^{-1}, the CBr group to bands at 680–515 cm^{-1}, and the CI group to bands at 610–485 cm^{-1}.

13.25   Near Infrared Region Correlation Chart

For instrumental and theoretical reasons Kaye[1] has assigned the near infrared region from 0.7 to 3.5 microns (14,285 to 2860 cm^{-1}). Kaye has reviewed this region in two papers; the first paper[1] dealt with spectral identification and analytical applications and contained a correlation chart with many references. The second paper[2] reviewed instrumentation and technique. More recent correlation charts have been published by Goddu and Delker[3] and the Anderson Physical Laboratory, Champaign, Illinois. In 1960 a new bibliography was published by Kaye[4] and in 1961 a review paper on analytical applications of near infrared absorption spectroscopy was presented by White.[5]

[1] W. Kaye, *Spectrochim. Acta* 6, 257 (1954)

[2] W. Kaye, *Spectrochim. Acta* 7, 181 (1955).

[3] R. F. Goddu and D. A. Delker, *Anal. Chem.* 32, 140 (1960).

[4] W. Kaye, *in* "The Encyclopedia of Spectroscopy" (G. L. Clark, ed.), p. 409. Reinhold, New York, 1960.

[5] R. G. White, paper presented at infrared spectroscopy institute at Canisius College, August, 1961.

Most of the absorption bands observed in this region are X—H stretching vibrations and overtone or combination bands of these vibrations. Since the C—H fundamental stretching vibrations as well as the O—H and N—H fundamental stretching vibrations are covered in more detail on subsequent charts [see the following sections], the main emphasis in the following discussion will concern the overtone bands and to a lesser degree the combination bands in the near infrared region.

A chart similar to that of Goddu and Delker is shown in Fig. 13.1. A few comments on this chart are in order. If one considers the paraffinic CH_3 , CH_2 and aromatic C—H vibrations, Evans, Hibbard, and Powell[6] report that the most useful CH_3 band falls between 8375 and 8360 cm^{-1} while the CH_2 band falls between 8255 and 8220 cm^{-1} and the aromatic CH band between 8740 and 8670 cm^{-1}. The average value for the aromatic C—H was 8710 cm^{-1} which is somewhat less than the 8755 cm^{-1} value previously reported by Hibbard and Cleaves.[7] The bands shown in the approximate range of 4075–4450 cm^{-1} are combination bands of saturated CH_2 and CH_3 groups.

Powers, Harper, and Tai[8] report that aromatic aldehydes are characterized by a band at 4525 cm^{-1}, which is possibly a combination of formyl C—H and of C=O, and two bands at 4445 and 8000 cm^{-1}.

Goddu[9] has reported that terminal methylene groups may be determined at 4740 or 6135 cm^{-1} with a sensitivity within 0.01%. Cis-double bonds may be determined at 4675 cm^{-1} with a sensitivity of about 1%. The trans-isomer has no unique band. Holman and Edmondson[10] have determined cis-unsaturation in nonconjugated fatty acids at 4565, 4675, or 8475 cm^{-1}.

The chart published by Goddu and Delker[3] shows three bands for cyclopropyl compounds. Washburn and Mahoney[11] report for nine cyclopropyl compounds a band in the range 4505–4405 cm^{-1} and a second band in the range 6135–6060 cm^{-1}, undoubtedly the first overtone of the C–H fundamental at approximately 3080 cm^{-1}. The band between 6135 and 6060 cm^{-1} is about five times as intense as the first one mentioned. In a study of sixteen simple cyclopropyl compounds Gassman[12] found that the range was 6160–6060 cm^{-1} and the empirical absorptivity constant (extinction coefficient) is 0.30 for each unsubstituted cyclopropyl methylene group. For example, eleven compounds

[6] A. Evans, R. R. Hibbard, and A. S. Powell, *Anal. Chem.* **23**, 1604 (1951).

[7] R. R. Hibbard and A. P. Cleaves, *Anal. Chem.* **21**, 486 (1949).

[8] R. M. Powers, J. L. Harper, and H. Tai, *Anal. Chem.* **32**, 1287 (1960); correction, *ibid.* **32**, 1598 (1960).

[9] R. F. Goddu, *Anal. Chem.* **29**, 1790 (1957).

[10] R. T. Holman and P. R. Edmondson, *Anal. Chem.* **28**, 1533 (1956).

[11] W. H. Washburn and M. J. Mahoney, *J. Am. Chem. Soc.* **80**, 504 (1958).

[12] P. G. Gassman, *Chem. Eng. News* **40**, 49 (April 9, 1962).

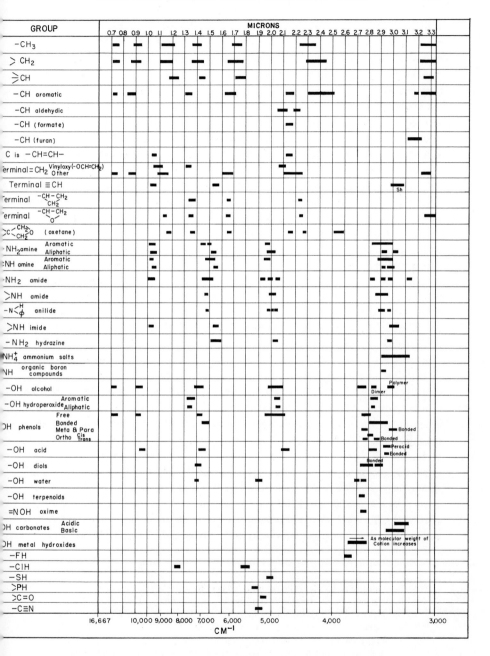

Fig. 13.1.   Correlation chart for the near-infrared region.

with two groups had absorptivity constants of 0.57–0.70 vs. the predicted 0.60. Seven nortricyclenes had peaks between 6010 and 6040 cm⁻¹ and although norbornenes (which lack a cyclopropyl group) absorb in the same region, they can be distinguished because the absorptivity constants are half those of the nortricyclenes.

Goddu and Delker[13] have determined terminal epoxides by measurement of the bands at 4545 and 6060 cm⁻¹. The combination band at 4545 is more intense than the band at 6060 cm⁻¹ which is the first overtone of the C–H stretching vibration of the terminal epoxide group. With regard to N—H bands, Whetsel, Roberson, and Krell,[14] have studied forty primary aromatic amines and have reported intensities for a combination band near 5070 cm⁻¹, the first overtone asymmetric and symmetric stretching bands near 6915 cm⁻¹ and 6700 cm⁻¹ respectively, and the second overtone symmetric near 9810 cm⁻¹. These authors were able to correlate variations in band intensity and position with the electronic nature and position of the substituents on the ring. Solvent effects on the bands at 6700 cm⁻¹ and 5070 cm⁻¹ of aniline, *m*-toluidine, *o*-chloroaniline, and *m*-chloroaniline have also been reported by the same authors.[15] Sauvageau and Sandorfy[16] comment that broad bands between 4600 and 4500 cm⁻¹ serve to identify amine hydrohalides. They assign this band to a combination band of a $\overset{+}{N}H_3$ asymmetric bend with either a $\overset{+}{N}H_3$ stretch or a CH_2 stretch or possibly both.

In connection with O—H absorptions Kaye[4] has done some interesting work on cellulose and its derivatives. He has pointed out that the fundamental vibration at 3300 cm⁻¹ is most advantageous for studying hydrogen bonded OH groups and the overtone region of the free OH band at approximately 7100 cm⁻¹ is better for the study of unbonded compounds. The determination of hydroperoxides (O—O—H groups) at approximately 4810 and 6850 cm⁻¹ has been discussed by Holman and Edmondson.[17,18] The first overtone of the OH stretching band of phenol has been assigned by Wulf, Jones, and Deming[19] to the band at 7050 cm⁻¹. In tri- and penta-halogenated phenols the overtone band is between 6890 and 6760 cm⁻¹ and in *ortho*-halogenated phenols between 6910 and 6805 cm⁻¹. A combination band of medium intensity for mono-, tri-, and penta-halogenated phenols is located between 8250 and 8000 cm⁻¹.

[13] R. F. Goddu and D. A. Delker, *Anal. Chem.* 30, 2013 (1958).

[14] K. B. Whetsel, W. E. Roberson, and M. W. Krell, *Anal. Chem.* 30, 1598 (1958).

[15] K. B. Whetsel, W. E. Roberson, and M. W. Krell, *Anal. Chem.* 32, 1281 (1960).

[16] P. Sauvageau and C. Sandorfy, *Can. J. Chem.* 38, 1901 (1960).

[17] R. T. Holman and P. R. Edmondson, *Anal. Chem.* 28, 1533 (1956).

[18] R. T. Holman, C. Nickell, O. S. Privett, and P. R. Edmondson, *J. Am. Oil Chemists' Soc.* 35, 422 (1958).

[19] O. R. Wulf, E. J. Jones, and L. S. Deming, *J. Chem. Phys.* 8, 753 (1940).

13.26   Carbon-Hydrogen Stretching Region Correlation Chart

This region has been reviewed by Wiberley, Bunce, and Bauer[20] and the main correlations have been covered in previous chapters; so this discussion will be brief. As shown in Fig. 13.2 the CH_3 bands occur at 2960 and 2870 cm^{-1} and the CH_2 bands at 2930 and 2860 cm^{-1}. In many compounds only one band in the region 2870–2860 cm^{-1} can be resolved. In oxygenated and sulfur–containing compounds the methyl and methylene bands are approximately 7 cm^{-1} higher and the extinction coefficients are greater than for the corresponding hydro-

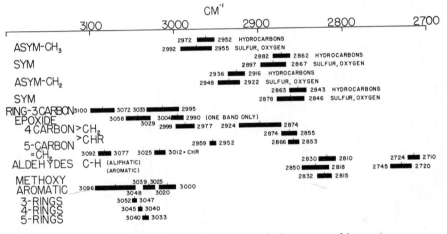

FIG. 13.2.   Correlation chart for the carbon-hydrogen stretching region.

carbons. In a given straight chain homologous series the asymmetric stretching CH_3 band at 2960 cm^{-1} is stronger than the corresponding CH_2 band when the ratio of methylene to methyl groups is 3 to 1 or less. With larger ratios the 2930 cm^{-1} band is more intense although exceptions may occur if the methyl group is adjacent to a carboxyl group.

Cyclopropyl CH_2 bands occur at approximately 3085 cm^{-1} for the unsymmetrical stretching frequency and at 3020 cm^{-1} for the symmetric stretch. Epoxides also have a distinct band above 2990 cm^{-1}. CH_2 groups in a four-membered ring have bands intermediate between the three– and five-membered ring systems. In five-membered rings the symmetric CH_2 band lies in the normal

[20] S. E. Wiberley, S. C. Bunce, and W. H. Bauer, *Anal. Chem.* **32**, 217 (1960).

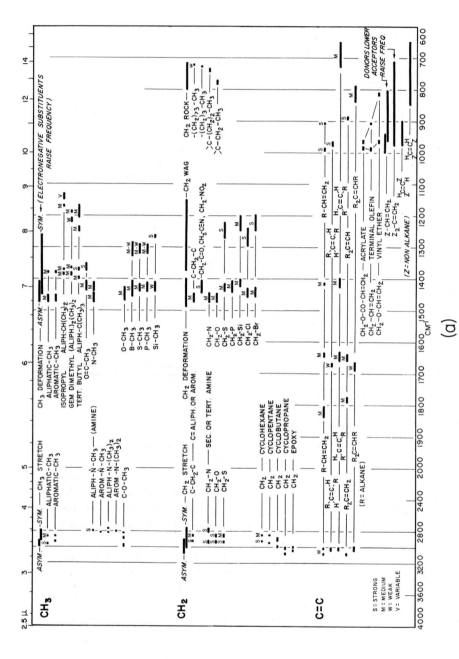

Fig. 13.3(a–f). Correlation charts for the rock salt region.

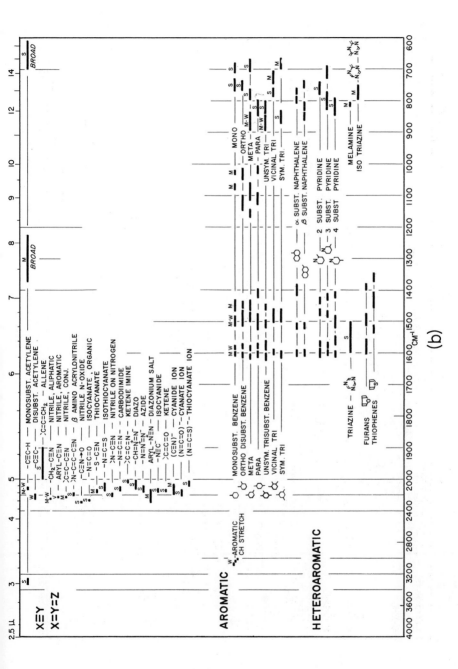

(b)

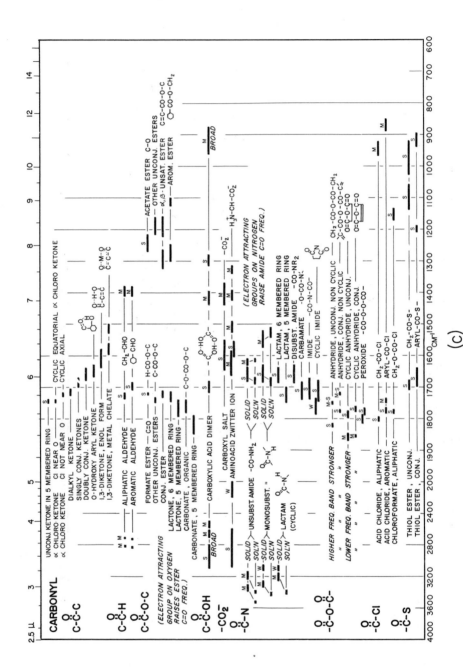

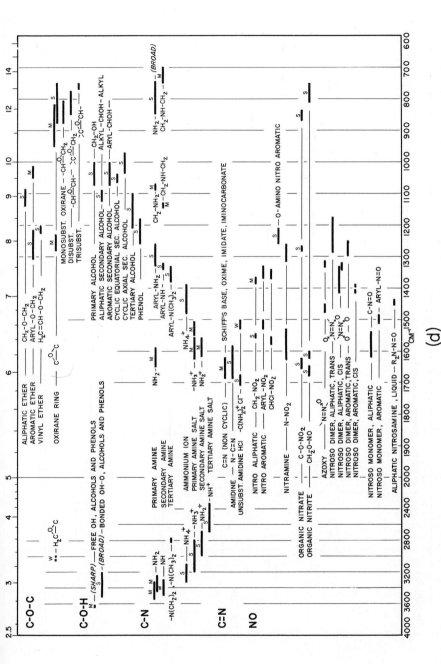

(d)

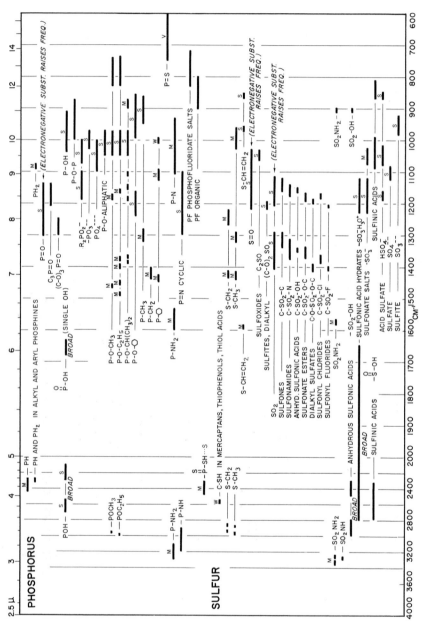

(e)

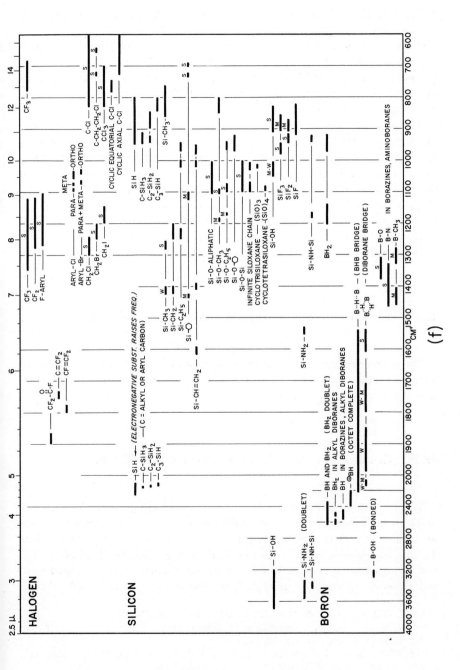

(f)

CH_2 range for straight chain hydrocarbons; however, the unsymmetric CH_2 band occurs at a higher value than the maximum CH_2 range shown for oxygenated and sulfur-containing compounds. The $=CH_2$ group in compounds containing $RHC=CH_2$ groups absorbs from 3192–3077 cm^{-1} while the $=CHR$ group absorbs in the 3025–3012 cm^{-1} range. The CH group in aldehydes gives rise to two bands at approximately 2820 and 2720 cm^{-1}. In aromatic aldehydes the bands occur at somewhat higher values.

Aromatic compounds contain one or more bands between 3100 and 3000 cm^{-1} and hence are readily distinguished from aliphatic compounds. As mentioned, the main exceptions are cyclopropyl derivatives, epoxides, alkenes and compounds such as chloroform where the inductive effect of the chlorine atoms shifts the C-H stretching vibration to 3019 cm^{-1}. In general, for unsubstituted fused rings the aromatic $C-H$ stretching vibration shifts to lower frequencies as the number of fused rings increases. For further details on the spectra of polynuclear aromatic compounds in the $C-H$ stretching region the paper by Wiberley and Gonzalez[21] should be consulted.

13.27 Sodium Chloride Region Correlation Charts

The correlation charts for this region are shown in Fig. 13.3(a–f). Since the previous chapters have discussed this region in great detail, additional comments on these correlations are not warranted.

13.28 Cesium Bromide Region Correlation Charts

A brief discussion of this wavelength region has been prepared by Stewart[22] and a general bibliography has been published by Palik.[23] The correlation charts are divided into three sections: organic [Fig. 13.4(a) and (b)], inorganic [Fig. 13.4(c)], and solvents useful in the far infrared [Fig. 13.4(d)]. The basis for the first section, the organic portion, is a chart for alkanes, alkenes, cycloalkanes, and aromatic compounds published by Bentley and co-authors.[24] Silicone

[21] S. E. Wiberley and R. D. Gonzalez, *J. Appl. Spectry.* 15, 174 (1961).

[22] J. E. Stewart, Beckman Applications Data Sheet 1R–94–MI.

[23] E. D. Palik, *J. Opt. Soc. Am.* 50, 1329 (1960).

[24] F. F. Bentley, E. F. Wolfarth, N. E. Srp, and W. R. Powell, *Spectrochim. Acta* 13, 1 (1958); WADC Technical Report 57–359, September, 1957.

compounds have been arbitrarily placed in the inorganic section although some correlation bands for organosilanes have been included in this section. The band intensities shown on the charts are relative intensities.

(a) ORGANIC SECTION [See Figs. 13.4(a) and (b).]

a. *Alkanes.* The frequencies shown for the normal, branched and substituted alkanes[24] are mostly due to their chain bending. The absorption bands for *n*-alkanes (458–452 cm⁻¹ and 538–485 cm⁻¹) shift to lower wavelengths as the chain length increases. The bands for branched and substituted alkanes are considerably stronger than those of the straight chain alkanes.

Many papers have been published on the halogenated alkanes[25-36] and the results, with relative intensities and types of vibrations are shown on the chart. Edgell and May[31] also report a C—Cl band at 293 cm⁻¹ and a C—I absorption at 286 cm⁻¹ in addition to the ranges indicated on the chart.

b. *Cycloalkanes.* The absorption regions shown are attributed to the non-planar modes of vibration as compared to the planar vibrations in the rock salt region.[37] However, cyclopropane does not absorb in the far infrared and bands which do appear are usually caused by substituents on the ring.

c. *Alkenes.* The alkenes give rise to strong bands in the far infrared with considerable shift in wavelength from *cis*- to *trans*-alkenes.[37] Alkene absorption is generally stronger than alkane absorption.

Information for only one cycloalkene was found in the literature and was not included on the chart. Cyclopentadiene, in various biscyclopentadienyl-metallic compounds, has strong absorption attributed to ring tilting from 478–440 cm⁻¹ and 528–492 cm⁻¹.[38]

[25] J. R. Nielsen, C. Y. Liang, D. C. Smith, and M. Alpert, *J. Chem. Phys.* 21, 1070 (1953).
[26] L. J. Bellamy, "The Infrared Spectra of Complex Molecules." Wiley, New York, 1958.
[27] E. K. Plyler and W. S. Benedict, *J. Res. Natl. Bur. Standards* 47, 202 (1951).
[28] D. C. Smith, G. M. Brown, J. R. Nielsen, R. M. Smith, and C. Y. Liang, *J. Chem. Phys.* 20, 473 (1952).
[29] E. Catalano and K. S. Pitzer, *J. Phys. Chem.* 62, 838 (1958).
[30] J. R. Nielsen, H. H. Claassen, and N. B. Moran, *J. Chem. Phys.* 23, 329 (1955).
[31] W. F. Edgell and C. E. May, *J. Chem. Phys.* 22, 1808 (1954).
[32] P. Klaboe and J. R. Nielsen, *J. Mol. Spectry.* 6, 379 (1961).
[33] J. R. Nielsen, C. Y. Liang, R. M. Smith, and D. C. Smith, *J. Chem. Phys.* 21, 383 (1953).
[34] J. R. Nielsen, C. Y. Liang, and D. C. Smith, *J. Chem. Phys.* 21, 1060 (1953).
[35] I. A. Rao and V. R. Rao, *J. Mol. Spectry.* 6, 447 (1961).
[36] O. Risgin and R. C. Taylor, *Spectrochim. Acta* 15, 1036 (1959).
[37] F. F. Bentley and E. F. Wolfarth, *Spectrochim. Acta* 15, 165 (1959).
[38] E. R. Lippincott, J. Xavier, and D. Steele, *J. Am. Chem. Soc.* 83, 2262 (1961).

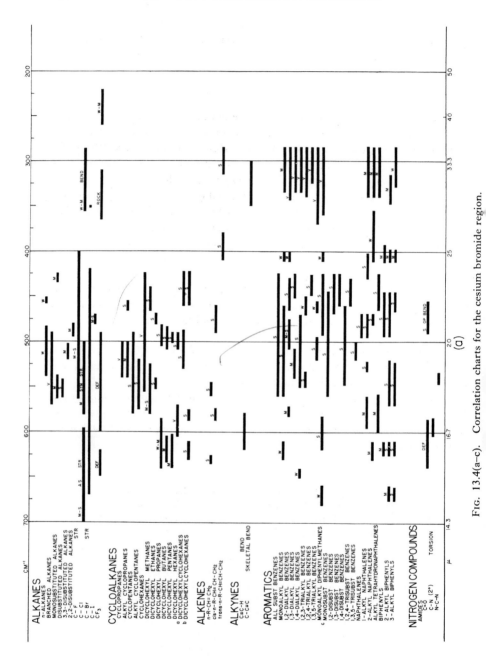

FIG. 13.4(a–c).   Correlation charts for the cesium bromide region.

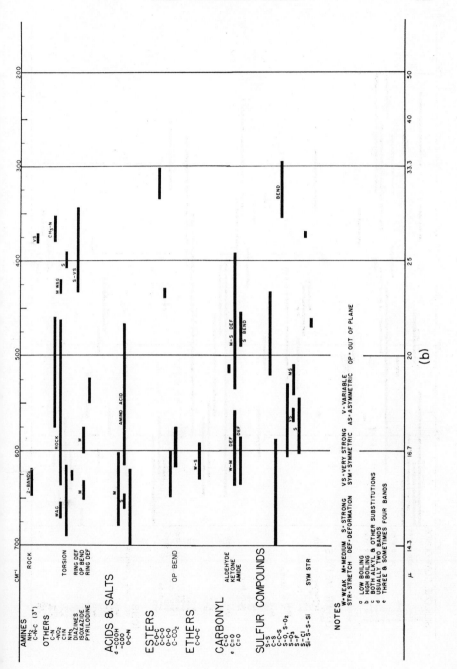

(b)

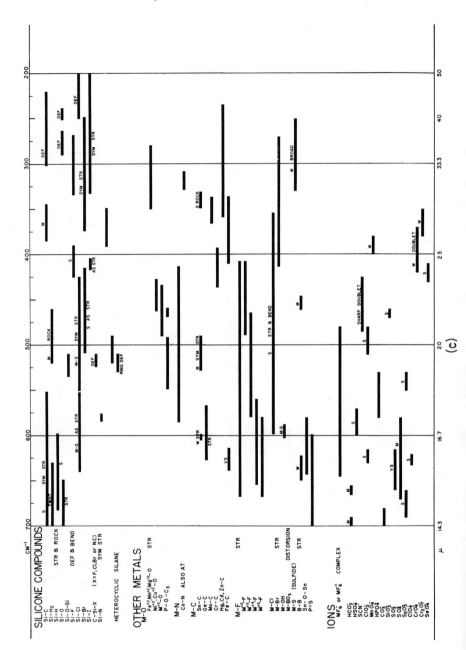

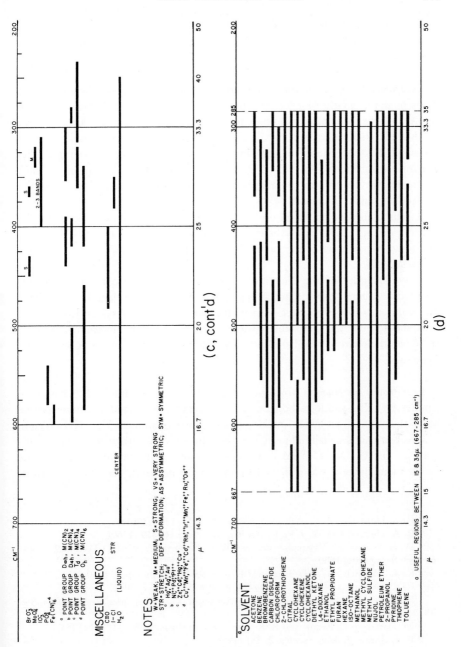

(c, cont'd)

(d)

d. *Alkynes.* The terminal C≡C—H group has been observed in the 618–578 cm^{-1} region.[26,39,40] As in the alkanes, a band attributed to skeletal bend has also been observed.

e. *Aromatics.* Most of the bands are caused by the out-of-plane deformations of the aromatic ring.[37,41–43] The strong band between 571-455 cm^{-1} in the spectra of the monoalkyl benzenes tends to broaden as the molecular weight of the side chain increases. As the size of the alkyl groups increases, the four *o*-dialkyl benzene bands increase in intensity. The strong *m*- and *p*-dialkyl benzene absorptions from 479–450 cm^{-1} and 571–481 cm^{-1} respectively shift to lower wavelengths in the ranges shown and become more intense as the molecular weight increases.

A fourth alkyl substitution on the "5" position does not seem to affect the spectra of the 1,2,3–trialkyl benzenes. The 1,3,5–trialkyl benzenes absorb at the long wavelengths of the range 513–488 cm^{-1} as the molecular weight increases.

The remainder of the aromatic bands follow a similar pattern. *Para*-substituted benzenes absorb more strongly, but at shorter wavelengths, than either the *meta*- or *ortho*-isomers. However, the *para*-bands are less consistent.

It should be noted that some of these bands are variable and are marked with a "v" on the chart. These bands are inconsistent and often do not appear in the spectra.

f. *Nitrogen compounds.* More work has been done with amides[44–48] than with amines.[48,49] The amide carbonyl and C—N regions presented are more reliable than the C-N-C and NH$_2$ rocking regions of the amines. The NH$_2$ region, where two bands usually appear, has been observed for ethylene diamine complexes. The O—N—C band listed under amines is found in trimethylamine oxide[49] and, since it was observed in only one compound, may not be reliable.

[39] G. R. Hunt and M. K. Wilson, *J. Chem. Phys.* **34**, 1301 (1961).

[40] R. A. Nyquist and W. J. Potts, *Spectrochim. Acta* **16**, 419 (1960).

[41] W. S. Wilcox, C. V. Stephenson, and W. C. Coburn, Jr., WADD Technical Report 60–333, September, 1960.

[42] R. J. Jakobsen, WADD Technical Report 60–204, September, 1960.

[43] R. J. Jakobsen, Report No. ASD-TDR-62-895, October, 1962.

[44] R. B. Penland, S. Mizushima, C. Curran, and J. V. Quagliano, *J. Am. Chem. Soc.* **79**, 1575 (1957).

[45] M. Davies, J. C. Evans, and R. L. Jones, *Trans. Faraday Soc.* **51**, 761 (1955).

[46] R. L. Jones, *J. Mol. Spectry.* **2**, 581 (1958).

[47] T. Miyazawa, *J. Mol. Spectry.* **4**, 155 (1960).

[48] A. E. Parsons, *J. Mol. Spectry.* **6**, 201 (1961).

[49] P. A. Giguère and D. Chin, *Can. J. Chem.* **39**, 1214 (1961).

The NO_2 band was observed[50,51] in N_2O_4 and in nitrocomplexes.[52] The band around 400 cm^{-1} for C≡N was observed in octacyano molybdenum, and tungsten complexes and is considerable stronger in anhydrous than in the hydrated complexes.[53] Hexadiaminecobalt(III) halides give rise to the NH_3 band shown on the chart.[54]

Some cyclic nitrogen compounds have been included; 1,2-diazine absorbs at 319 cm^{-1} and 370 cm^{-1}, 1,3-diazine (pyrimidine) has bands at 344 cm^{-1} and 624 cm^{-1}, and 1,4-diazine (pyrazine) absorbs from 432–400 cm^{-1}. These compounds are placed in one range listed as diazines.[55] Pyrrolidone, in addition to the region shown, has a carbonyl band in the same range as the other amides.[48]

g. *Acids.* In a study of the spectra of twenty-eight acids, there was at least one band and usually there were two bands around 665 cm^{-1}. Aluminum di-soaps of twelve of these acids showed a marked decrease in these bands. Furthermore, sodium acetate has a carboxyl band in this region.[56] The amino acid carboxyl band also occurs in this general region.[57] The carboxyl bands from 680–600 cm^{-1} in acids are of medium intensity.

The O—N—C band listed under the acids has been observed in formhydroxamic acid.[58]

h. *Esters.* J. K. Wilmshurst studied the absorption maxima of two esters[59] and assigned the ranges shown. Because of the small number of examples, the reliability and the complete ranges of the bands are not yet known.

i. *Ethers.* The spectra of the seven ethers have been studied by S. Levine at Rensselaer Polytechnic Institute. Six of these ethers have a band in the region from 627–602 cm^{-1}. Since this range seems to agree with the C—O—C of esters[59] and of dimethoxymethane,[60] this range has been tentatively assigned to the C—O—C bending vibration of ethers. However, the reliability of this assignment could be questioned.

[50] R. G. Snyder and I. C. Hisatsune, *J. Mol. Spectry.* 1, 139 (1957).

[51] G. M. Begun and W. H. Fletcher, *J. Mol. Spectry.* 4, 388 (1960).

[52] K. Nakamoto, J. Fujita, and H. Murata, *J. Am. Chem. Soc.* 80, 4817 (1958).

[53] E. G. Brame, Jr., F. A. Johnson, E. M. Larson, and V. W. Meloche, *J. Inorg. and Nucl. Chem.* 6, 99 (1958).

[54] E. P. Bertin, I. Nakagawa, S. Mizushima, T. J. Lane, and J. V. Quagliano, *J. Am. Chem. Soc.* 80, 525 (1958).

[55] R. C. Lord, A. L. Marston, and F. A. Miller, *Spectrochim. Acta* 9, 113 (1957).

[56] L. H. Jones and E. McLaren, *J. Chem. Phys.* 22, 1796 (1954).

[57] M. Tsuboi, T. Onishi, I. Nakagawa, T. Shimanouchi, and S. Mizushima, *Spectrochim. Acta* 12, 253 (1958).

[58] W. J. Orville-Thomas and A. E. Parsons, *J. Mol. Spectry.* 2, 203 (1958).

[59] J. K. Wilmshurst, *J. Mol. Spectry.* 1, 201 (1957).

[60] J. K. Wilmshurst, *Can. J. Chem.* 36, 285 (1958).

j. *Carbonyl.* The 517–509 cm^{-1} aldehyde carbonyl band has been observed only in acetaldehyde[61] in the vapor and solid states.

Bellamy[26] mentions the appearance of ketone carbonyl bands at 400, 500, and 600 cm^{-1}. The spectra of fifteen ketones have been studied by Levine and the bands for twelve more ketones were found in the literature.[62] Combining these results, the regions 557–636 cm^{-1} and 393–535 cm^{-1} have been assigned to the deformation vibrations of the ketonic carbonyl group. Three and sometimes four bands appear in the spectra with the intensity generally being medium to strong although in some cases the third or fourth band may be weak.

The amide carbonyl band is the same as that which has been discussed under amides.

k. *Organosulfur compounds.* The S—S stretching frequency from 430–520 cm^{-1},[26,63–65] and the C—S stretch from 587–708 cm^{-1} have been well studied.[66] A C=S rocking band at 668 cm^{-1} has also been reported.

The thiophosphoryl group absorbs in the rock salt region from 760–710 cm^{-1}.[67]

The SO_2 bands [68–70] at 610–530 cm^{-1} usually appear as a doublet attributed to both rocking and bending motions. The SO_3^- bands have been attributed to SO_3 deformation.[71] The sodium salt of methane sulfonic acid absorbs at 563 and 536 cm^{-1}.

The S—F wag has been studied in only two compounds.[72,73] The S—Cl band is more reliable as it has been observed in many compounds.[64,69]

The Si—S—S—Si linkage in disilyl sulfides produces a band with three branches, which is attributed to symmetric stretching. Asymmetric stretching for this group appears at 515 cm^{-1}.[74]

[61] J. C. Evans and H. J. Bernstein, *Can. J. Chem.* 34, 1083 (1956).
[62] J. Lecomte, M. L. Josien, and J. Lascombe, *Bull. Soc. Chim. France* 1956, 163.
[63] J. Cymerman and J. B. Willis, *J. Chem. Soc.* 1951, 1332.
[64] S. N. Nabi and N. Sheppard, *J. Chem. Soc.* 1959, 3439.
[65] D. W. Scott and J. P. McCullough, *J. Am. Chem. Soc.* 80, 3554 (1958).
[66] C. A. Frenzel, D. W. Scott, and J. P. McCullough, Bureau of Mines Report 5658 (1960).
[67] L. W. Daasch and D. C. Smith, *Anal. Chem.* 23, 853 (1951).
[68] P. A. Giguère and M. Falk, *Can. J. Chem.* 34, 1833 (1956).
[69] N. S. Ham, A. N. Hambly and R. H. Laby, *Australian J. Chem.* 13, 443 (1960).
[70] W. D. Perkins and M. K. Wilson, *J. Chem. Phys.* 20, 1791 (1952).
[71] W. G. Palmer, *J. Chem. Soc.* 1961, 1552.
[72] L. H. Cross, H. L. Roberts, P. Goggin, and L. A. Woodward, *Trans. Faraday Soc.* 56, 945 (1960).
[73] R. E. Dodd, L. A. Woodward, and H. L. Roberts, *Trans. Faraday Soc.* 53, 1545 (1957).
[74] H. R. Linton and E. R. Nixon, *J. Chem. Phys.* 29, 921 (1958).

(b) INORGANIC SECTION [See Fig. 13.4(c)].

The second section of the correlation chart includes the inorganic compounds and ions. Although some of the bands shown have been observed in organic silanes, silicone compounds have been included in this section.

A great number of inorganic compounds and ions have strong absorption bands in the cesium bromide region as well as in the rock salt region and some absorb beyond 250 cm^{-1}. A recent text[75] covers the infrared spectra of inorganic compounds primarily in the rock salt region but some references cited contain data on compounds in the cesium bromide region also.

a. *Silicone compounds.* Because of their ever increasing importance in modern day chemistry, a great deal of work has been done on the silicones. Using Grenoble and Launer[76] and Janz and Mikawa[77] as principal sources of information and reference, many absorption maxima have been found. The three Si—C regions shown on the chart have been observed in many aromatic and aliphatic silanes.[76-83] The strong symmetric stretching region overlaps the rock salt region by extending from 764-555 cm^{-1}, and inclusion of the asymmetric stretch increases this range to 805 cm^{-1}. A second Si—C deformation band appears below 250 cm^{-1}. The Si—H$_2$ twisting region also extends into the rock salt region[76] to 740 cm^{-1} and at lower values is overlapped by the SiH band.[74,84] SiO extends into the rock salt region as far as 851 cm^{-1}.[76]

Of the halogenated silicones, Si—F compounds absorb[85,86] at about 525 cm^{-1} but chlorosilanes have been the most widely studied.[76,77,79,82,87,88] The Si—Cl deformation extends to 169 cm^{-1} and the bond gives rise to another

[75] K. E. Lawson, "Infrared Absorption of Inorganic Substances." Reinhold, New York, 1961.

[76] M. E. Grenoble and P. J. Launer, *Appl. Spectry.* 14, 85 (1960).

[77] G. J. Janz and Y. Mikawa, Unpublished Report, "Silanes. Vibrational Assignments and Frequency Correlations."

[78] G. D. Oshesky and F. F. Bentley, *J. Am. Chem. Soc.* 79, 2057 (1957).

[79] E. A. V. Ebsworth, M. Onyszchuk and N. Sheppard, *J. Chem. Soc.* 1958, 1453.

[80] H. Kriegsmann and K. H. Schowtka, *Z. Physik. Chem.* (*Leipzig*) 209, 261 (1958).

[81] H. R. Linton and E. R. Nixon, *Spectrochim. Acta* 10, 299 (1958).

[82] K. Shimizu and H. Murata, *J. Mol. Spectry.* 4, 201 (1960).

[83] K. Shimizu and H. Murata, *J. Mol. Spectry.* 5, 44 (1960).

[84] E. A. V. Ebsworth, R. Taylor, and L. A. Woodward, *Trans. Faraday Soc.* 55, 211 (1959).

[85] E. A. Jones, J. S. Kirby-Smith, P. J. H. Woltz, and A. H. Nielsen, *J. Chem. Phys.* 19, 242 (1951).

[86] C. Newman, S. R. Polo, and M. K. Wilson, *Spectrochim. Acta* 15, 793 (1959).

[87] N. A. Chumaevskii, *Opt. Spectry.* (*USSR*) (*English Transl.*) 10, 33 (1961).

[88] A. L. Smith, *J. Chem. Phys.* 21, 1997 (1953).

deformation band at lower wavenumbers. The Si—Br bond has two deformation regions beyond 250 cm^{-1}.[77,79,89]

Halogenated phenyl silanes have been studied and the phenylsilicone and triphenyl-silicone bands have been observed.[76,80] It should be noted that the Si—N region may not be reliable as the assignment is based on one compound, tetrasilylhydrazine.

b. *Metal-oxygen.* All of the metal-oxygen regions shown on the chart have been attributed to the stretching motion of the M—O bond. The Fe^{2+}, Mn^{2+}, Mg^{2+}—O bands were observed in the spectra of garnets. Ionic Ca—O bonds do not give rise to discrete bands in the far infrared.[90] The M—O bands were studied in the spectra of metal(III) acetylacetonates.[91-93] and benzoylacetonates.[93]

c. *Metal-nitrogen.* This band has been studied in various complexes.[52,54,94,95] The M(III)—N bonds usually absorb at the higher end of the range 585–413 cm^{-1} for M—N stretch. In addition to a band in this range, a second band for Co—N has been observed in the 328–308 cm^{-1} region.

d. *Metal-carbon.* Much work has been done on organo-tin compounds[96-99] and the three regions shown on the chart have been observed for the Sn—C absorptions. Because tin and germanium are in the same family, it might be expected that their spectra would be somewhat similar. As can be seen on the chart, both have a band around 600 cm^{-1} but the Ge—C region[96] is larger than the Sn—C region. The Mo—C and Cr—C bands were observed in the spectra of octahedral complexes of the type $M(XY)_6$.[100]

Zn—C has two bands at 315 cm^{-1} and 359 cm^{-1}; Cd—C has two at 316 cm^{-1} and 250 cm^{-1}; and Hg—C has two at 330 cm^{-1} and 235 cm^{-1}. The bands were observed in solid $K_2M(CN)_4$ complexes[101] and this IIB family has been presented

[89] D. W. Mayo, H. E. Opitz, and J. S. Peake, *J. Chem. Phys.* **23**, 1344 (1955).

[90] P. Tarte, *Nature* **186**, 234 (1960).

[91] C. Djordjevic, *Spectrochim. Acta* **17**, 448 (1961).

[92] K. Nakamoto, P. J. McCarthy, A. Ruby, and A. E. Martell, *J. Am. Chem. Soc.* **83**, 1066 (1961).

[93] K. Nakamoto, P. J. McCarthy, and A. E. Martell, *Nature* **183**, 459 (1959).

[94] D. B. Powell and N. Sheppard, *Spectrochim. Acta* **17**, 68 (1961).

[95] D. B. Powell and N. Sheppard, *J. Chem. Soc.* **1961**, 1112.

[96] M. P. Brown, R. Okawara, and E. G. Rochow, *Spectrochim. Acta* **16**, 595 (1960).

[97] C. R. Dillard and J. R. Lawson, *J. Opt. Soc. Am.* **50**, 1271 (1960).

[98] W. F. Edgell and C. H. Ward, *J. Am. Chem. Soc.* **77**, 6486 (1955).

[99] M. C. Tobin, *J. Mol. Spectry.* **5**, 65 (1960).

[100] H. Murata and K. Kawai, *J. Chem. Phys.* **27**, 605 (1957).

[101] L. H. Jones, *Spectrochim. Acta* **17**, 188 (1961).

in one range headed Hg, Zn, Cd—C. Fe—C bands were observed in iron carbonyl spectra.[102–104] A band for Co—C has been observed at 528–526 cm^{-1} and at 390 cm^{-1} but is not on the chart.

As one can observe, no over-all general range can be assigned to the metal-carbon frequencies. As more work is done, it is possible that general ranges for the M—C bond for a family of metals can be assigned as has been done for Periodic Group IIB family. Two members of the VIB Group (Cr, Mo) and the IVA Group (Be, Sn) have been included in this section.

It should be noted that some papers which list one band at one wavelength have been published but not referred to because no range for that particular M–C band could be obtained.

e. *Metal-fluorine.* Peacock and Sharp[105] have done extensive work with metal fluoride complexes. The M^{2+}—F region is 489–407 cm^{-1}, M^{3+}—F is 579–464 cm^{-1}, M^{4+}–F is 654–560 cm^{-1}, and M^{5+}—F is 580–667 cm^{-1}. With the band from the lithium fluoride dimer,[106] NF_3 and PF_3 having been observed[107], the over-all M—F range is 667–407 cm^{-1}.

f. *Metal-chlorine.* The M—Cl band has been observed in the spectra of many metal chlorides[26,106,109–112] leading to the large 597–354 cm^{-1} range shown with one band being reported at 293 cm^{-1}.[110] Most compounds show two bands in this region, one attributed to stretch and the other to bend.

There are many variations in this region; so the M—Cl range can not be broken down as the M—F range was. Although there are many exceptions, the heavier metals seem to absorb at the lower end of the range.

g. *Metal-bromine.* Metal bromides have not been as extensively studied[106,108,113] as the chlorides. The M—Br stretching region, 271–413 cm^{-1}, in which two bands usually appear, overlaps to a large extent into the M—Cl region.

h. *Metal-hydroxide.* The spectra of eleven metal hydroxides were observed but water masked any bands which may have appeared in all but the three

---

[102] W. G. Fateley and E. R. Lippincott, *ibid.* **10**, 8 (1957).

[103] M. F. O'Dwyer, *J. Mol. Spectry.* **2**, 144 (1958).

[104] R. K. Sheline and K. S. Pitzer, *J. Am. Chem. Soc.* **72**, 1107 (1950).

[105] R. D. Peacock and D. W. A. Sharp, *J. Chem. Soc.* **1959**, 2762.

[106] W. Klemperer and W. G. Norris, *J. Chem. Phys.* **34**, 1071 (1961).

[107] M. K. Wilson and S. R. Polo, *ibid.* **20**, 1716 (1952).

[108] F. A. Miller and W. K. Baer, *Spectrochim. Acta* **17**, 112 (1961).

[109] F. A. Miller, G. L. Carlson, and W. B. White, *Spectrochim. Acta* **15**, 709 (1959).

[110] F. A. Miller and G. L. Carlson, *Spectrochim. Acta* **16**, 1148 (1960).

[111] A. Büchler and W. Klemperer, *J. Chem. Phys.* **29**, 121 (1958).

[112] J. K. Wilmshurst, *J. Mol. Spectry.* **5**, 343 (1960).

[113] F. A. Miller and G. L. Carlson, *Spectrochim. Acta* **16**, 6 (1960).

listed (Ba, Cu, Zn). The only band consistent to all three hydroxides was between 588 and 602 cm^{-1}. Because of the small number of examples and lack of proof such as deuteration shifts, the assignment of this band to a M—OH vibration is very tentative.

i. *Metal-borate.* Lippincott and Weir[114] observed the spectra of fourteen metal borates mainly of the rare earth metals. The range shown on the chart (588–551 cm^{-1}) has been assigned to a distortion vibration.

j. *Metal-sulfur.* The evaporated layers on polyethylene of ZnS and CdS have been studied.[115] The spectra of eleven metal sulfides, three of which were too highly colored to transmit, were observed. Six of eight sulfides which transmitted light gave a weak broad band in the same regions as CdS and ZnS. This region (357–251 cm^{-1}) has been tentatively assigned to the M—S stretching frequency of sulfides. All the sulfides observed gave one or two bands between 586 and 654 cm^{-1} but no definite assignment has been given to this region.

k. *Miscellaneous.* Decaborane gives rise to two bands between 446 and 461 cm^{-1} and three between 623 and 649 cm^{-1}.[116] All have been attributed to B—B stretch.

Only one alkyl tin oxide was measured to obtain the assignment given for the Sn—O—Sn region[96] causing the reliability to be very questionable.

The P=S band presented on the chart overlaps into the rock salt region to 840 cm^{-1} according to Bellamy.[26]

l. *Ions.* Eleven alkali salts of complex fluorides were studied and the MF_6^- or MF_6^{2-} bands were observed from 645–480 cm^{-1}.[105] The MF_6^- ion absorbs from 645–524 cm^{-1} and MF_6^{2-} ion in the rest of the region. FeF_6^{2-} absorbs between 492 and 458 cm^{-1}.

Two hundred and eight inorganic compounds were studied in order to obtain ranges for the anions shown.[117] Various minerals were studied[118] and Bellamy[26] reports the SO_4^{2-} band also.

It is reported that the ranges for MnO_4^-, CO_3^{2-}, and PO_4^{3-} are not reliable but no explanation is given. The ranges for the $B_4O_7^-$, HCO_3^-, HSO_4^-, SeO_4^-, ClO_3^-, BrO_3^-, IO_3^-, MoO_4^{2-}, WO_4^{2-}, and $Fe(CN)_6^{4-}$ anions were found in only two or three compounds.

[114] C. E. Weir and E. R. Lippincott, *J. Res. Natl. Bur. Standards* **65A**, 173 (1961).

[115] A. Mitsuishi, H. Yoshinaga, and S. Fujita, *J. Phys. Soc. Japan* **13**, 1235 (1958).

[116] W. E. Keller and H. L. Johnston, *J. Chem. Phys.* **20**, 1749 (1952).

[117] F. A. Miller, G. L. Carlson, F. F. Bentley, and W. H. Jones, *Spectrochim. Acta* **16**, 135 (1960).

[118] J. M. Hunt, M. P. Wisherd, and L. C. Bonham, *Anal. Chem.* **22**, 1478 (1950).

The NH_4^+, NO_2^-, NO_3^-, and CN^{-1} are transparent in the 700–300 cm^{-1} range.[117] However, a band attributed to NH_3^+ torsion at 516 cm^{-1} has been reported for α-glycine.[57]

Hidalgo and Mathieu[119] have observed a band attributed to the cations in their cyanide complexes. The intensity varies greatly throughout the range and therefore, is not indicated on the chart.

It should be noted that the complexes were separated into their appropriate point groups and cations are shown on the chart in this manner.

m. *Miscellaneous bands.* The range shown for the C=O bond had been observed in the various carbonyls.[102,120] Certain iodine monochloride complexes give rise to the I—Cl band on the chart.[121]

Liquid water absorbs throughout the entire CsBr region[122] but atmospheric water has many distinct bands which are valuable for calibration purposes.

(c) SOLVENT SECTION [See Fig. 13.4(d).]

The third and final section of this chart lists twenty-six solvents and their useful regions in the 650–250 cm^{-1} range. Only cyclohexanol, methanol, and 2-propanol as well as Nujol[24] are valuable over this entire range. Many solvents[123] are transparent from 500 to 250 cm^{-1} and the rest have smaller ranges in which they are transparent.

13.29 Selected Infrared Spectra Illustrating Functional Group Frequencies

(a) PURPOSE OF THE SPECTRA

This collection of infrared spectra was run on an NaCl prism spectrometer. It does not pretend to be a complete library of spectra by any means. Its purpose is to provide one or two examples of most of the important functional group frequencies used in qualitative analysis. These are labeled directly on the spectra.

Since these spectra are not nearly enough to establish group frequencies by correlations in most cases, the order of the spectra has been arranged so the group

[119] A. Hidalgo and J. P. Mathieu, *Compt. rend.* **249**, 233 (1959).

[120] E. A. Jones and T. G. Burke, *J. Chem. Phys.* **18**, 1308 (1950).

[121] W. B. Person, R. E. Humphrey, W. A. Deskin, and A. I. Popov, *J. Am. Chem. Soc.* **80**, 2049 (1958).

[122] E. K. Plyler and N. Acquista, *J. Opt. Soc. Am.* **44**, 505 (1954).

[123] P. Torkington and H. W. Thompson, *Trans. Faraday Soc.* **41**, 184 (1945).

frequency assignments given will seem reasonable by interspectral comparisons. The per cent transmission coordinate has been condensed to facilitate inter-spectral comparisons and to maximize the total number of spectra presented. The spectra are not intended to be used for quantitative analysis and not suitable for this purpose.

In a few cases, enough spectra are presented of a group to illustrate a group frequency correlation. Examples of this would include groups such as methyl, tertiary butyl, phenyl and a few others. Spectra 1–12 illustrate a spectra-structure correlation of a long chain aliphatic group.

(b) SPECTRAL PRESENTATION

The spectrum number is given in the upper left corner of each spectrum. In the lower left corner is given the sample thickness or preparation, explanations of which are given below.

.015	liquid, .015 mm thick
.17, .01	liquid, two thicknesses, .17 mm and .01 mm
cap	liquid between plates without spacers
smear	viscous liquid, between plates without spacers
10 cm, 25 mm	gas run in 10 cm cell at 25 mm pressure
.08 M, CCl_4–CS_2, 1 mm	solution, .08 M concentration in 1 mm cell run in CCl_4 from 4000–1300 cm^{-1} and in CS_2 from 1400–650 cm^{-1}, solvent bands compensated
N	solid run as Nujol mull, Nujol bands marked N
N, HC	solid run as a Nujol mull and a halocarbon mull, halocarbon used only, at 3100–2750, and 1490–1350 cm^{-1}, the rest of the spectrum being that of the Nujol mull
N, HCBD	same as above substituting hexachlorobutadiene for halocarbon (both are satisfactory)
N, melt	same as above substituting a melted and resolidified film for HC or HCBD
KBr	solid run in a KBr pressed pellet
molten	low melting solid run in the liquid molten state
melt	solid run as a melted and resolidified film

(c) BAND ASSIGNMENT

The assignments on the spectra are for the most part, those discussed and referenced in the text. The description of the vibrations are necessarily brief. A description such as "C—O stretch" does not necessarily mean that the C—O bond stretches while the rest of the molecule stands still. It implies that the vibration giving rise to the band involves stretching of the C—O bond but may involve other bonds as well.

Certain vibrations have been drawn out with arrows representing in plane motion and "plus" and "minus" signs indicating out of plane motion.

In some cases such as the phenyl group (ϕ), the whole group is indicated as being the origin of the band rather than always specifying the vibration within the group.

A dotted line in the description "OH def – – – C—O str" implies interaction so that at least to some extent, both bands involve both OH deformation and C—O stretch.

In some cases where vertain vibrations are inactive in the infrared, the Raman frequency of the vibration in question is indicated.

Significant infrared bands beyond the NaCl region such as C—Br and C—I bands are indicated on the spectra.

The abbreviations used include:

asym asymmetric
sym symmetric
str stretch
def deformation-scissors motion of an NH_2 or CH_2 group
wag a bending motion out of the plane of the group
rk rock–a bending motion in the plane of the group in the CH_2 case; in the CH_3 case, a rotation of the CH_3 group opposed by counter motion of the attached atom
adj adjacent-applied to hydrogens on neighboring carbon atoms in an aromatic ring
ar aromatic ring

(d) TABLE OF CONTENTS OF FUNCTIONAL GROUPS ILLUSTRATED IN THE SPECTRA

The number of the spectrum which is the primary example of a given functional group is given to the left of the group. Due to the fact that most molecules contain more than one functional group, secondary examples are given as cross references after the functional group.

1–39 Aliphatic Groups

1–12 long chain aliphatic group attached to various other functional groups, cf. 73, 191, 192, 215, 220, 232, 251, 481–485
13–14 short chain CH_2 group, cf. 16
13–14 methyl group on carbon, cf. 1–12, 31, 75–78, 83, 85–98, 102-104
14 gem dimethyl group on carbon

15   isopropyl group, cf. 300, 522, 523, 595–597
16   tertiary butyl group, cf. 51, 59, 106, 129, 130, 137, 138, 142–144, 301, 323, 534
17   methyl group on oxygen, cf. 44, 56, 150, 151
18   methyl group on nitrogen, cf. 57, 58
19   methyl group on iodine
—   methyl group on silicon, cf. 473, 474, 479
—   methyl group on phosphorus, cf. 495, 498
—   methyl group on sulfur, cf. 55, 61, 338, 518, 519, 536, 540, 556, 561
20–30   the group $Z-CH_2-CH_2-Z$ where Z represents different functional groups
31–33   cyclic CH_2 (6, 5, and 4 membered ring) cf. 20, 81, 84, 116–118, 303
34–39   cyclopropane ring

40–63 Triple Bonds

40   acetylene, monosubstituted, conjugated, cf. 26
42, 43 acetylene, monosubstituted, conjugated with aryl group
44   acetylene, monosubstituted, conjugated with double bond
45   acetylene, monosubstituted, conjugated with carbonyl
41, 47 acetylene, symmetrically disubstituted
46   acetylene, unsymmetrically disubstituted
48–49   nitrile, unconjugated, cf. 27, 33, 34, 494–497, 543, 547, 620
48–49 $CH_2-C\equiv N$, cf. 27
50–52   nitrile with electronegative group in the α position
53–54   nitrile, conjugated, cf. 101–104, 343–346, 395, 396
55–57   nitrile, conjugated, with group in the β position, cf. 111, 112
58   nitrile on nitrogen
59–60   isocyanide
61   thiocyanate, organic
62   cyanide, inorganic
63   diazonium group

64–72 Cumulated Double Bonds $X=Y=Z$

64   allene group
65   isocyanate, organic
66   isothiocyanate, organic
67   cyanate, inorganic
68   thiocyanate, inorganic
69   carbodiimide
70–71   azide
72   diazoacetate

73–84 Carbon-Carbon Double Bonds

73–74   vinyl group, cf. 25, 53, 79, 110, 198, 221, 252, 263, 264, 283, 311, 475, 541, 550, 572, 573
75   trans disubstituted ethylene, cf. 57, 111, 200, 201, 378
76   cis disubstituted ethylene, cf. 55, 56, 81, 112, 202
77   vinylidene group (1,1-disubstituted ethylene), cf. 54, 80, 113, 124, 199
78   trisubstituted double bond
79–80   double bond, aryl conjugated
81–84   cyclic double bond

85–104 Aromatic Rings

85–96   benzene ring, methyl substituted, o, m, p, etc.
85   monosubstituted benzene, cf. 32, 42, 43, 60, 63, 65, 66, 79, 80, 101, 114, 115, 135, 136, 148, 149, 160, 165, 167, 172, 203, 204, 222, 233, 305–309, 354, 465–472, 487–492, 621, 622
86   o-disubstituted benzene, cf. 102, 150, 159, 161, 286, 355, 358, 535, 574–578, 580, 581, 604, 605, 610
87   m-disubstituted benzene, cf. 103, 223, 356, 359, 582, 583, 606, 607, 611
88   p-disubstituted benzene, cf. 71, 104, 137, 151, 162, 275, 276, 357, 360, 366, 446, 448, 534, 558, 560, 564, 584, 585, 608, 609, 612
89–96   more highly substituted benzene ring, cf. 138
97–100 condensed rings, cf. 365
101–104 benzonitrile, methyl substituted

105–124 Ethers and Related C—O—C Groups

105–106 ether, aliphatic, unbranched and branched on α carbon, cf. 3, 18, 21, 224, 225
107–109 orthoformate, orthoacetate, acetal
110–113 vinyl ether, cf. 44
114–115 aromatic ether, cf. 150, 151
116–118 cyclic ether, (6,5, and 4 membered ring) cf. 21
119–124 epoxy ring

125–141 Alcohols, Phenols and Related OH Compounds

125–126 primary alcohol, cf. 4, 229, 403, 586
127–128 secondary alcohol, cf. 226–228
129–130 tertiary alcohol, cf. 170
131–132 cyclic secondary alcohol
133–134 cyclic tertiary alcohol

135–138   phenol, cf. 161, 162
139–140   poly–ol, cf. 23
141   water

142–144 Peroxides

142   hydroperoxide
143   peroxide
144   perester

145–151 Aldehydes

145–146   aldehyde, aliphatic, cf. 5
147   aldehyde, electronegative substituent
148–151   aldehyde, conjugated
150   benzaldehyde, *ortho* substituted

152–177 Ketones

152–155   ketone, aliphatic, cf. 28
152–153 $CH_3-C=O$, cf. 155–157, 160–164, 171, 180–185
153–156 $CH_2-C=O$, cf. 145, 173–177
156   ketone, α chloro
157   ketone, conjugated
158   ketone, doubly conjugated
159   ketone, doubly conjugated in strained ring
160   ketone, aromatic
161–169   ketone, hydrogen bonded and conjugated (hydroxy acetophenones, enols of 1,3 diketones, tropolone, etc.)
170   ketone-alcohol
171–172   1,2 diketone
173–177   ketone, cyclic (8-4 membered rings)

178–218 Esters

178–179   formate
178       $CH_3-O-C=O$ cf. 180, 186, 189, 190, 198-200, 205-207
179       $C_2H_5-O-C=O$ cf. 45, 181, 191, 194, 196, 197, 201–203, 208
– $n-C_3H_7-O-C=O$ cf. 187
180–181   acetate
182–183   acetate, branched substituent
184–185   acetate, election withdrawing substituent cf. 52, 144
186–187   propionate
188   butyrate

189   isobutyrate
190–192   long chain ester, cf. 7
193   α chloro ester, election withdrawing substituent
194   oxalate
195   dithio oxalate
196   malonate
197   succinate
198   acrylate
199   methacrylate
200   crotonate
201   fumarate
202   maleate
203   benzoate
204   thiobenzoate
205   phthalate
206   isophthalate
207   terephthalate
208   carbonate, (organic)
209–210   xanthate ester and salt
211   trithio carbonate, (organic)
212–215   cyclic lactones (6–4 membered rings)
216–217   cyclic carbonate
218   cyclic trithio carbonate
—   propiolate cf. 46
—   diazoacetate cf. 72
—   peracetate cf. 144
—   acetoacetate cf. 169

219–241 Carboxylic Acids and Salts

219–223   carboxylic acid dimer, cf. 6, 46, 47
224–229   carboxylic acid with alternate hydrogen bonded forms, cf. 238, 239
230   carboxylic acid, electronegative substituent
231–234   carboxyl salt
235–237   amino acid zwitter ion
238–239   amino acid hydrochloride
240   carbonate salt
241   bicarbonate salt

242–248 Anhydrides

242–243   anhydride, noncyclic, unconjugated
244–245   anhydride, noncyclic, conjugated

246   anhydride, cyclic, unconjugated
247–248   anhydride, cyclic, conjugated

249–265 Amides and Related Compounds

249–256   amide, unsubstituted, cf. 378, 587
254   thio amide, unsubstituted
257–259   amide, N-monosubstituted, noncyclic
260–261   amide, N-monosubstituted, cyclic lactam
262   amide, N-disubstituted
263–264   lactam, N-vinyl
265   hydroxamic acid

266–270 Carbamates

266–267   carbamate, N-unsubstituted
268   carbamate, N-monosubstituted
269   thiocarbamate, N-monosubstituted
270   carbamate, cyclic

271–281 Ureas

271   urea, monosubstituted
272–273   urea, N,N-disubstituted
274–277   urea, N,N′–disubstituted
276   urea, N,N′-disubstituted with electron withdrawing group
278–281   thio urea

282–291 Imides and Related Compounds

282–283   imide, noncyclic
284–286   imide, cyclic
287–288   hydantoin
289   N-acetyl benzamide
290   biuret
291   dithiobiuret

292–297 Chloro Carbonyl Compounds

292–293   acid chloride, unconjugated
294   acid chloride, aryl conjugated
295–296   chloroformate
297   chloroformamide

298–320 Amines and Amine Salts

298–301   primary amine, aliphatic cf. 24
302–303   secondary amine, aliphatic cf. 22
304   tertiary amine, aliphatic cf. 17
305   aniline, N-unsubstituted, cf. 358-360, 535, 581, 583, 585
306–307   aniline, N-monosubstituted
308–309   aniline, N-disubstituted
310   ethylene imine
311   N-vinyl, aromatic amine
312   hydroxyl amine
313   ammonium ion
314–315   primary amine salt, aliphatic cf. 235–239
316   secondary amine salt, aliphatic
317   tertiary amine salt, aliphatic cf. 234
318   quaternary amine salt, aliphatic
319–320   aniline salt cf. 516, 517

321–353 C=N Compounds

321–323   C=N aliphatic substituents
324   C=N aromatic substituents
325–327   oxime
328–329   amide oxime
330–332   imidate
331   imidate salt
333   imino carbonate
334–335   amidine salt
336   substituted formamidine
337   iso urea salt
338   iso thiourea salt
339–340   guanidines and salt
345   iso urea, N–cyano
346   iso thiourea, N-cyano
347–483   biguanide and salt
349–350 $S_2C=N$ and salt
351–353   cyclic $N=C-N$

354–373 N=O Compounds

354–360   nitro, aromatic cf. 276, 386, 387
361–362   nitro, aliphatic cf. 367
363   nitrate, organic cf. 8
364   nitramine

365–367   C-nitroso group
368   nitrite, organic cf. 9
369–371   N-nitroso group
372   nitrate ion
373   nitrite ion

374–381 N=N Compounds

374–375   azo group
376   azoxy group
377–379   azo carbonyl compounds
380–381   N—N=N

382–423 Nitrogen Heteroaromatics

382–390   pyridine rings
383   pyridine hydrochloride
384–385   pyridine, N-oxide
391–394   quinolines and isoquinolines
395–396   pyrimidines
397   pyridazides
398   pyrazines
399–418   s-triazines, normal (3 double bonds in ring) and iso (one or more external double bonds), cf. 579
419–423   s-tetrazines, symmetrically and unsymmetrically substituted

424–441 Five Membered Rings with Two Double Bonds

424–426   cyclopentadiene derivatives, cf. 167
427–430   furan and thiophene rings
431–441   rings containing 1, 2, 3, and 4 nitrogens

442–465 Boron Compounds

442–443   borane
442–443   B—H cf. 453–455, 457, 461
444   boric acid
444–451   B—O cf. 452, 454
445–446   boronic acid
447–448   boroxole
449–451   borate ester
452–455   coordinated boron and boron salt
456–461   borazine
456–464   B—N
459–460   B—Cl cf. 464, 465
462–464   amino borane
464–465   chloro borane

466–480 Silicon Compounds

466–468	SiH_3 , SiH_2 , and SiH
466–472	Si-phenyl
469	Si—OH
470	Si—NH_2
471	siloxane (mono)
472–473	Si—Cl
473–474	Si $(CH_3)_3$
474	Si—NH—Si
475	Si-vinyl
476	silicate ester
477	trisiloxane, cyclic
478	tetrasiloxane, cyclic
479	siloxane polymer
480	silica gel

481–531 Phosphorus Compounds

481–483	phosphine, aliphatic
481	PH_2 cf. 487, 494
482	PH cf. 485–488, 500, 509, 516
481–486	CH_2—P cf. 493–497, 507, 508, 510–515, 520, 521
484–485	phosphine oxide, aliphatic
484–485	P=O cf. 490, 496, 498, 500-503, 505, 507-514, 526, 527
486	phosphine sulfide, aliphatic
486	P=S, cf. 491, 497, 506, 520, 522, 524, 525
487–489	phosphine, aromatic
487–492	P-phenyl, cf. 498, 509, 516, 526–528
490	phosphine oxide, aromatic
491	phosphine sulfide, aromatic
492	phosphonium salt
493	P-ethyl
495	P-methyl cf. 498
494–497	cyanoethyl phosphine, oxide, and sulfide
498	dimethyl phenyl phosphine oxide
499–500	CH_3—O—P cf. 510, 519, 524, 525
501	C_2H_5—O—P cf. 507, 616–619
502–503	n-C_4H_9—O—P cf. 506
—	$(CH_3)_2CH$—O—P cf. 522, 523
503	P—O—P cf. 512
504–505	phenyl-O—P
500–503	C—O—P=O cf. 505, 507

506   dithio phosphoric acid ester
507   phosphinate ester
508–512   phosphinic acid and other POOH acids
513–514   phosphonic acid
515–519   acid salts
518–519 CH_3-S-P
520–523   dithio acids and salts
524   thiophosphoryl chloride
525–528 $P-N$
529–531   inorganic salts

532–578 Sulfur Compounds

532   mercaptan
533–535   thiophenol
536–539   sulfides and disulfides, aliphatic
536   CH_3-S cf. 540, 542, 556, 561
537–538 C_2H_5-S
540   sulfide, phenyl
541   sulfide, vinyl
542–544   sulfoxide
545–546   sulfite ester
545–546   alkyl-$O-S$ cf. 552, 555, 565
547–558 $-SO_2-$
547–548   sulfone
549–551   sulfonamide
550   vinyl on oxidized sulfur
552   sulfonate ester
553–554   sulfonyl chloride
555   sulfate ester
556–558   sulfonic acid, anhydrous
559–560   sulfonic acid, hydrate
561–564   sulfonic acid salt
565   alkyl sodium sulfate
566   sulfinic acid salt
567–570   inorganic sulfate, bisulfate, sulfite and bisulfite
571–578   thiazole ring
571–572 $C=S$ cf. 209, 211, 218, 254, 269, 278–281, 291, 412, 415, 575

579–588 Fluorine Compounds

579–585 CF_3group, cf. 230, 234, 256
586   CF_2 group cf. 587
587   trifluoro vinyl group

588   NF
—   F-aryl cf. 610–612

589–614 Chlorine, Bromine, and Iodine Compounds

589–591   chloromethanes
592–594   *n*-alkyl halides cf. 10–12, 19, 29, 30
595–597   isopropyl halides
598–600   benzyl halides
601–603   other C—Cl groups cf. 36–39, 49, 50, 147, 156, 193, 255, 399–401
604–612   aryl halides cf. 275, 375, 376, 580, 582, 584
613–614   chlorate and bromate ions

615–620 Metal Carbonyls

615   metal carbonyl
616–619   metal carbonyl–phosphorus complexes
620   bridged metal carbonyl

621–622 Arsenic Compounds

623–624 Tin Compounds

Inorganic Ions

62	$C{\equiv}N^-$
63	BF_4^-
67	NCO^-
68	NCS^-
240	CO_3^{2-}
241	HCO_3^-
313, 521	NH_4^+
372	NO_3^-
373	NO_2^-
455	BH_4^-
529	PO_4^{3-}
530	HPO_4^{2-}
531	$H_2PO_4^-$
567, 320, 348	SO_4^{2-}
568	HSO_4^-
569	SO_3^{2-}
570	HSO_3^-
613	ClO_3^-
614	BrO_3^-

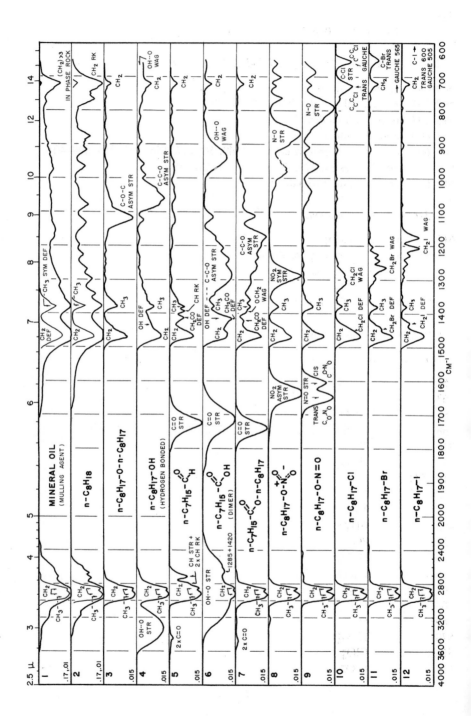

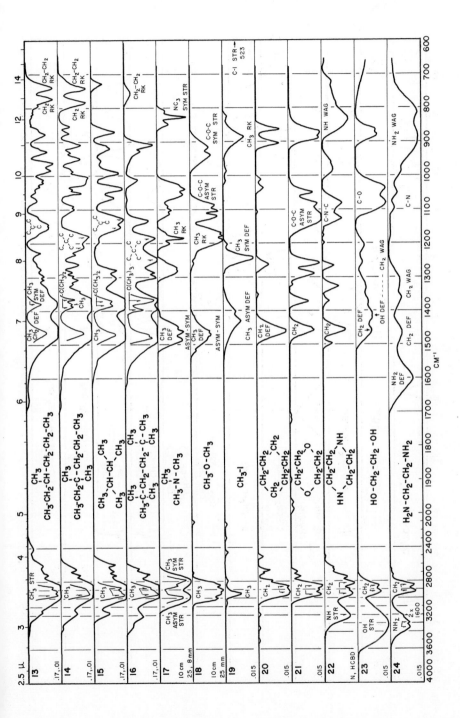

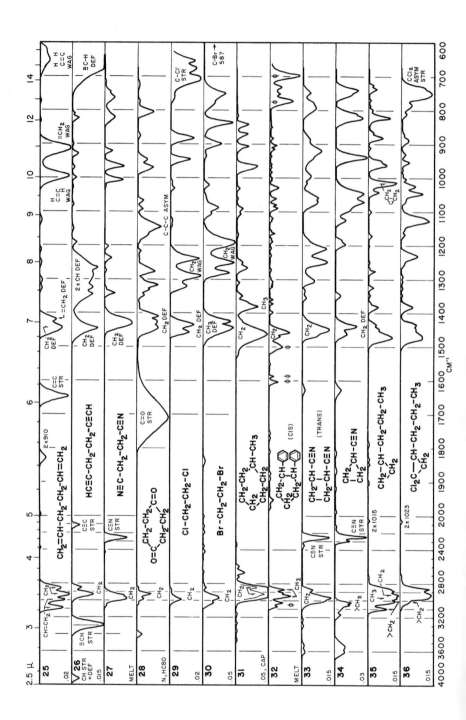

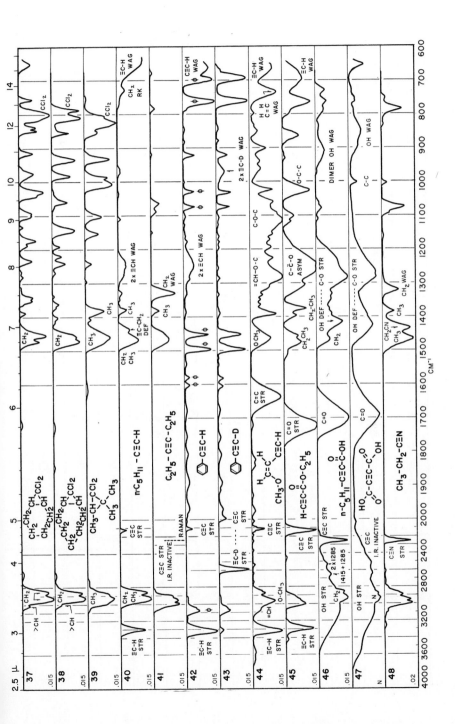

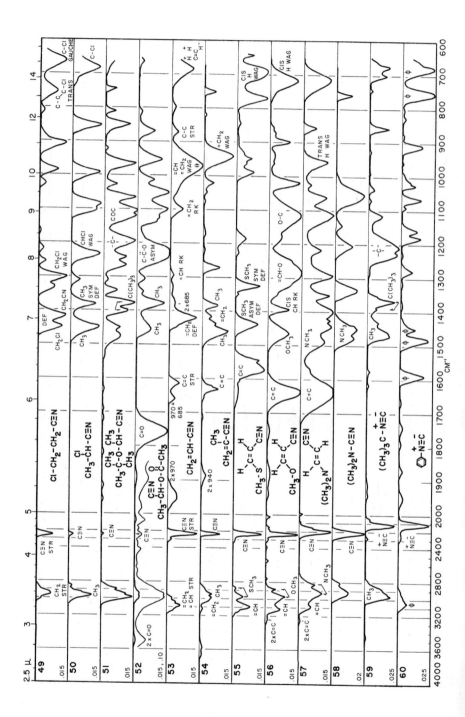

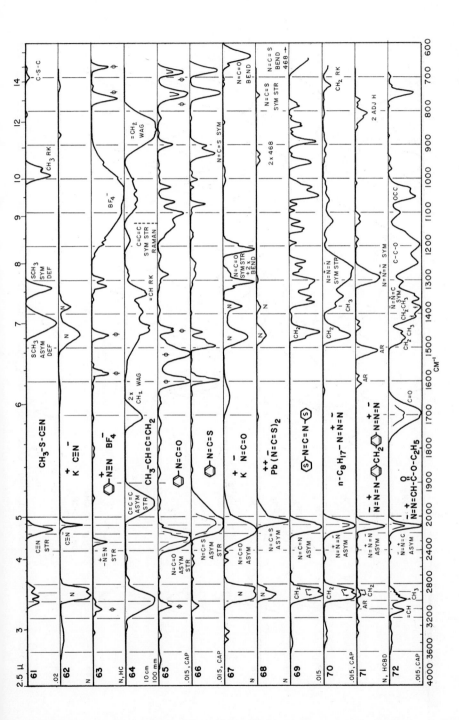

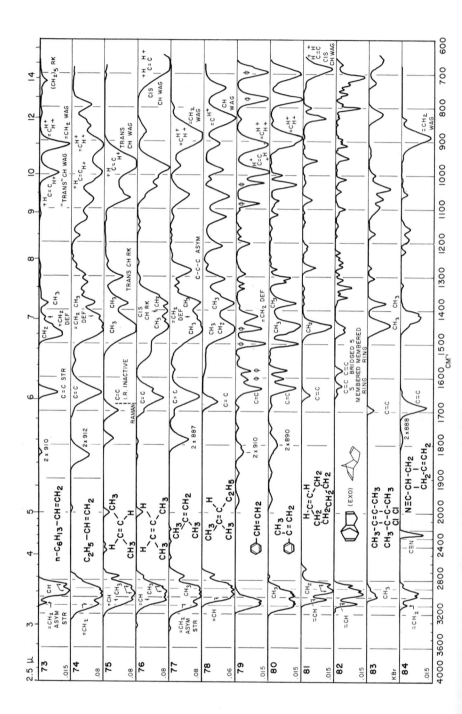

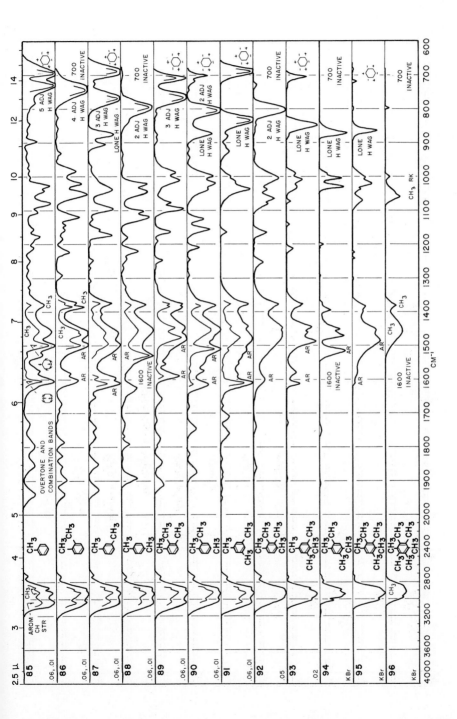

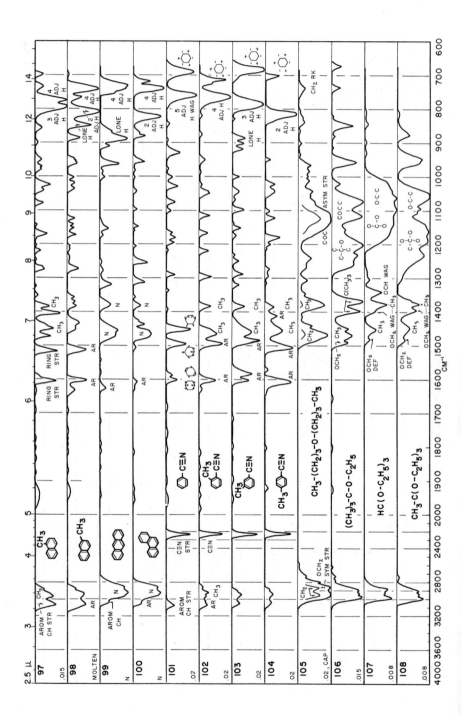

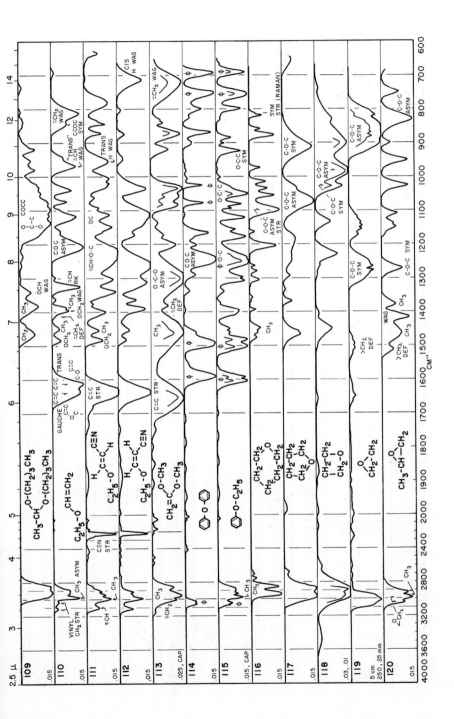

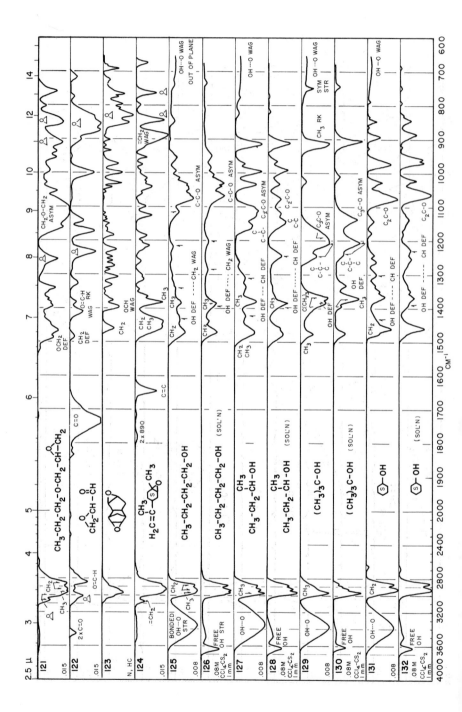

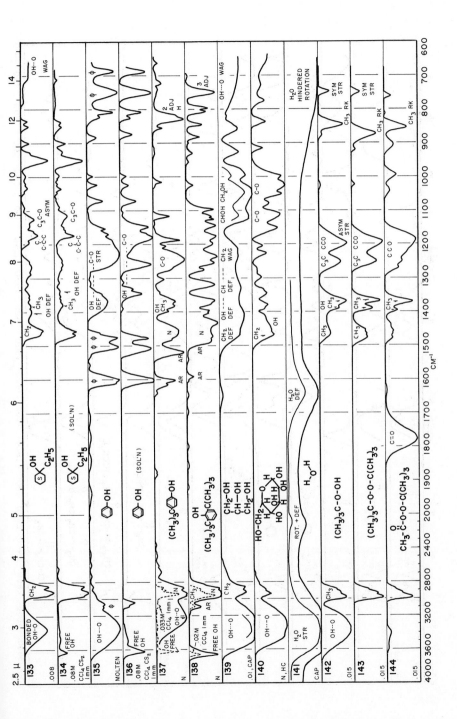

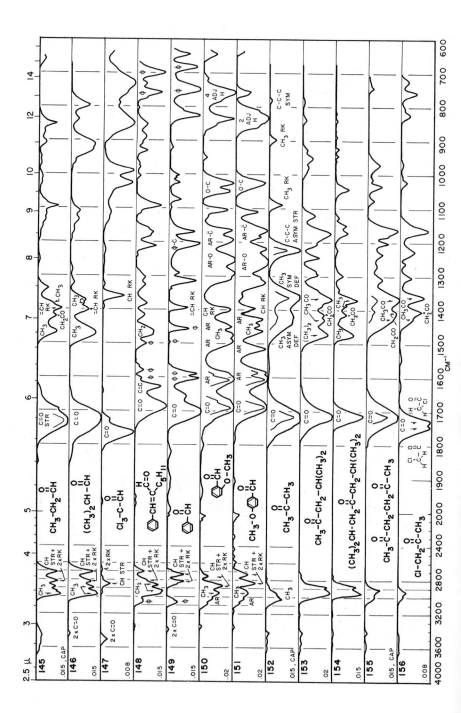

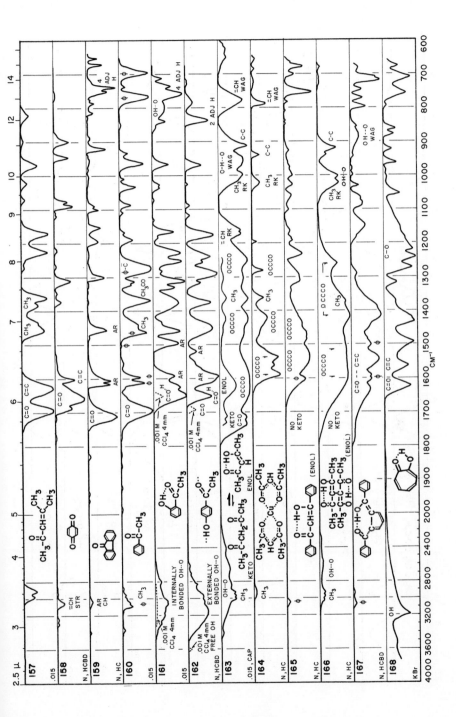

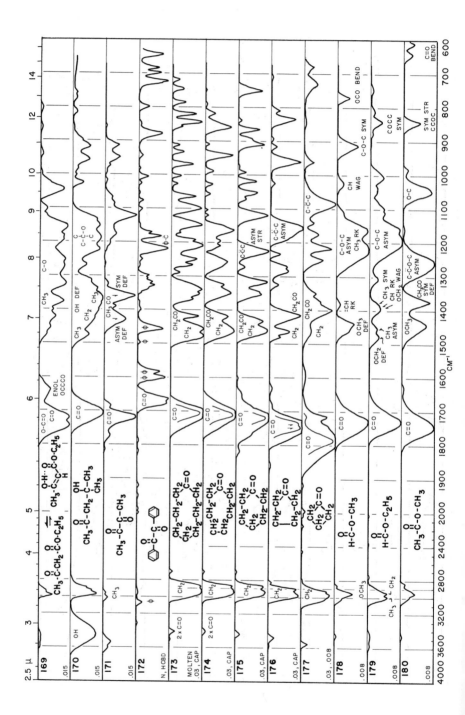

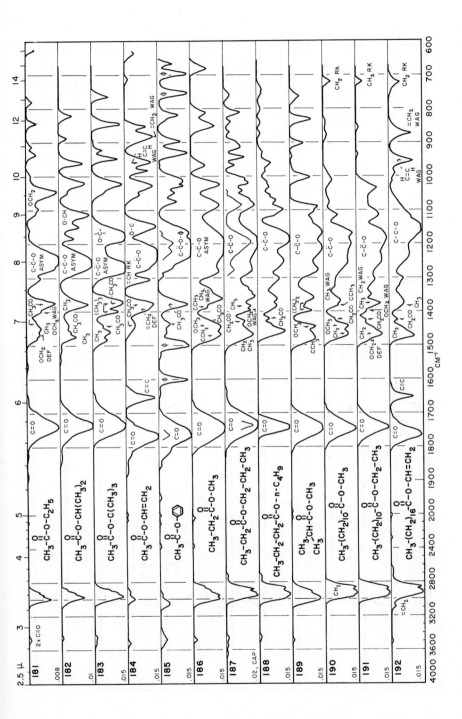

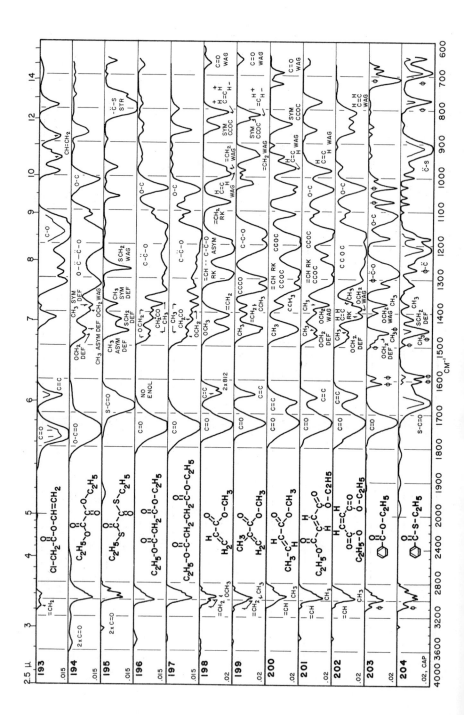

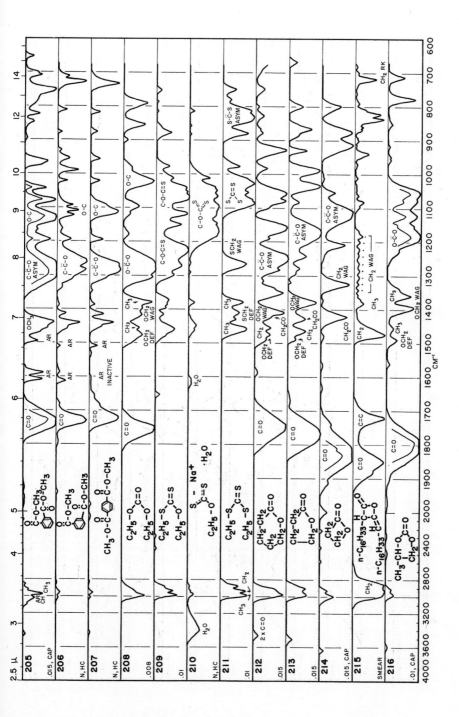

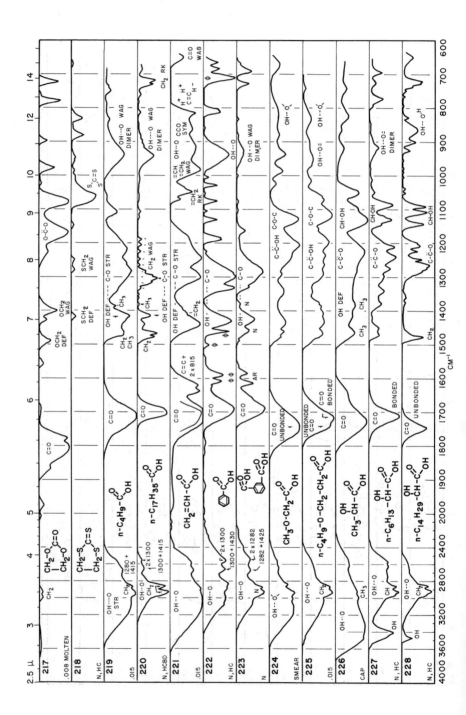

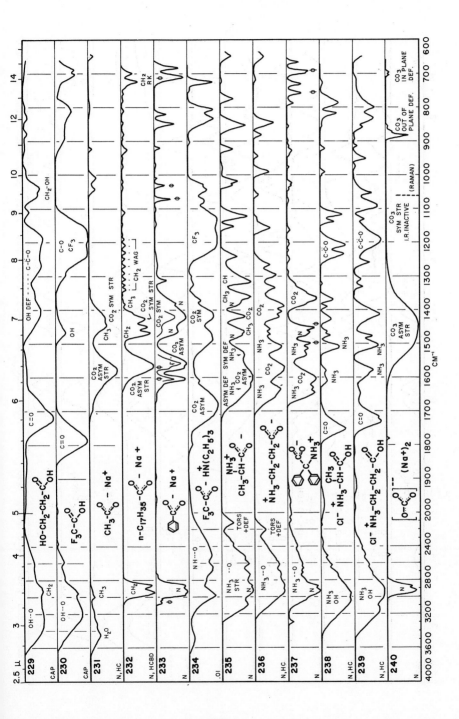

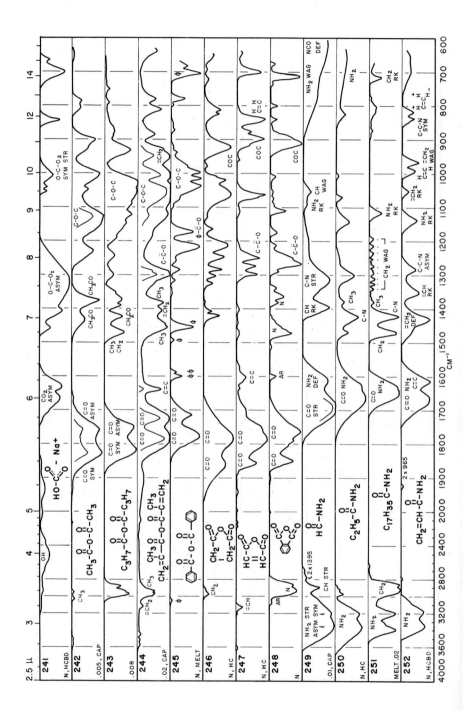

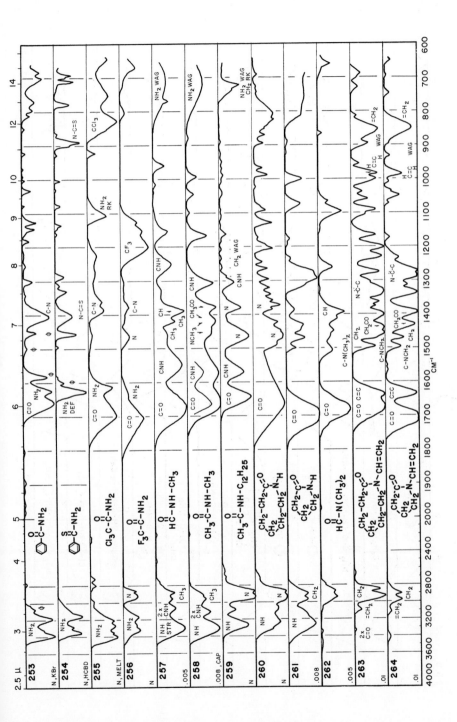

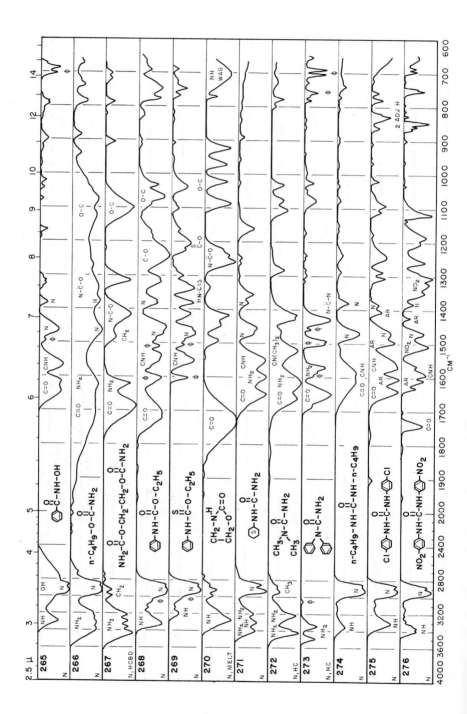

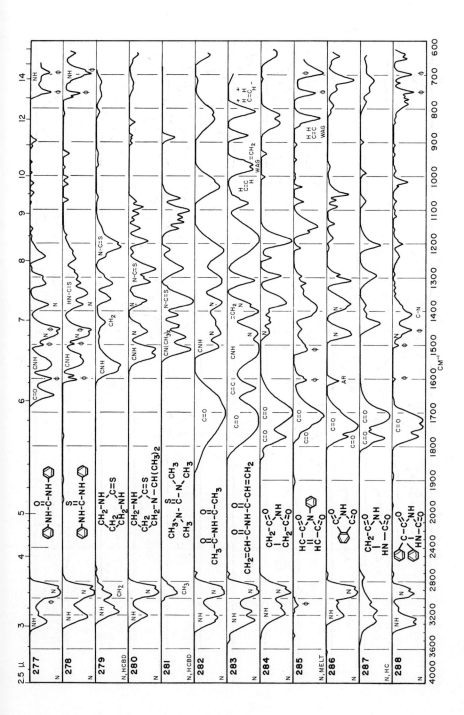

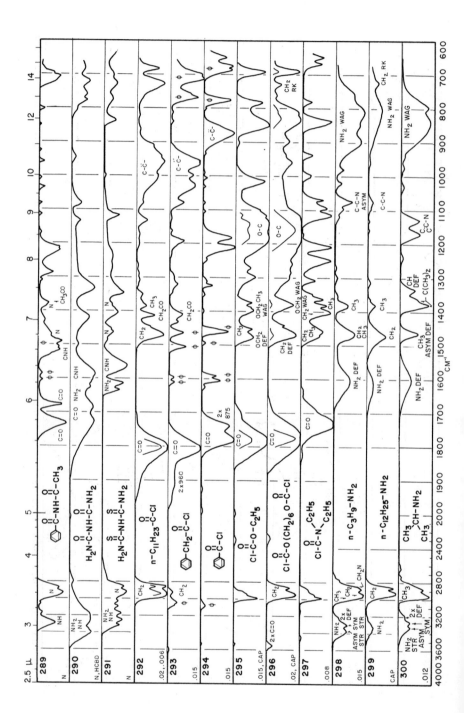

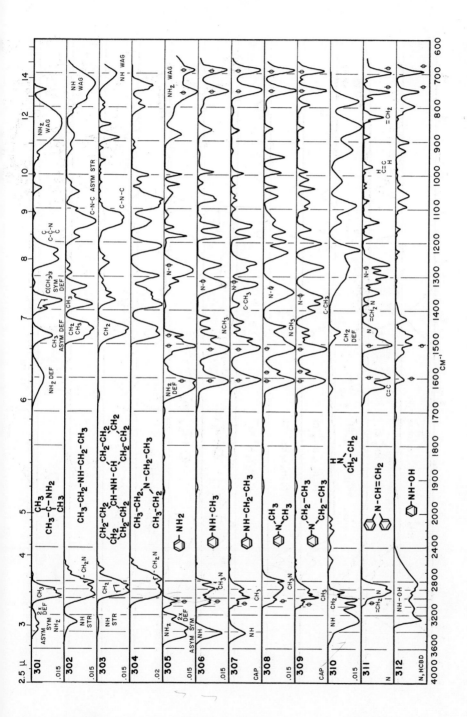

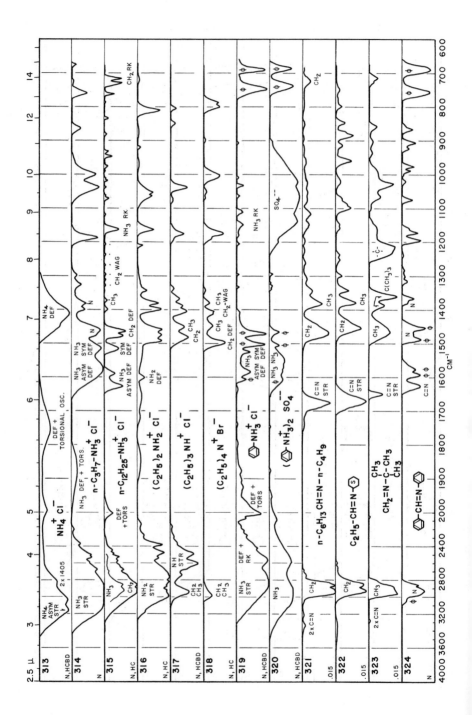

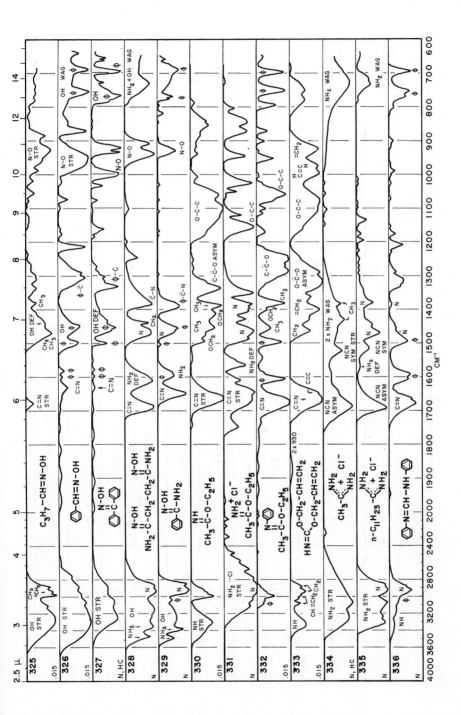

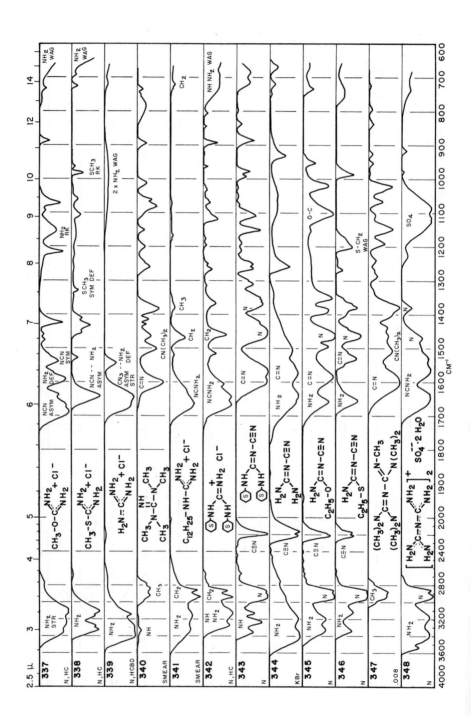

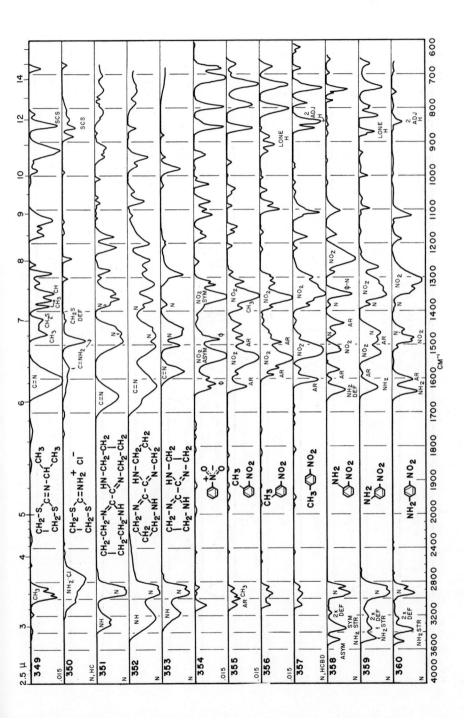

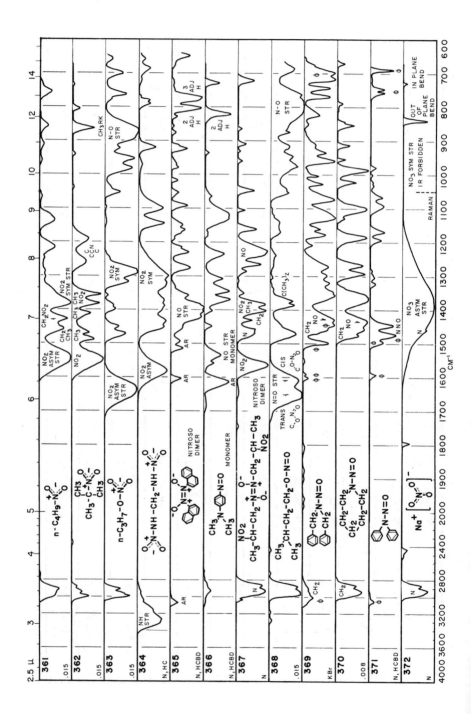

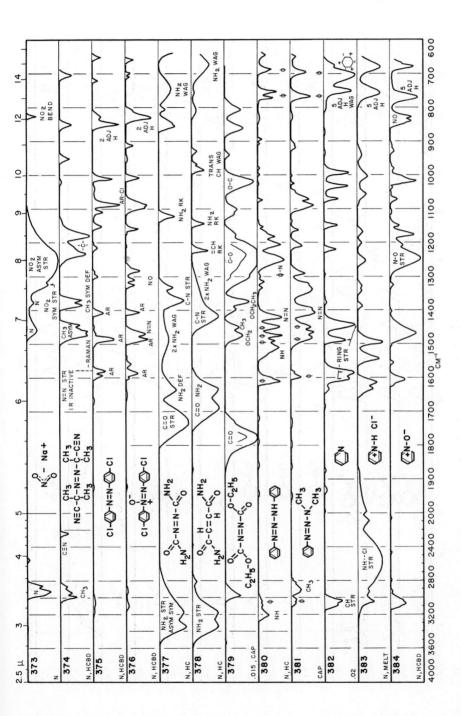

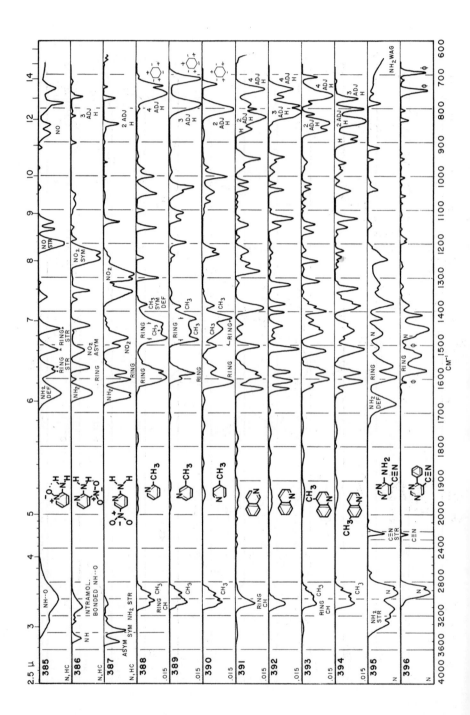

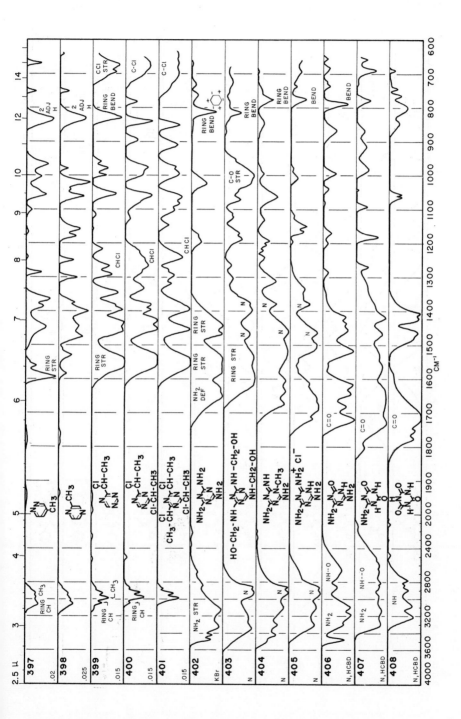

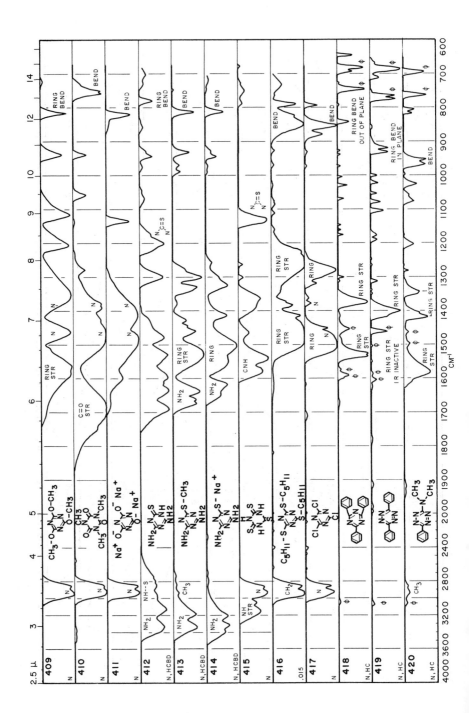

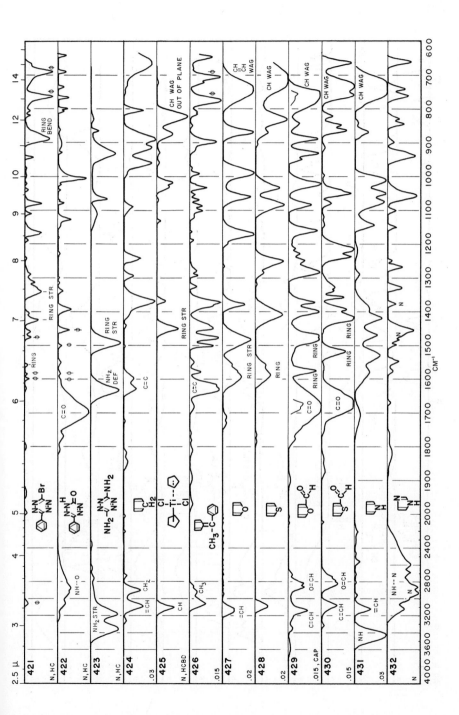

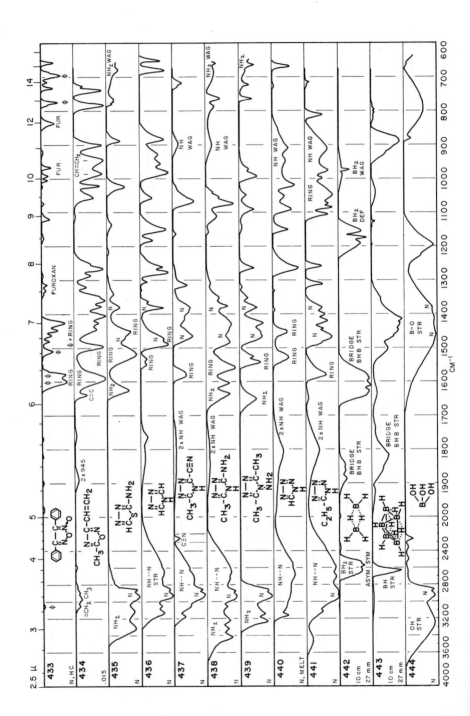

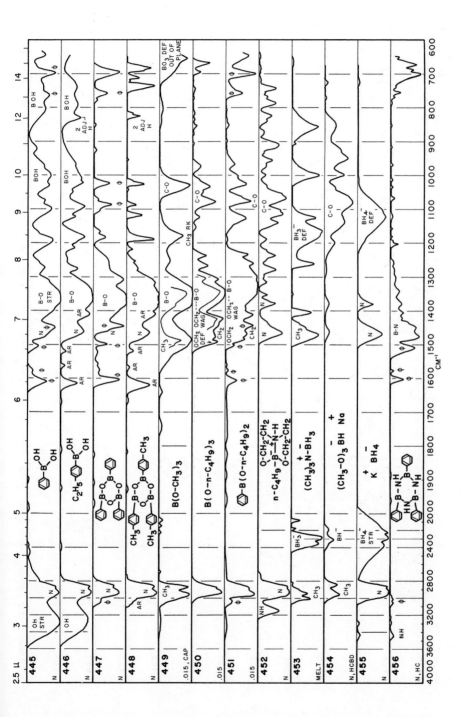

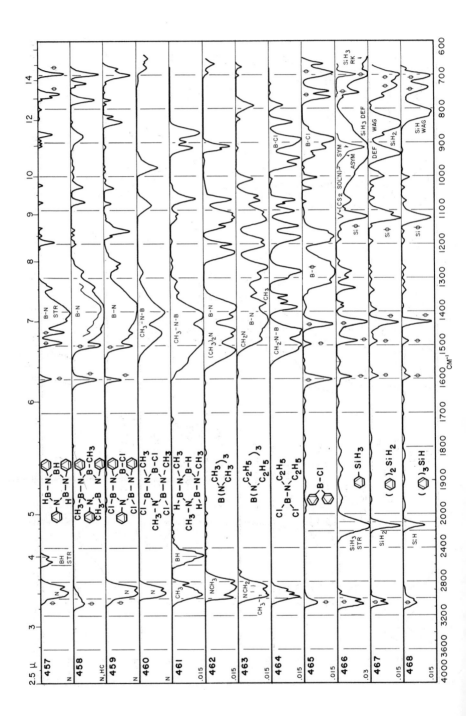

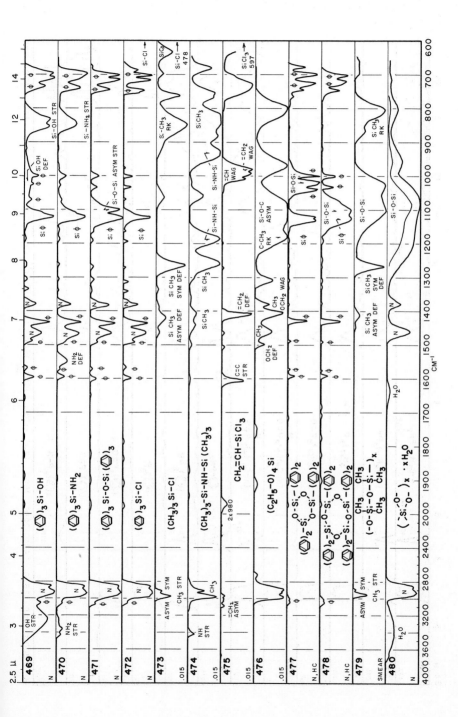

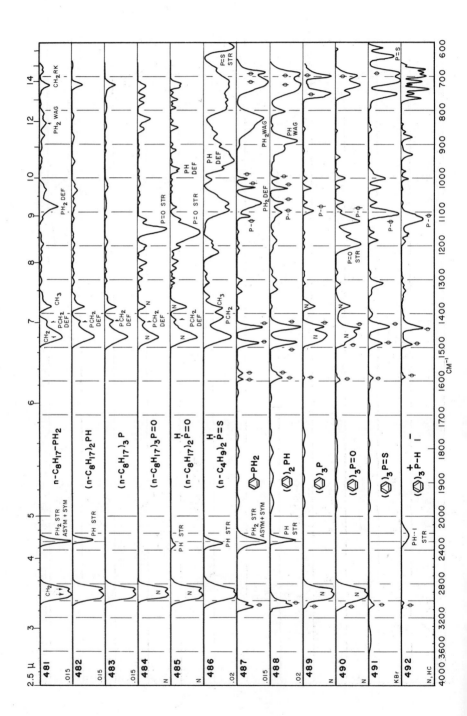

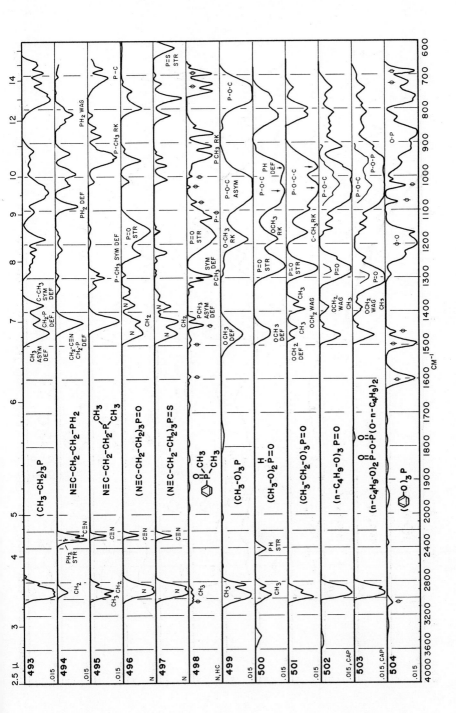

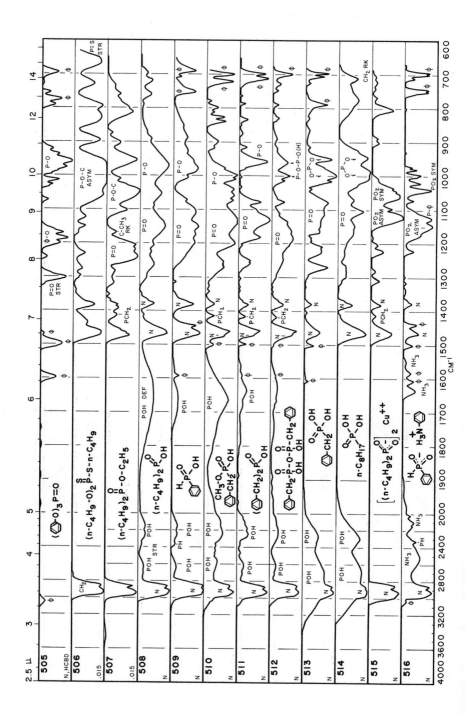

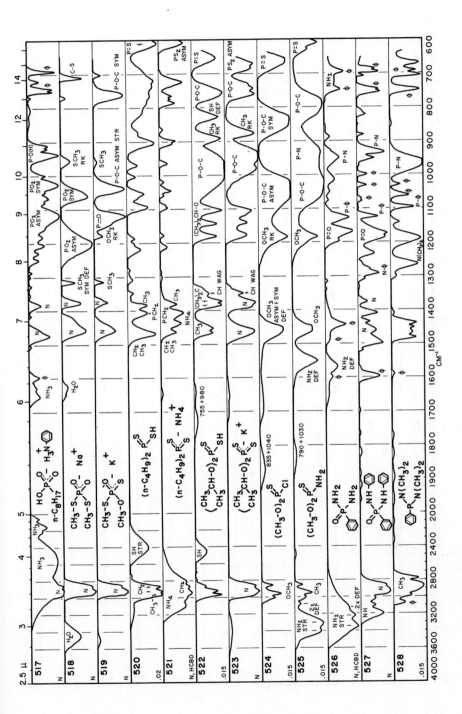

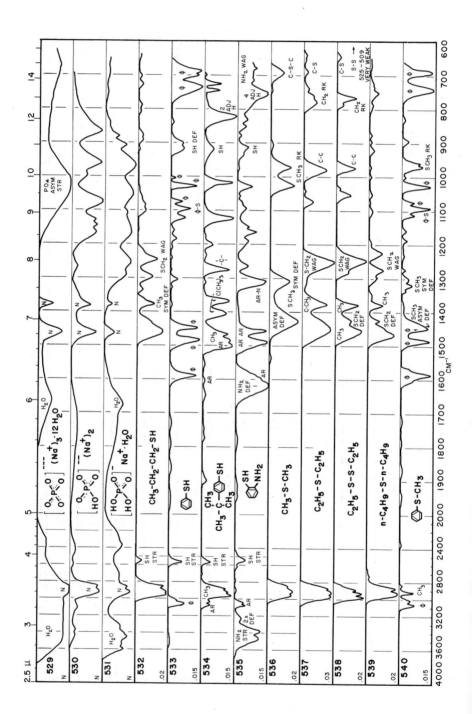

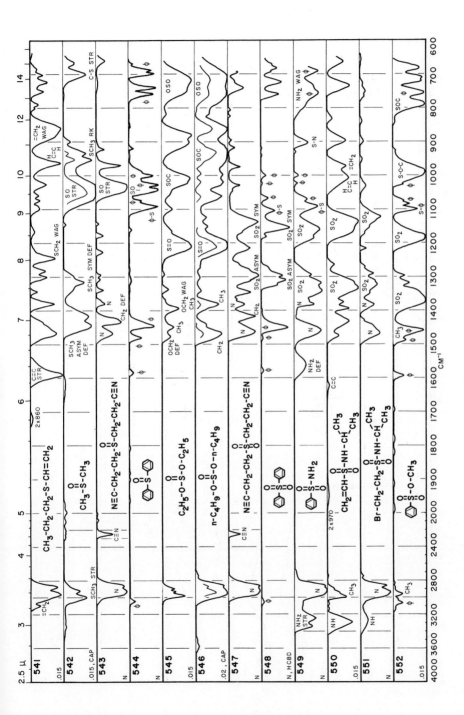

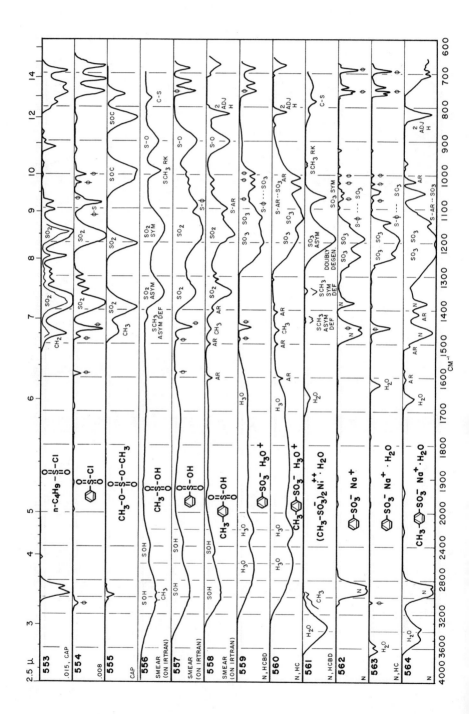

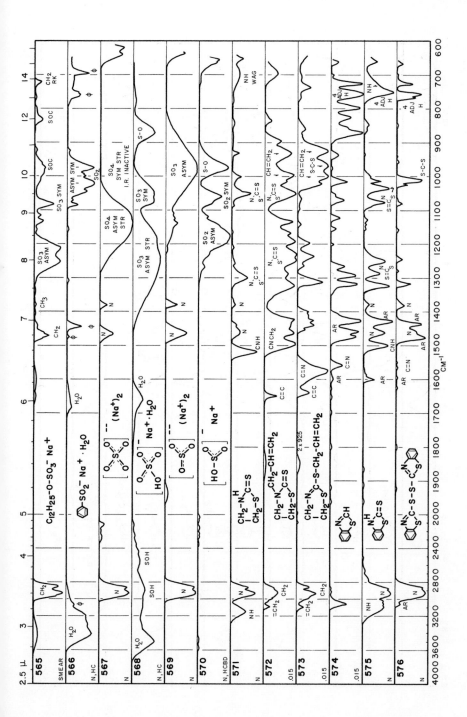

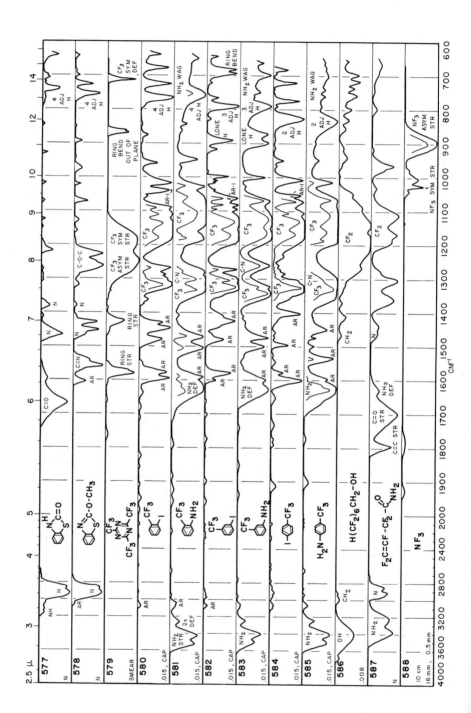

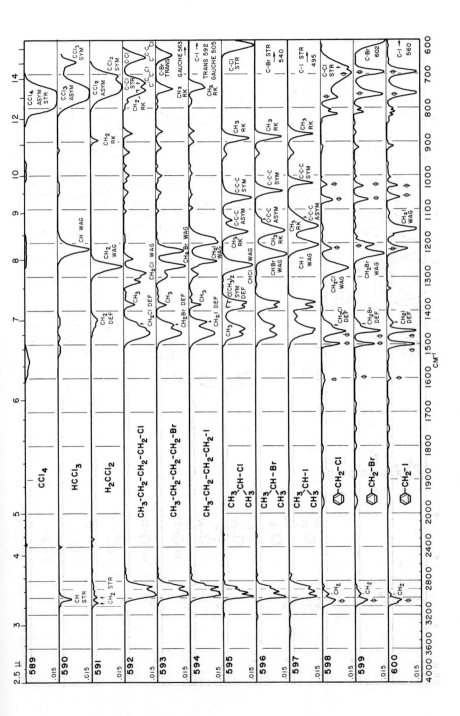

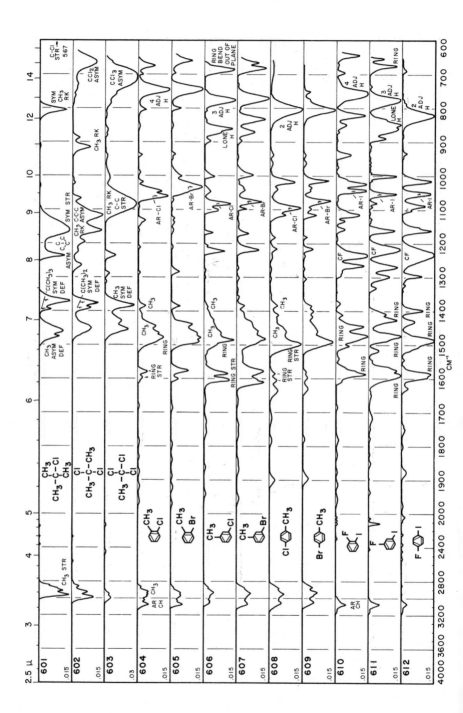

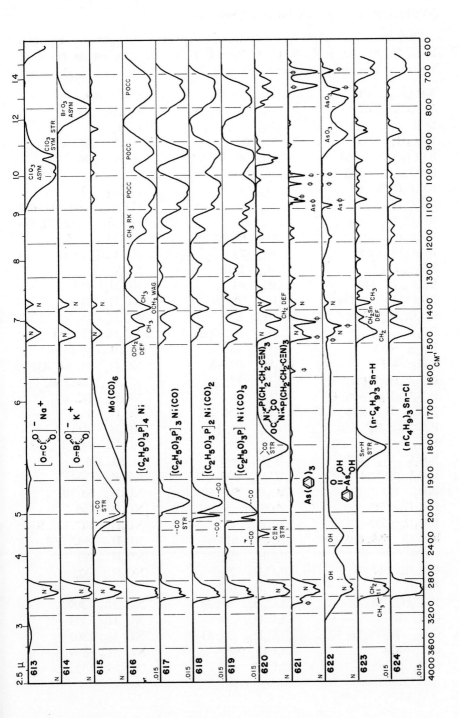

(e) MOLECULAR FORMULA INDEX OF SPECTRA

Elements in each of the molecular formulas appear in the following sequence: B, Si, Bi, Sb, As, P, N, S, O, I, Br, Cl, F, C, H, then metals (in salts). Molecular formulas are indexed alphabetically.

$AsC_{18}H_{15}$ 621	C_6H_{10} 25, 41	Cl_4C 589
$AsO_3C_6H_7$ 622	C_6H_{12} 20, 35, 78	DC_8H_5 43
$BClC_{12}H_{10}$ 465	C_6H_{14} 15	ICH_3 19
BNC_3H_{12} 453	C_7H_8 85	IC_3H_7 597
$BNCl_2C_4H_{10}$ 464	C_7H_{12} 40, 81	IC_4H_9 594
$BNO_2C_8H_{18}$ 452	C_7H_{14} 31	IC_7H_7 600
$BN_2F_4C_6H_5$ 63	C_7H_{16} 13	IC_8H_{17} 12
$BN_3C_6H_{18}$ 462	C_8H_6 42	IFC_6H_4 610, 611, 612
$BN_3C_{12}H_{30}$ 463	C_8H_8 79	$IF_3C_7H_4$ 580, 582, 584
$BO_2C_6H_7$ 445	C_8H_{10} 86, 87, 88	MoO_6C_6 615
$BO_2C_8H_{11}$ 446	C_8H_{16} 73	$NBrC_8H_{20}$ 318
$BO_2C_{14}H_{23}$ 451	C_8H_{18} 2, 14	NCK 62
$BO_3C_3H_9$ 449	C_9H_{10} 80	NC_2H_5 310
$BO_3C_3H_{10}Na$ 454	C_9H_{12} 89, 90, 91	NC_3H_3 53
$BO_3C_{12}H_{27}$ 450	$C_{10}H_{12}$ 82	NC_3H_5 48
BO_3H_3 444	$C_{10}H_{14}$ 92, 93, 94	NC_3H_9 17, 300
BH_4K 455	$C_{10}H_{22}$ 16	NC_3H_{11} 298
B_2H_6 442	$C_{11}H_{10}$ 97, 98	NC_4H_5 34, 54, 431
$B_3N_3C_3H_{12}$ 461	$C_{11}H_{16}$ 95	NC_4H_{11} 301, 302
$B_3N_3C_{18}H_{18}$ 456, 457	$C_{12}H_{18}$ 96	NC_5H_5 382
$B_3N_3C_{21}H_{24}$ 458	$C_{13}H_{12}$ 426	NC_5H_9 59
$B_3N_3Cl_3C_3H_9$ 460	$C_{14}H_{10}$ 99, 100	NC_5H_{11} 323
$B_3N_3Cl_3C_{18}H_{15}$ 459	$C_{17}H_{18}$ 32	NC_6H_7 84, 305, 388,
$B_3O_3C_{18}H_{15}$ 447	ClC_3H_7 595	389, 390
$B_3O_3C_{21}H_{21}$ 448	ClC_4H_9 592, 601	NC_6H_{15} 304
B_5H_9 443	ClC_7H_7 598, 604, 606,	NC_7H_5 60, 101
BrC_3H_7 596	608	NC_7H_9 306
BrC_4H_9 593	ClC_8H_{17} 10	NC_8H_7 102, 103, 104
BrC_7H_7 599, 605, 607,	ClO_3Na 613	NC_8H_{11} 307, 308
609	Cl_2CH_2 591	NC_9H_7 391, 392
BrC_8H_{17} 11	$Cl_2C_2H_4$ 29	NC_9H_{17} 322
BrO_3K 614	$Cl_2C_3H_6$ 602	$NC_{10}H_9$ 393, 394
$Br_2C_2H_4$ 30	$Cl_2C_6H_{10}$ 36, 39	$NC_{10}H_{15}$ 309
C_4H_6 64	$Cl_2C_7H_{10}$ 37	$NC_{11}H_{23}$ 321
C_4H_8 74, 75, 76, 77	$Cl_2C_8H_{12}$ 38, 83	$NC_{12}H_{23}$ 303
C_5H_6 424	Cl_3CH 590	$NC_{12}H_{27}$ 299
C_6H_6 26	$Cl_3C_2H_3$ 603	$NC_{13}H_{11}$ 324

$NC_{14}H_{13}$ 311
$NClC_3H_4$ 49, 50
$NClC_3H_{10}$ 314
$NClC_4H_{12}$ 316
$NClC_5H_6$ 383
$NClC_6H_8$ 319
$NClC_6H_{16}$ 317
$NClC_{12}H_{28}$ 315
$NClH_4$ 313
NF_3 588
$NF_3C_7H_6$ 581, 583, 585
$NOCH_3$ 249
$NOCK$ 67
NOC_2H_5 257
NOC_3H_5 252
NOC_3H_7 250, 258, 262
NOC_4H_5 56
NOC_4H_7 261
NOC_4H_9 325, 330
NOC_5H_5 384
NOC_5H_7 111, 112
NOC_6H_7 312
NOC_6H_9 264
NOC_6H_{11} 260
NOC_7H_5 65
NOC_7H_7 253, 326
NOC_7H_{13} 51
NOC_8H_{13} 263
$NOC_{10}H_{13}$ 332
$NOC_{13}H_{11}$ 327
$NOC_{14}H_{29}$ 259
$NOC_{18}H_{37}$ 251
$NOClC_4H_{10}$ 331
$NOClC_5H_{10}$ 297
$NOCl_3C_2H_2$ 255
$NOF_3C_2H_2$ 256
$NOF_5C_4H_2$ 587
$NO_2C_3H_5$ 270
$NO_2C_3H_7$ 235, 236
$NO_2C_4H_5$ 284

$NO_2C_4H_7$ 282
$NO_2C_4H_9$ 361, 362
$NO_2C_5H_7$ 52
$NO_2C_5H_{11}$ 266, 368
$NO_2C_6H_5$ 354
$NO_2C_6H_7$ 283
$NO_2C_7H_7$ 265, 355, 356, 357
$NO_2C_7H_{11}$ 333
$NO_2C_8H_5$ 286
$NO_2C_8H_{17}$ 9
$NO_2C_9H_9$ 289
$NO_2C_9H_{11}$ 268
$NO_2C_{10}H_7$ 285
$NO_2C_{14}H_{13}$ 237
$NO_2ClC_3H_8$ 238, 239
$NO_2F_3C_8H_{16}$ 234
NO_2Na 373
$NO_3C_3H_7$ 363
$NO_3C_8H_{17}$ 8
NO_3Na 372
$NSCPb_{1/2}$ 68
NSC_2H_3 61
NSC_4H_5 55
NSC_6H_7 535
NSC_7H_5 66, 574
NSC_7H_7 254
$NSOC_7H_5$ 577
$NSOC_8H_7$ 578
$NSOC_9H_{11}$ 269
$NSO_2BrC_5H_{12}$ 551
$NSO_2C_5H_{11}$ 550
$NSO_2C_6H_7$ 549
$NS_2C_3H_5$ 571
$NS_2C_6H_9$ 572, 573
$NS_2C_6H_{11}$ 349
$NS_2C_7H_5$ 575
$NS_2ClC_3H_6$ 350
$N_2C_2H_8$ 24
$N_2C_3H_4$ 432
$N_2C_3H_6$ 58
$N_2C_4H_4$ 27

$N_2C_4H_{10}$ 22
$N_2C_5H_6$ 397, 398
$N_2C_5H_8$ 57
$N_2C_6H_6$ 33
$N_2C_{13}H_{12}$ 336
$N_2C_{13}H_{22}$ 69
$N_2ClC_2H_7$ 334
$N_2ClC_{12}H_{27}$ 335
$N_2Cl_2C_{12}H_8$ 375
$N_2OC_3H_8$ 272
$N_2OC_5H_6$ 385, 434
$N_2OC_5H_{10}$ 370
$N_2OC_7H_8$ 329
$N_2OC_7H_{14}$ 271
$N_2OC_8H_{10}$ 366
$N_2OC_9H_{20}$ 274
$N_2OC_{12}H_{10}$ 371
$N_2OC_{13}H_{12}$ 273, 277
$N_2OC_{14}H_{14}$ 369
$N_2OClC_2H_7$ 337
$N_2OClC_{13}H_{10}$ 275
$N_2OCl_2C_{12}H_8$ 376
$N_2O_2C_3H_4$ 287
$N_2O_2C_4H_6$ 72, 378
$N_2O_4C_4H_8$ 267
$N_2O_2C_6H_6$ 358, 359, 360
$N_2O_2C_{14}H_{10}$ 433
$N_2O_2C_{15}H_{12}$ 288
$N_2O_2C_{20}H_{14}$ 365
$N_2O_4C_6H_{10}$ 379
$N_2SC_4H_8$ 279
$N_2SC_5H_{12}$ 281
$N_2SC_7H_{14}$ 280
$N_2SC_{13}H_{12}$ 278
$N_2SClC_2H_7$ 338
$N_2SOC_6H_8$ 543
$N_2SO_2C_6H_8$ 547
$N_2SO_4C_{12}H_{16}$ 320
$N_2S_4C_{14}H_8$ 576
$N_3C_2H_3$ 436
$N_3C_5H_{13}$ 340

$N_3C_8H_{11}$ 381
$N_3C_8H_{17}$ 70
$N_3C_{11}H_7$ 396
$N_3C_{12}H_{11}$ 380
$N_3C_{21}H_{15}$ 418
N_3ClCH_6 339
$N_3ClC_5H_6$ 399
$N_3ClC_{13}H_{26}$ 342
$N_3ClC_{13}H_{30}$ 341
$N_3Cl_2C_7H_9$ 400
$N_3Cl_3C_3$ 417
$N_3Cl_3C_9H_{12}$ 401
$N_3F_9C_6$ 579
$N_3OC_4H_7$ 345
$N_3O_2C_2H_5$ 290
$N_3O_2C_5H_5$ 386, 387
$N_3O_3C_3H_3$ 408
$N_3O_3C_6H_9$ 409, 410
$N_3O_3C_3Na_3$ 411
$N_3SC_2H_3$ 435
$N_3SC_4H_7$ 346
$N_3S_2C_2H_5$ 291
$N_3S_3C_3H_3$ 415
$N_3S_3C_{18}H_{33}$ 416
$N_4BrC_8H_5$ 421
N_4CH_2 440
$N_4C_2H_4$ 344
$N_4C_3H_6$ 438, 441
$N_4C_4H_4$ 437
$N_4C_4H_8$ 439
$N_4C_5H_4$ 395
$N_4C_6H_{10}$ 353
$N_4C_8H_{12}$ 374
$N_4C_8H_{14}$ 352
$N_4C_{10}H_{18}$ 351
$N_4C_{14}H_{10}$ 419
$N_4C_{14}H_{24}$ 343
$N_4OC_8H_6$ 422
$N_4O_2C_2H_4$ 377
$N_4O_2C_3H_4$ 407
$N_4O_2C_4H_{10}$ 328
$N_4O_5C_{13}H_{10}$ 276

$N_4O_4CH_4$ 364
$N_4O_6C_6H_{12}$ 367
$N_5C_9H_{21}$ 347
$N_5C_{10}H_{11}$ 420
$N_5OC_3H_5$ 406
$N_5SC_3H_4Na$ 414
$N_5SC_3H_5$ 412
$N_5SC_4H_7$ 413
$N_6C_2H_4$ 423
$N_6C_3H_6$ 402
$N_6C_4H_8$ 404
$N_6C_{13}H_{10}$ 71
$N_6ClC_3H_7$ 405
$N_6O_3C_6H_{12}$ 403
$N_{10}SO_4C_4H_{16}$ 348
OC_2H_4 119
OC_2H_6 18
OC_3H_6 118, 120, 145, 152
OC_4H_4 427
OC_4H_6 177
OC_4H_8 110, 117, 146
OC_4H_{10} 125–130
OC_5H_6 44
OC_5H_8 176
OC_5H_{10} 116
OC_6H_6 135, 136
OC_6H_{10} 157, 175
OC_6H_{12} 131, 132, 153
OC_6H_{14} 106
OC_7H_6 149
OC_7H_{12} 174
OC_8H_8 160
OC_8H_{10} 115
OC_8H_{14} 173
OC_8H_{16} 5, 133, 134
OC_8H_{18} 4, 105
OC_9H_{18} 154
$OC_{10}H_{14}$ 137
$OC_{10}H_{16}$ 124
$OC_{12}H_{10}$ 114
$OC_{13}H_8$ 159

$OC_{14}H_{18}$ 148
$OC_{14}H_{22}$ 138
$OC_{16}H_{34}$ 3
$OClC_3H_5$ 156
$OClC_7H_5$ 294
$OClC_8H_7$ 293
$OClC_{12}H_{23}$ 292
OCl_3C_2H 147
$OF_{12}C_7H_4$ 586
OH_2 141
$O_2C_2H_4$ 178
$O_2C_2H_6$ 23
$O_2C_3H_4$ 122, 214, 221
$O_2C_3H_6$ 179, 180
$O_2C_4H_6$ 171, 184, 198, 213
$O_2C_4H_8$ 21, 113, 181, 186
$O_2C_4H_{10}$ 142
$O_2C_5H_4$ 429
$O_2C_5H_6$ 45
$O_2C_5H_8$ 163, 199, 200, 212
$O_2C_5H_{10}$ 182, 189, 219
$O_2C_6H_4$ 158
$O_2C_6H_8$ 28
$O_2C_6H_{10}$ 155
$O_2C_6H_{12}$ 121, 170, 183, 187
$O_2C_7H_6$ 168, 222
$O_2C_8H_8$ 150, 151, 161, 162, 185
$O_2C_8H_{12}$ 46
$O_2C_8H_{16}$ 6, 188
$O_2C_8H_{18}$ 143
$O_2C_9H_{10}$ 203
$O_2C_{10}H_{12}$ 123
$O_2C_{10}H_{22}$ 109
$O_2C_{13}H_{26}$ 190
$O_2C_{14}H_{10}$ 172
$O_2C_{14}H_{28}$ 191

$O_2C_{15}H_{12}$ 165
$O_2C_{16}H_{32}$ 7
$O_2C_{18}H_{36}$ 220
$O_2C_{19}H_{14}$ 167
$O_2C_{20}H_{38}$ 192
$O_2C_{36}H_{68}$ 215
$O_2C_2H_3Na$ 231
$O_2C_7H_5Na$ 233
$O_2C_{18}H_{35}Na$ 232
$O_2ClC_3H_5$ 295
$O_2ClC_4H_5$ 193
$O_2F_3C_2H$ 230
$O_3C_3H_4$ 217
$O_3C_3H_6$ 224, 226, 229
$O_3C_3H_8$ 139
$O_3C_4H_2$ 247
$O_3C_4H_4$ 246
$O_3C_4H_6$ 216, 242
$O_3C_5H_{10}$ 208
$O_3C_6H_{10}$ 169
$O_3C_6H_{12}$ 144
$O_3C_7H_{14}$ 225
$O_3C_7H_{16}$ 107
$O_3C_8H_4$ 248
$O_3C_8H_{10}$ 244
$O_3C_8H_{14}$ 243
$O_3C_8H_{16}$ 227
$O_3C_8H_{18}$ 108
$O_3C_{14}H_{10}$ 245
$O_3C_{16}H_{32}$ 228
O_3CHNa 241
O_3CNa 240
$O_4C_4H_2$ 47
$O_4C_6H_{10}$ 194
$O_4C_7H_{12}$ 196
$O_4C_8H_6$ 223
$O_4C_8H_{12}$ 201, 202
$O_4C_8H_{14}$ 197
$O_4C_{10}H_{10}$ 205, 206, 207
$O_4C_{10}H_{14}$ 166
$O_4C_{10}H_{14}Cu$ 164

$O_4Cl_2C_8H_{12}$ 296
$O_6C_6H_{12}$ 140
PC_6H_7 487
PC_6H_{15} 493
PC_8H_{19} 481
$PC_{12}H_{11}$ 488
$PC_{16}H_{35}$ 482
$PC_{18}H_{15}$ 489
$PC_{24}H_{51}$ 483
$PIC_{18}H_{16}$ 492
PNC_3H_6 494
PNC_5H_{10} 495
$PNO_2C_{12}H_{14}$ 516
$PNO_3C_{14}H_{26}$ 517
$PNSO_2C_2H_8$ 525
$PNS_2C_8H_{22}$ 521
$PN_2C_{10}H_{17}$ 528
$PN_2OC_6H_9$ 526
$PN_2OC_{18}H_{17}$ 527
$PN_3C_9H_{12} \cdot NiOC$ 620
$PN_3OC_9H_{12}$ 496
$PN_3SC_9H_{12}$ 497
POC_8H_{11} 498
$POC_{16}H_{35}$ 485
$POC_{18}H_{15}$ 490
$POC_{24}H_{51}$ 484
$PO_2C_6H_7$ 509
$PO_2C_8H_{18}Cu_{1/2}$ 515
$PO_2C_8H_{19}$ 508
$PO_2C_{10}H_{23}$ 507
$PO_2C_{14}H_{15}$ 511
$PO_3C_2H_7$ 500
$PO_3C_3H_9$ 499
$PO_3C_6H_{15} \cdot 1/2NiO_2C_2$ 618
$PO_3C_6H_{15} \cdot NiO_3C_3$ 619
$PO_3C_7H_9$ 513
$PO_3C_8H_{11}$ 510
$PO_3C_8H_{19}$ 514
$PO_3C_{18}H_{15}$ 504

$PO_4C_6H_{15}$ 501
$PO_4C_{12}H_{27}$ 502
$PO_4C_{18}H_{15}$ 505
PO_4H_2Na 531
PO_4HNa_2 530
PO_4Na_3 529
PSC_8H_{19} 486
$PSC_{18}H_{15}$ 491
$PSClO_2C_2H_6$ 524
$PS_2C_8H_{19}$ 520
$PS_2O_2C_2H_6K$ 519
$PS_2O_2C_2H_6Na$ 518
$PS_2O_2C_6H_{14}K$ 523
$PS_2O_2C_6H_{15}$ 522
$PS_2O_2C_{12}H_{27}$ 506
$P_2O_5C_{14}H_{16}$ 512
$P_2O_7C_{16}H_{36}$ 503
$P_3O_9C_{18}H_{45} \cdot NiOC$ 617
$P_4O_{12}C_{24}H_{60} \cdot Ni$ 616
SC_2H_6 536
SC_3H_8 532
SC_4H_4 428
SC_4H_{10} 537
SC_5H_{10} 541
SC_6H_6 533
SC_7H_8 540
SC_8H_{18} 539
$SC_{10}H_{14}$ 534
SOC_2H_6 542
SOC_5H_4 430
SOC_9H_{10} 204
$SOC_{12}H_{10}$ 544
$SO_2C_6H_5Na$ 566
$SO_2C_{12}H_{10}$ 548
$SO_2ClC_4H_9$ 553
$SO_2ClC_6H_5$ 554
$SO_3CH_3Ni_{1/2}$ 561
SO_3CH_4 556
$SO_3C_4H_{10}$ 545
$SO_3C_6H_5Na$ 562, 563
$SO_3C_6H_6$ 557, 559

$SO_3C_7H_7Na$ 564	$S_2OC_5H_{10}$ 209	$(SiOC_2H_6)_x$ 479
$SO_3C_7H_8$ 552, 558, 560	$S_2O_2C_6H_{10}$ 195	$SiOC_{18}H_{16}$ 469
$SO_3C_8H_{18}$ 546	$S_3C_3H_4$ 218	$(SiO_2)_x$ 480
SO_3HNa 570	$S_3C_5H_{10}$ 211	$SiO_4C_8H_{20}$ 476
SO_3Na_2 569	SiC_6H_8 466	$Si_2NC_6H_{19}$ 474
$SO_4C_2H_6$ 555	$SiC_{12}H_{12}$ 467	$Si_2OC_{36}H_{30}$ 471
$SO_4C_{12}H_{25}Na$ 565	$SiC_{18}H_{16}$ 468	$Si_3O_3C_{36}H_{30}$ 477
SO_4HNa 568	$SiClC_3H_9$ 473	$Si_4O_4C_{48}H_{40}$ 478
SO_4Na_2 567	$SiClC_{18}H_{15}$ 472	$SnC_{12}H_{28}$ 623
$S_2C_4H_{10}$ 538	$SiCl_3C_2H_3$ 475	$SnClC_{12}H_{27}$ 624
$S_2OC_3H_5Na$ 210	$SiNC_{18}H_{17}$470	$TiCl_2C_{10}H_{20}$ 425

(f) UNKNOWNS FOR INTERPRETATION

Spectra A—L are presented without labels or interpretation as an exercise for the reader in functional group analysis. These are all pure liquids (no Nujol or solvent) 0.01–0.3 mm thick. For interpretations of these see Section 13.29 (g).

(g) INTERPRETATION OF UNKNOWNS A—L

(A) Aromatic ring, 3100–3000 cm^{-1}, 1608 cm^{-1}, and 1500 cm^{-1}. Mono-substituted aromatic ring, 700, 767, 1032, 1085 cm^{-1} and 2000–1700 cm^{-1} (overtones). Aliphatic group, 2960–2870 cm^{-1}, 1470 cm^{-1}. Isopropyl group 1388, 1368 cm^{-1}. *Isopropyl benzene.*

(B) Carboxylic acid, 3100 cm^{-1} (broad) (OH), 1712 cm^{-1} (C=O), 1420, 1300–1200, and 930 cm^{-1} (broad). Aliphatic group, 2960–2860 and 1468 cm^{-1}. Methyl group on a carbon 1380 cm^{-1}. *Propionic acid.*

(C) Aromatic ring, 3100–3000, 1605, 1583, 1490 cm^{-1}. Ortho substituted aromatic ring 740 cm^{-1}. Aliphatic group, 2960–2860, 1465, and 1380 cm^{-1}. (CH$_3$). Conjugated ester, 1725 cm^{-1} (C=O). Aromatic ester, ca. 1280 and 1120 cm^{-1}. *Di (2-ethyl-hexyl) phthalate.*

(D) Monosubstituted aromatic ring, 3100–3000, 1592, 1505, 750, and 700 cm^{-1}. Aliphatic group 2930–2880 cm^{-1}. Conjugated ester 1727 cm^{-1} (C=O). Unsaturated ester, ca. 1190 cm^{-1}. Vinyl group, 1635, 1412, 985, 968 cm^{-1}. Acrylate 812 cm^{-1} and 1620 cm^{-1} (overtone). *Benzyl acrylate.*

(E) Aromatic ring, 3100–3000, 1602, 1582, 1520 cm^{-1}. Substituted naphthalene 810 cm^{-1} (3 adjacent hydrogens) and 780 cm^{-1} (4 adjacent hydrogens). Aldehyde, 2860 cm^{-1}, 2740 cm^{-1} (CH), 1692 cm^{-1}(C=O). *1-Naphthaldehyde.*

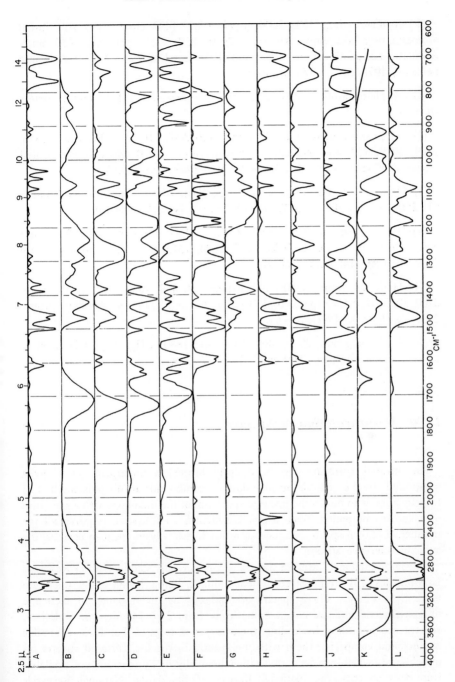

(F) Aromatic ring, 3100–3000, 1597, 1585, 1497 cm⁻¹. *Para* substituted aromatic ring, 825 cm⁻¹. Aliphatic, 2960–2830 cm⁻¹, methoxy, 2830 cm⁻¹. Aromatic-*o*-aliphatic ether, 1252 and 1035 cm⁻¹. *Para* substituted bromo benzene, 1075 cm⁻¹. *p-Bromo anisole.*

(G) Aliphatic groups 2970–2850 cm⁻¹. Aliphatic ether 1130 cm⁻¹. *Diethyl ether.*

(H) Monosubstituted aromatic ring, 3100–3000, 1605, 1590, 1502, 1458, 1069, 1029, 733, and 693 cm⁻¹. Aliphatic group 2930 cm⁻¹. Unconjugated nitrile, 2250 cm⁻¹, CH_2—$C \equiv N$, 1420 cm⁻¹. *Phenyl acetonitrile.*

(I) Monosubstituted aromatic ring [see (H)]. Aliphatic group, 2930 cm⁻¹. SH 2560 cm⁻¹, CH_2—S, 1433 and 1255 cm⁻¹. *Benzyl mercaptan.*

(J) Hydroxyl group, 3300 cm⁻¹ (broad) (OH), aromatic OH, 1225 cm⁻¹ *para* substituted aromatic, 3030, 1617, 1604, 1515, 817 cm⁻¹ aliphatic group 2930–2870 and 1460 cm⁻¹. *p-Cresol.*

(K) Hydroxyl group, 3350 cm⁻¹, primary alcohol, 1030 cm⁻¹, vinyl group, 3100–3000, 1855 (overtone), 1655 (C=C), 995 and 922 cm⁻¹. Aliphatic group, 2930, 2880 cm⁻¹. *Allyl alcohol.*

(L) Aliphatic group, 2960–2860, 1470, and 1830 (CH_3) cm⁻¹. CH_2 next to tertiary amine nitrogen, 2800 cm⁻¹. *Tributyl amine.*

13.30 Documentation of Spectra

An infrared spectrum has been aptly termed a fingerprint of a given compound. In the analysis of an unknown compound, an obvious method of identification is to match the infrared spectrum of the unknown with a spectrum of a known compound. Such a positive identification system requires a large number of known spectra. A good deal of effort has been spent in establishing suitable reference spectra.

One large catalog of infrared spectra is commercially sold by Sadtler Research Laboratories, 1517 Vine Street, Philadelphia 2, Pennsylvania under the trade name Spec-Finder. These spectra are indexed by major bands in each one micron interval and are coded numerically from 2 to 14 microns. Unknown spectra are identified by coding their major absorption bands in a similar manner and comparing them with the spectra in the file. Infrared spectra on punch cards which can be sorted either manually or by machine are available from two sources, the National Bureau of Standards—National Research

Council publication and the "Documentation of Molecular Spectroscopy" (DMS) published by Butterworths Scientific Publication, London, England. The DMS system is available in the United States from Spex Industries, Inc. 205 — 02 Jamaica Avenue, Hollis 23, New York and contains approximately 80% spectral cards and 20% literature cards.

Even edge–punch cards become unwieldy when the number of spectra exceed the 10,000 mark. L. Kuentzel[124] has coded IBM cards with infrared spectra. These IBM cards have been adopted by ASTM Committee E–13 and are distributed through ASTM Headquarters at 1916 Race Street, Philadelphia, Pennsylvania.

Infrared spectra of approximately 2400 compounds and Raman spectra of approximately 350 compounds of high purity are available from the American Petroleum Institute, Data Distribution Office, Agricultural and Mechanical College of Texas, College Station, Texas.

Some of the large industrial companies have combined all the catalogs mentioned on IBM cards so that a quick sort of many thousand spectra can be made in a matter of minutes.

An index to 43,500 published infrared spectra, ASTM Special Technical Publication No. 331, has recently been published by the American Society for Testing and Materials, 1916 Race Street, Philadelphia 3, Pennsylvania.

[124] L. E. Kuentzel, *Anal. Chem.* **23**, 1413 (1951).

CHAPTER 14

THE THEORETICAL ANALYSIS
OF MOLECULES

As discussed in Chapter 1, a molecule may have $3N$-6 (or $3N$-5) normal modes of vibration or fundamental frequencies. In a normal mode of vibration the motion of the atoms is simple harmonic in nature, and each atom vibrates with the same frequency. For nondegenerate vibrations, the atoms also vibrate in phase, that is, all atoms pass through their equilibrium positions simultaneously and reach their maximum (but not necessarily equal) amplitudes simultaneously.

The purpose of this chapter is to show how the normal or fundamental vibrations of a molecule may be determined mathematically. The calculations require a knowledge of the interatomic forces (force constants) and the configuration (bond lengths and angles) of the molecule. The first section (14.1) introduces the most direct approach but is not expanded due to mathematical complications. Other texts may be consulted for further discussion.[1-4] The remaining sections (14.2–14.14) describe the internal coordinate treatment in detail. The method is outlined and then discussed in detail, using chloroform as an example. Some use is made of group theory and matrix algebra but no detailed previous knowledge of these fields is necessary. For those interested in further discussion of the mathematical principles involved, other sources[5,6] are available.

[1] E. T. Whittaker, "Analytical Dynamics of Particles and Rigid Bodies," 3rd ed., Chapter 7. Cambridge Univ. Press, London and New York, 1927.

[2] S. Glasstone, "Theoretical Chemistry." Van Nostrand, New York, 1944.

[3] E. B. Wilson, Jr., J. C. Decius, and P. C. Cross, "Molecular Vibrations." McGraw-Hill, New York, 1955.

[4] G. Herzberg, "Infrared and Raman Spectra of Polyatomic Molecules," Van Nostrand, New York, 1945.

[5] H. Margenau and G. M. Murphy, "The Mathematics of Physics and Chemistry," 2nd ed. Van Nostrand, New York, 1956.

[6] J. E. Rosenthal and G. M. Murphy, *Rev. Mod. Phys.* 8, 317 (1936).

14.1 Normal Modes of Vibration

During a vibration the movement of the N atoms in a molecule from their equilibrium positions will generally be very complex but their displacements may be represented by a set of coordinates x_1, y_1, z_1, x_2, y_2, z_2, $\cdots$, x_N, y_N, z_N, or more generally, by q_1, q_2, q_3, q_4, $\cdots$, q_{3N}. The $3N$ coordinates, q_i, where i is 1, 2, 3, $\cdots$, $3N$ may be used to express the potential energy, V, and the kinetic energy, T. The appropriate relations are:

$$2V = \sum_{i,j=1}^{3N} b_{ij} q_i q_j , \qquad (14.1)$$

and

$$2T = \sum_{i,j=1}^{3N} a_{ij} \dot{q}_i \dot{q}_j , \qquad (14.2)$$

where $\dot{q}$ is dq/dt and q_i and q_j are the ith and jth coordinates and are not necessarily the same (i.e., $i = j$ or $i \neq j$). The b_{ij} values are constants and the a_{ij} values are functions of the atomic masses. An equation of motion, the Lagrange equation, can be written which involves both V and T as functions related to the coordinates q_i. Numerous references are available for this treatment and it will not be discussed in detail here.[1-4]

A set of $3N$ differential equations results which have the general solution:

$$q_j = A_j \sin (\sqrt{\lambda} t + \alpha) , \qquad (14.3)$$

which is an equation characteristic of wave motion with a frequency ν' equal to $\sqrt{\lambda}/2\pi$, amplitude A, and phase constant α. The q_j values of Eq. (14.3) may be substituted into the $3N$ differential equations mentioned above to obtain a set of $3N$ algebraic equations of the form:

$$\sum_{i=1}^{3N} (b_{ij} - a_{ij}\lambda) A_j = 0, \qquad (14.4)$$

where j is 1, 2, 3, $\cdots$ $3N$. For nontrivial solutions (not zero) for A_j the determinant of the coefficients in Eq. (14.4) must equal zero, that is:

$$\begin{vmatrix} b_{11} - a_{11}\lambda & b_{12} - a_{12}\lambda & \dots & b_{13N} - a_{13N}\lambda \\ b_{21} - a_{21}\lambda & b_{22} - a_{22}\lambda & \dots & b_{23N} - a_{23N}\lambda \\ \dots & \dots & \dots & \dots \\ b_{3N1} - a_{3N1}\lambda & b_{3N2} - a_{3N2}\lambda & \dots & b_{3N3N} - a_{3N3N}\lambda \end{vmatrix} = 0. \qquad (14.5)$$

Equation (14.5), called the secular determinant, may be solved for $3N$ values of λ and each value of λ can then be put back into Eq. (14.4) to calculate the corresponding values for A_j. Actually only the ratios of the A_j values, that is, the ratio of the amplitudes for each λ, can be determined but this is sufficient to describe the vibration. The results indicate that each atom is oscillating about its equilibrium position with amplitude A_j, generally different for each coordinate, but with the same frequency, $\sqrt{\lambda}/2\pi$, and phase constant, α. A vibration of this type, as already defined, is a normal mode of vibration or a fundamental frequency of the molecule.

The normal modes of vibration for the chloroform molecule are shown in Fig. 14.1. The actual job of calculating the frequencies $(\sqrt{\lambda}/2\pi)$ and amplitudes (A_j) by the method outlined is very difficult even for molecules with as few as four or five atoms and many improvements have been proposed. Other methods make use of different coordinate systems which serve to make the calculations somewhat less difficult. One method uses a linear transformation

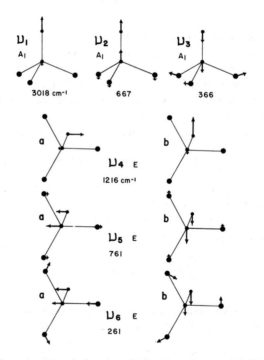

FIG. 14.1.   Normal modes of vibration of chloroform (schematic). Two components of each degenerate mode (E) are illustrated. ν_1 is mainly a C-H stretching vibration and ν_4 is mainly a C-H bending vibration. ν_2 and ν_5 involve C—Cl stretching but also involve some deformation. ν_3 and ν_6 are mainly CCl_3 deformation vibrations.

of the q coordinates to a new set of *normal coordinates* which affords some simplification by eliminating cross product terms in the kinetic and potential energy expressions (i.e., terms where $i \neq j$). The final equations, however, are still of $3N$ order and difficult to handle. The largest simplification comes from the symmetry characteristics of the molecule and may be approached by introduction of internal coordinates and symmetry coordinates. This method, introduced by Wilson,[7,8] will be briefly outlined and then discussed in detail using chloroform as an example.

14.2 Internal Coordinates

Internal coordinates are changes in bond lengths and in interbond angles. A method for obtaining complete sets has been given by Decius.[9] There are four general types; bond stretching, interbond angle deformation, torsion, and out-of-plane bending. Bond stretching, r, is a change in the interatomic bond distance and the number of coordinates of this type is given by:

$$n_r = b, \tag{14.6}$$

where b is the number of bonds (disregarding type, i.e., single, double, or triple) in the molecule. Angle deformation, ϕ, is a change in the interbond angle and the number of internal coordinates of this type is:

$$n_\phi = 4b - 3a + a_1, \tag{14.7}$$

where b is again the number of bonds, a is the number of atoms, and a_1 is the number of atoms of multiplicity one. The multiplicity of an atom is equal to the number of bonds meeting at the atom, again ignoring bond type. Torsion, τ, is a change in the dihedral angle formed by the planes which include atoms 1, 2, and 3 and atoms 2, 3, and 4 respectively in Fig. 14.2. The number of torsional coordinates would be:

$$n_\tau = b - a_1, \tag{14.8}$$

where b and a_1 are as previously defined. Out-of-plane bending, ϕ', occurs

[7] E. B. Wilson, Jr., *J. Chem. Phys.* **7**, 1047 (1937).
[8] E. B. Wilson, Jr., *J. Chem. Phys.* **9**, 76 (1941).
[9] J. C. Decius, *J. Chem. Phys.* **17**, 1315 (1949).

only in the case of a linear molecule or a linear subsection within a molecule. In the event of a linear molecule, one of the torsions is replaced by an out-of-plane bending for each linear subsection.

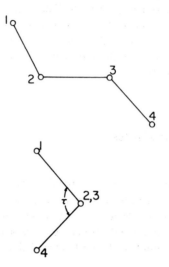

FIG. 14.2.   Dihedral angle for the internal coordinate involving torsion about a bond.

14.3 Symmetry Coordinates

Symmetry coordinates are linear combinations of the internal coordinates. The symmetry coordinates picked are not necessarily unique but must have definite properties. They must be normal, orthogonal, and they must transform properly; as will be described below. A symmetry coordinate has the form:

$$S_j = \sum_k U_{jk} r_k , \tag{14.9}$$

where S_j is the jth symmetry coordinate, r_k the kth internal coordinate and U_{jk} is a suitable coefficient for r_k . Since coordinates are not necessarily unique, a perfectly general method for obtaining them cannot be given. Several methods are available for obtaining trial coordinates. For example, a coordinate S_j^i may be given by[10]:

$$S_j^i = \sum_R \chi_i(R)\, RL_k , \tag{14.10}$$

[10] J. R. Nielson and L. H. Berryman, *J. Chem. Phys.* **17**, 659 (1949).

where $\chi_i(R)$ is the character for the vibration species $i(A_1$, etc.) and covering operation $R(C_3$, etc.) and is obtained from the group character table. RL_k is the coordinate which the generating coordinate, L_k, becomes when each operation, R, is performed and the equation is summed over all operations of the group. L_k is the "generating coordinate." L_k may be a single internal coordinate or some linear combination of internal coordinates.

The trial coordinates must be shown to have the necessary properties. The condition for normality is:

$$\sum_k U_{jk} U_{jk} = 1, \tag{14.11}$$

where U_{jk} is a coefficient in the jth symmetry coordinate and the summation is carried over the k internal coordinates. The condition therefore requires the sum of the squares of the coefficients in each symmetry coordinate be one.

The coordinates will be orthogonal if:

$$\sum_k U_{jk} U_{lk} = 0, \tag{14.12}$$

where l and j refer to different symmetry coordinates. That is, the coefficient of an internal coordinate in one symmetry coordinate is multiplied by the corresponding (same internal coordinate) coefficient in another symmetry coordinate and these products are summed over all internal coordinates. The summation must be zero and the same result must hold true for every symmetry coordinate applied to all the others for them to be mutually orthogonal.

The correctness of transformation can be shown by use of the point group character table and a table of transformations of the internal coordinates for each symmetry operation. The table of transformations lists what happens to each of the internal coordinates as a result of each of the covering operations. The coordinates may remain unchanged or become one of the other internal coordinates. Each of the covering operations is performed on the symmetry coordinate and the result is either no change (represented by a factor $+1$) or a new coordinate differing by a factor (-1 for nondegenerate vibrations). The factor (1 or -1) must be the same as the character of the covering operation for the vibration species to which the symmetry coordinate belongs. The case for degenerate species is somewhat more involved and will be discussed with the chloroform example.

14.4 The Calculation of Frequencies

The method for obtaining fundamental frequencies will only be outlined here and discussed in detail with the chloroform example. The potential energy of a molecule is expressed by the **F** matrix, which is given by the matrix multiplication:

$$\mathbf{F} = \mathbf{U}\mathbf{f}\mathbf{U}', \tag{14.13}$$

where **U** is the matrix formed by the coefficients of the symmetry coordinates, **U**′ is the transpose of **U**, and **f** is the matrix formed by the force constants.*

The kinetic energy is expressed by the **G** matrix and is a function of the atomic masses and molecular configuration, that is, the bond lengths and bond angles. The elements of the **G** matrix, for nondegenerate vibrations, are given by[†]:

$$G_{ij} = \sum_p \mu_p g_p S_i^{(t)} \cdot S_j^{(t)} , \tag{14.14}$$

* In matrix multiplication row elements on the left hand matrix, **A**, are multiplied by the corresponding column elements of the right hand matrix, **B**. The sums of the products of the corresponding elements give the elements of the resulting matrix, **C**. For example, the sum of the products for the first row (of **A**) and column (of **B**) gives the first element of the first row in **C**. The first row (of **A**) and second column (of **B**) gives the second element of the first row of **C**, etc. The second row (in **A**) is then multiplied by each column (in **B**) to give the second row elements of **C**, and the process continues for each row of **A**. The number of elements in the rows in **A** must be the same as the number of elements in the columns of **B**.

As an example, if

$$\mathbf{A} = \begin{Vmatrix} a & b & c \\ d & e & f \\ g & h & i \end{Vmatrix},$$

and

$$\mathbf{B} = \begin{Vmatrix} j & k \\ l & m \\ n & o \end{Vmatrix} :$$

AB = **C**, or

$$\begin{Vmatrix} a & b & c \\ d & e & f \\ g & h & i \end{Vmatrix} \begin{Vmatrix} j & k \\ l & m \\ n & o \end{Vmatrix} = \begin{Vmatrix} aj + bl + cn & ak + bm + co \\ dj + el + fn & dk + em + fo \\ gj + hl + in & gk + hm + io \end{Vmatrix}.$$

The transpose of a matrix is obtained by exchanging rows and columns. Thus the matrix,

$$\mathbf{A} = \begin{Vmatrix} a & b & c \\ d & e & f \\ g & h & i \end{Vmatrix},$$

has a transpose,

$$\mathbf{A}' = \begin{Vmatrix} a & d & g \\ b & e & h \\ c & f & i \end{Vmatrix}.$$

† The G elements for doubly degenerate vibrations are given by

$$G_{ij} = \frac{1}{2} \sum_p \mu_p g_p (S_{ia}^{(t)} \cdot S_{ja}^{(t)} + S_{ib}^{(t)} \cdot S_{jb}^{(t)}),$$

where the a and b subscripts refer to pairs of symmetry coordinates (see Section 14.7).

where i and j refer to the ith and jth symmetry coordinates, p refers to a set of equivalent atoms, t being a typical atom of the set, μ_p is the reciprocal mass of the typical atom, t, and g_p is the number of equivalent atoms in the pth set. The summation is carried over all sets. The dot indicates the scalar product of the **S** vectors. The **S** vectors are:

$$S_j^{(t)} = \sum_k U_{jk} s_{kt}, \qquad (14.15)$$

where j refers to the jth symmetry coordinate, t to the typical atom, U_{jk} to the coefficient of the kth internal coordinate, and the summation extends over all internal coordinates.

The s_{kt} vectors are expressed in terms of unit vectors along chemical bonds and their value depends on the type of motion involved. Referring to Fig. 14.3, the s_{kt} vectors for bond stretching are:

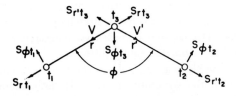

FIG. 14.3. s_{kt} vectors for bond stretching and angle bending.

$$s_{rt_1} = \mathbf{V},$$

$$s_{r't_2} = \mathbf{V'}, \qquad (14.16)$$

$$s_{rt_3} = -\mathbf{V},$$

and

$$s_{r't_3} = -\mathbf{V'},$$

where r and r' are the bond stretching coordinates and $\mathbf{V}$ and $\mathbf{V'}$ are the unit vectors. For angle deformation the s_{kt} vectors are:

$$s_{\phi t_1} = \frac{\cos\phi\ V - V'}{r\sin\phi}$$

$$s_{\phi t_2} = \frac{\cos\phi\ V' - V}{r'\sin\phi} \qquad (14.17)$$

$$s_{\phi t_3} = \frac{(r - r'\cos\phi)\,V - (r' - r\cos\phi)\,V'}{rr'\sin\phi}$$

where ϕ is the interbond angle and r and r' are the bond lengths. For a complete treatment of this type see, for example, Wilson, Decius, and Cross,[3] Chapter 4, or Meister and Cleveland.[11]

The **G** matrix, which has the form:

$$\mathbf{G} = \begin{Vmatrix} G_{11} & G_{12} & \dots & G_{1j} \\ G_{21} & G_{22} & \dots & G_{2j} \\ \dots & \dots & \dots & \dots \\ G_{i1} & G_{i2} & \dots & G_{ij} \end{Vmatrix} \tag{14.18}$$

is, however, more conveniently determined from known tabulated values. The method is similar to that used for obtaining the **F** matrix. The **G** matrix is given by the relation:

$$\mathbf{G} = \mathbf{UgU'} \tag{14.19}$$

where **U** and **U'** are the same matrices as defined in Eq. (14.13) and **g** is a matrix similar to the **f** matrix in form but involves kinetic energy elements, as described below. The elements of the **g** matrix are given in terms of the internal coordinates, such as bond stretching, r, and angle deformation, ϕ. Thus the element $g_{r\phi}$ would involve a stretching coordinate and a bending coordinate. Wilson, Decius, and Cross[3] have suggested a notation describing each element and have tabulated values for each.

As an example, the element, $g_{r\phi}$, above could be of three possible common types, depending on the structure involved. If both atoms, involved in the stretching coordinate, are also involved in the bending coordinate, the designation is $g_{r\phi}^2$. The superscript, two, indicates two common atoms. If, however, only one of the atoms involved in stretching also takes part in the bending, there are two possible situations. The common atom may be either, an end atom in the bending, or the central atom. The two elements are called $g_{r\phi}^1(_2^1)$ and $g_{r\phi}^1(_1^1)$, respectively. Representations of the commonly used kinetic energy elements, similar to that in Wilson, Decius, and Cross,[3] are shown in Fig. 14.4 The subscripts, r or ϕ, give the internal coordinates involved and the superscript the number of atoms common to both coordinates. (Here restricted to stretching and bending coordinates). The representations are schematic with atoms common to both coordinates shown as double circles on a horizontal line. Noncommon atoms for the first coordinate (first subscript) are on 45° lines above the horizontal and the noncommon atoms of the second coordinate on 45° lines below. A pair of numbers in parentheses, for example $g_{r\phi}(_2^1)$, gives the number of atoms on the top left line (top number) and on the bottom left line (bottom number). Each atom is identified by a number.

General formulas for g element values can be found in Appendix VI of Wilson, Decius, and Cross.[3]

[11] A. G. Meister and F. F. Cleveland, *Am. J. Phys.* **14**, 13 (1946).

Wilson, Decius, and Cross[3] also give special formulas for tetrahedral bond angles and 120° bond angles. Their use will be discussed in more detail in Section 14.9. For more complete tables, including torsion, out-of-plane bending, and cyclic structures, see Decius[9,12]. Ferigle and Meister[13] have discussed g elements for linear cases.

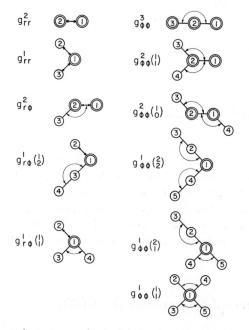

FIG. 14.4. Schematic representations of the g elements. (Redrawn from "Molecular Vibrations" by Wilson, Decius and Cross. Copyright 1955, McGraw-Hill Book Company, Inc. Used by permission.)

Once the **F** and **G** matrices are known, the secular determinant may be written. The determinant is of the form:

$$
\begin{vmatrix}
\sum_i G_{1i}F_{i1} - \lambda & \sum_j G_{1j}F_{j2} & \cdots & \sum_k G_{1k}F_{kn} \\
\sum_i G_{2i}F_{i1} & \sum_j G_{2j}F_{j2} - \lambda & \cdots & \sum_k G_{2k}F_{kn} \\
\cdots & \cdots & \cdots & \cdots \\
\sum_i G_{ni}F_{i1} & \sum_j G_{nj}F_{j2} & \cdots & \sum_k G_{nk}F_{kn} - \lambda
\end{vmatrix} = 0, \quad (14.20)
$$

[12] J. C. Decius, *J. Chem. Phys.* **16**, 1025 (1948).
[13] S. M. Ferigle and A. G. Meister, *J. Chem. Phys.* **19**, 982 (1951).

where the λ values are in sec^{-2}. Numerical values for the summations are obtained and an nth order determinant results which may be expanded to give a polynomial of order n. The equation may be solved using the Groeffe root squaring method (see Margenau and Murphy[5]) or some other convenient method to give n values for λ. The frequencies, ν, in cm^{-1}, are related to the λ values by the relation:

$$\lambda = 4\pi^2 c^2 \nu^2, \qquad (14.21)$$

where c is the velocity of light.

14.5   The $CHCl_3$ Molecule

The chloroform molecule has one threefold axis of symmetry, C_3, and three σ_v planes of symmetry. Chloroform thus belongs to the C_{3v} point group as discussed in Chapter 3. The symmetry elements, symmetry operations, selection rules, and vibration types have been discussed in detail in Section 3.6 where it was shown that chloroform has nine fundamental vibrations, three A_1 vibrations and three doubly degenerate type E vibrations.

14.6   The Internal Coordinates for $CHCl_3$

The chloroform molecule has five atoms, four having a multiplicity of one, and four bonds. Thus a is 5, b is 4, and a_1 is 4. Substitution of these values in the equations of Section 14.2 gives:

$$n_r = b = 4,$$
$$n_\phi = 4b - 3a + a_1 = 16 - 15 + 4 = 5, \qquad (14.22)$$

and

$$n_\tau = b - a_1 = 4 - 4 = 0,$$

giving chloroform only two types of internal coordinates, bond stretching and angle deformation. The internal coordinates are shown in Fig. 14.5 and are $r, t_1, t_2, t_3, \alpha_1, \alpha_2, \alpha_3, \beta_1, \beta_2$, and β_3; giving a total of ten internal coordinates or one more than necessary. (Since there are only nine fundamental vibrations.) However, in order to take advantage of the symmetry of the molecule, all ten will be used even though they are not all independent.

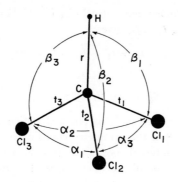

FIG. 14.5. Internal coordinates for chloroform.

14.7 The Symmetry Coordinates for CHCl₃

Symmetry coordinates for chloroform may be obtained from Eq. (14.10). The characters $[\chi_i(R)$ values] are obtained from the C_{3v} character table, shown in Table 14.1, and the generating coordinates, L_k, from the internal coordinates.

TABLE 14.1

C_{3v} CHARACTER TABLE

C_{3v}	I	C_3	σ_v
A_1	1	1	1
A_2	1	1	-1
E	2	-1	0 .

For example, using r as L_k and the $\chi_i(R)$ values for the A_1 class, Eq. (14.10) is:

$$S_j^i = \sum_R \chi_i(R)\, RL_k$$

$$S_1^{A_1} = (1)r + (1)r + (1)r + (1)r + (1)r + (1)r, \qquad (14.23)$$

since none of the symmetry operations, R, effect r, and all the characters for A_1 vibrations are one.* The correct coordinate, however, would be:

$$S_1 = r, \qquad (14.24)$$

* See Table 14.2 to conveniently obtain the RL_k values.

since Eq. (14.23) is obviously not normal ($\sum_k U_{jk}^2 \neq 1$) and the A_1 superscript has been omitted. Using t_1 as L_k gives:

$$S_2 = t_1 + t_2 + t_3 + t_1 + t_2 + t_3 = 2(t_1 + t_2 + t_3) \qquad (14.25)$$

which would be:

$$S_2 = 1/\sqrt{3}(t_1 + t_2 + t_3), \qquad (14.26)$$

since $(1/\sqrt{3})^2 + (1/\sqrt{3})^2 + (1/\sqrt{3})^2$ is one and the coordinate would then be normal. It can be seen that the symmetry coordinates from Eq. (14.10) have the correct ratio for the internal coordinates but the actual coefficient must be picked to give a normal coordinate. Two more A_1 symmetry coordinates are given by using $\alpha_1 - \beta_1$ and $\alpha_1 + \beta_1$ as L_k values to give:

$$S_3 = (\alpha_1 - \beta_1) + (\alpha_3 - \beta_3) + (\alpha_2 - \beta_2) + (\alpha_2 - \beta_2)$$
$$+ (\alpha_3 - \beta_3) + (\alpha_1 - \beta_1), \qquad (14.27)$$

and

$$S_4 = (\alpha_1 + \beta_1) + (\alpha_3 + \beta_3) + (\alpha_2 + \beta_2) + (\alpha_2 + \beta_2)$$
$$+ (\alpha_3 + \beta_3) + (\alpha_1 + \beta_1), \qquad (14.28)$$

respectively. The two normalized coordinates would then be:

$$S_3 = 1/\sqrt{6}(\alpha_1 + \alpha_2 + \alpha_3 - \beta_1 - \beta_2 - \beta_3), \qquad (14.29)$$

and

$$S_4 = 1/\sqrt{6}(\alpha_1 + \alpha_2 + \alpha_3 + \beta_1 + \beta_2 + \beta_3). \qquad (14.30)$$

There are only three A_1 vibrations for $CHCl_3$ and thus only three symmetry coordinates are necessary, indicating that one of the four is redundant and is either equal to zero or not independent of the others. This point will be discussed later in this section. The coordinates must first be shown to be orthogonal and transform properly. S_1 is orthogonal with S_2 since:

$$\sum_k U_{jk}U_{lk} = (1)(0) + (0)(1/3) + (0)(1/3) + (0)(1/3) = 0 \qquad (14.31)$$

and S_1 would also be orthogonal with S_3 and S_4 because no other internal coordinate appears in S_1 and r is not present in any other symmetry coordinate. The same is also true of S_2 since t_1, t_2, and t_3 are not present in any other symmetry coordinate and either U_{jk} or U_{lk} would always be zero. S_3 and S_4 are orthogonal because:

$$\sum_k U_{jk}U_{lk} = (1/\sqrt{6})(1/\sqrt{6}) + (1/\sqrt{6})(1/\sqrt{6}) + (1/\sqrt{6})(1/\sqrt{6})$$
$$+ (-1/\sqrt{6})(1/\sqrt{6}) + (-1/\sqrt{6})(1/\sqrt{6}) + (-1/\sqrt{6})(1/\sqrt{6}) = 0 \qquad (14.32)$$

and thus all four coordinates are mutually orthogonal.

TABLE 14.2

TRANSFORMATION OF INTERNAL COORDINATES

	I	C_3^+	C_3^-	σ_1	σ_2	σ_3
r	r	r	r	r	r	r
t_1	t_1	t_3	t_2	t_1	t_3	t_2
t_2	t_2	t_1	t_3	t_3	t_2	t_1
t_3	t_3	t_2	t_1	t_2	t_1	t_3
α_1	α_1	α_3	α_2	α_1	α_3	α_2
α_2	α_2	α_1	α_3	α_3	α_2	α_1
α_3	α_3	α_2	α_1	α_2	α_1	α_3
β_1	β_1	β_3	β_2	β_1	β_3	β_2
β_2	β_2	β_1	β_3	β_3	β_2	β_1
β_3	β_3	β_2	β_1	β_2	β_1	β_3

Correctness of transformation can be shown by use of Table 14.2 which is the table of transformations for the internal coordinates of chloroform. For example taking S_2 and performing the indicated symmetry operations:

$$(I)\ S_2 = 1/\sqrt{3}(t_1 + t_2 + t_3) = (1)\ S_2$$

$$(C_3^+)S_2 = 1/\sqrt{3}(t_3 + t_1 + t_2) = (1)\ S_2 \qquad (14.33)$$

$$(\sigma_{v_1})\ S_2 = 1/\sqrt{3}(t_1 + t_3 + t_2) = (1)\ S_2$$

which means the transformed coordinate is the same as the original or multiplication of the original coordinate by one gives the transformed coordinate. The characters for all covering operations for A_1 vibrations are one and thus S_2 transforms as an A_1 vibration. Referring to Table 14.2 it can easily be shown that all four coordinates are unchanged by all transformations and thus all have the plus one character necessary for A_1 vibrations.

The four coordinates which have been shown to have all the necessary characteristics for symmetry coordinates are:

$$S_1 = r$$

$$S_2 = 1/\sqrt{3}(t_1 + t_2 + t_3)$$

$$S_3 = 1/\sqrt{6}(\alpha_1 + \alpha_2 + \alpha_3 - \beta_1 - \beta_2 - \beta_3) \qquad (14.34)$$

$$S_4 = 1/\sqrt{6}(\alpha_1 + \alpha_2 + \alpha_3 + \beta_1 + \beta_2 + \beta_3) = 0$$

Since only three coordinates are necessary for the A_1 vibrations, S_4 may be picked as the redundant coordinate. This is permissible because the sum of all the changes around a point (the carbon atom) would be zero and thus not affect the kinetic or potential energies.

The E type vibrations introduces a somewhat different approach to the symmetry coordinates. There are also three E vibrations for chloroform but, since they are doubly degenerate, six symmetry coordinates are needed. The six will be three pairs, usually designated a and b. Generally each pair will involve the same type internal coordinate.

Taking t_1 as a generating coordinate and again using Eq. (14.10) of Section 14.3 with the characters for E vibrations gives:

$$S_{1a} = (2)t_1 + (-1)t_2 + (-1)t_3 + (0)t_1 + (0)t_3 + (0)t_2 = 2t_1 - t_2 - t_3$$
$$(14.35)$$

which must be multiplied by $1/\sqrt{6}$ to give the normal coordinate:

$$S_{1a} = 1/\sqrt{6}(2t_1 - t_2 - t_3). \qquad (14.36)$$

Similar coordinates may be obtained using α_1 and β_1 as generating coordinates to give:

$$S_{2a} = 1/\sqrt{6}(2\alpha_1 - \alpha_2 - \alpha_3) \qquad (14.37)$$

and

$$S_{3a} = 1/\sqrt{6}(2\beta_1 - \beta_2 - \beta_3) \qquad (14.38)$$

respectively.

The second coordinate of the first pair may be obtained using $t_2 - t_3$ as L_k to give:

$$\begin{aligned} S_{1b} &= 2(t_2 - t_3) + (-1)(t_1 - t_2) + (-1)(t_3 - t_1) + (0)(t_3 - t_2) + (0)(t_2 - t_1) \\ &\quad + (0)(t_1 - t_3) \\ &= 2t_2 - 2t_3 - t_1 + t_2 - t_3 + t_1 \\ &= 3(t_2 - t_3), \end{aligned} \qquad (14.39)$$

which multiplied by $1/3\sqrt{2}$ gives the normal coordinate:

$$S_{1b} = 1/\sqrt{2}(t_2 - t_3). \qquad (14.40)$$

Following the same procedure with $\alpha_2 - \alpha_3$ and $\beta_2 - \beta_3$ as generating coordinates gives:

$$S_{2b} = 1/\sqrt{2}(\alpha_2 - \alpha_3) \qquad (14.41)$$

and

$$S_{3b} = 1/\sqrt{2}(\beta_2 - \beta_3) \qquad (14.42)$$

respectively.

The six coordinates must be proved orthogonal. S_{1a} and S_{1b} are orthogonal since:

$$\sum_k U_{jk}U_{lk} = (2/\sqrt{6})(0) + (-1/\sqrt{6})(1/\sqrt{2}) + (1/\sqrt{6})(-1/\sqrt{2}) = 0$$
$$(14.43)$$

S_{1a} and S_{1b} are obviously orthogonal with the other four coordinates because no t appears in S_{2a}, S_{2b}, S_{3a}, or S_{3b}. In the same way S_{2a} and S_{2b} and S_{3a} and S_{3b} can be shown to be orthogonal with each other.

The correctness of transformation for the coordinates of degenerate vibrations differs from the A_1 coordinates because a covering operation applied to one of a pair of E coordinates does not give the same coordinate or its negative. Instead a linear combination of the two coordinates forming the pair is produced. For example when the identity operation, I, is applied to S_{1a}:

$$(I)S_{1a} = 1/\sqrt{6}(2t_1 - t_2 - t_3) = AS_{1a} + BS_{1b} \qquad (14.44)$$

or

$$1/\sqrt{6}(2t_1 - t_2 - t_3) = A(2t_1 - t_2 - t_3)\,1/\sqrt{6} + B(t_2 - t_3)\,1/\sqrt{2} \qquad (14.45)$$

where A and B are constants. Doing the same for S_{1b} gives:

$$(I)S_{1b} = 1/\sqrt{2}(t_2 - t_3) = A'S_{1a} + B'S_{1b} \qquad (14.46)$$

or

$$1/\sqrt{2}(t_2 - t_3) = A'(2t_1 - t_2 - t_3)\,1/\sqrt{6} + B'(t_2 - t_3)\,1/\sqrt{2} \qquad (14.47)$$

where A' and B' are constants. By equating coefficients the constants may be found. For example using t_1 in Eq. (14.45) gives:

$$2A/\sqrt{6} = 2/\sqrt{6}$$
$$A = 1 \qquad (14.48)$$

or using t_2 in the same equations:

$$-A/\sqrt{6} + B/\sqrt{2} = -1/\sqrt{6} \qquad (14.49)$$

and since A is one

$$B/\sqrt{2} = -1/\sqrt{6} + 1/\sqrt{6} = 0 \qquad (14.50)$$
$$B = 0$$

In the same way A' can be shown to be zero and B' to be one. Then, forming the matrix:

$$\left\|\begin{matrix} A & B \\ A' & B' \end{matrix}\right\| = \left\|\begin{matrix} 1 & 0 \\ 0 & 1 \end{matrix}\right\| \qquad (14.51)$$

in which the sum of the elements along the principal diagonal is two, it can be seen that this is the character for E vibrations under the identity operation and thus S_{1a} and S_{1b} transform properly.

Following the same procedure with the C_3^+ operations gives:

$$(C_3^+)\,S_{1a} = (2t_3 - t_1 - t_2)\,1/\sqrt{6} = A(2t_1 - t_2 - t_3)\,1/\sqrt{6} + B(t_2 - t_3)\,1/\sqrt{2} \qquad (14.52)$$

and

$$(C_3^+) \, S_{1b} = (t_1 - t_2) \, 1/\sqrt{2} = A'(2t_1 - t_2 - t_3) \, 1/\sqrt{6} + B'(t_2 - t_3) \, 1/\sqrt{2} \tag{14.53}$$

Equating coefficients for t_1 in Eq. (14.52):

$$2A/\sqrt{6} = -1/\sqrt{6}$$
$$A = -1/2 \tag{14.54}$$

and for t_2 in the same equation:

$$-A/\sqrt{6} + B/\sqrt{2} = -1/\sqrt{6} \tag{14.55}$$

and since A is $-1/2$:

$$\tfrac{1}{2}/\sqrt{6} + B/\sqrt{2} = -1/\sqrt{6}$$
$$B = -\sqrt{3}/2. \tag{14.56}$$

In the same way, using Eq. (14.53), A' is $\sqrt{3}/2$ and B' is $-1/2$ to give the matrix:

$$\left\| \begin{matrix} A & B \\ A' & B' \end{matrix} \right\| = \left\| \begin{matrix} -1/2 & -\sqrt{3}/2 \\ \sqrt{3}/2 & -1/2 \end{matrix} \right\| \tag{14.57}$$

in which the principal diagonal is -1 in agreement with the character for E vibrations under C_3^+.

The matrix for the C_3^- operation is:

$$\left\| \begin{matrix} A & B \\ A' & B' \end{matrix} \right\| = \left\| \begin{matrix} -1/2 & \sqrt{3}/2 \\ -\sqrt{3}/2 & -1/2 \end{matrix} \right\| \tag{14.58}$$

again giving the correct -1 character. The matrices for the three σ_v reflections are:

$$\left\| \begin{matrix} A & B \\ A' & B' \end{matrix} \right\| = \left\| \begin{matrix} 1 & 0 \\ 0 & -1 \end{matrix} \right\|$$

$$\left\| \begin{matrix} A & B \\ A' & B' \end{matrix} \right\| = \left\| \begin{matrix} -1/2 & -\sqrt{3}/2 \\ -\sqrt{3}/2 & 1/2 \end{matrix} \right\| \tag{14.59}$$

$$\left\| \begin{matrix} A & B \\ A' & B' \end{matrix} \right\| = \left\| \begin{matrix} -1/2 & \sqrt{3}/2 \\ \sqrt{3}/2 & 1/2 \end{matrix} \right\|$$

in which the sum of the elements along the principal diagonal is zero for all three, which is the character for E vibrations under σ_v.

Before leaving the discussion of symmetry coordinates it should be mentioned that the choice of generating coordinates has been somewhat arbitrary and others might have been tried first.

For example if $t_1 - t_2$ were used instead of $t_2 - t_3$ the S_{1b} coordinate would be:

$$S_{1b}^* = 1/\sqrt{2}(t_1 - t_2) \tag{14.60}$$

instead of Eq. (14.40). However this coordinate would not be orthogonal with S_{1a} since:

$$\sum_k U_{jk} U_{1k} = (2/\sqrt{6})(1/\sqrt{2}) + (-1/\sqrt{6})(-1/\sqrt{2}) + (-1/\sqrt{6})(0) \neq 0 \tag{14.61}$$

and the pair S_{1b}^* and S_{1a} would not transform properly since:

$$\left\| \begin{matrix} A & B \\ A' & B' \end{matrix} \right\| = \left\| \begin{matrix} -1/2 & 0 \\ -3 & 1 \end{matrix} \right\| \tag{14.62}$$

is the matrix for the C_3^+ operation and the sum of the elements along the principal diagonal is not -1 as it should be for an E vibration.

On the other hand it is possible that several generating coordinates may give identical symmetry coordinates. The problem then is to try various generating coordinates until a sufficient number of proper symmetry coordinates is obtained. The symmetry coordinates are represented in Fig. 14.6.

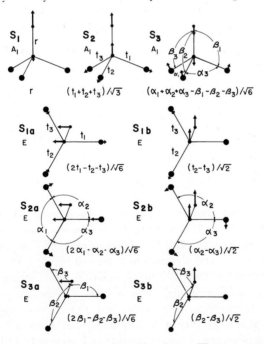

Fig. 14.6. Symmetry coordinates for chloroform. These symmetry coordinate drawings indicate schematically the major motions resulting from specified combinations of internal coordinates. The normal modes of vibration can be expressed as combinations of symmetry coordinates, with appropriate coefficients.

14.8   The F Matrix for $CHCl_3$

The potential energy of a molecule has been shown to have the form of Eq. (14.1) and can be expressed as:

$$2V = \sum f_{ik} r_i r_k , \tag{14.63}$$

where f_{ik} equals f_{ki} and the summation is extended over all coordinates. Here internal coordinates are used and the f_{ik} values are corresponding force constants. For the chloroform molecule the expression for the potential energy (the potential function) is:

$$
\begin{aligned}
2V = {} & f_r[r^2] + f_t[(t_1)^2 + (t_2)^2 + (t_3)^2] + d^2 f_\alpha[(\alpha_1)^2 + (\alpha_2)^2 + (\alpha_3)^2] + d^2 f_\beta[(\beta_1)^2 \\
& + (\beta_2)^2 + (\beta_3)^2] + 2f_{rt}[(r)(t_1) + (r)(t_2) + (r)(t_3)] + 2f_{tt}[(t_1)(t_2) \\
& + (t_1)(t_3) + (t_2)(t_3)] + 2d^2 f_{\alpha\alpha}[(\alpha_1)(\alpha_2) + (\alpha_1)(\alpha_3) + (\alpha_2)(\alpha_3)] \\
& + 2d^2 f_{\beta\beta}[(\beta_1)(\beta_2) + (\beta_1)(\beta_3) + (\beta_2)(\beta_3)] + 2df_{r\alpha}[(r)(\alpha_1) + (r)(\alpha_2) \\
& + (r)(\alpha_3)] + 2df_{r\beta}[(r)(\beta_1) + (r)(\beta_2) + (r)(\beta_3)] + 2df'_{t\alpha}[(t_1)(\alpha_1) \\
& + (t_2)(\alpha_2) + (t_3)(\alpha_3)] + 2df_{t\alpha}[(t_1)(\alpha_2) + (t_1)(\alpha_3) + (t_2)(\alpha_1) \\
& + (t_2)(\alpha_3) + (t_3)(\alpha_1) + (t_3)(\alpha_2)] + 2df_{t\beta}[(t_1)(\beta_1) + (t_2)(\beta_2) \\
& + (t_3)(\beta_3)] + 2df'_{t\beta}[(t_1)(\beta_2) + (t_1)(\beta_3) + (t_2)(\beta_1) + (t_2)(\beta_3) \\
& + (t_3)(\beta_1) + (t_3)(\beta_2)] + 2d^2 f'_{\alpha\beta}[(\alpha_1)(\beta_1) + (\alpha_2)(\beta_2) + (\alpha_3)(\beta_3)] \\
& + 2d^2 f_{\alpha\beta}[(\alpha_1)(\beta_2) + (\alpha_1)(\beta_3) + (\alpha_2)(\beta_1) + (\alpha_2)(\beta_3) \\
& + (\alpha_3)(\beta_1) + (\alpha_3)(\beta_2)] , \tag{14.64}
\end{aligned}
$$

where any force constants involving an angle deformation have been multiplied by a distance d (or d^2) to allow consistant units, for the force constants, in dynes per centimeter. See Section 14.10 for further discussion. The potential function, as written, is complete and all terms but one will be used. However, generally many of the force constants for the interaction terms would be unavailable and would have to be neglected. This is because there are many more force constants than frequencies. If possible, only those terms having little effect on the potential energy should be neglected. See Crawford and Brinkley[14] for a discussion of choice of force constants and Section 14.14 for approximate potential functions.

[14] B. E. Crawford and S. R. Brinkley, *J. Chem. Phys.* **9**, 69 (1941).

Instead of expressing the potential energy in terms of internal coordinates, symmetry coordinates can be used. Following the procedure of Meister and Cleveland,[11] the expression, corresponding to Eq. (14.63), would be:

$$2V = \sum F_{jl} S_j S_l ,\qquad (14.65)$$

where F_{jl} equals F_{lj} and the summation extends over all symmetry coordinates. Equations (14.63) and (14.65) may be written in matrix form,* to give:

$$2V = \mathbf{r'fr}\qquad (14.66)$$

and

$$2V = \mathbf{S'FS},\qquad (14.67)$$

where $\mathbf{f}$ is the force constant matrix, $\mathbf{r}$ and $\mathbf{S}$ are matrices of the internal coordinates and symmetry coordinates respectively, and $\mathbf{r'}$ and $\mathbf{S'}$ their corresponding transposes. $\mathbf{F}$ is a matrix whose elements are linear combinations of the force constants. Equation (14.9) of Section 14.3, in matrix form, is:

$$\mathbf{S} = \mathbf{Ur},\qquad (14.68)$$

and multiplication by the inverse matrix, U^{-1}, gives:

$$\mathbf{U^{-1} S} = \mathbf{U^{-1} U r} \equiv \mathbf{I r} \equiv \mathbf{r},\qquad (14.69)$$

where $\mathbf{I}$ is the identity matrix (which also defines the inverse, i.e., $\mathbf{U^{-1} U} = \mathbf{I}$). Since the symmetry coordinates are normal and orthogonal, the inverse, $\mathbf{U^{-1}}$, is equal to the transpose, $\mathbf{U'}$, and Eq. (14.69) can be written:

$$\mathbf{r} = \mathbf{U^{-1} S} = \mathbf{U' S}.\qquad (14.70)$$

Using Eq. (14.70) for $\mathbf{r}$, its transpose, $\mathbf{r'}$, is:

$$\mathbf{r'} = \mathbf{(U' S)'} = \mathbf{S'U},\qquad (14.71)$$

since the transpose of a product is the product of the transposes, taken in reverse order. Equating (14.66) and (14.67) gives:

$$\mathbf{r'fr} = \mathbf{S'FS},\qquad (14.72)$$

* See Margenau and Murphy[5] for an introduction to matrices.

and using (14.70) and (14.71) for $\mathbf{r}$ and $\mathbf{r}'$, gives:

$$\mathbf{S'U f U'S = S'F S},\qquad(14.73)$$

or

$$\mathbf{F = U F U'},\qquad(14.74)$$

which is the $\mathbf{F}$ matrix, as introduced in Eq. (14.13). In general an $\mathbf{F}$ matrix will be determined for each vibrational species, which for chloroform are A_1 and E. Only A_1 symmetry coordinates are used for the $\mathbf{U}$ matrix when calculating the $\mathbf{F}$ matrix for A_1 vibrations and correspondingly, only the E coordinates, when determining the $\mathbf{F}$ matrix for E vibrations. The complete $\mathbf{f}$ matrix is used in each case.

The $\mathbf{f}$ matrix for chloroform is:

		r	t_1	t_2	t_3	α_1	α_2	α_3	β_1	β_2	β_3
	r	f_r	f_{rt}	f_{rt}	f_{rt}	$df_{r\alpha}$	$df_{r\alpha}$	$df_{r\alpha}$	$df_{r\beta}$	$df_{r\beta}$	$df_{r\beta}$
	t_1		f_t	f_{tt}	f_{tt}	$df'_{t\alpha}$	$df_{t\alpha}$	$df_{t\alpha}$	$df_{t\beta}$	$df'_{t\beta}$	$df'_{t\beta}$
	t_2			f_t	f_{tt}	$df_{t\alpha}$	$df'_{t\alpha}$	$df_{t\alpha}$	$df'_{t\beta}$	$df_{t\beta}$	$df'_{t\beta}$
	t_3				f_t	$df_{t\alpha}$	$df_{t\alpha}$	$df'_{t\alpha}$	$df'_{t\beta}$	$df'_{t\beta}$	$df_{t\beta}$
$f =$	α_1	Symmetric				d^2f_α	$d^2f_{\alpha\alpha}$	$d^2f_{\alpha\alpha}$	$d^2f'_{\alpha\beta}$	$d^2f_{\alpha\beta}$	$d^2f_{\alpha\beta}$
	α_2	about					d^2f_α	$d^2f_{\alpha\alpha}$	$d^2f_{\alpha\beta}$	$d^2f'_{\alpha\beta}$	$d^2f_{\alpha\beta}$
	α_3	diagonal						d^2f_α	$d^2f_{\alpha\beta}$	$d^2f_{\alpha\beta}$	$d^2f'_{\alpha\beta}$
	β_1								d^2f_β	$d^2f_{\beta\beta}$	$d^2f_{\beta\beta}$
	β_2									d^2f_β	$d^2f_{\beta\beta}$
	β_3										d^2f_β ,

$$(14.75)$$

and corresponds to the potential function written in Eq. (14.64). The $\mathbf{U}$ matrix for the A_1 vibrations, derived from the symmetry coordinates of Eq. (14.34), is:

A_1	r	t_1	t_2	t_3	α_1	α_2	α_3	β_1	β_2	β_3
S_1	1	0	0	0	0	0	0	0	0	0
$\mathbf{U} = S_2$	0	$\dfrac{1}{\sqrt{3}}$	$\dfrac{1}{\sqrt{3}}$	$\dfrac{1}{\sqrt{3}}$	0	0	0	0	0	0
S_2	0	0	0	0	$\dfrac{1}{\sqrt{6}}$	$\dfrac{1}{\sqrt{6}}$	$\dfrac{1}{\sqrt{6}}$	$\dfrac{-1}{\sqrt{6}}$	$\dfrac{-1}{\sqrt{6}}$	$\dfrac{-1}{\sqrt{6}}$,

$$(14.76)$$

and exchanging rows and columns gives the transpose, $\mathbf{U}'$:

$$\mathbf{U}' = \begin{Vmatrix} 1 & 0 & 0 \\ 0 & \dfrac{1}{\sqrt{3}} & 0 \\ 0 & \dfrac{1}{\sqrt{3}} & 0 \\ 0 & \dfrac{1}{\sqrt{3}} & 0 \\ 0 & 0 & \dfrac{1}{\sqrt{6}} \\ 0 & 0 & \dfrac{1}{\sqrt{6}} \\ 0 & 0 & \dfrac{1}{\sqrt{6}} \\ 0 & 0 & \dfrac{-1}{\sqrt{6}} \\ 0 & 0 & \dfrac{-1}{\sqrt{6}} \\ 0 & 0 & \dfrac{-1}{\sqrt{6}} \end{Vmatrix} \qquad (14.77)$$

The $\mathbf{F}$ matrix for the $\hat{A}_1$ vibrations may now be obtained by matrix multiplication. The product $\mathbf{fU}'$ is first obtained and then the product of $\mathbf{U}$ and $\mathbf{fU}'$ to give $\mathbf{UfU}'$, that is, the $\mathbf{F}$ matrix. The first step is:

$$\mathbf{fU}' = \begin{Vmatrix} f_r & 1/\sqrt{3}\,(3f_{rt}) & 1/\sqrt{6}\,(3df_{r\alpha} - 3df_{r\beta}) \\ f_{rt} & 1/\sqrt{3}\,(f_t + 2f_{tt}) & 1/\sqrt{6}\,(df'_{t\alpha} + 2df_{t\alpha} - df_{t\beta} - 2df'_{t\beta}) \\ f_{rt} & 1/\sqrt{3}\,(f_t + 2f_{tt}) & 1/\sqrt{6}\,(df'_{t\alpha} + 2df_{t\alpha} - df_{t\beta} - 2df'_{t\beta}) \\ f_{rt} & 1/\sqrt{3}\,(f_t + 2f_{tt}) & 1/\sqrt{6}\,(df'_{\alpha} + 2df_{t\alpha} - df_{t\beta} - 2df'_{t\beta}) \\ df_{r\alpha} & 1/\sqrt{3}\,(df'_{t\alpha} + 2df_{t\alpha}) & 1/\sqrt{6}\,(d^2f_{\alpha} + 2d^2f_{\alpha\alpha} - d^2f'_{\alpha\beta} - 2d^2f_{\alpha\beta}) \\ df_{r\alpha} & 1/\sqrt{3}\,(df'_{t\alpha} + 2df_{t\alpha}) & 1/\sqrt{6}\,(d^2f_{\alpha} + 2d^2f_{\alpha\alpha} - d^2f'_{\alpha\beta} - 2d^2f_{\alpha\beta}) \\ df_{r\alpha} & 1/\sqrt{3}\,(df'_{\alpha} + 2df_{t\alpha}) & 1/\sqrt{6}\,(d^2f_{\alpha} + 2d^2f_{\alpha\alpha} - d^2f'_{\alpha\beta} - 2d^2f_{\alpha\beta}) \\ df_{r\beta} & 1/\sqrt{3}\,(df_{t\beta} + 2df'_{t\beta}) & 1/\sqrt{6}\,(d^2f'_{\alpha\beta} + 2d^2f_{\alpha\beta} - d^2f_{\beta} - 2d^2f_{\beta\beta}) \\ df_{r\beta} & 1/\sqrt{3}\,(df_{t\beta} + 2df'_{t\beta}) & 1/\sqrt{6}\,(d^2f'_{\alpha\beta} + 2d^2f_{\alpha\beta} - d^2f_{\beta} - 2d^2f_{\beta\beta}) \\ df_{r\beta} & 1/\sqrt{3}\,(df_{t\beta} + 2df'_{t\beta}) & 1/\sqrt{6}\,(d^2f'_{\alpha\beta} + 2d^2f_{\alpha\beta} - d^2f_{\beta} - 2d^2f_{\beta\beta}) \end{Vmatrix}$$

$$(14.78)$$

where each entry of the rows of the **f** matrix are multiplied by the corresponding column entry of the **U**′ matrix. Equation (14.78) is then multiplied by **U** to give:

$$\mathbf{UfU'} = \begin{Vmatrix} f_r & \sqrt{3}f_{rt} & 3/\sqrt{6}\,(df_{r\alpha} - df_{r\beta}) \\ \sqrt{3}f_{rt} & f_t + 2f_{tt} & 1/\sqrt{2}\,(2df_{t\alpha} - df_{t\beta} \\ & & + df'_{t\alpha} - 2df'_{t\beta}) \\ 3/\sqrt{6}\,(df_{r\alpha} - df_{r\beta}) & 1/\sqrt{2}\,(2df_{t\alpha} - df_{t\beta} & 1/2\,(d^2f_\alpha + d^2f_\beta + 2d^2f_{\alpha\alpha} \\ & + df'_{t\alpha} - 2df'_{t\beta}) & + 2d^2f_{\beta\beta} - 2d^2f'_{\alpha\beta} - 4d^2f_{\alpha\beta}) \end{Vmatrix}$$

$$(14.79)$$

which is the **F** matrix for the A_1 vibrations.

The **F** matrix for the E vibrations is obtained in the same way except that the **U** and **U**′ matrices from the E symmetry coordinates are used. Either the a or the b sets may be used and will give the same final result for the **F** matrix. The **U** matrix from the b set of E coordinates would be:

E	r	t_1	t_2	t_3	α_1	α_2	α_3	β_1	β_2	β_3
S_{1b}	0	0	$1/\sqrt{2}$	$-1/\sqrt{2}$	0	0	0	0	0	0
S_{2b}	0	0	0	0	0	$1/\sqrt{2}$	$-1/\sqrt{2}$	0	0	0
S_{3b}	0	0	0	0	0	0	0	0	$1/\sqrt{2}$	$-1/\sqrt{2}$

$$(14.80)$$

and the **U**′ matrix would be:

$$\mathbf{U'} = \begin{Vmatrix} 0 & 0 & 0 \\ 0 & 0 & 0 \\ 1/\sqrt{2} & 0 & 0 \\ -1/\sqrt{2} & 0 & 0 \\ 0 & 0 & 0 \\ 0 & 1/\sqrt{2} & 0 \\ 0 & -1/\sqrt{2} & 0 \\ 0 & 0 & 0 \\ 0 & 0 & 1/\sqrt{2} \\ 0 & 0 & -1/\sqrt{2} \end{Vmatrix}$$

$$(14.81)$$

The matrix multiplication of $\mathbf{f}\,\mathbf{U}'$ gives:

$$\mathbf{fU}' = \begin{Vmatrix} 0 & 0 & 0 \\ 0 & 0 & 0 \\ \dfrac{1}{\sqrt{2}}(f_t - f_{tt}) & \dfrac{1}{\sqrt{2}}(df'_{t\alpha} - df_{t\alpha}) & \dfrac{1}{\sqrt{2}}(df_{t\beta} - df'_{t\beta}) \\ \dfrac{1}{\sqrt{2}}(f_{tt} - f_t) & \dfrac{1}{\sqrt{2}}(df_{t\alpha} - df'_{t\alpha}) & \dfrac{1}{\sqrt{2}}(df'_{t\beta} - df_{t\beta}) \\ 0 & 0 & 0 \\ \dfrac{1}{\sqrt{2}}(df'_{t\alpha} - df_{t\alpha}) & \dfrac{1}{\sqrt{2}}(d^2f_\alpha - d^2f_{\alpha\alpha}) & \dfrac{1}{\sqrt{2}}(d^2f'_{\alpha\beta} - d^2f_{\alpha\beta}) \\ \dfrac{1}{\sqrt{2}}(df_{t\alpha} - df'_{t\alpha}) & \dfrac{1}{\sqrt{2}}(d^2f_{\alpha\alpha} - d^2f_\alpha) & \dfrac{1}{\sqrt{2}}(d^2f_{\alpha\beta} - d^2f'_{\alpha\beta}) \\ 0 & 0 & 0 \\ \dfrac{1}{\sqrt{2}}(df_{t\beta} - df'_{t\beta}) & \dfrac{1}{\sqrt{2}}(d^2f'_{\alpha\beta} - d^2f_{\alpha\beta}) & \dfrac{1}{\sqrt{2}}(d^2f_\beta - d^2f_{\beta\beta}) \\ \dfrac{1}{\sqrt{2}}(df'_{t\beta} - df_{t\beta}) & \dfrac{1}{\sqrt{2}}(d^2f_{\alpha\beta} - d^2f'_{\alpha\beta}) & \dfrac{1}{\sqrt{2}}(d^2f_{\beta\beta} - d^2f_\beta) \end{Vmatrix} \quad (14.82)$$

and multiplication by $\mathbf{U}$, Eq. (14.80), gives:

$$\mathbf{UfU}' = \begin{Vmatrix} f_t - f_{tt} & df'_{t\alpha} - df_{t\alpha} & df_{t\beta} - df'_{t\beta} \\ df'_{t\alpha} - df_{t\alpha} & d^2f_\alpha - d^2f_{\alpha\alpha} & d^2f'_{\alpha\beta} - d^2f_{\alpha\beta} \\ df_{t\beta} - df'_{t\beta} & d^2f'_{\alpha\beta} - d^2f_{\alpha\beta} & d^2f_\beta - d^2f_{\beta\beta} \end{Vmatrix}, \quad (14.83)$$

which is the $\mathbf{F}$ matrix for the E vibrations.

14.9 The G Matrix for CHCl₃

As shown by Eq. (14.19), the $\mathbf{G}$ matrix is given by matrix multiplication from the relation:

$$\mathbf{G} = \mathbf{U}\,\mathbf{g}\,\mathbf{U}', \quad (14.84)$$

in a manner similar to that for the **F** matrix. The **g** matrix for chloroform would be:

	r	t_1	t_2	t_3	α_1	α_2	α_3	β_1	β_2	β_3
r	g_{rr}	g_{rt_1}	g_{rt_2}	g_{rt_3}	$g_{r\alpha_1}$	$g_{r\alpha_2}$	$g_{r\alpha_3}$	$g_{r\beta_1}$	$g_{r\beta_2}$	$g_{r\beta_3}$
t_1		$g_{t_1t_1}$	$g_{t_1t_2}$	$g_{t_1t_3}$	$g_{t_1\alpha_1}$	$g_{t_1\alpha_2}$	$g_{t_1\alpha_3}$	$g_{t_1\beta_1}$	$g_{t_1\beta_2}$	$g_{t_1\beta_3}$
t_2			$g_{t_2t_2}$	$g_{t_2t_3}$	$g_{t_2\alpha_1}$	$g_{t_2\alpha_2}$	$g_{t_2\alpha_3}$	$g_{t_2\beta_1}$	$g_{t_2\beta_2}$	$g_{t_2\beta_3}$
t_3				$g_{t_3t_3}$	$g_{t_3\alpha_1}$	$g_{t_2\alpha_2}$	$g_{t_3\alpha_3}$	$g_{t_3\beta_1}$	$g_{t_3\beta_2}$	$g_{t_3\beta_3}$
α_1	Symmetric				$g_{\alpha_1\alpha_1}$	$g_{\alpha_1\alpha_2}$	$g_{\alpha_1\alpha_3}$	$g_{\alpha_1\beta_1}$	$g_{\alpha_1\beta_2}$	$g_{\alpha_1\beta_3}$
α_1		about				$g_{\alpha_2\alpha_2}$	$g_{\alpha_2\alpha_3}$	$g_{\alpha_2\beta_1}$	$g_{\alpha_2\beta_2}$	$g_{\alpha_2\beta_3}$
α_3			diagonal				$g_{\alpha_3\alpha_3}$	$g_{\alpha_3\beta_1}$	$g_{\alpha_3\beta_2}$	$g_{\alpha_3\beta_3}$
β_1								$g_{\beta_1\beta_1}$	$g_{\beta_1\beta_2}$	$g_{\beta_1\beta_3}$
β_2									$g_{\beta_2\beta_2}$	$g_{\beta_2\beta_3}$
β_3										$g_{\beta_3\beta_3}$

$$(14.85)$$

where the same designations for internal coordinates, as was used in the **f** matrix, are included. However, due to the symmetry of the molecule, many of the **g** elements are equivalent. The equivalent elements are listed in the following equations:

$$g_{rr} = g_r = [g_{rr}^2], \tag{14.86}$$

$$g_{rt_1} = g_{rt_2} = g_{rt_3} = g_{rt} = [g_{rr}^1], \tag{14.87}$$

$$g_{r\alpha_1} = g_{r\alpha_2} = g_{r\alpha_3} = g_{r\alpha} = [g_{r\phi}^1\binom{1}{1})], \tag{14.88}$$

$$g_{r\beta_1} = g_{r\beta_2} = g_{r\beta_3} = g_{r\beta} = [g_{r\phi}^2], \tag{14.89}$$

$$g_{t_1t_1} = g_{t_2t_2} = g_{t_3t_3} = g_t = [g_{rr}^2], \tag{14.90}$$

$$g_{t_1t_2} = g_{t_1t_3} = g_{t_2t_3} = g_{tt} = [g_{rr}^1], \tag{14.91}$$

$$g_{t_1\alpha_1} = g_{t_2\alpha_2} = g_{t_3\alpha_3} = g'_{t\alpha} = [g_{r\phi}^1\binom{1}{1})], \tag{14.92}$$

$$g_{t_1\alpha_2} = g_{t_1\alpha_3} = g_{t_2\alpha_1} = g_{t_2\alpha_3} = g_{t_3\alpha_1} = g_{t_3\alpha_2} = g_{t\alpha} = [g_{r\phi}^2], \tag{14.93}$$

$$g_{t_1\beta_1} = g_{t_2\beta_2} = g_{t_3\beta_3} = g_{t\beta} = [g_{r\phi}^2], \tag{14.94}$$

$$g_{t_1\beta_2} = g_{t_1\beta_3} = g_{t_2\beta_1} = g_{t_2\beta_3} = g_{t_3\beta_1} = g_{t_3\beta_2} = g'_{t\beta} = [g^1_{r\phi}(^1_1)], \quad (14.95)$$

$$g_{\alpha_1\alpha_1} = g_{\alpha_2\alpha_2} = g_{\alpha_3\alpha_3} = g_\alpha = [g^3_{\phi\phi}], \quad (14.96)$$

$$g_{\alpha_1\alpha_2} = g_{\alpha_1\alpha_3} = g_{\alpha_2\alpha_3} = g_{\alpha\alpha} = [g^2_{\phi\phi}(^1_1)], \quad (14.97)$$

$$g_{\alpha_1\beta_1} = g_{\alpha_2\beta_2} = g_{\alpha_3\beta_3} = g'_{\alpha\beta} = [g^1_{\phi\phi}(^1_1)], \quad (14.98)$$

$$g_{\alpha_1\beta_2} = g_{\alpha_1\beta_3} = g_{\alpha_2\beta_3} = g_{\alpha\beta} = [g^2_{\phi\phi}(^1_1)], \quad (14.99)$$

$$g_{\beta_1\beta_1} = g_{\beta_2\beta_2} = g_{\beta_3\beta_3} = g_\beta = [g^3_{\phi\phi}], \quad (14.100)$$

and

$$g_{\beta_1\beta_2} = g_{\beta_1\beta_3} = g_{\beta_2\beta_3} = g_{\beta\beta} = [g^2_{\phi\phi}(^1_1)], \quad (14.101)$$

where the equivalent g elements are listed and given a common symbol, which will give a **g** matrix consistent with that for the **f** matrix. See Fig. 14.5, showing the internal coordinates, for justification of the equivalencies listed. The Decius[3] notation for each element is also included in brackets. See Fig. 14.4 and Fig. 14.5. The **g** matrix, simplified by use of the single symbol for equivalent elements, is:

$$\mathbf{g} = \begin{Vmatrix} g_r & g_{rt} & g_{rt} & g_{rt} & g_{r\alpha} & g_{r\alpha} & g_{r\alpha} & g_{r\beta} & g_{r\beta} & g_{r\beta} \\ & g_t & g_{tt} & g_{tt} & g'_{t\alpha} & g_{t\alpha} & g_{t\alpha} & g_{t\beta} & g'_{t\beta} & g'_{t\beta} \\ & & g_t & g_{tt} & g_{t\alpha} & g'_{t\alpha} & g_{t\alpha} & g'_{t\beta} & g_{t\beta} & g'_{t\beta} \\ & & & g_t & g_{t\alpha} & g_{t\alpha} & g'_{t\alpha} & g'_{t\beta} & g'_{t\beta} & g_{t\beta} \\ & \text{Symmetric} & & & g_\alpha & g_{\alpha\alpha} & g_{\alpha\alpha} & g'_{\alpha\beta} & g_{\alpha\beta} & g_{\alpha\beta} \\ & \text{about} & & & & g_\alpha & g_{\alpha\alpha} & g_{\alpha\beta} & g'_{\alpha\beta} & g_{\alpha\beta} \\ & & \text{diagonal} & & & & g_\alpha & g_{\alpha\beta} & g_{\alpha\beta} & g'_{\alpha\beta} \\ & & & & & & & g_\beta & g_{\beta\beta} & g_{\beta\beta} \\ & & & & & & & & g_\beta & g_{\beta\beta} \\ & & & & & & & & & g_\beta \end{Vmatrix} \quad (14.102)$$

and again is symmetric about the diagonal.

The **G** matrices for the A_1 and for the E vibrations may now be determined from the matrix multiplication of Eq. (14.84). The **U** and **U**′ matrices, the same as used for the **F** matrix, were given in Eqs. (14.76) and (14.77).

The first multiplication step gives:

$$\mathbf{gU'} = \begin{Vmatrix} g_r & \dfrac{3}{\sqrt{3}}g_{rt} & \dfrac{3}{\sqrt{6}}g_{r\alpha} - \dfrac{3}{\sqrt{6}}g_{r\beta} \\[2ex] g_{rt} & \dfrac{1}{\sqrt{3}}g_t + \dfrac{2}{\sqrt{3}}g_{tt} & \dfrac{1}{\sqrt{6}}g'_{t\alpha} + \dfrac{2}{\sqrt{6}}g_{t\alpha} - \dfrac{1}{\sqrt{6}}g_{t\beta} - \dfrac{2}{\sqrt{6}}g'_{t\beta} \\[2ex] g_{rt} & \dfrac{1}{\sqrt{3}}g_t + \dfrac{2}{\sqrt{3}}g_{tt} & \dfrac{1}{\sqrt{6}}g'_{t\alpha} + \dfrac{2}{\sqrt{6}}g_{t\alpha} - \dfrac{1}{\sqrt{6}}g_{t\beta} - \dfrac{2}{\sqrt{6}}g'_{t\beta} \\[2ex] g_{rt} & \dfrac{1}{\sqrt{3}}g_t + \dfrac{2}{\sqrt{3}}g_{tt} & \dfrac{1}{\sqrt{6}}g'_{t\alpha} + \dfrac{2}{\sqrt{6}}g_{t\alpha} - \dfrac{1}{\sqrt{6}}g_{t\beta} - \dfrac{2}{\sqrt{6}}g'_{t\beta} \\[2ex] g_{r\alpha} & \dfrac{1}{\sqrt{3}}g'_{t\alpha} + \dfrac{2}{\sqrt{3}}g_{t\alpha} & \dfrac{1}{\sqrt{6}}g_\alpha + \dfrac{2}{\sqrt{6}}g_{\alpha\alpha} - \dfrac{1}{\sqrt{6}}g'_{\alpha\beta} - \dfrac{2}{\sqrt{6}}g_{\alpha\beta} \\[2ex] g_{r\alpha} & \dfrac{1}{\sqrt{3}}g'_{t\alpha} + \dfrac{2}{\sqrt{3}}g_{t\alpha} & \dfrac{1}{\sqrt{6}}g_\alpha + \dfrac{2}{\sqrt{6}}g_{\alpha\alpha} - \dfrac{1}{\sqrt{6}}g'_{\alpha\beta} - \dfrac{2}{\sqrt{6}}g_{\alpha\beta} \\[2ex] g_{r\alpha} & \dfrac{1}{\sqrt{3}}g'_{t\alpha} + \dfrac{2}{\sqrt{3}}g_{t\alpha} & \dfrac{1}{\sqrt{6}}g_\alpha + \dfrac{2}{\sqrt{6}}g_{\alpha\alpha} - \dfrac{1}{\sqrt{6}}g'_{\alpha\beta} - \dfrac{2}{\sqrt{6}}g_{\alpha\beta} \\[2ex] g_{r\beta} & \dfrac{1}{\sqrt{3}}g_{t\beta} + \dfrac{2}{\sqrt{3}}g'_{t\beta} & \dfrac{1}{\sqrt{6}}g'_{\alpha\beta} + \dfrac{2}{\sqrt{6}}g_{\alpha\beta} - \dfrac{1}{\sqrt{6}}g_\beta - \dfrac{2}{\sqrt{6}}g_{\beta\beta} \\[2ex] g_{r\beta} & \dfrac{1}{\sqrt{3}}g_{t\beta} + \dfrac{2}{\sqrt{3}}g'_{t\beta} & \dfrac{1}{\sqrt{6}}g'_{\alpha\beta} + \dfrac{2}{\sqrt{6}}g_{\alpha\beta} - \dfrac{1}{\sqrt{6}}g_\beta - \dfrac{2}{\sqrt{6}}g_{\beta\beta} \\[2ex] g_{r\beta} & \dfrac{1}{\sqrt{3}}g_{t\beta} + \dfrac{2}{\sqrt{3}}g'_{t\beta} & \dfrac{1}{\sqrt{6}}g'_{\alpha\beta} + \dfrac{2}{\sqrt{6}}g_{\alpha\beta} - \dfrac{1}{\sqrt{6}}g_\beta - \dfrac{2}{\sqrt{6}}g_{\beta\beta} \end{Vmatrix}$$

$$(14.103)$$

and multiplication of $\mathbf{gU'}$ and $\mathbf{U}$, Eq. (14.76), gives the $\mathbf{G}$ matrix $(\mathbf{UgU'})$ for the A_1 vibrations in terms of the g elements.

$$UgU' = \begin{Vmatrix} g_r & \dfrac{3}{\sqrt{3}}g_{rt} & \dfrac{3}{\sqrt{6}}g_{r\alpha} - \dfrac{3}{\sqrt{6}}g_{r\beta} \\[3ex] \dfrac{3}{\sqrt{3}}g_{rt} & g_t - 2g_{tt} & \dfrac{1}{\sqrt{2}}g'_{t\alpha} + \dfrac{2}{\sqrt{2}}g_{t\alpha} \\[1ex] & & -\dfrac{1}{\sqrt{2}}g_{t\beta} - \dfrac{2}{\sqrt{2}}g'_{t\beta} \\[3ex] \dfrac{3}{\sqrt{6}}g_{r\alpha} - \dfrac{3}{\sqrt{6}}g_{r\beta} & \dfrac{1}{\sqrt{2}}g'_{t\alpha} + \dfrac{2}{\sqrt{2}}g_{t\alpha} & \dfrac{1}{2}g_\alpha + g_{\alpha\alpha} - g'_{\alpha\beta} \\[1ex] & -\dfrac{1}{\sqrt{2}}g_{t\beta} - \dfrac{2}{\sqrt{2}}g'_{t\beta} & -2g_{\alpha\beta} + \dfrac{1}{2}g_\beta + g_{\beta\beta} \end{Vmatrix}$$

$$(14.104)$$

The values tabulated by Decius[3] for tetrahedral bond angles,* shown in Table 14.3, can now be used to evaluate the g elements. The results are:

TABLE 14.3^a

g ELEMENTS FOR $\phi = 109°28'$

$$g_{rr}^{2} \qquad \mu_1 + \mu_2$$

$$g_{rr}^{1} \qquad -\frac{1}{3}\mu_1$$

$$g_{r\phi}^{2} \qquad -\frac{2\sqrt{2}}{3}\rho_{23}\mu_2$$

$$g_{r\phi}^{1}\binom{1}{2} \qquad \frac{2\sqrt{2}}{3}\rho_{13}\mu_1 \cos \tau$$

$$g_{r\phi}^{1}\binom{1}{1} \qquad \frac{\sqrt{2}}{3}(\rho_{13} + \rho_{14})\mu_1$$

$$g_{\phi\phi}^{3} \qquad \rho_{12}^{2}\mu_1 + \rho_{23}^{2}\mu_3 + \frac{1}{3}(3\rho_{12}^{2} + 3\rho_{23}^{2} + 2\rho_{12}\rho_{23})\mu_2$$

$$g_{\phi\phi}^{2}\binom{1}{1} \qquad -\frac{1}{6}\{3\rho_{21}^{2}\mu_1 + [3\rho_{21}^{2} + (\rho_{23} + \rho_{24})\rho_{21} - 5\rho_{23}\rho_{24}]\mu_2\}$$

$$g_{\phi\phi}^{2}\binom{1}{0} \qquad -\frac{1}{3}\rho_{12}\cos\tau[(3\rho_{12} + \rho_{14})\mu_1 + (3\rho_{12} + \rho_{23})\mu_2]$$

$$g_{\phi\phi}^{1}\binom{2}{2} \qquad -\frac{1}{3}(3\sin\tau_{25}\sin\tau_{34} - \cos\tau_{25}\cos\tau_{34})\rho_{12}\rho_{14}\mu_1$$

$$g_{\phi\phi}^{1}\binom{2}{1} \qquad -\frac{1}{3}[(3\cos\tau_{35} + \cos\tau_{34})\rho_{14} + (3\cos\tau_{34} + \cos\tau_{35})\rho_{15}]\rho_{12}\mu_1$$

$$g_{\phi\phi}^{1}\binom{1}{1} \qquad -\frac{2}{3}(\rho_{12} + \rho_{14})(\rho_{13} + \rho_{15})\mu_1$$

^{a} From "Molecular Vibrations," by Wilson, Decius, and Cross. Copyright (1955). McGraw-Hill Book Company, Inc. used by permission.

$$g_r = [g_{rr}^{2}] = \mu_C + \mu_H , \qquad\qquad (14.105)$$

$$g_{rt} = [g_{rr}^{1}] = -\frac{1}{3}\mu_C , \qquad\qquad (14.106)$$

* The bond angles for CHCl$_3$ are not exactly tetrahedral (see Chapter 15, page 479) but are assumed tetrahedral for convenience in calculation.

$$g_{r\alpha} = [g^1_{r\phi}(^1_1)] = \frac{2\sqrt{2}}{3} \rho_{CCl}\mu_C , \tag{14.107}$$

$$g_{r\beta} = [g^2_{r\phi}] = -\frac{2\sqrt{2}}{3} \rho_{CCl}\mu_C , \tag{14.108}$$

$$g_t = [g^2_{rr}] = \mu_C + \mu_{Cl} , \tag{14.109}$$

$$g_{tt} = [g^1_{rr}] = -\frac{1}{3}\mu_C , \tag{14.110}$$

$$g'_{t\alpha} = [g^1_{r\phi}(^1_1)] = \frac{2\sqrt{2}}{3} \rho_{CCl}\mu_C , \tag{14.111}$$

$$g_{t\alpha} = [g^2_{r\phi}] = -\frac{2\sqrt{2}}{3} \rho_{CCl}\mu_C , \tag{14.112}$$

$$g_{t\beta} = [g^2_{r\phi}] = -\frac{2\sqrt{2}}{3} \rho_{CH}\mu_C , \tag{14.113}$$

$$g'_{t\beta} = [g^1_{r\phi}(^1_1)] = \frac{\sqrt{2}}{3} (\rho_{CH} + \rho_{CCl}) \mu_C , \tag{14.114}$$

$$g_\alpha = [g^3_{\phi\phi}] = \frac{8}{3} \rho^2_{CCl}\mu_C + 2\rho^2_{CCl}\mu_{Cl} , \tag{14.115}$$

$$g_{\alpha\alpha} = [g^2_{\phi\phi}(^1_1)] = -\frac{1}{2} \rho^2_{CCl}\mu_{Cl} , \tag{14.116}$$

$$g'_{\alpha\beta} = [g^1_{\phi\phi}(^1_1)] = -\frac{4}{3}(\rho^2_{CCl} + \rho_{CH}\rho_{CCl}) \mu_C , \tag{14.117}$$

$$g_{\alpha\beta} = [g^2_{\phi\phi}(^1_1)] = -\left(\frac{2}{3}\rho^2_{CCl} - \frac{2}{3}\rho_{CH}\rho_{CCl}\right) \mu_C - \frac{1}{2} \rho^2_{CCl}\mu_{Cl} , \tag{14.118}$$

$$g_\beta = [g^3_{\phi\phi}] = \rho^2_{CH}\mu_H + \rho^2_{CCl}\mu_{Cl} + \left(\rho^2_{CH} + \rho^2_{CCl} + \frac{2}{3}\rho_{CH}\rho_{CCl}\right)\mu_C , \tag{14.119}$$

and

$$g_{\beta\beta} = [g^2_{\phi\phi}(^1_1)] = -\frac{1}{2} \rho^2_{CH}\mu_H - \frac{1}{6}(3\rho^2_{CH} + 2\rho_{CH}\rho_{CCl} - 5\rho^2_{CCl}) \mu_C \tag{14.120}$$

where μ_H, μ_C, and μ_{Cl} are the reciprocals of the atomic masses of hydrogen, carbon, and chlorine and ρ_{CH} and ρ_{CCl} are the reciprocals of the C—H and

C—Cl bond distances. Making use of the above equations, the G_{ij} elements may be calculated to give the **G** matrix for the A_1 vibrations from Eq. (14.104):

$$
\mathbf{G} = \begin{Vmatrix} G_{11} & G_{12} & G_{13} \\ G_{21} & G_{22} & G_{23} \\ G_{31} & G_{32} & G_{33} \end{Vmatrix} = \begin{Vmatrix} \mu_H + \mu_C & -\dfrac{1}{\sqrt{3}}\mu_C & \dfrac{4}{\sqrt{3}}\rho_{CCl}\mu_C \\[2mm] -\dfrac{1}{\sqrt{3}}\mu_C & \dfrac{1}{3}\mu_C + \mu_{Cl} & -\dfrac{4}{3}\rho_{CCl}\mu_C \\[2mm] \dfrac{4}{\sqrt{3}}\rho_{CCl}\mu_C & -\dfrac{4}{3}\rho_{CCl}\mu_C & \dfrac{16}{3}\rho_{CCl}^2\mu_C + 2\rho_{CCl}^2\mu_C \end{Vmatrix}
$$

$$(14.121)$$

where it is noted that G_{ij} is equal to G_{ji} .

The **G** matrix for the E vibrations is derived in the same way, using the **U** and **U'** matrices for the E vibrations as shown in Eqs. (14.80) and (14.81). The same **g** matrix, Eq. (14.102), is used as in the A_1 calculation, above. The corresponding matrix multiplication, **UgU'**, gives:

$$
\mathbf{UgU'} = \begin{Vmatrix} g_t - g_{tt} & g'_{t\alpha} - g_{t\alpha} & g_{t\beta} - g'_{t\beta} \\[1mm] g'_{t\alpha} - g_{t\alpha} & g_\alpha - g_{\alpha\alpha} & g'_{\alpha\beta} - g_{\alpha\beta} \\[1mm] g_{t\beta} - g'_{t\beta} & g'_{\alpha\beta} - g_{\alpha\beta} & g_\beta - g_{\beta\beta} \end{Vmatrix}
$$

$$(14.122)$$

which is the **G** matrix for the E vibrations in terms of the g elements. Equations (14.105)–(14.120) are again used to evaluate the g elements and the result is:

$$
\mathbf{G} = \begin{Vmatrix} \dfrac{4}{3}\mu_C + \mu_{Cl} & \dfrac{4\sqrt{2}}{3}\rho_{CCl}\mu_C & -\left[\sqrt{2}\rho_{CH} + \dfrac{\sqrt{2}}{3}\rho_{CCl}\right]\mu_C \\[3mm] \dfrac{4\sqrt{2}}{3}\rho_{CCl}\mu_C & \dfrac{8}{3}\rho_{CCl}^2\mu_C + \dfrac{5}{2}\rho_{CCl}^2\mu_{Cl} & -\dfrac{2}{3}\left[\rho_{CCl}^2 + \rho_{CH}\rho_{CCl}\right]\mu_C \\ & & +\dfrac{1}{2}\rho_{CCl}^2\mu_{Cl} \\[3mm] -\left[\sqrt{2}\rho_{CH} & -\dfrac{2}{3}\left[\rho_{CCl}^2 + \rho_{CH}\rho_{CCl}\right]\mu_C & \dfrac{3}{2}\rho_{CH}^2\mu_H + \rho_{CCl}^2\mu_{Cl} \\ +\dfrac{\sqrt{2}}{3}\rho_{CCl}\right]\mu_C & +\dfrac{1}{2}\rho_{CCl}^2\mu_{Cl} & +\left[\dfrac{3}{2}\rho_{CH}^2 + \dfrac{1}{6}\rho_{CCl}^2 \right. \\ & & \left. +\rho_{CH}\rho_{CCl}\right]\mu_C \end{Vmatrix}
$$

$$(14.123)$$

which is the **G** matrix for the E vibrations.

14.10 The Secular Determinants for $CHCl_3$

With the **F** and **G** matrices determined, a secular determinant of the form given by Eq. (14.20) of Section 14.4 can be written for each vibration type. Generally it is easier to first obtain numerical values for each of the F and G elements before the secular determinant is written.

In order to evaluate the F elements, the force constants for the molecule must be known and this may be a difficult requirement. The force constant problem will be discussed later. The force constants, as determined by Zeitlow,[15] will be used for the chloroform molecule. The values are listed in Table 14.4, using the same designations as in the **f** matrix. The second column of Table 14.4

TABLE 14.4

FORCE CONSTANTS FOR THE CHLOROFORM MOLECULE

f_{ij}	Value (Zeitlow[15]) (dyn/cm)	df_{ij} or d^2f_{ij} ($d = 1.77 \times 10^{-8}$ cm)	Value (ergs)
f_r	4.8540×10^5		
f_t	3.4782×10^5		
f_α	0.51275×10^5	d^2f_α	1.6064×10^{-11}
f_β	0.20834×10^5	d^2f_β	0.6525×10^{-11}
f_{rt}	0.0880×10^5		
f_{tt}	0.3526×10^5		
$f_{r\alpha} - f_{r\beta}$	0.31208×10^5	$df_{r\alpha} - df_{r\beta}$	0.5524×10^{-3}
$f_{t\alpha}$	0.23378×10^5	$df_{t\alpha}$	0.4138×10^{-3}
$f_{t\beta}$	0.18319×10^5	$df_{t\beta}$	0.3243×10^{-3}
$f'_{t\alpha}$	-0.11123×10^5	$df'_{t\alpha}$	-0.1968×10^{-3}
$f'_{t\beta}$	-0.0927×10^5	$df'_{t\beta}$	-0.1641×10^{-3}
$f_{\alpha\alpha}$	0.14287×10^5	$d^2f_{\alpha\alpha}$	0.4476×10^{-11}
$f_{\beta\beta}$	0.00287×10^5	$d^2f_{\beta\beta}$	0.00899×10^{-11}
$f_{\alpha\beta}$	0		
$f_{\alpha\beta}$	0.049242×10^5	$d^2f_{\alpha\beta}$	0.1543×10^{-11}

lists all of the force constant values, in the customary units of dyn/cm. Reference to the potential function, Equation (14.64), shows that terms such as $f_r[r^2]$,

[15] J. P. Zeitlow, M. S. Thesis, Illinois Institute of Technology, Chicago, 1949.

were r is a change in bond length (i.e., units in cm) will give the correct energy unit, dyn/cm times cm^2, or ergs, but terms such as $f_\alpha[\alpha^2]$ involve no unit of length and must be multiplied by cm^2, that is a length squared, to give energy units. The distance generally used is that of one the bonds forming the angle. Correspondingly for terms of the type, $f_{r\alpha}$, the constant must be multiplied by a single length, d, in cm. The third column of the table lists the constants multiplied by d or d^2, if required. The value of d chosen was the C—Cl bond length, 1.77×10^{-8} cm. Note that in writing out the potential function, it would be the internal coordinate (α or β) which would be multiplied by d. Here, for convenience in calculation, d is included directly with the force constant.

Using the values of Table 14.4 and Eq. (14.79) for the **F** matrix, the values for the F elements for the A_1 vibrations are:

$$F_{11} = f_r = 4.8540 \times 10^5, \tag{14.124}$$

$$F_{12} = \sqrt{3}\,f_{rt} = 0.1524 \times 10^5, \tag{14.125}$$

$$F_{13} = \frac{3}{\sqrt{6}}(df_{r\alpha} - df_{r\beta}) = 0.6765 \times 10^{-3}, \tag{14.126}$$

$$F_{22} = f_t + 2f_{tt} = 4.1834 \times 10^5, \tag{14.127}$$

$$F_{23} = \frac{1}{\sqrt{2}}(2df_{t\alpha} - df_{t\beta} + df'_{t\alpha} - 2df'_{t\beta}) = 0.4487 \times 10^{-3}, \tag{14.128}$$

and

$$F_{33} = \frac{1}{2}(d^2 f_\alpha + d^2 f_\beta + 2d^2 f_{\alpha\alpha} + 2d^2 f_{\beta\beta} - 2d^2 f'_{\alpha\beta} - 4d^2 f_{\alpha\beta})$$
$$F_{33} = 1.2776 \times 10^{-11}, \tag{14.129}$$

where $f'_{\alpha\beta}$ is unknown and has been set equal to zero.

The G elements can be evaluated using Eq. (14.120) and the following values for the reciprocal masses and bond distances:

$$\mu_C = 5.0153 \times 10^{22} \text{ gm}^{-1}, \tag{14.130}$$

$$\mu_H = 5.9762 \times 10^{23} \text{ gm}^{-1}, \tag{14.131}$$

$$\mu_{Cl} = 1.6988 \times 10^{22} \text{ gm}^{-1}, \tag{14.132}$$

$$\rho_{CH} = \frac{1}{C - H} = \frac{1}{1.093 \times 10^{-8}} = 9.149 \times 10^7 \text{ cm}^{-1}, \tag{14.133}$$

and

$$\rho_{CCl} = \frac{1}{C - Cl} = \frac{1}{1.77 \times 10^{-8}} = 5.650 \times 10^7 \text{ cm}^{-1}. \tag{14.134}$$

The G elements for the A_1 vibrations are then:

$$G_{11} = \mu_H + \mu_C = 6.4777 \times 10^{23}, \tag{14.135}$$

$$G_{12} = -\frac{1}{\sqrt{3}}\mu_C = -2.8956 \times 10^{22}, \tag{14.136}$$

$$G_{13} = \frac{4}{\sqrt{3}}\rho_{CCl}\mu_C = 6.5434 \times 10^{30}, \tag{14.137}$$

$$G_{22} = \frac{1}{3}\mu_C + \mu_{Cl} = 3.3706 \times 10^{22}, \tag{14.138}$$

$$G_{23} = -\frac{4}{3}\rho_{CCl}\mu_C = -3.7779 \times 10^{30}, \tag{14.139}$$

and

$$G_{33} = \frac{16}{3}\rho_{CCl}^2\mu_C + 2\rho_{CCl}^2\mu_{Cl} = 9.6205 \times 10^{38}. \tag{14.140}$$

The secular determinant, defined in Eq. (14.20), is:

$$\begin{vmatrix} \sum_i G_{1i}F_{i1} - \lambda & \sum_j G_{1j}F_{j2} & \sum_k G_{1k}F_{k3} \\ \sum_i G_{2i}F_{i1} & \sum_j G_{2j}F_{j2} - \lambda & \sum_k G_{2k}F_{k3} \\ \sum_i G_{3i}F_{i1} & \sum_j G_{3j}F_{j2} & \sum_k G_{3k}F_{k3} - \lambda \end{vmatrix} = 0, \tag{14.141}$$

for the A_1 vibrations of chloroform. Summing each term with the numerical values of Eqs. (14.124)–(14.129) and (14.135)–(14.140) gives the values:

$$\sum_i G_{1i}F_{i1} - \lambda = G_{11}F_{11} + G_{12}F_{21} + G_{13}F_{31} - \lambda = 318.414 \times 10^{27} - \lambda, \tag{14.142}$$

$$\sum_i G_{2i}F_{i1} = G_{21}F_{11} + G_{22}F_{21} + G_{23}F_{31} = -16.0927 \times 10^{27}, \tag{14.143}$$

$$\sum_i G_{3i}F_{i1} = G_{31}F_{11} + G_{32}F_{21} + G_{33}F_{31} = 37.6942 \times 10^{35}, \tag{14.144}$$

$$\sum_j G_{1j}F_{j2} = G_{11}F_{12} + G_{12}F_{22} + G_{13}F_{32} = 0.6959 \times 10^{27}, \tag{14.145}$$

$$\sum_j G_{2j}F_{j2} - \lambda = G_{21}F_{12} + G_{22}F_{22} + G_{23}F_{32} - \lambda = 11.9641 \times 10^{27} - \lambda, \tag{14.146}$$

$$\sum_j G_{3j}F_{j2} = G_{31}F_{12} + G_{32}F_{22} + G_{33}F_{32} = -10.4905 \times 10^{35}, \tag{14.147}$$

$$\sum_k G_{1k}F_{k3} = G_{11}F_{13} + G_{12}F_{23} + G_{13}F_{33} = 50.8823 \times 10^{19}, \tag{14.148}$$

$$\sum_k G_{2k}F_{k3} = G_{21}F_{13} + G_{22}F_{23} + G_{23}F_{33} = -5.2731 \times 10^{19}, \tag{14.149}$$

and

$$\sum_k G_{3k}F_{k3} - \lambda = G_{31}F_{13} + G_{32}F_{23} + G_{33}F_{33} - \lambda = 15.0227 \times 10^{27} - \lambda. \quad (14.150)$$

Substitution of these values in Eq. (14.141) gives the secular determinant:

$$\begin{vmatrix} 318.414 \times 10^{27} - \lambda & 0.6959 \times 10^{27} & 50.8823 \times 10^{19} \\ -16.0972 \times 10^{27} & 11.9641 \times 10^{27} - \lambda & -5.2731 \times 10^{19} \\ 37.6942 \times 10^{35} & -10.4905 \times 10^{35} & 15.0227 \times 10^{27} - \lambda \end{vmatrix} = 0, \quad (14.151)$$

which may be expanded to give the equation:

$$\lambda^3 - 3.4540 \times 10^{29} \lambda^2 + 6.8105 \times 10^{57} \lambda - 2.5290 \times 10^{85} = 0. \quad (14.152)$$

Equation (14.152) may be solved for three values of λ. For example, using the Graefe root squaring method (see Margenau and Murphy[5]), the roots are:

$$\lambda_1 = 3.2466 \times 10^{29} \text{ sec}^{-2}, \quad (14.153)$$

$$\lambda_2 = 1.5810 \times 10^{28} \text{ sec}^{-2}, \quad (14.154)$$

and

$$\lambda_3 = 4.9271 \times 10^{27} \text{ sec}^{-2}. \quad (14.155)$$

Equation (14.21) can then be used to obtain the corresponding frequencies, ν, from the λ values. The results are:

$$\nu_1 = \frac{\sqrt{\lambda_1}}{2\pi c} = 3025 \text{ cm}^{-1}, \quad (14.156)$$

$$\nu_2 = 668 \text{ cm}^{-1}, \quad (14.157)$$

and

$$\nu_3 = 373 \text{ cm}^{-1}. \quad (14.158)$$

The solution of the secular determinant is, in many cases, more difficult. If the order of the determinant is four or larger, special methods, involving computers in some cases, may be required. See Wilson, Decius, and Cross,[3] Chapter 9, for a comprehensive discussion.

The F and G elements for the E vibrations are determined in the same way as for the A_1 vibrations. Using Eq. (14.83) for the **F** matrix and Table 14.4 for the force constants, the F elements are:

$$F_{11} = f_t - f_{tt} = 3.1256 \times 10^5, \quad (14.159)$$

$$F_{12} = df'_{t\alpha} - df_{t\alpha} = -0.6106 \times 10^{-3}, \quad (14.160)$$

$$F_{13} = df_{t\beta} - df'_{t\beta} = 0.4884 \times 10^{-3}, \quad (14.161)$$

$$F_{22} = d^2 f_\alpha - d^2 f_{\alpha\alpha} = 1.1588 \times 10^{-11}, \quad (14.162)$$

$$F_{23} = d^2 f'_{\alpha\beta} - d^2 f_{\alpha\beta} = -0.1543 \times 10^{-11}, \quad (14.163)$$

and

$$F_{33} = d^2 f_\beta - d^2 f_{\beta\beta} = 0.6473 \times 10^{-11}. \qquad (14.164)$$

Using equation (14.123) for the **G** matrix, the G elements are:

$$G_{11} = \mu_{Cl} + \frac{4}{3}\mu_C = 8.3858 \times 10^{22}, \qquad (14.165)$$

$$G_{12} = \frac{4\sqrt{2}}{3}\rho_{CCl}\mu_C = 5.3427 \times 10^{30}, \qquad (14.166)$$

$$G_{13} = -\left[\sqrt{2}\,\rho_{CH} + \frac{\sqrt{2}}{3}\rho_{CCl}\right]\mu_C = -7.8249 \times 10^{30}, \qquad (14.167)$$

$$G_{22} = \frac{8}{3}\rho_{CCl}^2\mu_C + \frac{5}{2}\rho_{CCl}^2\mu_{Cl} = 5.6244 \times 10^{38}, \qquad (14.168)$$

$$G_{23} = -\frac{2}{3}[\rho_{CCl}^2 + \rho_{CH}\rho_{CCl}]\mu_C + \frac{1}{2}\rho_{CCl}^2\mu_{Cl} = -5.9809 \times 10^{38}, \qquad (14.169)$$

and

$$G_{33} = \frac{3}{2}\rho_{CH}^2\mu_H + \rho_{CCl}^2\mu_{Cl}$$
$$+ \left[\frac{3}{2}\rho_{CH}^2 + \frac{1}{6}\rho_{CCl}^2 + \rho_{CH}\rho_{CCl}\right]\mu_C = 84.739 \times 10^{38}, \qquad (14.170)$$

where Eqs. (14.129)–(14.133) have again been used for numerical values.

The G and F products are summed, in the same way as for the A_1 vibrations, to give:

$$\begin{vmatrix} 19.1267 \times 10^{27} - \lambda & 2.2781 \times 10^{19} & -1.7657 \times 10^{19} \\ 10.3437 \times 10^{35} & 4.1782 \times 10^{27} - \lambda & -2.1083 \times 10^{27} \\ 20.5809 \times 10^{35} & -15.2280 \times 10^{27} & 51.6481 \times 10^{27} - \lambda \end{vmatrix} = 0, \qquad (14.171)$$

for the secular determinant for the E vibrations. Expansion of the determinant gives the equation:

$$\lambda^3 - 7.4953 \times 10^{28}\lambda^2 + 1.2642 \times 10^{57}\lambda - 2.6275 \times 10^{84} = 0. \qquad (14.172)$$

The three roots of the equation are:

$$\lambda_4 = 5.1316 \times 10^{28} \text{ sec}^{-2}, \qquad (14.173)$$

$$\lambda_5 = 2.1224 \times 10^{28} \text{ sec}^{-2}, \qquad (14.174)$$

and

$$\lambda_6 = 2.4123 \times 10^{27} \text{ sec}^{-2}, \tag{14.175}$$

which correspond to:

$$\nu_4 = 1203 \text{ cm}^{-1}, \tag{14.176}$$

$$\nu_5 = 773 \text{ cm}^{-1}, \tag{14.177}$$

and

$$\nu_6 = 261 \text{ cm}^{-1}, \tag{14.178}$$

for the frequencies in cm^{-1}, of the E vibrations.

14.11 The Infrared and Raman Spectra of CHCl₃ and CDCl₃

The observed infrared and Raman spectra for CHCl₃ and CDCl₃ are given in Table 14.5 and in Table 14.6 respectively. Values are in wavenumbers and

TABLE 14.5
INFRARED AND RAMAN SPECTRA OF CHCl₃ (LIQUID)^a

ν	Infrared intensity	Type	Assignment	$\Delta\nu$	Raman intensity-polarization
3683	w	A_1	$\nu_1 + \nu_2$		
3019	s	A_1	ν_1	3018	s (polarized)
2400	m	$A_1 + E$	$2\nu_4$		
1521	m	$A_1 + E$	$2\nu_5$	1518	w
1475	w	$A_1 + A_2 + E$	$\nu_4 + \nu_6$	1501	vw
1423	m	E	$\nu_2 + \nu_5$	1420	vw
1334	w	A_1	$2\nu_2$		
1216	vs	E	ν_4	1216	m (depolarized)
1032	w	A_1	$\nu_2 + \nu_3$	1024	vw
1019	w	$A_1 + A_2 + E$	$\nu_5 + \nu_6$		
929	m	E	$\nu_2 + \nu_6$		
849	w	E	$\nu_4 - \nu_3$		
757	vs	E	ν_5	761	s (depolarized)
668	s	A_1	ν_2	667	s (polarized)
627	m	E	$\nu_3 + \nu_6$	622	vw
497	w	$A_1 + A_2 + E$	$\nu_5 - \nu_6$	497	vw
407	w	E	$\nu_2 - \nu_6$		
392	w	$A_1 + E$	$\nu_5 - \nu_3$		
368	m	A_1	ν_3	366	s (polarized)
303	vw	A_1	$\nu_2 - \nu_3$		
261	w	E	ν_6	261	vs (depolarized)
230	w	$A_1 + A_2 - 2E$	$\nu_5 - 2\nu_6$		

^{a} The frequencies given are in cm^{-1} and the band intensities are abbreviated as follows: vs—very strong; s—strong; m—moderate; w—weak; vw—very weak.

TABLE 14.6

INFRARED AND RAMAN SPECTRA OF $CDCl_3$ (LIQUID)[a]

ν	Infrared intensity	Type	Assignment	Raman frequencies $(\Delta\nu)$
3155	w	E	$\nu_1 + \nu_4$	
2983	w	E	$\nu_1 + \nu_5$	
2902	w	A_1	$\nu_1 + \nu_2$	
2255	s	A_1	ν_1	2255
1817	w	$A_1 + E$	$\nu_3 + 2\nu_5$	
1795	w	$A_1 + E$	$2\nu_4$	1796
1643	vw	$A_1 + A_2 + E$	$\nu_4 + \nu_5$	1642
1562	vw	E	$\nu_2 + \nu_4$	
1468	m	$A_1 + E$	$2\nu_5$	1463
1382	m	E	$\nu_2 + \nu_5$	
1295	w	A_1	$2\nu_2$	
1168	w	$A_1 + A_2 + E$	$\nu_4 + \nu_6$	
1097	m	E	$\nu_3 + \nu_5$	
989	w	$A_1 + A_2 + E$	$\nu_5 + \nu_6$	
905	vs	E	ν_4	908
740	vs	E	ν_5	736
650	s	A_1	ν_2	650
627	m	$A_1 + A_2 + E$	$\nu_3 + \nu_6$	
545	w	E	$\nu_4 - \nu_3$	
475	w	$A_1 + A_2 + E$	$\nu_5 - \nu_6$	
366	m	A_1	ν_3	366
				262

[a] The frequencies given are in cm^{-1} and the band intensities are abbreviated as in Table 14.5.

relative intensities are given as very strong, strong, medium, weak, and very weak. All frequencies are for the liquid state. The data given are best estimates taken from the data of Plyler,[16] Cleveland,[17,18] and unpublished data.[19] The spectra for $CHCl_3$ and $CDCl_3$ are shown in Fig. 14.7.

14.12   Band Assignments for $CHCl_3$ and $CDCl_3$

The frequency assignments for $CHCl_3$ are given in Table 14.5. There are six strong Raman lines and these are taken as the six fundamentals. This procedure

[16] E. K. Plyler and W. S. Benedict, *J. Res. Natl. Bur. Standards* **47**, 202 1951).

[17] J. R. Madigan and F. F. Cleveland, *J. Chem. Phys.* **19**, 119 (1951).

[18] J. R. Madigan and F. F. Cleveland, *J. Chem. Phys.* **18**, 1081 (1950).

[19] Data from Laboratories at Rensselaer Polytechnic Institute, Troy, New York, 1963.

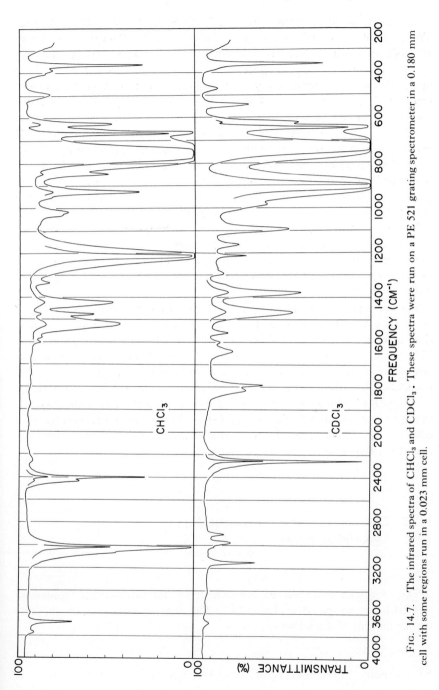

FIG. 14.7. The infrared spectra of CHCl₃ and CDCl₃. These spectra were run on a PE 521 grating spectrometer in a 0.180 mm cell with some regions run in a 0.023 mm cell.

is by no means always correct but here is supported by the rest of the data. The 3018, 667, and 366 cm^{-1} lines are polarized in the Raman and therefore are assigned to the completely symmetric A_1 type species and listed as ν_1, ν_2, and ν_3 in order of decreasing frequency. The 1216, 761, and 261 cm^{-1} lines in the Raman are completely depolarized and are the three type E vibrations listed as ν_4, ν_5, and ν_6. The 3019 cm^{-1} frequency for ν_1, may be associated with C—H stretching and occurs in the region expected. The next highest frequency, ν_4, is also related to the hydrogen atom and is essentially C—H bending against the rest of the molecule. These assignments are supported by their disappearance in the spectra of the deuterated compound. The lowest symmetric and degenerate frequencies ν_3 and ν_6 are mainly CCl_3 deformation vibrations. The symmetric and degenerate frequencies ν_2 and ν_5 involve C—Cl stretching but also involve some deformation.[20]

Essentially all of the observed frequencies may be accounted for on the basis of the given assignment as resulting from allowed combinations or overtones of the six fundamental frequencies. The selection rules for a C_{3v} molecule were given in Chapter 3. The complete assignment for $CHCl_3$ is in Table 14.5.

The corresponding assignment for $CDCl_3$ is given in Table 14.6. It may be noted that ν_1, and ν_4 are much lower, as would be expected from an isotopic shift involving replacement of hydrogen by deuterium. The values are now 2255 cm^{-1} for C—D stretching and 905 cm^{-1} for C—D deformation against the rest of the molecule. The low values for ν_3 and ν_6 are essentially unaltered and the CCl_3 deformation vibrations occur at the same frequencies as in $CHCl_3$. The higher stretching frequencies would interact with the rest of the molecule to a greater extent and might be expected to change somewhat. The bands at 650 cm^{-1} and 736 cm^{-1} are assigned to symmetric and degenerate CCl_3 stretching, ν_2 and ν_5, respectively.

14.13   Comparison of Experimental and Calculated Values

The calculated and observed assignments for the fundamental frequencies of $CHCl_3$ are compared in Table 14.7. The close agreement again supports the assignment of experimental values.

---

[20] I. Nakagawa, *J. Chem. Soc. (Japan), Pure Chem. Sect.* **75**, 535 (1954).

TABLE 14.7

COMPARISON OF OBSERVED AND CALCULATED FUNDAMENTAL FREQUENCIES FOR CHCl$_3$

Assignment	Observed^a	Calculated
ν_1	3019	3025
ν_2	668	668
ν_3	368	373
ν_4	1216	1203
ν_5	757	773
ν_6	261	261

^{a} The infrared frequencies are given (see Table 14.5).

14.14 The General Application of Theoretical Analysis

The detailed example for chloroform was used to illustrate a complete theoretical calculation using the entire potential function. It was, however, pointed out that a complete set of force constants necessary for the computations would not generally be available. A number of approaches may be made to the problem. The most direct would be to make a complete frequency assignment first and then calculate force constants which will fit the secular equation. This is adequate for the principal force constants but is only approximate since exact values will require the complete potential function. Many of the interaction constants cannot be obtained because there are nearly always many more constants than frequencies and therefore many must be left out. Several authors, such as Crawford and Brinkly,[14] have suggested methods for choosing the potential function. For example, interaction constants for two widely separated frequencies can usually be ignored and set equal to zero. In some cases isotopic analogs may be made which will have frequencies differing from those in the "normal" molecules. Assuming force constants are not altered, additional equations may be obtained and further force constants calculated.

An alternative and somewhat qualitative approach would be to assume force constants from analogous bonds in similar molecules which are known. Since force constants are not independent, the method is not strictly quantitative but may be adequate for an aid in assigning observed frequencies. The method will probably not serve for a complete vibrational assignment but as an aid; along with frequency correlation charts, observation of band envelopes, and selection rules; it may be very useful.

Several approximation methods which are in general use assume particular force fields acting in the molecule. The force fields commonly assumed are valence forces, central forces, and what is referred to as a Urey-Bradley[21] force field. For more comprehensive discussions of these treatments see Herzberg,[4] Chapter II, part 4, and Wilson, Decius, and Cross,[3] Chapter 8.

The valence forces are strong restoring forces opposing changes in bond lengths and in bond angles. The treatment is similar to the internal coordinate treatment discussed for chloroform except, to a first approximation, the valence forces would include no interaction terms. This method has generally been favored by chemists in that the forces are "chemical bonding forces" and the results are generally good, when applied to molecular vibrations.

The central force assumption considers the force on an atom as being the resultant of interactions with all of the other atoms. The interactions are dependent only on the distances between the atoms, disregarding the presence or absence of connecting bonds. Both the valence force and central force approach have the advantage of simplifying the potential function but application of the central force field has been more limited probably due to less agreement with chemical structure and restrictions on its application to some molecules.

The Urey-Bradley force field offers some of the advantages of both approaches. It makes use of a combination of valence force terms and some central force terms between nonbonded atoms.

[21] H. C. Urey and C. A. Bradley, *Phys. Rev.* **38**, 1969 (1931).

CHAPTER 15

THE CALCULATION
OF THERMODYNAMIC FUNCTIONS

Once the vibrational frequencies of a molecule are known it is possible to calculate the contribution of the vibrational energy to the total energy possessed by a molecule. In like manner the rotational energy contribution can be calculated if the moments of inertia of the molecule are known. Thus, the spectroscopic measured frequencies and the moments of inertia are important variables in determining the thermodynamic functions of a molecule. This chapter is devoted, therefore, to a detailed consideration of how these calculations can be made using again as the example, the chloroform molecule.

15.1 The Partition Function

The total energy of a system of molecules, such as one mole of an ideal gas, may be approached from a statistical assignment of molecules to various energy states.* The number of molecules, n_1, having energy, ϵ_i, is:

$$n_i = \frac{N g_i e^{-\epsilon_i/(kT)}}{Q}, \tag{15.1}$$

where N is Avogadro's number, k is the Boltzmann constant, T is the absolute temperature, and g_i is the statistical weight. The statistical weight gives the

[1] W. J. Moore, "Physical Chemistry," 3rd ed., Chapter 15. Prentice-Hall, Englewood Cliffs, New Jersey, 1962.
[2] C. E. Reid, "Principles of Chemical Thermodynamics," Chapter 6. Reinhold, New York, 1960.
[3] G. Herzberg, "Infrared and Raman Spectra of Polyatomic Molecules," Van Nostrand, New York, 1945.
* See Moore[1] or Reid[2] for an introduction to chemical statistics. Standard texts on statistical mechanics may be used for more comprehensive discussions. The introduction here (15.1–15.2) follows Herzberg.[3]

degeneracy of the energy level, that is, the number of states having the same energy, ϵ_i . The quantity in the denominator, Q, is:

$$Q = \sum g_i e^{-\epsilon_i/(kT)}, \tag{15.2}$$

and is the *partition function*. All thermodynamic functions may be related to the partition function.[3]

15.2 The Partition Function and the Total Energy

The total internal energy, E^0, of one mole of an ideal gas can be given by:

$$E^0 = E_0^0 + RT^2 \frac{d \ln Q}{dT} , \tag{15.3}$$

where E_0^0 is the energy at absolute zero, R is the gas constant, and Q is the partition function. Equation (15.3) can be given in a convenient form as:

$$E^0 - E_0^0 = RT^2 \frac{d \ln Q}{dT} . \tag{15.4}$$

If no reference is made to the zero point energy or if it is not defined in the usual manner, Eq. (15.4) can be written:

$$E^0 = RT^2 \frac{d \ln Q}{dT} . \tag{15.5}$$

15.3 The Partition Function and the Thermodynamic Functions

All thermodynamic functions determined in this chapter will be calculated for an ideal gas in its standard state. This will be indicated by a superscript zero, as in Eqs. (15.3)–(15.5).

(a) THE ENTHALPY FUNCTION

The enthalpy, H^0, is given by the relation:

$$H^0 = E^0 + RT, \tag{15.6}$$

for one mole of an ideal gas. Subtracting E_0^0 from each side of Eq. (15.6) gives:

$$H^0 - E_0^0 = E^0 - E_0^0 + RT, \tag{15.7}$$

and dividing each side of the equation by T gives:

$$\frac{H^0 - E_0^0}{T} = \frac{E^0 - E_0^0}{T} + R, \tag{15.8}$$

which defines the enthalpy or heat content function. From Eq. (15.4) for the internal energy, Eq. (15.8) becomes:

$$\frac{H^0 - E_0^0}{T} = RT \frac{d \ln Q}{dT} + R, \tag{15.9}$$

which gives the enthalpy function in terms of the partition function.

(b) HEAT CAPACITY

The heat capacity at constant volume, C_v^0, is given by the relation:

$$C_v^0 = \left(\frac{dE}{dT} \right)_v. \tag{15.10}$$

Both the heat capacity and the entropy are independent of the energy zero chosen, and Eq. (15.5) may be used for E. The heat capacity at constant volume is then:

$$C_v^0 = \left(\frac{dE}{dT} \right)_v = \frac{d}{dT} \left[RT^2 \left(\frac{d \ln Q}{dT} \right) \right], \tag{15.11}$$

which may be differentiated to give:

$$C_v^0 = \frac{R}{T^2} \left[\frac{d^2 Q/d(1/T)^2}{Q} - \left(\frac{dQ/d(1/T)}{Q} \right)^2 \right]. \tag{15.12}$$

The heat capacity at constant pressure, C_p^0, is given by adding R to C_v^0. In practice, the heat capacities are calculated by differentiation of the energy expressions after they have been evaluated rather than by use of Eq. (15.12). The actual calculations will be shown in Section (15.4).

(c) ENTROPY

The entropy may be obtained as a function of energy. The heat change, dq, is given by:

$$dq = dE + P \, dV, \tag{15.13}$$

where the only work done is that of expansion against a constant pressure. Since the entropy change, dS, is given by dq/T, for a reversible process, the entropy change may be given by dividing Eq. (15.13) by T, to give:

$$dS = \frac{dq}{T} = \frac{dE + P\,dV}{T} \qquad (15.14)$$

which at constant volume becomes:

$$dS = \frac{dE}{T} \qquad (15.15)$$

or replacing dE by $C_v dT$:

$$dS = C_v \frac{dT}{T}. \qquad (15.16)$$

Integration of Eq. (15.16) between zero and T gives:

$$S^0 - S_0^0 = \int_0^T C_v \frac{dT}{T} \qquad (15.17)$$

but C_v in terms of the partition function is given by Eq. (15.11) and Eq. (15.17) may be written:

$$S^0 - S_0^0 = \int_0^T \frac{1}{T} \frac{d}{dT} \left[RT^2 \left(\frac{d \ln Q}{dT} \right) \right] dT. \qquad (15.18)$$

Integrating by parts:

$$S^0 - S_0^0 = \left(\frac{1}{T} \right) \left(RT^2 \frac{d \ln Q}{dT} \right) + \int_0^T RT^2 \left(\frac{d \ln Q}{dT} \right) \frac{dT}{T^2}$$

$$S^0 - S_0^0 = RT \frac{d \ln Q}{dT} + \int_0^T R\, d \ln Q \qquad (15.19)$$

$$S^0 - S_0^0 = RT \frac{d \ln Q}{dT} + R \ln Q - R \ln Q_0$$

where Q is the partition function per molecule at temperature T and Q_0 the corresponding value at absolute zero. S_0^0 may be eliminated by use of the relation between entropy and the thermodynamic probability, W:

$$S = k \ln W \qquad (15.20)$$

where k is the Boltzmann constant. If a gas could exist at absolute zero, all the molecules would be in the zero energy level and the thermodynamic probability per molecule would be given by the statistical weight, g_0, for the zero point level. For N distinguishable particles the total probability would be g_0^N but since the particles in a gas are not distinguishable, the total probability must be divided by $N!$.[4] Then the entropy at absolute zero, from Eq. (15.20) will be:

$$S_0^0 = k \ln W_0 = k \ln \frac{g_0^N}{N!} \tag{15.21}$$

but $N!$ may be approximated by the Stirling relation:

$$N! = \left(\frac{N}{e}\right)^N \quad \text{or} \quad \ln N! = N \ln N - N. \tag{15.22}$$

Then Eq. (15.21) becomes:

$$S_0^0 = k \ln g_0^N - kN \ln N + kN \tag{15.23}$$

but g_0 is equal to Q_0, the partition function per molecule at absolute zero, since

$$Q_0 = g_0 \, e^{-0/kT} = g_0. \tag{15.24}$$

Equation (15.23) may then be written:

$$S_0^0 = k \ln Q_0^N - kN \ln N + kN \tag{15.25}$$

or assuming N the number of molecules in a mole:

$$S_0^0 = R \ln Q_0 - R \ln N + R. \tag{15.26}$$

Substitution of Eq. (15.26) in equation (15.19) gives:

$$S^0 - S_0^0 = RT \frac{d \ln Q}{dT} + R \ln Q - R \ln Q_0$$

$$S^0 - (R \ln Q_0 - R \ln N + R) = RT \frac{d \ln Q}{dT} + R \ln Q - R \ln Q_0$$

$$S^0 + R \ln N - R = RT \frac{d \ln Q}{dT} + R \ln Q \tag{15.27}$$

$$S^0 = RT \frac{d \ln Q}{dT} + R \ln Q - R \ln N + R$$

which gives the entropy for an ideal gas in terms of the partition function Q.

(d) FREE ENERGY FUNCTION

The free energy of an ideal gas is given by the relation:

$$G^0 = H^0 - TS^0. \tag{15.28}$$

[4] S. Glasstone, "Textbook of Physical Chemistry," 2nd ed. Van Nostrand, New York, 1946.

Subtracting E_0^0 from each side of the equation and dividing through by T gives:

$$\frac{G^0 - E_0^0}{T} = \frac{H^0 - E_0^0}{T} - S^0 \qquad (15.29)$$

which defines the free energy function. By using Eq. (15.9) for the enthalpy function and Eq. (15.27) for the entropy, the free energy function becomes:

$$\frac{G^0 - E_0^0}{T} = RT\frac{d\ln Q}{dT} + R - \left[RT\frac{d\ln Q}{dT} + R\ln Q - R\ln N + R\right]$$

$$\frac{G^0 - E_0^0}{T} = -R\ln Q + R\ln N = -R\ln Q - R\ln\frac{1}{N}$$

$$\frac{G^0 - E_0^0}{T} = -R\ln\frac{Q}{N} \qquad (15.30)$$

which is the free energy function in terms of the partition function.

The thermodynamic functions derived from the partition function may be summarized as follows:

Energy: $\qquad\qquad E^0 - E_0^0 = RT^2\frac{d\ln Q}{dT}$

Enthalpy function: $\qquad \dfrac{H^0 - E_0^0}{T} = RT\dfrac{d\ln Q}{dT} + R$

Heat capacity: $\qquad C_v^0 = \dfrac{d}{dT}\left[RT^2\left(\dfrac{d\ln Q}{dT}\right)\right] \qquad (15.31)$

Entropy: $\qquad\qquad S^0 = RT\dfrac{d\ln Q}{dT} + R\ln Q - R\ln N + R$

Free energy function: $\dfrac{G^0 - E_0^0}{T} = -R\ln\dfrac{Q}{N}.$

It can be seen that once the enthalpy function and the free energy function have been evaluated, the entropy may be obtained directly by substraction since

$$S^0 = \frac{H^0 - E_0^0}{T} - \left[\frac{G^0 - E_0^0}{T}\right]. \qquad (15.32)$$

15.4 Evaluation of the Partition Function

The total energy in a system may be divided into the sum of the translational energy and the internal energy; where the internal energy is essentially vibrational, rotational, and electronic. The energy, ϵ, is then:

$$\epsilon = \epsilon_{tr.} + \epsilon_{rot.} + \epsilon_{vib.} + \epsilon_{elec.} \tag{15.33}$$

and since the partition function, Q, is related to the energy by an exponential function; the total partition function will be:

$$Q = Q_{tr.} Q_{rot.} Q_{vib.} Q_{elec.} \cdot \tag{15.34}$$

Each partition function may be evaluated separately and the corresponding thermodynamic functions calculated. Each contribution to the thermodynamic functions are then added to obtain the total value. The electronic contribution is generally small, since $\epsilon_{elec.}$ is large compared to kT at ordinary temperatures, and its contribution will be ignored.

(a) TRANSLATIONAL ENERGY

The translational energy levels may be given by:

$$\epsilon_i = \frac{n^2 h^2}{8 m V^{2/3}} \tag{15.35}$$

where n is a positive integer (quantum number) from 0 to ∞ for a particle of mass m in a volume V, and h is Planck's constant. The partition function would then be:

$$Q_{tr.} = \sum g_i e^{-\epsilon_i/kT} = \sum_0^\infty e^{-n^2 h^2/(8m V^{2/3} kT)} \tag{15.36}$$

where g_i is equal to unity. If the levels are close together, as they are for translational levels, the summation may be replaced by an integration and Eq. (15.36) becomes:

$$Q_{tr.} = \int_0^\infty e^{-n^2 h^2/(8m V^{2/3} kT)} \, dn \, . \tag{15.37}$$

The integral may be evaluated from the form:

$$\int_0^\infty e^{-ax^2} \, dx = \frac{1}{2} \sqrt{\frac{\pi}{a}} \tag{15.38}$$

where the constant, a, is equal to $h^2/(8mV^{2/3}kT)$. Integration of Eq. (15.37) gives:

$$Q_{tr.} = \frac{1}{2}\sqrt{\frac{\pi(8mV^{2/3}kT)}{h^2}} = \frac{1}{h}(2\pi mkT)^{1/2}\,V^{1/3} \tag{15.39}$$

for the translational partition function for one degree of freedom. For three degrees of freedom the partition function would be:

$$Q_{tr.} = \left[\frac{1}{h}(2\pi mkT)^{1/2}\,V^{1/3}\right]^3 = \frac{(2\pi mkT)^{3/2}\,V}{h^3} \tag{15.40}$$

and each of the translational contributions to the thermodynamic functions may be derived from it.

The energy, $E^0 - E_0^0$, from Eq. (15.4) is:

$$(E^0 - E_0^0)_{tr.} = RT^2\frac{d\ln Q}{dT} = RT^2\frac{d}{dT}\left[\ln\frac{(2\pi mkT)^{3/2}\,V}{h^3}\right]$$

$$(E^0 - E_0^0)_{tr.} = \frac{RT^2\left[\frac{3}{2}\frac{V}{h^3}(2\pi mkT)^{1/2}\,2\pi mk\right]}{V(2\pi mkT)^{3/2}/h^3}$$

$$(E^0 - E_0^0)_{tr.} = RT^2\frac{3}{2}\frac{1}{T} = \frac{3}{2}RT \tag{15.41}$$

for the translational energy. The enthalpy function is:

$$\left(\frac{H^0 - E_0^0}{T}\right)_{tr.} = \frac{E^0 - E_0^0}{T} + R = \frac{3}{2}\frac{RT}{T} + R = \frac{5}{2}R \tag{15.42}$$

and the free energy function from equation (15.30) is:

$$\left(\frac{G^0 - E_0^0}{T}\right)_{tr.} = -R\ln\frac{Q}{N} = -R\ln\left[\frac{(2\pi mkT)^{3/2}\,V}{Nh^3}\right]. \tag{15.43}$$

The heat capacity, C_v^0, from differentiation of the energy term is simply $3R/2$. The entropy is given by combination of Eq. (15.42) and (15.43) as indicated in Eq. (15.32):

$$(S^0)_{tr.} = \frac{H^0 - E_0^0}{T} - \left[\frac{G^0 - E_0}{T}\right] = \frac{5}{2}R + R\ln\left[\frac{(2\pi mkT)^{3/2}\,V}{Nh^3}\right]. \tag{15.44}$$

(b) ROTATIONAL ENERGY

The rotational energy levels for a linear molecule is given by:

$$\epsilon_{rot.} = \frac{h^2 J(J+1)}{8\pi^2 I} \tag{15.45}$$

where I is the moment of inertia and J the rotational quantum number. The rotational partition function is:

$$Q_{rot.} = \sum g_i e^{-\epsilon_{rot.}/kT} = \sum (2J+1) e^{-h^2 J(J+1)/(8\pi^2 IkT)} \tag{15.46}$$

where the degeneracy, g_i, is equal to $(2J+1)$. Replacing the summation by an integration, an approximation which improves at higher temperatures, the result is:

$$Q_{rot.} = \int_0^\infty (2J+1) e^{-h^2 J(J+1)/(8\pi^2 IkT)} \, dJ \tag{15.47}$$

which may be written as:

$$Q_{rot.} = \int_0^\infty e^{-h^2 (J^2+J)/(8\pi^2 IkT)} \, d(J^2 + J) . \tag{15.48}$$

At constant temperature, Eq. (15.48) may be integrated:

$$Q_{rot.} = -\frac{8\pi^2 IkT}{h^2} \int_0^\infty e^{-h^2(J^2+J)/(8\pi^2 IkT)} \left(-\frac{h^2}{8\pi^2 IkT} \right) d(J^2 + J)$$

$$Q_{rot.} = -\frac{8\pi^2 IkT}{h^2} [e^{-h^2(J^2+J)/(8\pi^2 IkT)}]_0^\infty \tag{15.49}$$

$$Q_{rot.} = -\frac{8\pi^2 IkT}{h^2} [0 - 1] = \frac{8\pi^2 IkT}{h^2}$$

but this value must be divided by a factor, σ, the symmetry number. The symmetry number is the number of equivalent orientations of the molecule which can be obtained by simple rotation. The rotational partition function which must be used is:

$$Q_{rot.} = \frac{8\pi^2 IkT}{\sigma h^2} \tag{15.50}$$

for a linear molecule.

The rotational contributions to the thermodynamic functions for linear molecules can now be calculated. The energy will be:

$$(E^0 - E_0^0)_{rot.} = RT^2 \frac{d \ln Q}{dT} = RT \frac{d}{dT} \left[\ln \left(\frac{8\pi^2 IkT}{\sigma h^2} \right) \right]$$

$$(E^0 - E_0^0)_{rot.} = RT^2 \left[\frac{8\pi^2 Ik}{\sigma h^2} \cdot \frac{\sigma h^2}{8\pi^2 IkT} \right] = RT . \tag{15.51}$$

The enthalpy function is easily determined from the relation:

$$\left(\frac{H^0 - E_0^0}{T}\right)_{rot.} = \frac{E^0 - E_0^0}{T} = \frac{RT}{T} = R \qquad (15.52)$$

where the contribution R of Eq. (15.9) has been omitted since it has already been included in the translational contribution. The heat capacity, C_v^0, would be:

$$(C_v^0)_{rot.} = \frac{d(E^0 - E_0^0)}{dT} = \frac{d}{dT}(RT) = R \qquad (15.53)$$

and the free energy function is:

$$\left(\frac{G^0 - E_0^0}{T}\right)_{rot.} = -R \ln \underset{\sim}{Q} = -R \ln \left[\frac{8\pi^2 IkT}{\sigma h^2}\right] \qquad (15.54)$$

where in this case the partition function for rotation is somewhat different than for translation, as given by equation (15.30). For contributions other than translational the enthalpy function is:

$$\frac{H^0 - E_0^0}{T} = RT \frac{d \ln \underset{\sim}{Q}}{dT} \qquad (15.55)$$

and the entropy, S^0, is:

$$S^0 = RT \frac{d \ln \underset{\sim}{Q}}{dT} + R \ln \underset{\sim}{Q} \qquad (15.56)$$

where all factors arising from inclusion of $N!$ in S_0 have been eliminated, since for rotation, the particles may be considered distinguishable. The free energy function from equation (15.29) is:

$$\frac{G^0 - E_0^0}{T} = \frac{H^0 - E_0^0}{T} - S^0 = RT \frac{d \ln \underset{\sim}{Q}}{dT} - \left[RT \frac{d \ln \underset{\sim}{Q}}{dT} + R \ln \underset{\sim}{Q}\right] \qquad (15.57)$$

as has been indicated in Eq. (15.54).

For a nonlinear polyatomic molecule the energy levels of a symmetric top would be:

$$(\epsilon_i)_{rot.} = \frac{h^2}{8\pi^2 I_B} J(J+1) + \left[\frac{h^2}{8\pi^2 I_A} - \frac{h^2}{8\pi^2 I_B}\right] K^2 \qquad (15.58)$$

where K has the values $J, J-1, \cdots, -J$; I_A is the moment of inertia about the symmetry axis; and I_B is one of the two equal moments of inertia. The partition function can then be written:

$$\underset{\sim}{Q}_{rot.} = \sum_{J=0}^{\infty} \sum_{K=-J}^{J} (2J+1) \exp \left\{\left[\frac{h^2 J(J+1)}{8\pi^2 I_B} + \left(\frac{h^2}{8\pi^2 I_A} - \frac{h^2}{8\pi^2 I_B}\right) K^2\right] \Big/ kT\right\} \qquad (15.59)$$

and is approximately equal to[3]:

$$Q_{\text{rot.}} \approx \frac{(\pi I_A I_B^2)^{1/2}}{\sigma} \left(\frac{8\pi^2 kT}{h^2} \right)^{3/2} \tag{15.60}$$

where the symmetry number, σ, has also been added. An expression for the rotational levels of an asymmetric top cannot easily be written. An approximation may be derived from Eq. (15.59) by using I_A and $\sqrt{I_B I_C}$ as the moments of inertia, where I_B and I_C are the two moments of inertia nearest each other in value. If I_A and I_B are closest, then I_C and $\sqrt{I_A I_B}$ are used in Eq. (15.59). The result, for the first case is:[3]

$$Q_{\text{rot.}} \approx (\pi I_A I_B I_C)^{1/2} \left(\frac{8\pi^2 kT}{h^2} \right)^{3/2} \tag{15.61}$$

or including the symmetry number, σ:

$$Q_{\text{rot.}} = \frac{(\pi I_A I_B I_C)^{1/2}}{\sigma} \left(\frac{8\pi^2 kT}{h^2} \right)^{3/2}. \tag{15.62}$$

Equation (15.62) can then be used to calculate the rotational contributions to the thermodynamic functions for an asymmetric polyatomic molecule or any nonlinear polyatomic molecule by use of the proper moments of inertia. The internal energy is then:

$$(E^0 - E_0^0)_{\text{rot.}} = RT^2 \frac{d \ln Q}{dT} = RT^2 \frac{d}{dT} \left[\ln \frac{(\pi I_A I_B I_C)^{1/2}}{\sigma} \left(\frac{8\pi^2 kT}{h^2} \right)^{3/2} \right] \tag{15.63}$$

and differentiating:

$$(E^0 - E_0^0)_{\text{rot.}} = RT^2 \left(\frac{3}{2} \right) \left(\frac{8\pi^2 kT}{h^2} \right)^{-1} \left(\frac{8\pi^2 k}{h^2} \right) = \frac{3}{2} RT. \tag{15.64}$$

The enthalpy function is:

$$\left(\frac{H^0 - E_0^0}{T} \right)_{\text{rot.}} = \frac{E^0 - E_0^0}{T} = \frac{3}{2} \frac{RT}{T} = \frac{3}{2} R \tag{15.65}$$

and the heat capacity, C_v, is:

$$(C_v^0)_{\text{rot.}} = \frac{d(E^0 - E_0^0)}{dT} = \frac{d}{dT} \left(\frac{3}{2} RT \right) = \frac{3}{2} R. \tag{15.66}$$

The free energy function is:

$$\left(\frac{G^0 - E_0^0}{T} \right)_{\text{rot.}} = -R \ln Q = -R \ln \left[\frac{(\pi I_A I_B I_C)^{1/2}}{\sigma} \left(\frac{8\pi^2 kT}{h^2} \right)^{3/2} \right]. \tag{15.67}$$

The corresponding functions for a symmetric top or spherical top may be derived in the same way by using the proper moments of inertia in the partition function.

(c) VIBRATIONAL ENERGY

The energy states for vibrational levels, assuming a harmonic oscillator and no interaction between vibration and rotation, is:

$$(\epsilon_i)_{\text{vib.}} = (v_i + \tfrac{1}{2})\, hv' \tag{15.68}$$

where v' is the frequency of vibration in sec^{-1} and v_i is the vibrational quantum number. The partition function is:

$$Q'_{\text{vib.}} = \sum g_i\, e^{-\epsilon_i/kT} = \sum_v e^{-(v+1/2)hv'/kT} \tag{15.69}$$

where g_i is unity. Equation (15.69) can be simplified by removing the constant term and noting that the summation of $e^{-v_i x}$ is $1/(1 - e^{-x})$ to give:

$$Q'_{\text{vib.}} = \exp\left[\frac{-hv'}{(2kT)}\right] \sum \exp\left[\frac{-v_i hv'}{(kT)}\right] = \exp\left[\frac{-hv'}{(2kT)}\right]\left(\frac{1}{1 - e^{-hv'/kT}}\right). \tag{15.70}$$

Equation (15.70) may be written:

$$Q'_{\text{vib.}} = e^{-x/2}\left(\frac{1}{1 - e^{-x}}\right) \tag{15.71}$$

where x is equal to hv'/kT or hvc/kT where v is the vibrational frequency in wavenumbers. The internal energy from Eq. (15.5), since the zero level ($v = 0$) is not zero energy, is:

$$E^0 = RT^2 \frac{d \ln Q'}{dT} = RT^2 \frac{d}{dT}\left[\ln\left(e^{-x/2}\right)\left(\frac{1}{1 - e^{-x}}\right)\right]$$

$$E^0 = RT^2 \frac{d}{dT}\left[\ln\left(\frac{1}{1 - e^{-x}}\right) + \ln\left(e^{-x/2}\right)\right] = RT^2 \frac{d}{dT}\left[\ln\left(\frac{1}{1 - e^{-x}}\right)\left(-\frac{x}{2}\right)\right] \tag{15.72}$$

$$E^0 = RT^2\left[\left(\frac{-(1 - e^{-x})^{-2}\,(-e^{-x})\,(-hvc/k)\,(-1/T^2)}{(1 - e^{-x})^{-1}}\right) + \left(\frac{-hvc}{2k}\right)\left(-T^{-2}\right)\right]$$

$$E^0 = RT\left[\frac{xe^{-x}}{(1 - e^{-x})}\right] + \frac{R}{k}\frac{hvc}{2}.$$

However, $Rhvc/2k$ is equal to $N(hv'/2)$, which is the zero point energy per mole, E_0, and thus Eq. (15.72) may be written:

$$(E^0 - E_0^0)_{\text{vib.}} = RT\left[\frac{xe^{-x}}{(1 - e^{-x})}\right] = RT\left[\frac{x}{e^x(1 - e^{-x})}\right]$$

$$(E^0 - E_0^0)_{\text{vib.}} = \frac{RTx}{e^x - 1}. \tag{15.73}$$

The same result can also be obtained by initially substracting ϵ_0, that is $\frac{1}{2} h\nu'$ from each side of Eq. (15.68):

$$(\epsilon_i - \epsilon_0)_{\text{vib.}} = (\epsilon_i')_{\text{vib.}} = \left(v_i + \tfrac{1}{2}\right) h\nu' - \tfrac{1}{2} h\nu' \qquad (15.74)$$

$$(\epsilon_i')_{\text{vib.}} = v_i h\nu'$$

which would conform to the usual zero level, that is, the quantum number zero corresponds to a zero energy level as was true for translation and rotation. Equation (15.4) can then properly be used with the partition function derived from energy levels based on Eq. (15.74), which is:

$$Q_{\text{vib.}} = \sum g_i e^{-\epsilon'_i/kT} = \sum_v e^{-v_i h\nu'/kT} = \frac{1}{1 - e^{-x}} \qquad (15.75)$$

to give the final result:

$$(E^0 - E_0^0)_{\text{vib.}} = RT^2 \frac{d \ln Q_{\text{vib.}}}{dT} = \frac{RTx}{e^x - 1}, \qquad (15.76)$$

which is the same result as Eq. (15.73).

The enthalpy function, omitting R, as in rotation is:

$$\left(\frac{H^0 - E_0^0}{T}\right)_{\text{vib.}} = \left(\frac{E^0 - E_0^0}{T}\right)_{\text{vib.}} = \frac{RTx}{(e^x - 1)\,T} = \frac{Rx}{e^x - 1} \qquad (15.77)$$

and the heat capacity, C_v^0, from differentiation of the energy is:

$$(C_v^0)_{\text{vib.}} = \frac{d(E^0 - E_0^0)}{dT} = \frac{d}{dT} \frac{RTx}{e^x - 1}$$

$$(C_v^0)_{\text{vib.}} = \frac{d}{dT}\left[R\left(\frac{h\nu c}{k}\right)(e^x - 1)^{-1}\right] = -R\left(\frac{h\nu c}{k}\right)\left[(e^x - 1)^{-2}(e^x)\left(\frac{h\nu c}{k}\right)\left(\frac{-1}{T^2}\right)\right]$$

$$(C_v^0)_{\text{vib.}} = R\left(\frac{h\nu c}{kT}\right)^2 \frac{e^x}{(e^x - 1)^2} = \frac{Rx^2 e^x}{(e^x - 1)^2}, \qquad (15.78)$$

where x is $h\nu c/kT$, as defined previously. The free energy function derived in the same way as for rotation is:

$$\frac{G^0 - E_0^0}{T} = \frac{H^0 - E_0^0}{T} - S^0 = RT\frac{d \ln Q}{dT} - \left[RT\frac{d \ln Q}{dT} + R \ln Q\right]$$

$$\frac{G^0 - E_0^0}{T} = -R \ln Q \quad \text{or} \quad \left(\frac{G^0 - E_0^0}{T}\right)_{\text{vib.}} = -R \ln Q_{\text{vib.}}$$

$$\left(\frac{G^0 - E_0^0}{T}\right)_{\text{vib.}} = -R \ln \left(\frac{1}{1 - e^{-x}}\right) = R \ln (1 - e^{-x}). \qquad (15.79)$$

In polyatomic molecules each of the $3N-6$ frequencies, ν, will give a corresponding value for x. The total vibrational contribution to each of the thermodynamic functions is obtained by summing the contributions from each frequency. The contribution from each degenerate vibration is multiplied by the degeneracy of the vibration.

15.5   Evaluation of the Thermodynamic Functions for $CHCl_3$

In this section the expressions obtained in the preceding sections will be used to calculate numerical values for the thermodynamic functions for chloroform.

(a) TRANSLATIONAL CONTRIBUTION

The translational contribution to the internal energy, from Eq. (15.41) is:

$$(E^0 - E_0^0)_{tr.} = \frac{3}{2} RT = 2.9808 \; T \tag{15.80}$$

and may be calculated for any absolute temperature, T. The enthalpy function from Eq. (15.42) is:

$$\left(\frac{H^0 - E_0^0}{T}\right)_{tr.} = \frac{5}{2} R = 4.9680 \tag{15.81}$$

and is a constant contribution. The heat capacity, C_v^0, is:

$$(C_v^0)_{tr.} = \frac{d(E^0 - E_0^0)}{dT} = \frac{3}{2} R = 2.9808 \tag{15.82}$$

and the corresponding value at constant pressure, C_p^0, is:

$$(C_p^0)_{tr.} = (C_v^0)_{tr.} + R = 2.9808 + 1.9872 = 4.9680. \tag{15.83}$$

The free energy function, from Eq. (15.43), is:

$$\left(\frac{G^0 - E_0^0}{T}\right)_{tr.} = -R \left[\ln \left(\frac{(2\pi mkT)^{3/2} \, V}{Nh^3}\right)\right]$$

$$= -R(2.303) \log \left(\frac{(2\pi mkT)^{3/2} \, RT}{Nh^3 P}\right), \tag{15.84}$$

where the volume, V, has been replaced by RT/P, assuming an ideal gas and 2.303 is introduced to convert from natural to common logarithms. Introducing the numerical values for the constants and simplifying, Eq. (15.84) becomes:

$$\left(\frac{G^0 - E_0^0}{T}\right)_{tr.} = -4.5757 \left[\log \frac{(2\pi k)^{3/2} R}{N^{5/2} h^3 P} + \log T^{5/2} + \log M^{3/2}\right]$$

$$\left(\frac{G^0 - E_0^0}{T}\right)_{tr.} = -4.5757 \left[\frac{3}{2} \log (8.6727 \times 10^{-16}) + \log 82.057 \right.$$

$$-\frac{5}{2} \log (6.023 \times 10^{23})$$

$$\left. - 3 \log (6.6237 \times 10^{-27}) + \frac{5}{2} \log T + \frac{3}{2} \log M\right]$$

$$\left(\frac{G^0 - E_0^0}{T}\right)_{tr.} = -4.5757 \left(-1.59156 + \frac{5}{2} \log T + \frac{3}{2} \log M\right)$$

$$\left(\frac{G^0 - E_0^0}{T}\right)_{tr.} = 7.28244 - 11.43916 \log T - 6.86350 \log M, \tag{15.85}$$

where m, the weight of a molecule, has been replaced by its equivalent; the molecular weight, M, over N. The gas constant, R, is in milliliter-atmospheres and the pressure, P, has been taken as 1 atm. The molecular weight of chloroform is 119.39 and substitution in Eq. (15.85) gives:

$$\left(\frac{G^0 - E_0^0}{T}\right)_{tr.} = 7.28244 - 11.43916 \log T - 6.86350 \log 119.39 \tag{15.86}$$

$$\left(\frac{G^0 - E_0^0}{T}\right)_{tr.} = -6.97280 - 11.4392 \log T$$

from which the free energy function may be calculated at any temperature, T. Calculated values for the thermodynamic functions at several temperatures are listed in Table 15.1. Values for the entropy, S^0, are also listed and were obtained by combination of the enthalpy function and free energy function as given in Eq. (15.32). The two values have been added, since the negative of the free energy function is listed.

(b) ROTATIONAL CONTRIBUTION

The rotational partition function was given by Eq. (15.62) as:

$$Q_{rot.} = \frac{(\pi I_A I_B I_C)^{1/2}}{\sigma} \left(\frac{8\pi^2 kT}{h^2}\right)^{3/2} \tag{15.87}$$

TABLE 15.1

THERMODYNAMIC FUNCTIONS FOR CHLOROFORM

(CAL/MOLE/$^\circ$K)

Temperature ($^\circ$K)	Contribution	$H^0 - E_0^0/T$	$-(G^0 - E_0^0)/T$	S^0	C_p^0
298.16	Translation	4.9680	35.2787	40.2467	4.9680
	Rotation	2.9808	22.1765	25.1573	2.9808
	Vibration	3.4222	1.8918	5.3140	7.7590
	Total^a	11.37	59.35	70.72	15.71
400	Translation	4.9680	36.7385	41.7065	4.9680
	Rotation	2.9808	23.0523	26.0331	2.9808
	Vibration	4.8063	3.0919	7.8982	9.8757
	Total^a	12.76	62.88	75.64	17.82
500	Translation	4.9680	37.8471	42.8151	4.9680
	Rotation	2.9808	23.7175	26.6983	2.9808
	Vibration	5.9815	4.3006	10.2821	11.3824
	Total^a	13.93	65.87	79.80	19.33
600	Translation	4.9680	38.7528	43.7208	4.9680
	Rotation	2.9808	24.2609	27.2417	2.9808
	Vibration	6.9797	5.4839	12.4636	12.4856
	Total^a	14.93	68.50	83.43	20.43
800	Translation	4.9680	40.1820	45.1500	4.9680
	Rotation	2.9808	25.1185	28.0993	2.9808
	Vibration	8.5823	7.7937	16.3760	13.9722
	Total^a	16.53	73.09	89.63	21.92
1000	Translation	4.9680	41.2906	46.2586	4.9680
	Rotation	2.9808	25.7836	28.7644	2.9808
	Vibration	9.7373	9.7579	19.4952	14.9134
	Total^a	17.69	76.83	94.52	22.86

^{a} Rounded to nearest significant figures.

for a polyatomic, nonlinear molecule and requires values for the moments of inertia and the symmetry number. Determination of the moments of inertia for a diatomic molecule was shown in Chapter 3. A polyatomic molecule, in general, has three moments, I_A, I_B, and I_C. Chloroform is a symmetric top and two of the moments should be equal, that is, $I_A = I_B \neq I_C$. The moments may be calculated by the method of Hirshfelder as follows[5]:

$$I_A I_B I_C = \begin{vmatrix} A & -D & -E \\ -D & B & -F \\ -E & -F & C \end{vmatrix} \tag{15.88}$$

[5] J. O. Hirshfelder, *J. Chem. Phys.* 8, 431 (1940).

where A, B, C, D, E, and F are defined by:

$$A = \Sigma\, m(y^2 + z^2) - \frac{1}{M}(\Sigma\, my)^2 - \frac{1}{M}(\Sigma\, mz)^2$$

$$B = \Sigma\, m(x^2 + z^2) - \frac{1}{M}(\Sigma\, mx)^2 - \frac{1}{M}(\Sigma\, mz)^2$$

$$C = \Sigma\, m(x^2 + y^2) - \frac{1}{M}(\Sigma\, mx)^2 - \frac{1}{M}(\Sigma\, my)^2$$

$$D = \Sigma\, mxy - \frac{1}{M}(\Sigma\, mx)(\Sigma\, my)$$ \hspace{2cm} (15.89)

$$E = \Sigma\, mxz - \frac{1}{M}(\Sigma\, mx)(\Sigma\, mz)$$

and

$$F = \Sigma\, myz - \frac{1}{M}(\Sigma\, my)(\Sigma\, mz),$$

where x, y, and z are the cartesian coordinates for each atom of mass m with reference to an arbitrary set of axes. The axes chosen for chloroform are shown in Fig. 15.1(a) with the z axis along the $C-H$ bond and the origin at the carbon atom. The bond lengths and angles are those used in Chapter 14 from the data of Zeitlow.[6] The $Cl-C-Cl$ angle is 112°, the $C-H$ distance 1.093 Å and the $C-Cl$ distance 1.77 Å. The length A [see Fig. 15.1(b)] is:

$$A = \sin 56°(1.77) = 1.467, \hspace{2cm} (15.90)$$

and from Fig. 15.1(c), the x coordinates for Cl_1, Cl_2, and Cl_3 are 1.467, 0, and -1.467 respectively. The y coordinate for Cl_2 is indicated by $-y''$ in Fig. 15.1(c) and is:

$$y'' = 1.467/\cos 30° = 1.694. \hspace{2cm} (15.91)$$

The y coordinates for Cl_1 and Cl_3 are identical and are:

$$y' = 1.467 \tan 30° = 0.8470. \hspace{2cm} (15.92)$$

The z coordinates for all three chlorine atoms are the same and are negative. The value, referring to Fig. 15.1(d), is:

$$a = 1.77 \cos 56° = 0.990$$
$$z^2 = (0.990)^2 - (0.8470)^2 = 0.262 \hspace{2cm} (15.93)$$
$$z = 0.512.$$

Table 15.2 lists the coordinates, in angstroms, for all atoms.

[6] J. P. Zeitlow, M. S. Thesis, Illinois Institute of Technology, Chicago, 1949.

Table 15.2 also lists the square of each coordinate and other data required for the determination of Eq. (15.89). The value for A is then:

$$A = \Sigma\, m(y^2 + z^2) - \frac{1}{M}(\Sigma\, my)^2 - \frac{1}{M}(\Sigma\, mz)^2$$

$$A = 30.169 \times 10^{-39} - (5.044 \times 10^{21})\,(0) - (5.044 \times 10^{21})\,(78.53 \times 10^{-62})$$

$$A = 26.21 \times 10^{-39}\ \text{gm-cm}^2,$$
(15.94)

where the coordinate values are in cm and the masses are in gm. The values for B and C are:

$$B = \Sigma\, m(x^2 + z^2) - \frac{1}{M}(\Sigma\, mx)^2 - \frac{1}{M}(\Sigma\, mz)^2$$

$$B = 30.171 \times 10^{-39} - (5.044 \times 10^{21})\,(0) - (5.044 \times 10^{21})\,(78.53 \times 10^{-62})$$

$$B = 26.21 \times 10^{-39}\ \text{gm-cm}^2,$$
(15.95)

and

$$C = \Sigma\, m(x^2 + y^2) - \frac{1}{M}(\Sigma\, mx)^2 - \frac{1}{M}(\Sigma\, my)^2$$

$$C = 50.68 \times 10^{-39} - (5.044 \times 10^{21})\,(0) - (5.044 \times 10^{21})\,(0)$$
(15.96)

$$C = 50.68 \times 10^{-39}\ \text{gm-cm}^2.$$

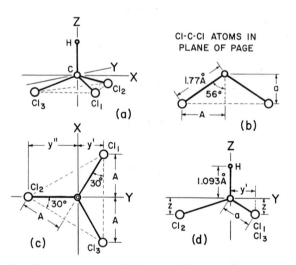

FIG. 15.1.   Coordinate system for $CHCl_3$. (a) XZ plane: H and C are in XZ plane (plane of paper); Cl_1 and Cl_3 are in front of plane; Cl_2 is behind plane. (b) Plane through any two chlorine atoms and the carbon atom. (c) XY plane: C atom is in XY plane (plane of paper); H atom is above plane; Cl_1, Cl_2, and Cl_3 are all in a plane below XY plane. (d) YZ plane: H, C, and Cl_2 are in YZ plane (plane of paper); Cl_1 is behind plane; Cl_3 is in front of plane.

TABLE 15.2[a]

COORDINATE VALUES AND RELATED DATA FOR THE CALCULATION OF THE
MOMENTS OF INERTIA FOR THE CHLOROFORM MOLECULE

Atom	x	y	z	x^2	y^2	z^2
H	0	0	1.093	0	0	1.195
C	0	0	0	0	0	0
Cl_1	1.467	0.847	−0.512	2.152	0.717	0.262
Cl_2	0	−1.694	−0.512	0	2.870	0.262
Cl_3	−1.467	0.847	−0.512	2.152	0.717	0.262

Atom	$y^2 + z^2$	$x^2 + z^2$	$x^2 + y^2$	$m(y^2 + z^2)$	$m(x^2 + z^2)$	$m(x^2 + y^2)$
H	1.195	1.195	0	0.200	0.200	0
C	0	0	0	0	0	0
Cl_1	0.979	2.414	2.869	5.764	14.214	16.893
Cl_2	3.132	0.262	2.870	18.441	1.543	16.898
Cl_3	0.979	2.414	2.869	5.764	14.214	16.893
Σ	6.285	6.285	8.608	30.169	30.171	50.684

Atom	my	mz	mx	mxy	mxz	myz
H	0	0.183	0	0	0	0
C	0	0	0	0	0	0
Cl_1	4.987	−3.015	8.638	7.316	−4.423	−2.553
Cl_2	−9.974	−3.015	0	0	0	5.107
Cl_3	4.987	−3.015	−8.638	−7.316	4.423	−2.553
Σ	0	−8.862	0	0	0	0
$(Σ)^2$	0	78.535	0			

[a] Bond lengths used are in angstrom units and atomic masses have been multiplied by 10^{23}: $m_H = 0.1674 = 0.1674 \times 10^{-23}$ gm; $m_{Cl} = 5.888 = 5.888 \times 10^{-23}$ gm.

Reference to Table 15.2 indicates that D, E, and F are all zero. The product of the three moments of inertia, from Eq. (15.88), is then:

$$I_A I_B I_C = \begin{matrix} 262.1 \times 10^{-40} \\ 262.1 \times 10^{-40} \\ 506.8 \times 10^{-40} \end{matrix}$$

$$I_A I_B I_C = 3480.2 \times 10^{-116}, \qquad (15.97)$$

and $I_A = I_B = 262.1 \times 10^{-40}$ gm-cm² and $I_C = 506.8 \times 10^{-40}$ gm-cm². The value reported by Smith and Unterberger[7] for I_B, from microwave data, is 254.1×10^{-40} gm-cm².

The enthalpy function, from Eq. (15.65), is:

$$\left(\frac{H^0 - E_0^0}{T}\right)_{rot.} = \frac{3}{2} R = 2.9808, \qquad (15.98)$$

[7] W. V. Smith and R. R. Unterberger, *J. Chem. Phys.* **17**, 1348 (1949).

and the heat capacity, C_v^0, from Eq. (15.66), is:

$$(C_v^0)_{\text{rot.}} = \frac{3}{2} R = 2.9808. \tag{15.99}$$

The free energy function, from Eq. (15.67):

$$\left(\frac{G^0 - E_0^0}{T} \right)_{\text{rot.}} = -R \ln \left[\frac{(\pi I_A I_B I_C)^{1/2}}{\sigma} \left(\frac{8\pi^2 kT}{h^2} \right)^{3/2} \right], \tag{15.100}$$

is more complex but it can be simplified. Introducing values for the constants and combining terms gives:

$$\left(\frac{G^0 - E_0^0}{T} \right)_{\text{rot.}} = -(1.9872)\,(2.3026) \left[\log \left(\frac{\pi^{7/2}(8k)^{3/2}}{h^3} \right) \right.$$

$$\left. + \frac{1}{2} \log \left(I_A I_B I_C \right) + \frac{3}{2} \log T - \log \sigma \right]$$

$$\left(\frac{G^0 - E_0^0}{T} \right)_{\text{rot.}} = -4.5757 \left[\frac{7}{2} \log 3.1416 + \frac{3}{2} \log \left(11.0424 \times 10^{-16} \right) \right.$$

$$\left. - 3 \log \left(6.6237 \times 10^{-27} \right) + \frac{1}{2} \log \left(I_A I_B I_C \right) + \frac{3}{2} \log T - \log \sigma \right]$$

$$\left(\frac{G^0 - E_0^0}{T} \right)_{\text{rot.}} = -264.66 - 2.2878 \log \left(I_A I_B I_C \right) - 6.8635 \log T + 4.5757 \log \sigma, \tag{15.101}$$

which is a general expression for the rotational contribution to the free energy. The product $I_A I_B I_C$, for chloroform, is 3480.2×10^{-116}, σ is equal to 3, and Eq. (15.101) becomes:

$$\left(\frac{G^0 - E_0^0}{T} \right)_{\text{rot.}} = -264.66 - 2.2878 \log \left(3480.2 \times 10^{-116} \right)$$

$$- 6.8635 \log T + 4.5757 \log 3 \tag{15.102}$$

$$\left(\frac{G^0 - E_0^0}{T} \right)_{\text{rot.}} = -5.1979 - 6.8635 \log T,$$

which may be used to calculate the free energy function for chloroform at the temperature, T. Table 15.1 lists the results for several temperatures. Table 15.1 also gives the constant values for the rotational contributions to the enthalpy function, $(H^0 - E_0^0)/T$, and to the heat capacity at constant pressure, C_p^0, which is equal to C_v^0, for rotation. Values for $S_{\text{rot.}}^0$ obtained from the enthalpy function and the free energy function are also listed and were calculated in the same way as was done for translation.

(c) VIBRATIONAL CONTRIBUTIONS

The vibrational contributions to the thermodynamic functions are given by Eqs. (15.87), (15.88), and (15.89) for the enthalpy, heat capacity, and free energy as:

$$\left(\frac{H^0 - E_0^0}{T}\right)_{\text{vib.}} = \frac{Rx}{e^x - 1},$$

$$(C_v^0)_{\text{vib.}} = (C_p^0)_{\text{vib.}} = \frac{Rx^2 e^x}{(e^x - 1)^2},$$

(15.103)

and

$$\left(\frac{G^0 - E_0^0}{T}\right)_{\text{vib.}} = R \ln (1 - e^{-x}),$$

where x was defined as hvc/kT. The fundamental frequencies, v, for chloroform are 3019, 668, and 368 cm^{-1} of type A_1 and 1216, 757, and 261 cm^{-1} of type E. Values of x must be calculated for each frequency at each temperature. For example, at 25^{0}C the value of x for the 3019 frequency is:

$$x = \frac{hvc}{kT} = \frac{(6.6237 \times 10^{-27})\,(3019)\,(2.9978 \times 10^{10})}{(1.3803 \times 10^{-16})\,(298.16)}$$

$$x = 14.57.$$

(15.104)

The calculated values of x are listed in the third column of Table 15.3. Using these values the functions $x/(e^x - 1)$, $-\ln(1 - e^{-x})$, and $x^2 e^x/(e^x - 1)^2$ may be obtained from tabulated values. (For example, see Taylor and Glasstone,[8] or Dole.[9])

Once the functions are known they are summed (counting each value for E vibrations twice) to give the totals listed in Table 15.3. Multiplication of the proper summation by R gives the corresponding thermodynamic function as indicated in Eq. (15.103). Table 15.1 lists the final values obtained as well as the entropy, $S_{\text{vib.}}^0$, again the sum of the enthalpy column, $(H^0 - E_0^0)/T$, and the free energy column, $-(G^0 - E_0^0)/T$ as was done in the preceding contributions.

Table 15.1 contains a summary of all the final calculations for translation, rotation, and vibration at the several temperatures and lists the total for each function at each temperature.

[8] H. S. Taylor and S. Glasstone, "Treatise on Physical Chemistry," 3rd ed., p. 655. Van Nostrand, New York, 1942.
[9] M. Dole, "Introduction to Statistical Thermodynamics," p. 223. Prentice-Hall, Englewood Cliffs, New Jersey 1954.

TABLE 15.3
VIBRATIONAL CONTRIBUTIONS TO THE THERMODYNAMIC FUNCTIONS

Temperature (°K) ν_i	x_i	$x_i/e^{x_i} - 1$	$-\ln(1 - e^{-x_i})$	$x_i^2 e^{x_i}/(e^{x_i} - 1)^2$
298.16 3019	14.57	0.00001	0.00000	0.00010
1216[a]	5.867	0.01662	0.00283	0.09782
757[a]	3.653	0.09740	0.02634	0.36499
668	3.223	0.13401	0.04078	0.44947
368	1.776	0.36222	0.18571	0.77415
261[a]	1.259	0.49893	0.33359	0.87758
Σ		1.72213	0.95199	3.90450
R Σ		3.4222	1.8918	7.7590
400 3019	10.858	0.00021	0.00002	0.00228
1216[a]	4.373	0.05599	0.01273	0.24783
757[a]	2.723	0.19130	0.06800	0.55790
668	2.403	0.23900	0.09480	0.63120
368	1.324	0.47969	0.30898	0.86570
261[a]	0.939	0.60257	0.49533	0.92951
Σ		2.41863	1.55591	4.96966
R Σ		4.8063	3.0919	9.8757
500 3019	8.687	0.00146	0.00017	0.01271
1216[a]	3.499	0.10898	0.03066	0.39331
757[a]	2.178	0.27820	0.12010	0.68330
668	1.922	0.32940	0.15840	0.74169
368	1.059	0.56193	0.42534	0.91140
261[a]	0.751	0.67144	0.63935	0.95442
Σ		3.01003	2.16415	5.72786
R Σ		5.9815	4.3006	11.3824
600 3019	7.239	0.00520	0.00072	0.03765
1216[a]	2.916	0.16706	0.05573	0.51489
757[a]	1.815	0.35304	0.17774	0.76540
668	1.602	0.40425	0.22502	0.81103
368	0.882	0.62302	0.53437	0.93759
261[a]	0.626	0.71984	0.76628	0.96807
Σ		3.51235	2.75960	6.28300
R Σ		6.9797	5.4839	12.4856
800 3019	5.429	0.02390	0.00439	0.13038
1216[a]	2.187	0.27600	0.11900	0.68130
757[a]	1.361	0.46958	0.29660	0.85914
668	1.201	0.51722	0.35838	0.88817
368	0.662	0.71984	0.76628	0.76628
261[a]	0.469	0.78334	0.98084	0.96807
Σ		4.31881	3.92193	7.03108
R Σ		8.5823	7.7937	13.9722

[a] Degenerate (type E) vibrations—each contribution counted twice in summations.

AUTHOR INDEX

Numbers in parentheses are footnote numbers. They are inserted to indicate the citation of an author's work when his name is not mentioned on the page.

Abel, E. W., 291
Abramovitch, R. A., 266
Acquista, N., 53, 132, 198, 349
Addison, C. C., 136
Alford, D., 304, 306(41)
Allen, G., 94, 304, 306(42)
Alpert, M., 133, 313, 337
Ambrose, E. J., 79, 81, 84 (77), 85
Anachenko, S. N., 245
Anderson, D. M. W., 275
Anderson, J. A., Jr., 198
Anderson, W. E., 151
Andreev, N. S., 317
Andrews, D. H., 4, 54
Angell, C. L., 153, 246, 253, 257(45)
Angelotti, N. C. 295
Aroney, M., 207
Aronovic, S. M., 261
Aronson, J. R., 149
Avery, D. G., 55

Backer, H. J., 205
Badger, G. M., 192
Badger, R. M., 27
Baer, W. K., 347
Bailey, C. R., 26, 139, 151, 153, 157
Baird, W S., 55
Bak, B., 9, 236, 311, 312(76)
Baker, A. W., 67 153
Baker, E. B., 53
Baldwin, S., 203
Barceló, J. D., 133
Barceló Matutano, J. R., 26
Barker, E. F., 133, 151
Barker, G. R., 255
Barker, S. A., 276

Barnard, D., 307, 308(53)
Barnes, R. B., 76
Barr, D. A., 266
Barr, E. E., 54
Barraclough, C. G., 318
Barrans, J., 237
Barton, D. H. R., 316
Bauer, S. H., 142
Bauer, W. H., 192, 196(5), 198(5), 199(5), 210, 226, 230(11), 269, 306, 329
Bauman, R. P., 78, 119, 149
Bavin, P. M. G., 308(57), 309
Baxter, J. N., 308(59), 309
Beard, J. A. T., 252, 253
Becker, J. A., 54
Beckett, C. W., 130, 139, 149
Beecher, L., 299, 305 (27)
Beer, M., 264
Begun, G. M., 343
Bell, E. E., 154
Bell, J. V., 299
Bell, M. F. 74
Bellamy, L. J., 194, 211, 242, 243(9) 245, 248, 249(10), 255, 256(51), 263(10), 265(10), 275, 278, 287, 291, 292(1), 293(1), 294(1), 299, 305(27), 308(62), 309, 311, 312(73), 315, 337, 342(26), 344(26), 347(26), 348(26)
Bellanato, J., 26
Bender, P., 131
Benedict, W. S., 337, 458
Ben Ishai, D., 266
Bentley, F. F., 226, 336, 337(24), 243(37), 345. 348, 349(24, 117)
Berezin, I. V., 245
Berkowitz, J. 233

Bernstein, H. J., 94, 131, 135, 146, 153, 159, 344
Berryman, L. H., 313, 314(86), 315(86), 426
Bertin, E. P., 343, 346(54)
Besnainou, S., 239, 241(1), 246(1)
Bethell, D. E., 147
Bethke, G. W., 141, 149
Billings, B. H., 54
Bindernagel, K. O., 309
Birdsall, C. M., 134
Birnbaum, S. M., 262
Blaine, L. R., 59
Blander, M., 142
Blau, E. J., 216
Blodgett, R. B., 316, 317(101)
Bogomolov, A. M., 220, 222(4), 225(4), 228(4), 231(4)
Bomstein, J., 273
Bonham, L. C., 348
Boord, C. E., 198
Bordium, W. G., 245, 247(23)
Borisevich, N. A., 266, 267(92)
Born, M., 35
Bortnick, N., 203
Bourne, E. J., 276
Boyer, J. H., 206
Brader, J. J., 311, 312(77)
Bradley, C. A., 462
Braithwaite, J. G. N., 51
Brame, E. G., Jr., 343
Brand, J. C. D., 32, 98, 113(2), 116(2), 119(2), 129, 132, 133
Brandmuller, J., 220, 222(5), 225(5), 228(5)
Bratoz, S., 239, 241(1), 246(1), 257, 258(54), 259(54), 260(54)
Brattain, R. R., 211, 213(7), 244, 245(18)
Brattain, W. H., 54
Braun, W. G., 93
Braunholtz, J. T., 232
Breslow, R., 218
Brice, T. J., 314
Briggs, L. H., 270
Brinkley, S. R., 440, 461(14)
Brissette, C., 281, 282(11)
Brockman, F. G., 54
Brockmann, H., 265
Brodersen, S., 236
Brown, C. A., 318
Brown, G. M., 313, 337
Brown, J. B., 233

Brown, J. F., Jr., 282, 285(18), 286(18), 289(18)
Brown, J. K., 129, 130, 133, 134, 145, 195, 213, 252, 261, 315, 316(98), 317 (96, 98)
Brown, M. P., 318, 346, 348(96)
Brown, T. L., 263
Brugel, W., 128
Büchler, A., 347
Bues, W., 95
Bunce, S. C., 192, 196(5), 198(5), 199(5), 210, 226, 230(11), 269, 306, 329
Burke, T. G., 131, 135, 162, 349
Byrd, W. E., 137

Caldow, G. L., 203, 204(13)
Campbell, J. E., 76
Cannon, C. G., 189, 228, 231(18), 232(18), 233(18), 264
Carlson, G. L., 347, 348, 349(117)
Carpanelli, C., 289
Carrigou-Lagrange, C., 226, 230(10)
Carrington, R. A. G., 286
Cartwright, C. H., 52
Catalano, E., 337
Cave, W. T., 133, 137, 300, 301(36), 304(36)
Cawthon, T. M., 129, 133
Cerato, C. C., 95
Cetina, R., 248
Chamberlain, M. M., 67
Chao, T. S., 206
Chapman, A. C., 302
Chapman, D., 261
Charette, J., 245, 246(27)
Charney, E., 81, 82(78)
Chasmar, R. P., 55
Chatt, J., 209
Chenon, B., 281, 282(12)
Chin, D., 342
Chittenden, R. A., 300, 301(33), 302(33), 303(33), 305(33)
Chiurdoglu, G., 216
Christen, P. J., 304
Christensen, B. E., 233
Chumaevskii, N. A., 345
Church, F. M., 227, 233(17)
Cilento, G., 141
Claassen, H. H., 134, 136, 137, 140, 151, 159, 162, 313, 314(86), 315(86), 337
Clark, H. M., 147

Clarke, H. T., 265
Cleaves, A. P., 326
Cleveland, F. F., 92, 122, 123(6), 124(6), 125(6), 136, 139, 148, 154, 202, 430, 441, 458
Cluff, C. L., 292
Coats, N. A., 270
Coburn, W. C., Jr., 342
Coggeshall, N. D., 192
Colclough, R. O., 304, 306(42)
Cole, A. R. H., 273
Cole, D. J., 70
Cole, J. O., 273
Colebrook, L. D., 270
Collins, R. L., 139, 142
Collman, J. P , 245, 246(26)
Colthup, N. B., 82, 83(82), 185(2), 186, 194, 199(11), 216, 217(12), 218(12), 226, 227(12), 231(12), 234, 243, 244(12), 248(12), 262(12)
Conduit, C. P., 285
Conn, G. K. T., 41, 55
Connelly, B. R., 255, 256(51)
Conrad, E. E , 295, 296(16)
Cook, G. L., 227, 233(17)
Corbridge, D. E. C., 299, 300(29), 301(29), 302(29), 304(29), 305(29)
Corish, P. J., 261
Coulson, C. A., 189
Cousins, L. R., 141
Cowan, R. D., 141
Craig, J C., 282
Craig, W. E., 204
Crawford, B. E., 440, 461(14)
Crawford, B. L., Jr., 59, 93, 136
Crawford, M. F., 86
Creighton. J. A., 141, 160
Criegee, R., 217, 218(19)
Cross, L. H., 143, 344
Cross, P. C., 422, 423(3), 430, 431, 455, 462
Culbertson, H., 233
Curran, C., 137, 311, 312(68), 342
Currie, C. C., 297
Curtis, H. W., 160
Cymerman-Craig, J., 308(59), 309, 344

Daasch, L. W., 133, 148, 153, 155, 299, 300(26), 301(26), 305(26), 308, 344
Daly, L. H., 134

Dandegaonker, S. H., 291, 294(4)
Dangl, R., 262, 263(71), 266(71), 311, 312(75)
Daniels, F., 316, 317(101)
Danti, A., 94
Dasent, W. E., 140
Dauben, W. G., 255, 256(50)
Dautel, R., 317
Davidson, D. W., 131
Davies, M., 311, 312(69), 342
Davis, A., 136
Davison, W. H. T., 203
Dawson, J. W. 292
Decius, J.' C., 129, 233, 422, 423(3), 425, 430, 431, 449, 455, 462
Delaroff, V. 283
Delker, D. A., 325, 326(3), 328
Deming, L. S., 328
Derfer, J. M., 198
de Roch, I. S., 317
Derwish, G. A. W., 139, 142
Deskin, W. A., 349
De Sorbo, W., 54
Detoni, S., 307, 308(54), 310(54)
De Waard, R., 52
Dewar, M. J. S., 135
Dijkstra, R., 205
Dillard, C. R., 346
Dilling, M., 262
Dizabo, P., 261
Djordjevic, C., 346
Dobriner, K., 74, 242, 243(8), 244, 247(19)
Dodd, R. E., 132, 136, 137, 150, 344
Doering, W. E., 218, 246
Doerr, R. C., 260
Dole, M., 483
Douglas, T., 255
Downie, A. R., 59
Duncan, N. E., 134
Dunderdale, J., 132, 289
DuVall, R. B., 228(21), 231

Ebers, E. S., 41
Ebsworth, E. A. V., 138, 282, 345, 346(79)
Eckstein, Z., 285
Edgell, W. F., 132, 137, 138, 140, 141, 155, 160, 337, 346
Edmondson, P. R., 326, 328
Edsall, J. T.. 92
Eggers, D. F., Jr., 217, 218, 247, 248(33)

Egorov, Y. P., 195
Eischens, R. P., 67
Elliot, A., 79, 81, 84(77) 85
Elliott, J. J., 278
El-Sabban, M. Z., 139
Emerson, W., 307, 308(55)
Englert, G., 289
Epstein, W. W., 255, 256(50)
Estep, P. A., 232
Evans, A., 326
Evans, G. E., 145
Evans, J. C., 136, 140, 342, 344
Evans, M. V., 139

Fabian, J., 282, 283(17), 284(17)
Fabian, J. M., 307, 308(53)
Fahrenfort, J., 67
Fales, H. M., 270
Falk, M., 344
Fano, L., 147
Farmer, V. C., 67
Fassel, V. A., 285, 295, 296(16)
Fateley, W. G., 347, 349(102)
Faure, K., 218
Feairheller, W. R., Jr., 146
Feldman, T., 85
Fenske, M. R., 93
Ferguson, E. E., 138, 139, 151, 152
Ferigle, S. M., 128, 154, 431
Ferraro, J. R., 300, 301
Ferris, F. C., 297
Fessenden, R., 298
Field, J. E., 273
Fitzgerald, W. E., 146
Fitzsimmons, R. V., 97
Fletcher, A. N., 62
Fletcher, W. H., 136, 137, 343
Foffani, A., 289
Folt, V. L., 316
Forbes, W. F., 244
Fowler, R. G., 248, 262, 263(71), 266(71), 311, 312(75)
Fox, J. J., 192, 196(3), 199(3)
Francel, R. J., 80, 82, 137, 285
Francis, S. A., 195
Fraser, R. D. B., 81, 84(80), 264
Frazer, R. T. M., 77
Freedman, H. H., 263
Freeman, N. K., 130, 139, 148, 155
Frei, K., 138, 239, 241(2), 246(2)

French, J. C., 205
Frenzel, C. A., 344
Friedel, R. A., 41
Fritz, H. P., 238
Fugger, J., 205, 206(21)
Fujita, J., 142, 160, 343, 346(52), 348
Fukushima, K., 262
Funk, E., 245
Fuson, N., 262, 263(71), 266(71), 311, 312(75)

Gallagher, B. S., 253
Gallaway, W. S., 139, 148
Gantert, G. E., 204
Gassman, P. G., 326
Gatehouse, B. M., 136, 153
Gaunt J., 162
Geiseler, G., 309
Gerrard, W., 291, 292(1), 293(1), 294(1,4)
Gibian, T. G., 140
Giguère, P. A., 260, 342, 344
Gillham, E. J., 54
Gilyarov, V. A., 305
Glass, W. K., 311
Glasstone, S., 422, 423(2), 467, 483
Glockler, G., 145
Gluzinsky, P., 285
Goddu, R. F., 325, 326(3), 328
Goggin, P. L., 132, 143, 344
Golay, M. J. E., 55
Goldenson, J., 299
Goldman, G. K., 243
Goldstein, J. H., 131
Gonzalez, R. D., 336
Gonzalez Barredo, J. M., 97
Gonzalez-Sanchez, F., 259
Gordon, J. M., 270
Gore, R. C., 76, 299, 301(30), 302(30)
Goubean, J., 234
Goulden, J. D. S., 257, 260(55)
Gowenlock, B. G., 289, 290(57)
Grant, G. A., 300
Gray, G. W., 308(57), 309
Greenberg, J., 70
Greene, F. T., 130
Greenlee, K. W., 154
Greenstein, J. P., 262
Grenoble, M. E., 345, 346(76)
Griffith, N. E., 202, 203(6)
Griffiths, V. S., 139, 142

Grivas, J. C., 283, 284(26)
Groenewege, M. P., 228, 233(19)
Grumprecht, W. H., 233
Grundmann, C., 234
Gudzinowicz, B. J., 198
Guillouzo, G., 311, 317(78)
Gullikson, C. W., 132
Gunthard, H. H., 138, 239, 241(2), 246(2)
Gurvich, I. A., 274
Guter, G. A., 245, 247(23)
Guthrie, R. D., 286, 309
Gutowsky, H. S., 154, 159
Gwinn, W. D., 148, 155

Haas, C., 67, 313
Hadzi, D., 245, 257, 258(54), 759(54), 260(54), 266, 279, 280(6), 282, 307, 308(54), 310(54), 312
Hale, J. B., 26
Hales, J. L., 255, 257(49), 311, 317(70)
Halford, J. O. 239, 241(3), 246(3), 247(3)
Halford, R. S., 79, 81
Hall, H. K., Jr., 241
Hall, J. R., 160
Hallgren, L. J., 70
Hallman, H., 81
Hals, L. J., 314
Halverson, F., 28, 80, 136, 137, 208, 272
Ham, N. S., 86, 204, 307, 344
Hambly, A. N., 307, 344
Hammer, W. F., 234
Hammond, G. S., 245, 247(23)
Hamner, W. F., 67
Hannan, R. B., Jr., 158
Hansen-Nygaard, L., 236, 311, 312(76)
Hansler, R. L., 15
Hanst, P. L., 260
Harper, J. L., 326
Harper, R., 302
Harris, F. W., 134
Hartwell, E. J., 248
Harvey, R. B., 304, 305(44)
Hastings, S. H., 198
Haszeldine, R. N., 266, 285, 287, 289, 290(42), 314
Hauptschein, M., 315
Hawkins, G. F., 206, 207(23)
Hawkins, J. G., 227, 231(13), 232(13)
Heacock, R. A. 282
Heckle, W. A., 236

Heether, M. R., 273, 277
Heigl, J. J., 74
Heisler, J., 299
Henbest, H. B., 192, 198, 233, 273
Henry, M. C., 318
Herling, F., 242, 243(8), 274
Herscher, L. W., 41
Herzberg, G., 26, 128, 129, 130, 131, 132, 133, 134, 135, 136, 137, 138, 139, 140, 141, 144, 145, 146, 147, 148, 149, 150, 153, 155, 157, 158, 159, 160, 162, 182, 216, 217(14), 218(14), 422, 423(4), 462, 463, 464(3), 473(3)
Hibbard, R. R., 326
Hidalgo, A., 349
Hill, R. D., 192, 280
Hirschfelder, J. O., 478
Hirt, R. C., 235
Hisatsune, I. C., 97, 343
Höver, H., 218
Hoffman, C. J., 159
Hoffman, C. W. W., 206
Holman, R. T., 326, 328
Holmstedt, B., 304
Holtzclaw, H. F., Jr., 245, 246(26)
Hooge, F. N., 304
Hornig, D. F., 71, 155, 160, 281
Horwitz, W., 93
Hough, L., 255
Hosse, L. R., 276
Hoyer, H., 203
Hrostowski, H. J., 143
Hubley, C. E., 300, 301(32, 37), 304(32), 305(32)
Hudson, R. L., 138, 151, 313, 314(86), 315(86)
Hückel, W., 274
Hughes, H. K., 73
Hughes, R. B., 248, 249(38, 39), 250(38, 39)
Humphrey, R. E. 349
Humphries, P., 244, 247(19)
Hunsberger, I. M., 244
Hunt, G. R., 342
Hunt, J. M., 348
Hunter, M. J., 295, 296(17), 297(17)
Hurowitz, M. D., 203
Hyde, W. L., 54

Ingold, C. K., 26, 139, 151, 153, 157
Isbell, H. S., 276

Ito, T., 253, 257(45)

Jahn, E. L., 234
Jakobsen, R. J., 342
James, D. W., 86, 96
Jameson, D. A., 244
Jander, J., 289
Janz, G. J., 86, 96, 131, 134, 141, 146, 345, 346(77)
Jeffries, P. R., 273
Jenkins, F. A., 45
Jenness, J. R., Jr., 53
Jesson, J. P., 202, 204(7)
Johnson, F. A., 343
Johnson, F. E., 206, 207(23)
Johnston, H. L., 348
Jonathan, N., 84
Jones, A. V., 135
Jones, E. A., 131, 135, 143, 162, 345, 349
Jones, E. J., 328
Jones, E. R. H., 233
Jones, F. E., 55
Jones, J. I., 255, 257(49), 311, 312(70)
Jones, L. H., 67, 343, 346
Jones, R. A., 266, 278, 279(3)
Jones, R. C., 53
Jones, R. L., 342
Jones, R. N., 74, 141, 195, 198(15), 242, 243(8), 244, 246, 247(19), 253, 257(45), 261, 274
Jones, W. D., 144
Jones, W. H., 348, 349(117)
Jones, W. J., 154, 311, 312(69)
Jorge, M. P., 133
Josien, M. L., 226, 230(9, 10), 261, 263, 344

Kabachnik, M. I., 302, 303(40), 305
Kaesz, H. D., 318
Kagarise, R. E., 130, 145, 241
Kaplan, I., 40
Karr, C., 232
Kasai, P. H., 218
Katayama, M., 154
Katritzky, A. R., 138, 139, 220, 224(1), 225(1), 226(1), 227(1), 228(1), 231(1), 233(1), 236(1), 237, 252, 253, 266, 270, 278, 279(3), 280(3), 317
Kawai, K., 346
Kaye, W., 325, 328(4)

Keir, D. S., 74
Keller, W. E., 348
Kellner, L., 189
Kennard, W., 227, 231(14)
Kessler, H. B., 264
Ketelaar, J. A. A., 67, 313
Kettering, C. F., 4
Khovratovich, N. N., 266, 267(92)
Kinell, P., 208
Kirby-Smith, J. S., 345
Kissman, H. M., 289
Kitson, R. E., 202, 203(6)
Kjaer, A., 204
Klaboe, P., 146, 337
Klanberg, F., 141
Klein, B., 233
Klemperer, W., 69, 347
Knight, H. B., 273, 277
Kniseley, R. N., 295, 296(16)
Knox, L. H., 246
Kobayashi, M., 142, 160
Koch, H. P., 307, 308(53)
Koegel, R. J., 262
Koehler, J. S., 160
Koelsch, C. F., 233
Kohlrausch, K. W. F., 222, 230(7), 258, 259(56), 272, 288
Kozima, K., 130, 146
Krainov, E. P., 198, 217, 218(20)
Krell, M. W., 328
Kresze, G., 311
Kreutzberger, A., 234
Kriegsmann, H., 345, 346(80)
Krimm, S., 275, 316
Kross, R. D., 285
Krueger, P. J., 246, 278, 279(5)
Kubler, R., 288
Kubo, M., 292
Kuentzel, L.E., 421
Kuhn, L. P., 276
Kumler, W. D., 287
Kynaston, W., 255, 257(49), 311, 312(70)

Laby, R. H., 307, 344
Lagemann, R. T., 131, 132, 136, 162
Lagowski, J. M., 252, 253, 317
Lancaster, J. E., 234
Landis, F. P., 51
Landolt-Börnstein, 217, 218(18)
Lane, T. J., 311, 312(68), 343, 346(54)

Langer, J., 257
Langley, B. W., 289
Langton, W. G., 54
Lappert, M. F., 291, 292(1), 293(1), 294(1, 4)
Larson, E. M., 343
Larson, L., 304
Lascombe, J., 344
Lauer, J. L., 95
Laune, J., 216
Launer, P. J., 345, 346(76)
Lauzon, R., 246
Lawson, K. E., 345
Lawson, J. R., 346
La Zerte, J. D., 314
Leandri, G., 289
Lebas, J. M., 226, 230(9, 10)
Lecomte, J., 344
Lee, D., 55
Le Fèvre, R. J. W., 206, 207, 288
Leggon, H. W., 66
Legrand, M., 282, 283(17), 284(17)
Lehmann, W. J., 134, 291, 292(8, 9), 293(7), 294(13)
Lehrer, E., 52
Leitch, L. C., 246
Leja, J., 312
Lesbre, M., 317
Levering, D. R., 206, 283, 287(22)
Lewis, J., 318
Liang, C. Y., 133, 141, 275, 337
Lide, D. R., Jr., 141, 317
Lieber, E., 204, 206, 207, 283 287(22)
Liebman, S. A., 198
Lingren, W. E., 247, 248(33)
Linsley, S. G., 76
Linton, H. R., 138, 344, 345(74)
Lippincott, E. R., 142, 146, 148, 152, 160, 288, 337, 347, 348, 349(102)
Little, L. H., 312
Livingstone, S. E., 153
Lohman, F. H., 72
Long, D. A., 136
Lord, R. C., 51, 52(13), 138, 139, 141, 143, 148, 149, 153, 189, 216, 217(11), 219(11, 16), 236, 282, 343
Louis, G., 217, 218(19)
Love, G. R., 86
Lowe, E. J., 305
Lozac'h, N., 311, 312(78)
Lüttke, W., 288, 289, 290(57)

Lunn, W. H., 285
Lurie, C., 243
Luskin, L. S., 203, 204
Luttringhaus, A., 311, 312(67, 72)
Lynch, M. A., Jr., 143
Lythgoe, B., 289

Maarsen, J. W., 300
McCallum, R. A., 262
McCarthy, P. J., 245, 246(28), 346
McCormick, R. H., 93
McCubbin, T. K., Jr., 51, 52(13)
McCullough, J. P., 344
McDowell, C. A., 131
Macfarlane, J. J., 154
McGinn, C. E., 267
McHard, J. A., 298
Machida, K., 266, 267(90)
McIvor, R. A., 300, 301(32, 37), 304(32), 305(32)
McKay, A. F., 261
McKinney, D. S., 140, 160
McLaren, E., 343
McMurry, H. L., 28, 194, 195(10), 198(10), 210, 212(5), 213(5), 228
Madigan, J. R., 458
Maeda, S., 130
Mageli, O. L., 276
Magoon, M. C., 59
Mahoney, C. L., 270
Mahoney, M. J., 326
Maier, W., 289
Maki, A., 144
Malherbe, F. E., 146
Mallion, K. B., 302
Mallory, H. D., 138
Malm, J. G., 162
Mancuso, D. E., 202
Mann, D. E., 132, 137, 139, 141, 147, 151, 158
Mann, F. G., 232, 302
Mannion, J. J., 202
Margenau, H., 32, 422, 432, 441, 455
Margoshes, M., 189
Margrave, J. L., 130
Mariner, T., 93
Marion, L., 282
Markov, M. N., 54
Marston, A. L., 343
Martell, A. E., 245, 246(28), 346

Martin, A. E., 192, 196(3), 199(3)
Martz, D. E., 131, 136
Marvel, C. S., 311, 312(77)
Maschke, A., 311
Mashima, M., 267, 268
Mason, G. W., 300
Mason, J., 132, 289
Mason, S. F., 278
Mastryukova, T. A., 302, 303(40)
Mateos, J. L., 248
Mathieu, J. P., 349
Mathis, R., 317
Mattinson, B. J. H., 287
Mattraw, H. C., 51, 70
Matze, J., 300
May, C. E., 140, 337
Mayhood, J. E., 304, 305(44)
Mayo, D. W., 346
Meakins, G. D., 192, 198, 205, 273, 280
Meal, J. H., 151
Mecke, R., 244, 245, 275, 311, 312(67, 72, 74)
Mecke, R., Jr., 311, 312(67, 72, 74)
Meiklejohn, R. A., 261
Meister, A. G., 122, 123(6), 124(6), 125(6), 128, 136, 154, 430, 431, 441
Mellon, M. G., 77
Meloche, V. W., 261, 343
Memefee, A., 304, 306(41)
Merian, E., 307, 308(51), 310(51)
Merrifield, R. E., 189, 282
Mesa, S., 248
Meyer, R. J., 261
Meyers, A. I., 284
Meyr, R., 207
Mikawa, Y., 86, 271, 272(5), 345, 346(77)
Mikkelson, L., 152
Milas, N. A., 276
Miller, F. A., 141, 149, 158, 201, 202(2), 208, 216, 217(11), 219(11), 236, 287, 310, 311(63), 343, 347, 348, 349(117)
Milton, R. M., 54
Minkoff, G. J., 70
Mirone, P., 236
Mitsuishi, A., 348
Miyazawa, T., 153, 239, 264, 265(82), 342
Mizushima, S., 137, 153, 154, 155, 262, 264, 265, 311, 312(68), 342, 343, 346(54), 349(57)
Mole, T., 218

Momose, T., 232
Moore, H., 287
Moore, W. J., 463
Moran, N. B., 134, 313, 337
Morgan, H. W., 131
Morino, Y., 154
Moritz, A. G., 192
Mortimer, F. S., 316, 317(101)
Mosher, H. S., 276, 277(29)
Moss, R. J., 205
Moss, T. S., 53
Mould, H. M., 22
Mueller, W. A., 244
Muller, G. T. A., 273
Murata, H., 160, 343, 345, 346(52)
Murphy, G. M., 32, 115, 422, 432, 441, 455
Murray, M. J., 92, 122, 123(6), 124(6), 125(6), 139, 148, 202
Musso, H., 265
Myers, R. J., 218

Nabi, S. N., 344
Nakagawa, I., 155, 343, 346(54), 349(57), 460
Nakagawa, T., 292
Nakamoto, K., 119, 142, 160, 189, 245, 246(28), 343, 346(52)
Narasimham, N. A., 134, 139
Narisada, M., 292
Nazarov, I. N., 274
Neidenzu, K., 292
Neilsen, M. L., 300, 304(36)
Newman, C., 345
Newman, R., 79
Nicholls, B., 192, 198, 273
Nickell, C., 328
Nielsen, A. H., 131, 135, 162, 345
Nielsen, H. H., 41
Nielsen, J. R., 132, 133, 134, 137, 138, 139, 141, 142, 146, 149, 151, 152, 313, 314(86), 315(86) 337, 426
Nist, B. J., 217
Nixon, E. R., 138, 344, 345(74)
Noack, K., 244, 246
Nodiff, E. A., 315
Noltes, J. G., 318
Nonnenmacher, G., 220, 222(5), 225(5), 228(5)
Norris, W. G., 347
Nowak, M., 59
Nuttall, R. H., 207

Nyholm, R. S., 153, 318
Nyquist, R. A., 201, 210, 213(2), 215(2), 254, 255(47), 257(47), 342

O'Brien, K. G., 291
O'Bryan, H. M., 55
O'Dwyer, M. F., 143, 288, 347
Oetjen, R. A., 15
Oftedahl, E., 207
Ogden, G., 55
Oh, W. T., 288
Okawara, R., 318, 346, 348(96)
Olivera, E., 248
Olmos, A. W., 260
Onak, T. O., 291, 293(7)
Onishi, T., 262, 343, 349(57)
Onyszchuk, M., 138, 345, 346(79)
Opitz, H. E., 346
O'Reilly, E. J., Jr., 152
Orville-Thomas, W. J., 154, 343
Ory, H. A., 257, 236
Oshesky, G. D., 345
Otero, C., 133
Overend, J., 136, 242, 257(7), 314

Pace, E. L., 140
Padgett, W. M., II, 67, 234
Page, J. E., 316
Palik, E. D., 336
Palm, A., 282
Palmer, W. G., 344
Papa, A. J., 232
Parsons, A. E., 342, 343(48)
Patterson, L. J., 206, 283, 287(22)
Patterson, W. A., 273
Paul, F. W., 53
Pauson, P. L., 209
Peacock, R. D., 347, 348(105)
Peake, J. S., 346
Pearlson, W. H., 314
Pearson, D. P., 129
Pecile, C., 208
Pedersen, C., 311, 317(76)
Peltier, D., 261
Penland, R. B., 137, 311, 312(68), 342
Peppard, D. F., 300
Perkins, W. D., 136, 344
Person, W. B., 148, 349
Peterson, E. M., 76
Petrov, A. D., 195

Pfund, A. H., 42
Philippe, R. J., 287
Philpotts, A. R., 255, 256(51), 277
Pichevin, A., 261
Pickett, E. E., 198
Pierce, L., 140
Pierson, R. H., 62
Pimentel, G. C., 143, 148
Pinchas, S., 199, 247, 248(32), 266
Pinkard, R. M., 276
Pintar, M., 260
Pitzer, K. S., 28, 139, 148, 149, 153, 154, 155, 160, 220, 337, 347
Pliskin, W. A., 67
Plumb, R. C., 160
Plyler, E. K., 22, 53, 59, 132, 151, 198, 337, 349, 458
Podall, H. E., 227, 233(16)
Poelmans, M., 216
Poirier, P., 282, 283(17), 284(17)
Poliakova, I. D., 258
Poling, G. W., 312
Polo, S. R., 345, 347
Ponomarenko, V. A., 317
Pontarelli, D. A., 131
Poole, H. G., 139, 151, 153, 157
Pope, M., 81
Popov, A. I., 349
Popov, E. M., 302, 303(40)
Posey, L. R., Jr., 133
Post, B., 82
Potts, W. J., 201, 210, 213(2, 3), 215(2), 254, 255(47), 257(47), 342
Powell, A. S., 326
Powell, D. B., 346
Powell, F. X., 288
Powell, R. L., 263
Powell, W. R., 336, 337(24), 349(24)
Powers, R. M., 326
Powling, J., 135, 159
Pozefsky, A., 192
Prevorsek, D., 266, 282, 283
Price, W. C., 22, 154, 264
Priddle, J. E., 255
Prigent, J., 54
Pristera, F., 286
Privett, O. S., 328
Pullin, A. D. E., 311
Purcell, T., 59
Pustinger, J. V., Jr., 300, 301(36), 304(36)

Quagliano, J. V., 137, 155, 311, 312(68), 342, 343, 346(54)
Quiggle, D., 93

Radzitsky, P., 311, 317(77)
Ramachandran, J., 204
Ramsay, D. A., 73, 74, 136, 141, 242, 243(8)
Randall, H. M., 262, 263(71), 266(71), 311, 312(75)
Randle, R. R., 220, 222(2), 224(2), 225(2), 226(2), 227(2), 228(2), 285
Rank, D. H., 93, 130, 145
Rao, C. N. R., 204, 206, 262, 311, 312(79)
Rao, I. A., 337
Rao, V. R., 337
Raskin, S. S., 258
Rasmussen, R. S., 211, 213(7), 244, 245(18)
Rathjens, G. W., Jr., 148, 155
Rayson, D., 227, 231(14)
Rea, D. G., 94, 95, 138
Reece, I. H., 288
Regan, J. F., 263
Reid, C. E., 463
Riad, Y., 274
Rice, B., 97
Rice, S. A., 69
Richards, R. E., 248, 263, 264(74), 265(74), 274, 275(15), 296, 297(18)
Riggs, N. V., 289
Risgin, O., 337
Rix, H. D., 145
Robb, C. D., 53
Roberson, W. E., 328
Roberts, E. R., 207
Roberts, H. L., 132, 137, 143, 150, 344
Robinson, D. W., 149
Robinson, D. Z., 73
Robinson, E. A., 308(58), 309
Rochow, E. G., 318, 346, 348(96)
Rodionova, N. P., 302, 303(40)
Rogasch, P. E., 311, 317(73)
Rolfe, J. A., 132, 136
Romanko, J., 85
Roosens, A., 234
Roper, R., 288
Rosenbaum, E. J., 95
Rosenthal, J. E., 115, 422
Ross, I. G., 154
Rossmy, G., 275

Ruby, A., 346
Rundle, R. E., 189
Ryason, R., 136
Ryskin, Y. I. 297
Rytina, A. W., 203

Saari, W. S., 270
Sakashita, K., 130
Salzman, C. F., Jr., 93
Sanders, J. M., 227, 231(15)
Sandorfy, C., 281, 282(11, 12), 328
Saunders, R. A., 149, 313
Sauvageau, P., 328
Sax, K. J., 270
Scherer, J. R., 210, 213(3), 242, 257(7), 314
Schmid, E. W., 220, 222(5), 225(5), 228(5)
Schmitt, R. G., 235
Schowtka, K. H., 345, 346(80)
Schroeder, H., 234
Schuette, H. A., 261
Schuetz, R. D., 263
Schumb, W. C., 143, 149
Scott, C., 304, 306(41)
Scott, D. W., 28, 220, 344
Scott, T. A., 311, 317(71)
Sears, F. W., 39, 47
Seel, F., 257
Servais, P. C., 297
Servoss, R. R., 147
Shabarova, Z. I., 297
Shapiro, B. L., 205, 206(21)
Shapiro, I., 134, 293, 294(13)
Shapiro, J., 291, 292(8, 9), 293(7)
Sharkey, A. G., Jr., 41
Sharp, D. W. A., 136, 141, 160, 207, 347, 348(105)
Sheinker, Y. N., 206
Sheline, R. K., 148, 153, 154, 160, 347
Sheppard, N., 129, 130, 133, 134, 138, 142, 145, 146, 147, 153, 191, 194(2), 195, 201, 202(2a), 210, 213(1), 245, 252, 257, 259(54), 260(54), 261, 282, 305, 306(48), 315, 316(97, 98), 317(96, 97, 98), 344, 345, 346(79)
Shimanouchi, T., 153, 262, 264, 265, 343, 349(57)
Shimizeu, K., 160, 345
Shindo, H. 232
Shipman J. J., 316
Shlyapochnikov, V. V., 195

Shoppee, C. W. 316
Short, L. N., 138, 234
Shreve, O. D., 273, 277
Shrewsbury, D. D., 275
Shuler, W. E., 137
Shull, E. R., 134
Shutts, L. W., 4
Siegle, L. A., 82
Siewers, I., J., 210
Simanouti, T., 154
Simpson, D. M., 191, 195, 201, 202(2a), 210, 213(!), 261
Sinclair, R. G., 261
Singer, G. H., 160
Sirkar, S. C., 148
Skrbljak, M., 279, 280(6)
Slaymaker, S. C., 233
Slowinski, E. J., Jr., 143
Smit, M. C., 300
Smith, A. G., 297
Smith, A. L., 138, 141, 142, 159, 294, 295(14), 296(14), 297(14), 298(14), 345
Smith, D. C., 133, 137, 138, 139, 141, 149, 151, 152, 299, 300(26), 301(26), 305(26), 313, 314(86), 315(86), 337, 344
Smith, D. F., 162
Smith, J. C., 218
Smith, L. G., 42, 149
Smith, R. A., 55
Smith, R. D., 246
Smith, R. J. D., 253, 257(45)
Smith, R. M., 133, 141, 248, 337
Smith, W. V., 481
Snyder, R. G., 343
Sobotka, W., 285
Sommer, A., 137, 147, 158
Sousa, J. B., 206
Speakman, J. C., 32, 98, 113(2), 116(2), 119(2)
Spedding, H., 286, 289, 309
Spicer, G. S., 245
Spinner, E., 244, 311, 312(66)
Spitzer, R., 149
Spoors, J. W., 255
Sprague, J. W., 76
Srp, N. E., 336, 337(24), 349(24)
Staats, P. A., 131
Stamm, R. F., 93, 234
Stansbury, E. J., 85
St. Clair Gantz, E., 62

Steel, G., 203
Steele, D., 288, 337
Steese, C. M., 141
Stephens, E. R., 260
Stephenson, A., 308(57), 309
Stephenson, C. V., 143, 342
Sternberg, J., 263
Stevens, C. L., 205
Stewart, J. E., 276, 278, 279(2), 336
Stoicheff, B. P., 85, 131
Stojiljkovic, A., 317, 318(102)
Stokes, C. S., 315
Stone, F. G. A., 318
Stone, P. J., 274, 282
Strandberg, B., 208
Strickland, J. D. H., 245
Stuart, A. V., 273, 275(13)
Sutherland, G. B. B. M., 228, 231(18) 232(18), 233(18), 264, 273, 275(13)
Suzuki, I., 265, 311, 312(80)
Svatek, E., 204
Sverdlov, L. M., 198, 217, 218(20)
Sweeny, D. M., 155
Swern, D., 273, 277
Syrkin, Y. K., 206
Szasz, G. J., 146
Szmant, H. H., 307, 308(55)

Tai, H., 326
Talbert, J. M., 67, 236
Tallent, W. H., 210
Tamura, S., 232
Tanaka, S., 142, 160
Tannenbaum, H., 299
Tarte, P., 287, 289, 290, 346
Taub, B., 267
Taurins, A., 283, 284(26)
Taylor, H. S., 483
Taylor, K. A., 141, 160
Taylor, K. J., 198, 273
Taylor, R., 138, 345
Taylor, R. C., 141, 292, 337
Temple, R. B., 79, 81, 84(77), 85, 136, 137, 140, 236, 314
Teyssié, P., 245, 246(27)
Thain, W., 277
Theimer, R., 132
Theobald, R. S., 255
Thomas, L. C., 300, 301(33), 302(33), 303(33), 305(33)

Thomas, T. R., 86
Thompson, H. W., 133, 136, 137, 138, 140, 141, 202, 203, 204(7, 13), 208, 213, 234, 236, 243, 244, 248(13), 249(13), 250(13), 263, 264(74), 265(74), 274, 275(15), 278, 279(5), 282, 296, 297(18), 306, 314, 349
Thompson, J. W., 26
Thornton, D. W., 273
Thornton, V., 28, 194, 195(10), 198(10), 210, 212(5), 213(5), 228
Thursack, R. A., 134
Tidwell, E. D., 22
Tipson, R. S., 276
Tobin, M. C., 148, 160, 346
Tong, B. P., 302
Torgov, I. V., 245
Torkington, P., 213, 243, 248(13), 249(13), 250(13), 314, 349
Trotman, L. 289
Trotter, I., F. 306
Tsuboi, M., 137, 141, 265, 343, 349(57)
Tsutsui, M., 274
Tsvetkov, E. N., 305
Tunnicliff, R. D., 244, 245(18)
Turco, A., 208
Turrell, G. C., 144

Ueda, Y., 232
Ugi, I. 207
Ultee, C. J., 132, 137, 141
Uno, J., 266, 267(90)
Unterberger, R. R., 481
Urbanski, T., 285
Urey, H. C., 462

van der Elsken, J., 67, 313
Vasil'ev, A. F., 274
Vedder, W., 313
Venanzi, L. M., 209
Venkataraghavan, R., 311, 312(79)
Venkateswarlu, P., 148
Voelz, F. L., 148
Voronkov, M. G., 297
Vratny, F., 262

Waddington, T. C., 140, 141, 208, 281
Wagland, A. A., 192
Wagner, E. L., 71, 155, 160, 281, 311, 312(71)

Wait, S. C., Jr., 131, 141
Wakefield, B. J., 203
Walker, R. W., 217, 219(16)
Walsh, A., 71, 86
Walsh, P. N., 137, 147, 158
Walton, W. L., 248, 249(38, 39), 250(38,39)
Wang, T. S., 202, 227, 231(15)
Ward, C. H., 346
Ward, E. R., 227, 231(13), 232(13)
Washburn, W. H., 326
Watanabe, H., 292
Watşon, A. T., 198
Watson, J. K. G., 132
Weckherlin, S., 288
Weiblen, D. G., 138, 313, 314(85), 315(85)
Weinstock, B., 162
Weir, C. E., 348
Weiss, H. G., 291, 292(8, 9)
Welsh, H. L., 85, 86
Werbin, H., 282
Werner, R. L., 206, 207, 227, 231(14), 288, 291
West, R., 247
Weston, R. E., Jr., 135
Whatley, L. S., 247
Wheatley, P. J., 98, 104(1)
Whetsel, K. B., 206, 207(23), 328
Whiffen, D. H., 138, 208, 220, 222(2), 224(2), 225(2), 226(2), 227(2), 228(2, 6, 22), 231(6,13),232(13),276,285,289,296, 317, 318(102)
Whistler, R. L., 276
White, C. E., 146
White, D., 137, 147, 158
White, H. E., 45
White, J. U., 74
White, R. G., 325
White, W. B., 347
Whittaker, E. T., 422, 423(1)
Wiberg, K. B., 217, 218
Wiberley, S. E., 76, 134, 192, 196(5), 198(5), 199(5), 210, 226, 230(11), 269, 306, 329, 336
Wiegand, R. V., 93
Wilcox, W. S., 342
Wildman, W. C., 270
Wiley, R. H., 203, 233
Wilkins, C. H., 208, 287, 310, 311(63)
Wilkinson, G. R., 22
Williams, E. F., 76

Williams, H. R., 276, 277(29)
Williams, R. B., 198
Williams, R. L., 141, 194, 242, 243(9), 248, 255, 256(51), 275, 278, 291, 292(1), 293(1), 294(1), 308(62), 309
Williams, V. Z., 42, 53(7), 55(7), 136, 208
Willis, J. B., 71, 204, 308(59), 309, 344
Willix, R. L. S., 273
Wilmshurst, J. K., 153, 160, 194, 239, 343, 347
Wilson, C. L., 139, 151, 153, 157
Wilson, C. O., 134
Wilson, E. B., Jr., 92, 422, 423(3), 425, 430, 431, 455, 462
Wilson, G. R., 297
Wilson, M. K., 136, 141, 149, 342, 344, 345, 347
Winitz, M., 262
Wisherd, M. P., 348
Witkop, B., 289
Wolfarth, E. F., 226, 336, 337(24), 342(37), 349(24)
Woltz, P. J. H., 131, 135, 345
Wood, D. L., 81
Wood, J. M., Jr., 131
Woodford, D. E., 273
Woodward, L. A., 132, 136, 137, 138, 141, 143, 150, 160, 344, 345
Wormser, E. M., 52

Wotiz, J. H., 201, 202, 202(2)
Wright, N., 228(21), 231, 295, 296(17), 297(17)
Wright, W. B., Jr., 192, 196(9), 280
Wulf, O. R., 328
Wystrach, V. P., 302

Xavier, J., 337

Yamaguchi, A., 153, 311, 312(68)
Yano, H., 232
Yates, P., 205, 206(21)
Yoda, N., 205, 206(21)
Yoshinaga, H., 348
Yoshino, T., 146
Young, C. W., 160, 228(21), 231, 297
Young, T. F., 97

Zahradnik, R., 204
Zanon, I., 289
Zbinden, R., 241
Zeil, W., 317
Zeiss, H., 274
Zeitler, V. A., 318
Zeitlow, J. P., 452, 479
Zueva, G. Y., 317
Zumwalt, L. R., 27
Zwerdling, S., 81

SUBJECT INDEX*

Absorbance, 72
Absorbancy, 72
Absorption law, 71
Absorptivity, 72
Acetals, 199, 276, 353
Acetates, 249, 250, 252, 354
Acetonitrile, gas phase, 26
Acetyl acetonates, 246
Acetylene, gas phase, 26
Acetylenes, disubstituted, 202, 352
    monosubstituted, 200, 342, 352
Acid chlorides, 256, 257, 356
Acid hydrazides, 267
Acrylamide, polarized infrared spectrum,
    83
Acrylates, 249–252, 355
Acrylonitrile, cis β chloro, 28
AlB_3H_{12} , aluminum borohydride, 154
Alcohols, 178
    $C-O$, 274, 353
    OH deformation, 199, 275, 353
    OH stretch, 273, 353
Aldehydes, 199, 247, 354
    Fermi resonance, 182
    near I.R. region, 326
$Al-H$, 317
Alkanes, low frequency bands, 337
Allenes, 202, 352
Amides, disubstituted, 265, 356
    low frequency bands, 342
    monosubstituted, 181, 264, 356
    unsubstituted, 263, 356
Amidines, 283, 357
Amido acids, 263
Amines, aliphatic band, 280
    α substituted, 199
    $C-N$, 176, 279, 280

low frequency bands, 342
near I.R. region, 328
NH, 279
NH_2 deformation, 278
NH_2 stretch, 278
salts, 281, 357
spectra, 357
Amino acids, 262, 355
Ammelide, 235
Ammeline, 235
Ammonium ion, 160, 281, 357, 361
Amplitude of vibrations, 423–424
Angstrom, 2
Angular dispersion, 44
Angular momentum, 14
Anharmonic oscillator, 12
Anharmonicity constant, 12
Anhydrides, 255, 256, 355
Anilines, 188, 278–280, 357
Anisotropic molecule, 32
Anthracenes, 232
Anti-Stokes lines, 30, 34
Aromatic acids, 261
Aromatic CH, near I.R. region, 326
Aromatics, low frequency bands, 342
Arsenic compounds, 361
Aryl halides, 317, 361
$AsBr_3$, arsenic bromide, 140
$AsCl_3$, arsenic chloride, 140
AsD_3 , arsine-d_3 , 140
AsF_3 , arsenic fluoride, 140
AsH_3 , arsine, 140
$AsO_4^=$, arsenate ion, 160
Asymmetrical top, vibration-rotation band,
    27
Asymmetrical top molecules, 17, 27
Asymmetric stretching, of CO_2 , 5

* See pages 414-418 for the molecular formula index of spectra shown on pages 362-413.

Attenuated total reflectance, 67
Avogadro's number, 169
Axis of symmetry, 99
Azides, 206, 352
Azo group, 287, 358
Azothio group, 289
Azoxy, 288, 358

Band intensities, 73
Barium fluoride, 44, 63
Base line method, 74
BBr_3, boron tribromide, 153
$B-CH_3$, 294
$BC_3H_9O_3$, methyl borate, 147
$B-Cl$, 293, 358
BCl_3, boron trichloride, 153
B_2Cl_4, diboron tetrachloride, 147
$BClF_3^-$, 141
B_5D_9, pentaborane-d_9, 143
Beckman spectrophotometer Model IR-7, 57
Beer's law, 72, 76
Bending vibration of CO_2, 5
Benzene, 157
    gas phase, 26
Benzene ring, 3100–3000 cm^{-1} region, 230
    2000–1750 cm^{-1} region, 228, 230
    1600 cm^{-1} region, 224, 225
    1500 cm^{-1} region, 224, 225
    1300–1000 cm^{-1} region, 228, 229
    900–675 cm^{-1} region, 225, 226
    450 cm^{-1} region, 226
Benzene ring compounds, spectra, 353
Benzene ring, hydrogen wagging vibrations,
    180, 226
    mass sensitive frequencies, 222
    Raman correlations, 230
Benzoquinone diazide, 206
Benzoates, 249, 251, 252, 355
BF_3, boron trifluoride, 153
BF_4^-, 361
BH, 293, 358
BH_4^-, 361
B_2H_6, diborane, 149, 151, 153
B_5H_9, pentaborane, 143
$B_3H_6N_3$, triborine-triamine, 153
Bicarbonate ion, 355
Bifluoride ion, 313
Biguanides, 283, 357
Bisulfate ion, 310, 360
Bisulfite ion, 360

Biuret, 356
Blackbody, 38
Blaze angle, 49, 50
$B-N$, 292, 358
$B-O$, 291
BO_2^-, metaborate ion, 158
B_2O_2, boron oxide, 158
B_2O_3, boric oxide, 137
$B_4O_7^-$, 348
$B-OH$, 292
Bolometer, 52–54
Boltzmann constant, 38, 463, 466
Boranes, alkoxy, 292
    amino, 292, 293, 358
Borates, 291, 358
Borazines, 292, 293, 358
Borinic acids, 291
Borohydride salts, 293
Boronates, 291
Boron compounds, spectra, 358
    correlations, 291
Boronic acids, 291, 292, 358
    anhydrides, 291
Boronites, 291
    chloro, 293
B-phenyl, 294
BrF_5, bromine pentafluoride, 143
BrO_3^-, 140, 348, 361
B_2S_3, boron trisulfide, 130
Butadiene, 211
Butyrates, 250, 354

Calcium fluoride, 44, 46, 63
Calibration, 59
Carbamates, 266, 356
Carbodiimides, 205, 352
Carbohydrates, 276
Carbonate ion, 355
Carbonates, organic, 254, 355
Carbon rod source, 42
Carbonyls, bond angle effects, 239, 246
    mass effects, 239
    metal, 209, 361
    mesomeric and inductive effects, 187,
        241, 242
    overtones, 319
    strained ring, 185, 241
Carboxylic acids, carbonyl, 258, 355
    CH_2 wag bands, 261
    low frequency bands, 343

OH bending and C—O stretch, 181, 259, 355
OH stretch, 257, 355
salts, 262, 355
Cary Raman spectrophotometer Model 81, 89–90
Cavity cells, 64
C—Br, 316, 361
CBr_4, carbon tetrabromide, 160
C_2Br_4 tetrabromoethylene, 151
C_2Br_6, hexabromoethane, 149, 153
$CBrCl_3$, bromo- trichloromethane, 140
CBr_2Cl_2, dibromo-dichloromethane, 102–103, 136
CBr_3Cl, tribromo-chloromethane, 140
CBr_2ClD, chloro-dibromomethane-d_1, 131
C_2BrClF_2, 1,1 difluoro-bromo chloroethylene, 132
$C_2Br_2ClF_3$, trifluoro-dibromo-chloroethane, 129
$CBrF_3$, bromo-trifluoromethane, 140
CBr_2F_2, dibromo-difluoromethane, 136
$C_2Br_2F_4$, dibromo-tetrafluorethane, 130, 145
$CBrN$, cyanogen bromide, 143
CBr_3NO_2, tribromonitromethane, 132
$C=CH$, near infrared region, 326
C—Cl, 315, 361
CCl_4, carbon tetrachloride, 159
   Raman spectrum, 31, 93
C_2Cl_6, hexachloroethane, 149, 153
C_6Cl_6, hexachlorobenzene, 157
$CClF_3$, trifluoro-chloromethane, 140
CCl_2F_2, dichloro-difluoromethane, 136
CCl_3F, trichloro-fluoromethane, 140
C_2ClF_3, 1,1,2 trifluoro-chloroethylene, 132
C_2ClF_5, pentafluoro-chloroethane, 133
$C_2Cl_2F_2$, dichloro-difluorethane, 137
$C_2Cl_2F_4$, tetrafluoro-dichloroethane, 130, 145
C_2Cl_3F, 1,1,2 trichloro-fluorethylene, 132
$C_2Cl_3F_3$, trichloro-trifluorethane, 129, 133, 141
$C_2Cl_4F_2$, tetrachloro-difluorethane, 133, 145
C_2Cl_5F, pentachloro-fluoroethane, 133
C_2Cl_2FN, dichloro-fluoroacetonitrile, 131
C_2ClF_2N, chloro-difluoroacetonitrile, 131
$CClFO$, chloro-fluoroformaldehyde, 131
$CClN$, cyanogen chloride, 143

C_2Cl_3N, trichloro-methyl cyanide, 141
CCl_3NO_2, trichloronitromethane, 132
CCl_2O, phosgene, 135
$C_2Cl_2O_2$, oxalyl chloride, 145
$C_2Cl_3O_2^-$, trichloroacetate ion, 132
CCl_2S, thiophosgene, 135
CD_4, methane-d_4, 159
C_2D_6, ethane-d_6, 149, 153
C_3D_6, cyclopropane-d_6, 153
C_4D_6, cyclobutene-d_6, 138
C_6D_6, benzene-d_6, 157
$CdBr_2$, cadmium bromide, 158
$CDBr_3$, heavy bromoform, 140
$CdBr_4^-$, cadmium tetrabromide ion, 160
CD_3Br, methyl bromide-d_3, 140
Cd—C, 346
$CdCl_2$, cadmium chloride, 158
$CDCl_3$, heavy chloroform, 140
   band assignments, 458
   infrared and Raman spectra, 457
CD_3Cl, methyl chloride-d_3, 140
C_2DF_3, trifluoroethylene-d_1, 132
$C_2D_2F_2$, difluoroethylene-d_2, 137
C_2DF_2H, difluoroethylene-d_1, 132
C_6DH_5, benzene-d_1, 139
$C_3D_2H_2$, 137
$C_6D_2H_4$, 1,4 benzene-d_2, 151
$C_6D_3H_3$, 1,3,5 benzene-d_-, 153
$C_6D_4H_2$, 1,2,4,5 benzene-d_4, 151
C_6D_5H, benzene-d_5, 139
$C_2D_5H_6B_2N$, $[(CH_3)_2NB_2D_5]$, 139
$CD_3H_3N^+$, methyl ammonium-d_3 ion, 153
$CDHO$, formaldehyde-d_1, 131
C_2D_3HO, acetaldehyde-d_3, 132
CdI_2, cadmium iodide, 158
CD_2N_2, deuterodiazomethane, 136
CD_6N^+, methyl ammonium-d_6 ion, 149
$CD_6N_3^+$, guanidium ion-d_6, 153
$C_3D_6N_6$, melamine-d_6, 154
CD_3NO_2, nitromethane-d_3, 132
CD_4N_2O, urea-d_4, 137
CD_2O, formaldehyde-d_2, 135
Cell thickness, determination of, 62
Center of symmetry, 99
Central force field, 462
Centrifugal distortion constant, 15
   stretching, 15, 22, 27
Cesium bromide, 44, 46, 47
   region correlations, 336
Cesium iodide, 44

CF, 314, 360
CF$_4$, carbon tetrafluoride, 159
C$_2$F$_4$, tetrafluoroethylene, 151
C$_3$F$_8$, octofluoropropane, 138
C$_4$F$_6$, hexafluoro-2-butyne, 149
C$_4$F$_8$, perfluorocyclobutane, 155
CF$_3$I, trifluoro-iodomethane, 140
C$_2$F$_3$N, trifluoro-methyl cyanide, 141
CF$_3$NO, trifluoro-nitrosomethane, 132
CF$_2$O, 135
CF$_4$O, 132
CH, 199
CH$_2$, 174, 178, 195–198, 351, 352
    near infrared region, 326
CH$_3$, 191–195, 351, 352
    near infrared region, 326
CH$_4$, methane, 159
C$_2$H$_6$ ethane, 149, 153
C$_3$H$_4$, allene, 102–103, 148
C$_3$H$_6$, cyclopropane, 153
C$_3$H$_6$, propylene, 133
C$_3$H$_8$, propane, 138
C$_4$H$_6$, butadiene, 138
C$_4$H$_6$, cyclobutene, 138
C$_4$H$_6$, dimethyl acetylene, 149
C$_4$H$_6$, ethyl acetylene, 134
C$_4$H$_8$, butene-1, 134
C$_4$H$_8$, butene-2, 138, 146
C$_4$H$_8$, cyclobutane, 148, 155
C$_5$H$_6$, cyclopentadiene, 138
C$_5$H$_8$, cyclopentene, 139
C$_5$H$_8$, spiropentane, 148
C$_5$H$_{10}$, 1,1 dimethylcyclopropane, 139
C$_5$H$_{12}$, 2,2 dimethyl propane, 160
C$_6$H$_6$, benzene, 157
C$_6$H$_6$, dimethyldiacetylene, 154
C$_6$H$_{10}$, cyclohexene, 130
C$_6$H$_{10}$, 2,2 dimethyl-3-butyne, 142
C$_6$H$_{12}$, cyclohexane, 149
C$_7$H$_8$, tropilidene, 139
C$_7$H$_{10}$, nortricyclene, 142
C$_8$H$_8$, cyclo-octatetraene, 148
C$_8$H$_{10}$, 1,3,5,7 octatetraene, 146
C$_8$H$_{14}$, bicyclo-(2,2,2)-octane, 154
Character of a matrix, 114, 121
    the dipole moment, 123
    the polarizability, 124
Character tables, 121, 128
    for CHCl$_3$, 433
CH$_8$B$_2$, monoethyldiborane, 134

C$_5$H$_5$BCl$_3$N, pyridine boron trichloride,
    139
C$_2$H$_{11}$B$_2$N, [(CH$_3$)$_2$NB$_2$H$_5$), 139
CH$_3$BO, 141
CHBr$_3$, bromoform, 140
CH$_2$−Br, 197, 198
CH$_2$Br$_2$, dibromomethane, 136
CH$_3$Br, methyl bromide, 140
C$_2$H$_2$Br$_2$, cis dibromoethylene, 137
    trans form, 145
C$_2$H$_2$Br$_4$, tetrabromoethane, 130
C$_2$H$_3$Br, monobromoethylene, 132
C$_2$H$_4$Br$_2$, dibromoethane, 130, 133, 145
C$_2$H$_5$Br, ethyl bromide, 133
C$_3$H$_3$Br, bromo-methylacetylene, 141
C$_3$H$_7$Br, propyl bromide, 129, 134
    isopropyl bromide, 134
C$_4$H$_5$Br, ethyl bromoacetylene, 134
C$_4$H$_9$Br, tertiary butyl bromide, 142
C$_6$H$_3$Br$_3$, 1,3,5 tribromobenzene, 153
C$_6$H$_4$Br$_2$, dibromobenze, 138
C$_6$H$_5$Br, bromobenzene, 138
C$_6$H$_{10}$Br$_2$, 1,2, dibromocyclohexane, 130
    1,4, dibromocyclohexane, 146
CHBrCl$_2$, dichloro-bromomethane, 131
CHBr$_2$Cl, dibromo-chloromethane, 131
CH$_2$BrCl bromo-chloromethane, 131
C$_2$H$_4$BrCl, bromo-chloroethane, 129, 133
CHBrClF, bromo-chloro-fluoromethane,
    129
C$_2$H$_3$BrClF, bromo-chloro-fluoroethane,
    129
C$_2$H$_4$BrD, bromo-ethane-d$_1$, 133
    ethyl bromide-d$_1$, 129
CHBrF$_2$, bromo-difluoromethane, 131
CHBr$_2$F, dibromo-fluoromethane, 131
C$_2$HBrF$_2$, 1,1 difluoro-bromoethylene, 132
C$_6$H$_4$BrF, para bromo-fluorobenzene, 139
CH$_2$BrI, bromo-iodomethane, 131
C$_2$H$_3$BrO, acetyl bromide, 132
C$_3$H$_5$BrO, propionyl bromide, 134
C$_2$H$_6$Cd, dimethyl cadmium, 154
CHCl$_3$, chloroform, 140
CHCl$_3$ band assignments, 458
    bond lengths and angles, 479
    f matrix, 442
    force constants, 452
    fundamental frequencies, 461
    g matrix, 446, 447
    G matrix, 445, 451

502 SUBJECT INDEX

infrared and Raman spectra, 457
moments of inertia, 480
number of fundamentals, 122
product rule application, 166
secular determinant, 452, 455
thermodynamic functions, 476, 478
U matrix, 442, 444
CH_2-Cl, 197, 198
CH_3Cl, methyl chloride, 140
C_2HCl_3, trichloro-ethylene, 132
C_2HCl_5, pentachloro-ethane, 133
$C_2H_2Cl_2$, cis dichloroethylene, 137
$C_2H_2Cl_4$, tetrachloroethane, 130, 137, 145
C_2H_3Cl, monochloroethylene, 132
$C_2H_3Cl_3$, trichloroethane, 141
$C_2H_4Cl_2$, 1,2 dichloroethane, 130, 137, 145
   1,1 dichloroethane, 133
C_2H_5Cl, ethyl chloride, 133
C_3H_3Cl, methyl chloroacetylene, 141
$C_3H_3Cl_3$, 3,3,3 trichloropropene, 134
C_3H_7Cl, propyl chloride, 129, 134
   isopropyl chloride, 134
$C_4H_4Cl_2$, 2,3 dichloro-1,3 butadiene, 146
C_4H_9Cl, tertiary butyl chloride, 142
C_6HCl_5, pentachlorobenzene, 138
$C_6H_2Cl_4$, tetrachlorobenzene, 138
$C_6H_3Cl_3$, 1,3,5 trichlorobenzene, 153
$C_6H_4Cl_2$, dichlorobenzene, 138
C_6H_5Cl, chlorobenzene, 138
$C_6H_{10}Cl_2$, 1,2 dichlorocyclohexane, 130
   1,4 dichlorocyclohexane, 146
$CHClF_2$, difluoro-chloromethane, 131
$CHCl_2F$, dichloro-fluoromethane, 131
CH_2ClF, chloro-fluoromethane, 131
C_2HClF_4, tetrafluoro-chloroethane, 129, 133
$C_2HCl_2F_3$, trifluoro-dichloroethane, 129
C_2HCl_4F, tetrachloro-fluoroethane, 129
C_2H_2ClF, 1-chloro-1-fluoroethylene, 132
$C_2H_2ClF_3$, trifluoro-chloroethane, 133
C_6H_4ClF, chloro-fluorobenzene, 139
   meta, 134
CH_2ClI, chloro-iodomethane, 131
C_2H_4ClI, 1,1 chloro-iodoethane, 129, 133
C_2HCl_2N, dichloroacetonitrile, 132
C_2H_2ClN, chloro-acetonitrile, 132
$C_2H_2Cl_3NO$, trichloroacetamide, 133
$C_2HCl_3O_2$, trichloroacetic acid, 133
C_2H_3ClO, acetyl chloride, 132
$C_2H_2Cl_2O_2$, dichloroacetic acid, 129
$C_2H_3ClO_2$, monochloroacetic acid, 133

C_2H_5ClO, ethylene chlorohydrin, 133
C_3H_5ClO, propionyl chloride, 134
CH_3Cl_3Si, methyl trichlorosilane, 141
$C_2H_3Cl_3Si$, vinyl trichlorosilane, 134
$C_2H_6Cl_2Si$, dimethyl dichlorosilane, 138
C_3H_9ClSi, trimethyl chlorosilane, 142
$C_4H_{12}Si$, tetramethyl silicon, 160
$C_6H_5Cl_3Sn$, phenyl tin trichloride, 142
$C_{12}H_{10}Cl_2Sn$, diphenyl tin dichloride, 139
$C_{18}H_{15}ClSn$, triphenyl tin chloride, 142
C_2H_5CN, ethyl cyanide, 134
C_2H_5D, ethane-d_1, 133
CH_3DO, methanol-d_1, 131
CHF_3, fluoroform, 140
CH_2F_2, difluoromethane, 136
CH_3F, methyl fluoride, 140
C_2HF_5, pentafluoroethane, 134
$C_2H_2F_2$, difluoroethylene, 137
$C_2H_2F_4$, tetrafluoroethane, 146
$C_2H_3F_3$, trifluoroethane, 141
$C_2H_4F_2$, difluoroethane, 146
C_2HF_3, trifluoroethylene, 132
$C_6H_4F_2$, 1,3 difluorobenzene, 139
   1,4 difluorobenzene, 151
C_6H_5F, fluorobenzene, 138
C_6H_4FI, 1-fluoro-4 iodobenzene, 139
$CHFO$, fluoroformaldehyde, 131
C_2HF_3O, trifluoroacetaldehyde, 132
$C_4H_{12}Ge$, tetramethyl germanium, 160
C_2H_6Hg, dimethyl mercury, 153, 154
CH_4HgO, methyl mercuric hydroxide, 132
CHI_3, iodoform, 140
CH_2-I, 197, 198
CH_2I_2, diiodomethane, 136
CH_3I, methyl iodide, 140
C_2H_3I, iodoethylene, 132
$C_2H_2I_2$, diiodoethylene, 137, 145
$C_2H_4I_2$, diiodoethane, 130, 133, 145
C_2H_5I, ethyl iodide, 133
C_3H_3I, methyl-iodoacetylene, 141
C_3H_7I, propyl iodide, 134
   isopropyl iodide, 134
C_4H_9I, tertiary butyl iodide, 142
C_6H_5I, iodobenzene, 138
Chloroalkanes, 316
Chloroboronites, 293
Chloroformamide, 356
Chloroformates, 257, 356
CH_2N_2, cyanamide, 131
   diazomethane, 136

CH_3N_3 , methyl azide,132
CH_5N, methyl amine, 132
CH_6N^+, methyl ammonium ion, 149, 153
$CH_6N_3^+$, guanidium ion, 153
C_2H_3N, methyl cyanide, 141
  methyl isocyanide, 141
C_2H_5N, ethylene imine, 133
C_2H_7N, dimethylamine, 134
  ethylamine, 134
$C_2H_8N_2$, diaminoethane, 138
C_3HN, cyanoacetylene, 143
$C_3H_2N_2$, dicyanomethane, 137
C_3H_3N, cyanoethylene, 132
C_3H_5N, ethyl cyanide, 133
  ethyl isocyanide, 133
C_3H_9N, trimethyl amine, 142
$C_3H_6N_6$, melamine, 154
$C_4H_2N_2$, dicyanoethylene, 145
$C_4H_4N_2$, pyrimidine, 138
  dicyanoethane, 138, 146
C_4H_5N, cyclopropyl cyanide, 134
  pyrrole, 138
  α and β methyl acrylonitriles, 134
C_5H_5N, pyridine, 138
$CHNO$, cyanic acid, 131
CH_3NO, (H_2CNOH), 132
  (H_2NCOH), formamide, 132
CH_3NO_2 , nitromethane, 132
CH_3NO_3 , methyl nitrate, 129, 133
CH_4N_2O, urea, 137
C_2H_3NO, methyl isocyanate, 132
C_2H_5NO, acetamide, 133
$C_2H_5NO_2$, nitroethane, 134
$C_3H_3NO_2$, cyanoacetic acid, 133
C_3H_5NO, ethyl isocyanate, 134
  hydroxypropionitrile, 134
C_3H_7NO, acetoxime, 138
C_5H_5NO, pyridine-1-oxide, 139
CH_4N_2S, thiourea, 137
C_2H_5NS, thioacetamide, 133
C_3H_5NS, ethylthiocyanates, 134
CHO_2^-, formate ion, 135
CH_2O, formaldehyde, 135
CH_4O, methanol, 131
C_2H_2O, ketene, 136
$C_2H_2O_2$, glyoxal, 145
$C_2H_2O_4$, oxalic acid, 137
C_2H_4O, acetaldehyde, 132
  ethylene oxide, 137
$C_2H_4O_2$, acetic acid, 133

C_2H_6O, dimethyl ether, 137
  ethanol, 133
$C_2H_6O_2$, ethylene glycol, 138
C_3H_2O, propynal, 132
$C_3H_2O_2$, propiolic acid, 132
C_3H_6O, acetone, 138
  propionaldehyde, 134
$C_3H_6O_2$, propionic acid, 129
C_4H_4O, furan, 137
C_4H_6O, crotonaldehyde, 134
  cyclobutanone, 138
$C_4H_6O_2$, cyclopropane carbonic acid, 134
  diacetyl, 138
$C_4H_8O_2$, p-dioxane, 146
$C_5H_8O_2$, 2,6 dioxaspiro (3,3) heptane, 148
C_2H_4OS, (CH_3COSH), thioacetic acid, 133
$C_4H_{12}Pb$, tetramethyl lead, 160
CH_2-S, 197, 198, 329
CH_4S, methyl mercaptan, 132
C_2H_4S, ethylene sulfide, 137
C_2H_6S, dimethyl sulfide, 137
  ethyl mercaptan, 133
C_4H_4S, thiophene, 137
C_2H_6Se, dimethyl selenide, 137
  ethyl hydrogen selenide, 133
C_2H_8Si, dimethyl silane, 138
$C_4H_{12}Si$, tetramethyl silicon, 160
CH_3SiF_3 , methyl trifluorosilane, 142
$C_4H_{12}Sn$, tetramethyl tin, 160
C_2H_6Zn, dimethyl zinc, 153, 154
$C-I$, 317, 361
C_2I_2 , diiodoacetylene, 135
CIN, cyanogen iodide, 143
$CIFO_3$, 141
$ClNO$, nitrosyl chloride, 131
$ClNO_2$, 136
ClO_3^-, chlorate ion, 140, 348, 361
ClO_4^-, perchlorate ion, 160
$ClSO_3^-$, 141
Cl_2SO, thionyl chloride, 131
$C=N$, 282-284
$C\equiv N^-$, 361
CNO^-, cyanate ion, 143
CNS^-, thiocyanate ion, 143
$CNSe^-$, selenocyanate ion, 143
CO_3^{2-}, 153, 348, 355, 361
CO_2 , dipole moment change with vibration, 5, 8
CO_2 , doubly degenerate bending vibration, 6

CO_2, Fermi resonance, 182
CO_2, mechanical model, 4
C_3O_2, carbon suboxide, 145, 158
$COBr_2$, 136
$CoBrH_{15}N_5O_4S$, 142
Combination bands, 12, 124
Co-N, 346
Condensed ring aromatics, 231
Connecticut Instrument Company, attenu-
    ated total reflectance, attachments, 68
COS, carbonyl sulfide, 143
Coupling, 171
Covering operation, 109
C_p, (C_2, C_3, C_4 etc.), 99
C_{ph}, 105
C_{pv}, 105
$Cr-C$, 346
$CrO_4^=$, chromate ion, 160
Crotonates, 250, 251, 355
$C-S$, 306, 346
$C=S$, 311, 344, 360
Cumulated double bonds, 200
Cyanamides, 204
Cyanate ion, 208, 352
Cyanide, 208, 352
Cyanoguanidines, 204
Cyclobutanes, 197, 198, 329
Cyclobutanone, 246, 354
Cyclobutenes, 185, 217
Cyclohexanes, 197, 198
Cyclohexanediones, 245
Cyclohexanone, 246, 354
Cyclohexenes, 185, 217, 218
Cyclopentadienyl ring, metal complexes,
    238, 358
Cyclopentanes, 197
Cyclopentanone, 246, 354
Cyclopentenes, 185, 217, 218
Cyclopropanes, 197, 198, 329
Cyclopropene, 185, 217, 218
Cyclopropyl ring, near I.R. region, 326

DCN, deuterium cyanide, 143
Debye, definition of, 7
Degenerate vibrations, 6
Depolarization ratios, 35, 92, 163
Detectors of infrared radiation, 52
Diatomic molecule rotational energy, 13, 17
Diazo compounds, 205, 352
Diazonium group, 207, 352

Diazooxide, 206
Diazines, low frequency bands, 343
Diborane, 293
Dicroism, infrared, 81, 84
Diene, 210
Difference bands, 12, 71
Diffraction grating, 48
1,3-diketones, 245, 354
1,3-diketones, metal chelates, 245, 354
Dioxolane rings, 276
Dipole moment, 7
Dispersion, 44, 45
    of alkali halides, 46, 47
Disulfides, 306, 360
Dithiobiuret, 356
Dixanthogens, 312
DNO_3, heavy nitric acid, 136
D_2O, heavy water, 135
Double bonds in strained rings, 185, 216
Doubly degenerate modes of vibration, 6,
    118, 126
D_p, 105
D_{pd}, 105
D_{ph}, 107
D_2Se, deuterium selenide, 135

Emissivity, 40
Energy of dissociation, chemical, 10
    spectroscopic, 10
Enthalpy function, 464–465
    rotational, 472–473
        for $CHCl_3$, 481
    translational, 470
        for $CHCl_3$, 476
    vibrational, 475
        for $CHCl_3$, 483
Entropy, 465–467, 470
Epoxides, near I.R. region, 328
Epoxy rings, 197, 273, 329, 353
Ethers, aliphatic, 176, 269, 353
    aromatic, 270, 353
    cyclic, 184, 272
    low frequency bands, 343
    vinyl, 271, 353
Ethylene oxide gas phase, 28
Esters, 248, 354
    low frequency bands, 343
Extinction, 72

F-aryl, 314, 361

$F-C=C$, 314, 360
$F-C=O$, 314
$F-CH$, 313
$Fe-C$, 347
$Fe(CN)_6^{4-}$, 348
FeC_5O_5, iron penta carbonyl, 143, 153
$Fe_2C_9O_9$, iron nona carbonyl, 154
$Fe_3C_{12}O_{12}$, iron tetracarbonyl, 148
FeF_6^{2-}, 348
Filters for infrared spectrometers, 50
Filters for Raman mercury source, 86
Fluorine compounds, spectra, 360
F matrix, 428, 441–442
F matrix for $CHCl_3$, 444, 445
f matrix, 428
f matrix for $CHCl_3$, 442
FNO_2, 136
Force constants, 8, 9, 422, 428, 441
    choice of, 440, 461
    dimensions of, 440, 453
    for $CHCl_3$, 452
F_2O, fluorine monoxide, 135
Formamides, 199
Formates, 199, 248, 250, 354
Free energy function, 467–468
    rotational, 472
        for $CHCl_3$, 482
    translational, 470
        for $CHCl_3$, 477
    vibrational, 475
        for $CHCl_3$, 483
Freeze drying technique, 66
Fresnel, 2
Frequency, 2
FSO_3^-, 141
F_2SO, thionyl fluoride, 131
Fulvenes, hydroxy, 246, 354
Fumarates, 249, 250, 355
Fundamental frequencies, 3, 122, 422
    calculation of, 422
    for A, vibrations of $CHCl_3$, 455
    for E, vibrations of $CHCl_3$, 457
    of CO_2, 6
Furans, 237, 358
Furazans, 237
Furoxans, 237

$GaBr_4^-$, gallium tetrabromide ion, 160
GaI_4^-, gallium tetraiodide ion, 160
Gas cells, 61

Gas contours, 26, 28, 163
$GeBr_4$, germanium tetrabromide, 160
$GeBr_3H$, tribromo-germane, 140
$Ge-C$, 346
$Ge-CH_3$, 318
$GeCl_4$, germanium tetrachloride, 160
$GeClH_3$, monochlorogermane, 141
$GeCl_3H$, trichloro-germane, 140
$Ge-H$, 317
GeH_4, germane, 160
Gem dimethyl group, 351
$Ge-O-Ge$, 318
Glass transmission limit, 44
Globar, 41, 59
G matrix, 428–430
    for A, vibrations of $CHCl_3$, 448, 451
    for E, vibrations of $CHCl_3$, 451
g matrix elements, 430, 431, 449
    for $CHCl_3$, 446, 447–450
Golay detector, 55
Grating, 48, 57–59
Group frequencies, 168
Group theory, 108
Guanamines, 235
Guanidines, 283, 357

Harmonic oscillator, 8
H_3BO_3, boric acid, 147
$H_3B_3O_6$, $(HBO_2)_3$, meta boric acid trimer, 147
HCl, anharmonic oscillator, 10
    dipole moment change with vibration, 7
    harmonic oscillator, 8
    internuclear distance, 16
    moment of inertia, 15, 23
    pure rotational spectrum, 15
    reduced mass of, 15
    rigid rotator, 12
    rotational constant, 23
    vibrational-rotational band, 21
$HClO_4$, perchloric acid, 132
HCN, hydrogen cyanide, 143
HCO_3^-, 348, 361
Heat capacity, 465
    rotational, 472
        for $CHCl_3$, 482
    translational, 470
        for $CHCl_3$, 476
    vibrational, 475
        for $CHCl_3$, 483

Heisenberg uncertainty principle, 10
$(HF_2)^-$, ion in potassium hydrogen fluoride, 143
$(HF)_2$, hydrogen fluoride dimer, 145
$HgBr_2$, mercuric bromide, 158
HgBrCl, HgBrI, HgClI, 143
$Hg-C$, 346
$HgCl_2$, mercuric chloride, 158
HgI_2, mercuric iodide, 158
High temperature infrared spectra, 69
   Raman spectra, 95
Hilger Raman spectrophotometer Model E 612, 88, 90
HNO_3, nitric acid, 136
Hooke's law, 9
H_2O, water, 135
H_2O_2, hydrogen peroxide, 130
HPO_3^{2-}, 141
HPO_4^{2-}, 361
$H_2PO_2^-$, 137
$H_2PO_4^-$, 361
H_2S, hydrogen sulfide, 135
H_2Se, hydrogen selenide, 135
HSO_3^-, 361
HSO_4^-, 348, 361
HSO_3Cl, 129
Hydantoin, 356
Hydrogen bonding, 189
Hydroperoxide, 276, 354
Hydroxamic acid, 266, 356

Identity, 103, 108, 112
   matrix, 441
Inductive effect, 186, 241
IF_5, iodine penta fluoride, 143
Imidates, 283, 357
Imides, 266, 356
Imino carbonates, 282, 357
Improper rotation, 121
Indoles, 233, 237
Infrared activity of vibrations, 123
Infrared spectrometers, 55
Inorganic ions, spectra, 361
Interaction, 171
Integrated band intensities, 73
Internal coordinates, 425
Internal coordinates for $CHCl_3$, 432, 433
Internal standard, 76
Inverse, 108–109
   matrix, 441

IO_3^-, iodate ion, 140, 348
IO_4^-, periodate ion, 160
Irreducible representation, 115, 117
Irtran-2, 43, 44, 63
Isobutyrates, 250, 355
Isocyanate dimers, 267
Isocyanides, 207, 352
Isocyanurates, 267
Isoxazoles, 237
Isophthalates, 251, 355
Isopropyl, 193–195, 352
Isothiocyanates, 204, 352
Isotope effects, 164
Isoureas, 283, 357

Ketenes, 208
Ketene imines, 205
Ketones, 243, 354
   α chloro, 188, 242, 243
   conjugated, 243, 354
   conjugated and hydrogen bonded, 244, 354
   di tertiary butyl, 247
   low frequency bands, 344
KRS-5, 44, 46, 47, 67

Lactams, 264, 356
Lactones, 253, 355
Lagrange equation, 423
Law of association, 111
Linear molecule, rotational energy, 16, 17
   vibrational-rotational band, 19
Liquid cells, 62
Lithium fluoride, 44, 46
Littrow prism arrangement, 48
Low temperature infrared spectra, 70
   Raman spectra, 97

Maleates, 250, 252, 355
Matrix, 112–114, 116
   multiplication, 428
Mechanical molecular models, 4
Melamines, 235, 358
Mercaptans, 305, 360
Mesomeric effect, 187, 242
Metal-borate, 348
Metal-bromine, 347
Metal-carbon, 346
Metal-carbonyls, 209

Metal-chlorine, 347
Metal-fluorine, 347
  complexes, 348
Metal-hydroxide, 347
Metal-nitrogen, 346
Metal-oxygen, 318, 346
Metal-sulfur, 348
Methacrylates, 249–251, 355
Methane vibrational-rotational band, 25
Methyl, 191–195, 351
Methylene, 195–198
Methylene 1,2 dioxy benzenes, 270
Mica transmission limit, 44
Microwave region, 2
  lamps, 86
Millimicron, 2
MnO_4^-, 348
$Mo-C$, 346
Models, vibrating molecular, 4
MoF_6, molybdenum hexafluoride, 162
Molar absorptivity, 73
Moment of inertia, 12, 14, 35, 463, 471
  calculated for $CHCl_3$, 478–481
  of HCl, 23
Monomeric acids, 260
$MoO_4^=$, molybdate ion, 160, 348
Multiplication, matrix, 114, 428
  table, 110

Naphthalenes, 227, 231, 232, 353
Naphthoquinone diazide, 206
N_3^-, azide ion, 158
NCS^-, 361
ND_3, ammonia-d_3, 140
$N_2D_6^{++}$, heavy hydrazinium ion, 149, 153
N_2D_5Br, hydrazine bromide-d_5, 129
ND_4Br, ammonium bromide-d_4, 155
ND_4Cl, ammonium chloride-d_4, 160
N_2D_5Cl, hydrazine monochloride-d_5, 129
$N_2D_3H_2^+$, hydrazinium ion-d_3, 132
Near infrared region correlations, 325
Nernst glower, 41
NF_3 nitrogen trifluoride, 140, 361
NH_3, ammonia, 140
NH_4^+, ammonium ion, 160, 281, 357, 361
N_2H_4, hydrazine, 129
$N_2H_5^+$, hydrazinium ion, 132
$N_2H_6^{++}$, hydrazinium ion, 149, 153
N_3H, hydrazoic acid, 131
NH_4Br, ammonium bromide, 155

N_2H_5Br, hydrazine bromide, 129
NH_4Cl, ammonium chloride, 160
N_2H_5Cl, hydrazine monochloride, 129
NH_4F, ammonium fluoride, 160
$Ni(CO)_4$, nickel tetracarbonyl, 160
NiP_4F_{12}, 160
Nitriles, 202, 352
  on a nitrogen atom, 204, 352
Nitrile N-oxides, 203
Nitramines, 287, 357
Nitrate ion, 287, 358
Nitrates, organic, 286, 357
Nitrite ion, 287, 358
Nitrites, organic, 287, 358
Nitro aromatics, 286, 357
  group, 285, 357
Nitrosamines, 290, 258
Nitroso group, 289, 358
$N = N$, 287, 358
$N - O$, 282, 286, 287
NO_2^-, 361
NO_3^-, 361
NO_2, nitrogen dioxide, 135
NO_2^-, nitrite ion, 135
NO_3^-, nitrate ion, 136, 153
Normal coordinates, 115, 119, 425
Normality of symmetry coordinates, 427, 434
Normal modes of vibration, 3, 422–424
N_4S_4, nitrogen tetrasulfide, 148
Nujol mull, 65, 76

Oblate rotator, 17, 18
O_h, 108
OH, near I.R. region, 328
Olefins, alkyl substituted, 212
  cyclic, 185, 216, 353
  fluorinated, 211
  hydrogen wagging vibrations, 213
  low frequency bands, 337
  non cyclic, 210, 353
O_3, ozone, 135
O, (point group), 108
Optical density, 72
Organometallic compounds, 317
Orthoacetates, 276, 353
Orthoformates, 199, 276, 353
Orthogonal coordinates, 427, 434
OsF_6, osmium hexafluoride, 162
OsO_4, osmium oxide, 160

OsO$_3$N$^-$, osmium nitrate ion, 141
Overtones, 12, 124
Oxadiazoles, 237
Oximes, 282, 357
Oxirane ring, 273, 329, 353

P$_4$, phosphorus, 159
Parallel band, 19, 26, 28
Para xylene gas phase, 28
Partition functions, 463, 464
  rotational, 471
  for linear molecules, 471
  for symmetric tops, 473
  for asymmetric tops, 473
  and thermodynamic functions, 464–468
  translational, 469
  vibrational, 475
P branch, 20
PBr$_3$, phosphorus tribromide, 140
P$-$C, 305
P$-$CH$_3$, 302, 352, 359
P$-$Cl, 305
PCl$_3$, phosphorus trichloride, 140
PCl$_5$, phosphorus pentachloride, 153
P$_3$Cl$_6$N$_3$, (PNCl$_2$)$_3$, phosphonitride dichloride trimer, 153
P$_4$Cl$_8$N$_4$, (PNCl$_2$)$_4$, phosphonitride dichloride tetramer, 148, 155
PCl$_3$O, phosphorus oxychloride, 140
PCl$_3$S, phosphorus sulfochloride, 141
PD$_3$, phosphine-d$_3$, 140
Pentadiene, 210
Perkin-Elmer Spectrometer, Model 137 Infracord, 56
  Model 421, 59
Peroxides, 199, 256, 276, 354
Peroxy acids, 260
Perpendicular band, 19, 26, 28
  of symmetrical tops, 25
P$-$F, 305
PF$_3$, phosphorus trifluoride, 140
P$-$H, 299, 359
PH$_3$, phosphine, 140
Phenanthrenes, 232
Phenetoles, 270
Phenols, 181, 273, 275, 354
Phosphate, trialkyl, 186
Phosphines, 299, 359
Phosphine oxide, 186, 299, 359
Phosphinic acids, 300, 360

Phosphonic acids, 300, 360
Phosphonitrilic trimers, 305
Phosphoric acids, 300
Phosphors, 53
Phosphorus acids, 299, 300
  acid esters, 299
  compounds, spectra, 359
  correlations, 298
Photoconductive cell, 53
Phthalates, 249, 251, 252, 355
Phthalhydrazides, 268
Planck's constant, 1, 10
Planck's radiation law, 38
Plane of symmetry, 99–101, 103
P$-$N, 304, 360
P$=$N, 305
Pneumatic cell, 55
P$=$O, 299, 359
PO$_4^{3-}$, 160, 348, 361
P$-$O-aliphatic, 301, 359
P$-$O-aromatic, 301, 359
P$-$OH, 300
Point group, 104, 106
  for CHCl$_3$, 432
Polarizability, 31, 162
  change, 33
  ellipsoid, 33
Polarized infrared radiation, 79, 164
Polarizers infrared, 79
  Raman, 92
Polishing alkali halide windows, 60
Polymers, polarized infrared spectra, 81, 84
Polystyrene, 59
P$-$O$-$P, 300, 359
Potassium bromide, 44, 46, 47
  disc, 65
Potential energy, 8
  function, 440
    central forces for, 462
    choice of, 440, 461
    for CHCl$_3$, 440, 442
    Urey-Bradley forces for, 462
    Valence forces for, 462
P-phenyl, 302, 359
Pressure broadening, 77
Prism, angular dispersion, 44
  resolving power, 47
Product rule, 164
Prolate rotator, 17, 18
Propane, gas phase, 28

Proper rotation, 121
Propionates, 250, 354
P=S, 302, 359
P—SH, 304
PtCl$_6^=$, chloroplatinate ion, 162
Pt(CN)$_4^=$, tetracyano-platinate (II) ion, 155
PtF$_6$, platinum hexafluoride, 162
Pyrazines, 358
Pyrazine, N-oxide, 233
Pyridine, N-oxide, 233, 358
Pyridines, 227, 233, 358
Pyrimidines, 234, 358
Pyrimidine, N-oxide, 233
Pyrroles, 237
Pyrrolines, 284

Q branch, 19
Quantitative analysis, 64, 71, 76
  of gases, 77
  multicomponent, 77
  single components, 74
Quartz transmission limit, 44
Quinazolines, 233
Quinolines, 233, 358
Quinone diazide, 206

Radiation law, 38
Raman activity of vibrations, 124
  effect, 29
  intensity measurements, 94
  sample techniques, 90
  sources, 85
  spectra, pure rotational, 34
  spectrographs, 88
Rayleigh-Jeans radiation law, 39
Rayleigh scattering, 27, 28, 31, 33, 34
R branch, 19
Reduced mass, 9, 13
Redundant coordinates, 432, 434
Reflectance cell, 70
Refractive index, 80
  of alkali halides, 46–47
Representation of a group, 115
Rigid rotator, 12
Rotational constant, 13, 18, 22
Rotational, axis of symmetry, 99
  energy contributions to thermodynamic
    functions, 471, 477
  of diatomic molecules, 12

Rotational, quantum number, 13, 18, 19
  Raman spectra, 34
Rotation-reflection axis of symmetry, 103

S$_8$, sulfur, 150
Sample holders, 61–63, 90–92
S-aryl, 307, 360
Sauereisen source, 41
SbBr$_3$, antimony tribromide, 140
SbCl$_3$, antimony trichloride, 140
SbCl$_6^-$, chloroantimonate ion, 162
Scattering coefficient, 94
S—CH$_2$, 306
S—CH$_3$, 306, 352, 360
Schiff bases, 282
Schoenflies notation, 104
S—Cl, 344
S$_2$Cl$_2$, sulfur chloride, 130
SClF$_5$, sulfur monochloride-pentafluoride, 143
Secular determinant, 424, 431, 452
  for A, vibrations of CHCl$_3$, 454
  for E, vibrations of CHCl$_3$, 456
Selection rules, 128, 163
SeF$_4$, selenium tetrafluoride, 136
SeF$_6$, selenium hexafluoride, 162
SeO$_4^-$, 160, 348
S—F, 307, 344
SF$_4$, sulfur tetrafluoride, 137
SF$_6$, sulfur hexafluoride, 162
S$_2$F$_{10}$, sulfur decafluoride, 150
S—H, 304, 305
Si—Br, 346
SiBr$_4$, silicon tetrabromide, 160
SiBrCl$_3$, bromotrichlorosilicane, 140
Si—CH$_2$, 296
Si—CH$_3$, 295, 352, 359
Si—Cl, 298, 345
SiCl$_4$, silicon tetrachloride, 159
Si$_2$Cl$_6$, silicon hexachloride, 149, 153, 154
Si$_2$D$_6$, disilicane-d$_6$, 149
Si$_2$D$_6$O, disiloxane-d$_6$, 149
Si$_2$D$_6$S, disilyl sulfide-d$_6$, 138
Si$_2$D$_6$Se, disilyl selenide-d$_6$, 138
Si—F, 297, 345
SiF$_4$, silicon tetrafluoride, 160
Si—H, 295, 359
SiH$_4$, silane, 160
SiHBr$_3$, silico-bromoform, 140
SiHCl$_3$, silico-chloroform, 140

Si_2H_6O, disiloxane, 149
Si_2H_6S, disilyl sulfide, 138
Si_2H_6Se, disilyl selenide, 138
Silanes, 345
Silicon compounds, spectra, 359
  correlations, 294
Siloxanes, 297, 359
Silver chloride, 44, 63, 68, 72
$Si-N$, 298, 359
SiO_4^{4-}, silicate ion, 160
$Si-OH$, 297, 359
$Si-O-R$, 296
$Si-O-Si$, 297
Si-phenyl, 296, 359
Si-vinyl, 296, 359
Slit width, 73
$SnBr_4$, tin tetrabromide, 160
$SnBr_6^{2-}$, bromostannate ion, 155
$SnCl_4$, tin tetrachloride, 160
$SnCl_6^{=}$, chlorostannate ion, 162
$Sn-C$, 346
$Sn-CH_3$, 318
$Sn-H$, 317
$SnHBr_3$, stanno-bromoform, 140
$SnHCl_3$, stanno-chloroform, 140
$Sn-O-Sn$, 318
SO, 307
SO_2, 135, 308, 309, 344, 360
S_2O_2, 135
SO_3, sulfur trioxide, 153
SO_3^{2-}, 311, 348; 361
SO_4^{2-}, 160, 311, 360
$S-O-CH_2$, 311
SO_2Cl_2, sulfuryl chloride, 136
Sodium chloride, 44, 46
SO_2F_2, sulfuryl fluoride, 136
Solids, infrared spectra, 64, 79
S_p, 103, 105
Spectrophotometers, 56–59
  Raman, 88–90
Spherical top, molecules, 17, 23, 25
  rotational energy, 16, 17
  vibrational-rotational bands, 23
$S-S$, 306, 344
Statistical weight, 463, 466
Stirling relation, 467
Stokes line, 30, 34
Stefan-Boltzmann law, 40
Sulfates, dialkyl, 309, 360
Sulfate ion, 311, 360

Sulfides, 306, 360
  disilyl, 344
Sulfinic acids, 310
Sulfite ion, 311, 348, 360
Sulfites, organic, 187, 307, 360
Sulfonamides, 308, 360
Sulfonates, 309, 360
Sulfones, 308, 360
Sulfonic acids, 310, 344, 360
Sulfonyl chlorides, 309, 360
  fluorides, 309
Sulfoxides, 187, 307, 360
Sulfur compounds, spectra, 360
Symmetrical stretching of CO_2, 5
Symmetrical top molecules, 17, 25, 35
  rotational energy, 16, 18
  vibrational-rotational band, 25
Symmetry coordinates, 425–426, 433
  for A, vibrations of $CHCl_3$, 434–435
  for E, vibrations of $CHCl_3$, 436–438
  normalization of, 426–427
  orthogonality of, 426–427
  transformation of, 426–427
Symmetry coordinates for $CHCl_3$, 433, 439
Symmetry number, 471
  operation, 101, 109
  species, 118, 162
S vectors, 429
s vectors, 429
S-vinyl, 307, 360

T, Td, 107
TeF_6, tellurium hexafluoride, 162
Te_2F_{10}, ditellurium decafluoride, 150
Teller-Redlich product rule, 164
Terephthalates, 251, 252, 255
Tertiary butyl, 193–195, 352
Tetralins, 232
Tetrazines, 236, 358
Thermocouples, 52, 53
Thiazole ring, 237, 360
Thioamides, 312
Thioammeline, 235, 358
Thiobenzoates, 355
Thiobenzophenones, 312
Thiocarbamates, 352
Thiocyanate ion, 208, 352
Thiocyanates, organic, 204, 352
Thiol acids, 254
  esters, 254

formates, 254
Thionitrites, 287
Thionylamine, 311
Thiophenes, 237, 358
Thiophenols, 305, 360
Thioureas, 312, 356
$TiCl_4$, titanium tetrachloride, 160
Tin compounds, 361
$Ti-O-Si$, 318
$Ti-O-Ti$, 318
Toronto lamp, 86–87
Total internal energy, 464
Translational energy contribution to thermodynamic functions, 469, 476
Transmittance, 71
Transpose of a matrix, 428
Triazines, alkyl or aryl substituted, 234
    chloro, 236
    oxysubstituted, 235
    spectra, 358
    thiosubstituted, 235
Trimethoxy benzene, 271
Trimethyl amine gas phase, 26
Triply degenerate vibrations, 118
Trithiocarbonates, 312
Tropolones, 246
Tyndall effect, 27

UF_6, uranium hexafluoride, 162
Ultraviolet region, 2
U matrix, 428, 442–444
Unicam SP. 100 infrared spectrometer, 58
UO_2^{++}, uranyl ion, 135

Ureas, 265, 356
Urey-Bradley force field, 462

Valence force, field, 462
Variable space cell, 64
Velocity of light, 1
Vibrational, energy contribution to thermodynamic functions, 474, 483
    quantum number, 10, 474
Vibrational-rotational band, 19
    of HCl, 21
    of methane, 25
Visible region, 2
$VOCl_3$, vanadium oxytrichloride, 141

Water, 354
Wavelength, 2
Wavenumber, 2
Welsbach mantle, 42
Wien's displacement law, 39
    radiation law, 38
WF_6, tungsten hexafluoride, 162
WO_4^{2-}, tungstate ion, 160, 348

Xanthates, 312

Zero-order frequency, 164
Zero point energy, 10, 464, 474
$ZnBr_2$, zinc bromide, 158
$Zn-C$, 346
$ZnCl_2$, zinc chloride, 158
$ZrCl_4$, zirconium tetrachloride, 160